HELL

JOHN HERSCHEL

HUYGENS

WILLIAM HERSCHEL

ESSEL

NEWTON

WATCHERS OF THE SKIES

AN INFORMAL HISTORY OF

ASTRONOMY FROM BABYLON TO THE SPACE AGE

Then felt I like some watcher of the skies
When a new planet swims into his ken.

— John Keats

OTHER BOOKS BY WILLY LEY

ROCKETS, MISSILES, AND SPACE TRAVEL

EXOTIC ZOOLOGY

ENGINEERS' DREAMS

THE CONQUEST OF SPACE
(WITH CHESLEY BONESTELL)

THE EXPLORATION OF MARS
(WITH WERNHER VON BRAUN)

WILLY LEY

WATCHERS OF THE SKIES

AN INFORMAL HISTORY OF ASTRONOMY FROM BABYLON TO THE SPACE AGE

ISTIMIRANT STELLA

NEW YORK
THE
VIKING PRESS

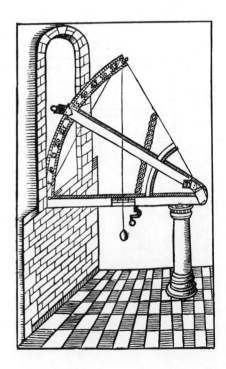

TO PASCAL COVICI

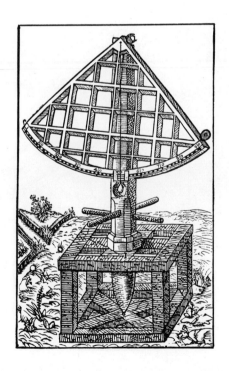

CONTENTS

Part III. APPROXIMATE INFINITY

ILLUSTRATIONS

FOREWORD

ASTRONOMY, all historians are agreed, is the oldest of the sciences, with the automatic result that its history is not only of great length but of extraordinary complexity.

To write a history of astronomy that is worth the reader's time is therefore anything but easy. A "complete" history of astronomy, if it is possible at all, would have to be the joint effort of a fairly large team of experts and, in physical size, would probably be a work of about ten volumes. And then it would be purely a reference work, which is consulted when a special point is to be clarified; it would not be a book which could be read. On the other hand, there have been—and probably still are—horrible examples of one-volume "stories of astronomy" which seemed designed to obscure its history. They tried to look "historical" by mentioning a few names and dates of the past but were far from historical in that they did not even discuss the thoughts, correct or mistaken, of the people mentioned. Instead they then went straight to what were at the time the latest results of research, often trying to convey the impression that all but a few of the problems had been solved.

The fact that in a history of any subject one should let the people who made that history speak for themselves had its influence on the arrangement of the present work. The history of astronomy proceeded in a reasonably straight line from the beginnings of the science to about the middle of the eighteenth century. At that point two things happened. The number of astronomers increased, and each one of them began to do work in various fields, sometimes starting a new branch of his science, even though he was not always aware of the fact. And, of course, the closer we come to the present, the greater the complexity, especially since other sciences, from atomic theory to rocket engineering, began to contribute to astronomy.

This book, therefore, is divided into three sections. The first section is the most nearly chronological in arrangement; it runs from the beginnings (as far as we know them) to about the time of the older Herschel. Ideas which did not contribute, even remotely, to the current science of astronomy have been left out. There is no need, for example, for a long discussion of the constellations of the Chinese. Such a discussion would be pertinent in a book on Chinese culture, but their constellations did not influence our own; in fact, the Chinese astronomers of today use the "Western" constellations. But the list of comet appearances compiled by the Chinese is another story, since their lists complemented the Western lists. Similarly the star myths which were developed by many "primitive" peoples have been disregarded. I don't say that they are not an interesting subject; I do say that they are not astronomy.

The second section deals with our own solar system, member by member. In this second section—the most voluminous part of the book, partly because the history of the solar system is especially comprehensive, partly because these nearby bodies acquire a special interest in the beginning years of the Space Age—each planet's history is treated separately for the purpose of making it especially clear.

The third section is devoted to the histories of a number of special problems of our own and other galaxies, again subject by subject.

Among these problems, however, questions of cosmogony are not included, for several reasons. The first is simply a matter of available space—a history of ideas about the origin of the universe would be a book in itself. Moreover, such a book belongs to the category of "history of natural philosophy" rather than that of "history of astronomy." Even now the proponents of the two leading theories of the origin of the universe—the origin from the explosion of a superatom, as first proposed by the Abbé Lemaître, and the less violent theory of "continuous creation"—defend their viewpoints in a manner highly suggestive of the theological disputes of the past. Of course there is some reason for this, in that the available scientific evidence is inconclusive. One week a recent discovery seems to favor one side, and a week later a new measurement, or a reappraisal of an older one, favors the other. And the fact that the debate is still going on is the strongest reason for omitting it from a history, since I believe that history should be written from some distance.

Finally, the appendix begins with a chronological list of astronomers, for the benefit of the people—of whom I am one—who have difficulty remembering who lived when, and whose problems may be increased by the arrangement of this book. It also includes two notes on subjects outside the scope of the text: radio astronomy and astronomical fantasies.

It is not only possible, but highly likely, that some of the "modern" accepted values for diameters, distances, etc., of celestial objects will have to be corrected once more as a result of measurements from space probes, manned ships, and, it is hoped, an observatory on the moon. Since science has been defined as a self-correcting process, any new item which replaces an old one is a piece of progress.

— WILLY LEY

September 1, 1963

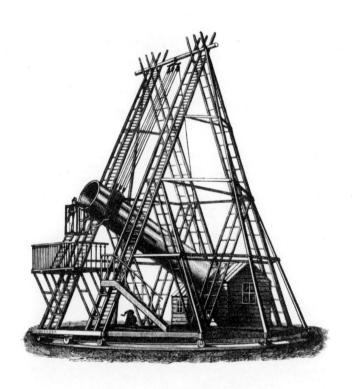

PART I

A SCIENCE GROWS UP

RAPHAEL:
Die Sonne tönt, nach alter Weise
In Brudersphären Wettgesang,
Und ihre vorgeschriebne Reise
Vollendet sie mit Donnergang.
Ihr Anblick gibt den Engeln Stärke,
Wenn keiner sie ergründen mag;
Die unbegreiflich hohen Werke
Sind herrlich wie am ersten Tag.

RAPHAEL:
In ancient chords the sun resounds
With kindred spheres a mingling air
And his divine-appointed rounds
Are climaxed with a thund'rous blare
This sight beyond all understanding
Gives angels strength; the great array
Of awesome works is as unending
As on that glorious primal day.

—JOHANN WOLFGANG VON GOETHE, *Faust*, Part I, Prologue in Heaven

1

FROM CHALDEA TO COS

So M E time ago, standing on the roof of a tall building with an unobstructed view toward the western horizon, I watched the setting sun.
This was not entirely for the purpose of esthetic enjoyment. I watched
in the faint hope of seeing the famous "green flash," which I have so
far seen only twice: once brilliantly from aboard a steamer in the Baltic
Sea and once indistinctly in Texas. The horizon, unfortunately, was not
quite clear; a heavy cloudbank was resting on it like a distant mountain
chain. But some observers had reported, I hopefully reminded myself,
that they had seen the green flash under such conditions: clouds heavy
enough can act like the horizon's rim.

There was no green flash.

But as the sky grew darker, Venus began to show, gradually growing
more luminous until even the most casual bystander could not have
missed the "evening star." Then I suddenly noticed—I don't know how
I had missed it before—the thin sickle of the moon to the south of
where the sun had by then disappeared, and also to the south of Venus.

At sight of the thin crescent, the thought presented itself (possibly in
consolation for the absence of the green flash) that I had just witnessed
what must have been the beginning of astronomy: three lights in the
sky, each bright enough so that it could not possibly be overlooked, but
each with pronounced peculiarities. One, the sun, unchanging in appearance and present in the sky with the greatest regularity. The second,
Venus, also unchanging in appearance to the naked eye, but not present
every night, shining brilliantly for a succession of evenings and then
absent for a long time. Finally the third, the moon, present in the sky
almost every night, and often in daytime, too, but forever changing its
appearance, from a thin sickle to a half-circle, then to a full circle, and
then back again to the sickle shape.

By the time men had reached the tool-making stage, they must have
started comparing the number of sunrises with the time that went by
between one full moon and the next. It is true that certain contemporary
primitive tribes until very recently had no number-words beyond *two*

or *five* and *many*. It is not certain whether these tribes could not count beyond that limit or whether the lack of higher-number words was merely a linguistic inadequacy which they somehow had managed to circumvent. But even if these tribes stopped counting at the figure "five" and called everything more numerous "many," other tribes evidently did learn to count higher. It must have been useful for primitive man, too, to know how many sunrises he had to wait for the next full moon, the time when he could go fishing at night.

The thought expressed by a Jewish rabbi (in the *Midrash*) that "the moon has been created for the counting of the days" must have occurred to quite a number of different people in different parts of the earth several thousand years earlier.

This proto-astronomy, concerned only with the counting of sunrises or sunsets between full moons, with succession of the seasons in countries where the seasons were important, and possibly with the appearance of Venus, must have been present almost anywhere. Under special conditions it must have extended to some stars—among coastal or insular tribes perhaps, where it became common knowledge that one had to sail in the direction of one group of stars in summer in order to reach a certain island, and in the direction of another group of stars in winter if the same island was to be reached.

But for proto-astronomy to change into early astronomy several conditions were needed. One was a sky which was clear most of the time. Another was a certain amount of leisure for at least some members of the population. Still another was the possibility of recording events, for later study of what had been written and for the purpose of passing information on to future generations. These three conditions came together for the first time in the land to the west of the Persian Gulf, which as a purely geographical area is best called Mesopotamia, since the names of political units, such as kingdoms and empires, kept shifting all the time. The two rival powers were Assyria and Babylon, and historians have said that it is impossible to write a history of Babylon *or* of Assyria. Such a history can be written only if both are considered simultaneously, for "the strength of one was the weakness of the other."

Here a few dates must be mentioned, Babylonian dates, because Babylon always re-emerged as the cultural center. Old Babylon, as it is usually called, is the Babylon of Hammurabi, who ruled from 1792 to 1750 B.C. The Babylon of Hammurabi and of his successors remained more or less unchanged until Assyria became the dominant power in that area under Tiglath-Pileser (745–727 B.C.), and the Assyrians steadily expanded their domain until finally the Assyrian king Sennacherib (705–682 B.C.) took Babylon itself and razed the city. The year was

689 B.C. But then the Assyrian empire crumbled and in 625 B.C. Babylon re-emerged under the Chaldean king Nabopolassar and his son Nebuchadnezzar. Finally, to finish this condensed survey of historical events, Cyrus of Persia took the city in 539 B.C.

Early astronomy, with written records and observations made for a specific purpose—time reckoning and religious ceremonies—then comprises approximately the period between 800 B.C. and the time of Pythagoras of Samos, who settled about 530 B.C. in a Greek colony in southern Italy. The time interval of not quite three centuries is much shorter than romanticized accounts, some old, some new, would lead the reader to believe. Of course the fact that Greek philosophers became important from around 500 B.C. does not mean that the inhabitants of Mesopotamia stopped their astronomical activities. The astronomy centered in Babylon continued for a few centuries.

The earliest collectors of astronomical data were the Assyrians. Of course there is always the possibility that we are misled by incomplete records, but at least we have records from Assyria, in the shape of the library of the Assyrian king Ashurbanipal (668–626 B.C.). One of the reasons why Ashurbanipal's library is so important is that the king himself had a strong sense of history; when he ordered a library established in his palace he also ordered the texts from the temples and sites of Old Babylon to be copied.

Among these copies is the "Venus tablet," found by Sir Henry Layard and deciphered in 1911 by a German Jesuit scholar, the astronomer F. X. Kugler. The original is believed to have been written during the first Babylonian dynasty, i.e., under Hammurabi's rule, or possibly somewhat earlier. The contents of the Venus tablet are, one might say, proto-astrological. It is stated that, when Venus appears, "rains will be in the heavens." Then the planet will be absent for three months and upon its return, "hostility will be in the land, the crops will prosper." As the Dutch astronomer Antonie Pannekoek remarks,[1] the statements made in the Venus tablet "cannot be observations or astronomical computations because the same time intervals always recur and the imaginary dates of beginning, regularly alternating between morning and evening phenomena, are always of one month and one day."

What probably happened is that priests had noted down the actual appearance and disappearance of Venus and the events that had accompanied the appearance. If the same event happened to coincide more than once with an appearance of Venus the one was taken for granted to be connected with the other. The Venus tablet in Ashurbanipal's

[1] In his *History of Astronomy* (New York: Interscience Publishers, Inc.; London: Allen & Unwin, Ltd., 1961).

library was most likely a copy of a copy of a copy, and even the original must have been a kind of summary.

In Old Babylon the emphasis of astronomical observation seems to have been on the moon for determining the beginning of a new month; among the Assyrians prediction seems to have been the main purpose. "When god Nergal [Mars] in its disappearing grows smaller . . . he will have mercy on Akkad." "When a planet [Mercury] approaches Li [Aldebaran] the king of Elam will die." "When Mars is dim, it is lucky; when bright, unlucky." "When Jupiter assumes a brilliance in the way of Bel and [becomes?] Nibiru, Akkad will overflow with plenty, the king of Akkad will grow powerful."

The future pattern of astrological beliefs can be seen emerging: Jupiter brings good luck; Mars and Mercury can bring bad luck.

While the priests of Old Babylon had paid attention only to Venus, the Assyrians knew all the naked-eye planets. Comets do not seem to have been mentioned; the "sudden bright stars" mentioned in one or two tablets probably refer to very bright meteors.

Observation of the moon probably had settled down to a routine matter by that time. The Assyrians knew that the time from full moon to full moon was about 29½ days. (Of course the time interval is the same for all corresponding phases.) The month began with the first appearance of the lunar crescent, and for this reason the day in Mesopotamia and adjacent lands began with sunset instead of with sunrise, which seems more natural to us.

But then something else was added, first, in all probability by the Babylonian priest-astronomers, before the Assyrians became the most influential power in the area. Even if the priests only watched the moon for purposes of time reckoning and the religious ceremonies which came to be attached to the time reckoning, they could not fail to notice that the moon does not stand still among the fixed stars. This led to naming the stars near the apparent path of the moon. We know a number of the names they used, but we cannot always be sure that a certain name refers to an individual star or to a group of stars. We know that one of these names, *Mulmul*, refers to a group, the one we call the Pleiades.

One result of the close observation of the moon was the division of the zodiac into twenty-eight "moon stations." These are about thirteen degrees apart and represent the distance which the moon travels during twenty-four hours. These moon stations were recognized by the Chinese as well as by the Indians and later the Arabs. That the Arabs "borrowed" the moon stations from the Mesopotamian priest-astronomers was taken for granted, but there has been a good deal of discussion as to whether the Chinese and the Indians did so, or whether they invented them independently. Something can be said for each side of the argument.

In the first place, the moon moves among the same stars whether it is observed from Ur, from Madras, or from Shanghai. In the second place, some of these stars happen to be conspicuous: the Hyades with Aldebaran, Regulus, Castor and Pollux, and so forth. Since the whole concept was based on the motion of the moon, the division of its path into twenty-eight "stations" was logical. And since certain stars and groups of stars along the path were so conspicuous, the choice was quite obvious in most cases. Those who insist that the Indians borrowed the moon stations and then passed them on to the Chinese base their case on the fact that the choice was not always obvious. In a number of cases the stars of a moon station are not conspicuous, and astronomers of different countries might be expected to pick somewhat different groupings for a moon station. But even the nonobvious groupings are identical. And it cannot be denied that there were mutual cultural influences between China and India and that knowledge from Mesopotamia could easily have reached India.

The early astronomers of Mesopotamia and their immediate successors had still another lunar problem on their hands. Building a calendar on the phases of the moon which can be directly observed is easy, but there are not many places on earth where the seasons can be wholly neglected. The rabbi who wrote in the *Midrash* that the moon has been created for the counting of days might have added "and for the purpose of furthering mathematics by trying to match the lunar periods and the solar years." The lunar period, as has been mentioned, is about 29½ days, while the time required for the earth to complete one orbit around the sun is about 365¼ days.[2] The year, therefore, is just about 11 days longer than 12 lunar periods. After only 3 years a purely lunar calendar of 12 periods to the "year" would be 33 days off, or more than a whole month. The first remedy was to make every third year a year of 13 lunar periods; such a 3-year period would be not quite 1092 days long. But since 3 solar years are 1095¾ days, even such a calendar would be nearly 134 days off in a single century. An 8-year period works a little better, using 5 years with 12 months and 3 with 13 months. Here the difference would amount to about 20 days per century.

A still closer approximation can be obtained with a 19-year period containing 235 months (6939.60 vs. 6939.69 days) with 7 of these 19

[2] The precise figures are 29.53059 days and 365.24220 days.

years being 13-month years. It was this 19-year period which became
the basis of the Jewish calendar. Much later, in the time of Sir Isaac
Newton and Dr. Edmond Halley, a similar period (one of 223 lunations
or 18 years and 11 days) came to be called the *saros*. Apparently
Halley thought that the ancient term *saros* referred to some such period
after which the moon returned to the same position in the sky, counting
only naked-eye accuracy. This was simply a mistake; in reality the term
saros, as used by the ancient Greek astronomers, seems to have referred
to something entirely different, namely a 3600-year period.

But let us return to the calendar of Mesopotamia.

We can't tell just when the peoples of this region went from one system of keeping the lunar calendar in step with the seasons to another
more precise one. A tablet from Ashurbanipal's library makes it quite
clear that a thirteenth month was added from time to time, but no
special system is mentioned; it sounds as if one of the observers decided
that the time had come to do so. The Arabs of a later date did the same
thing, the change being determined by a class of people designated as
Kalammas.[3]

While methods of time reckoning were developed and the appearance
of planets was noted along with terrestrial events, to find a basis for
predicting the future, there had been very nearly continuous war going
on in and around Mesopotamia. It did not end until all the small warring
states and cities had been incorporated into the Persian Empire. A non-
military result of this incorporation was that the priest-astronomers no
longer looked for omens. The Persians had their own religion in which
they believed fiercely; they had absolutely no use for signs from Ishtar
or Marduk. Since the Persians could do without such omens, they saw
no reason why the peoples in their provinces could not do the same.

The omens disappeared but the astronomical observations continued
and the Chaldeans became the first astronomers in our sense—people
who observed for the purpose of learning. They even began making the
first measurements.

Since the Old Testament often uses "Chaldeans" as a synonym for
Babylonians, a short linguistic explanation is in order. Originally the
Chaldeans were a separate tribe which settled at "Ur of the Chaldees."
They fought with the Assyrians, and they fought with the Babylonians
too, until in 625 B.C. Nabopolassar took Babylon. It is doubtful whether

---

[3] Mohammed stopped the practice of shifting from 12-month to 13-month years,
possibly to remove the influence of the *Kalammas* by making them unnecessary,
or possibly to avoid having the same calendar as the Jews. As a result, the
Mohammedan year still has 354 days, which makes each of their religious festivals
run through all the seasons within 33 years.

Nabopolassar was a pure Chaldean by ancestry; and in any event his son Nebuchadnezzar became king of Babylon. What happened was simply that the two nations had fused. The Chaldeans and the Babylonians were closely related racially. Their languages differed, if at all, only on very minor points, possibly somewhat in pronunciation. (Their languages were also nearly identical with the language spoken by the Assyrians, so that soldiers had no difficulty in freely insulting one another in battle.)

In short, after Nebuchadnezzar was king in Babylon and began building the famous Ishtar Gate, the term "Chaldeans" should have disappeared.

But it did not disappear. Instead it acquired a new meaning. The "Chaldeans" of Babylon became the "wise men." In the book of Daniel the word "Chaldean" means astronomer, astrologer, or magician in general. It is possible that the "Chaldeans" of the later Babylonian empire were originally Chaldeans by blood; in fact, one has to make that assumption in order to explain the shift in meaning at all. But it is unlikely that one had to have Chaldean ancestry to become a priest-astronomer in Babylon. The word had shifted from the name of a tribe to the designation of a profession.

Though the records are still fragmentary, we have somewhat better knowledge of Chaldean astronomy than we have of the earlier periods. We know, for example, just what periods they used for calendar-making purposes. Beginning in 530 B.C. they used the 8-year period; a century later the superior 19-year period was introduced and was used exclusively from 380 B.C.

The Chaldeans also made systematic lists of the constellations and their relative positions. When their writings were deciphered it seemed surprising at first glance that so many of their constellations had names we still use, e.g., the Bull (Taurus), the Twins (Gemini), the King (Regulus), the Scorpion, the Archer (Sagittarius), the Fish-Goat (Capricorn), the Hydra. The reason we still use the names is that the Greeks borrowed them from the Chaldeans and passed them on to posterity. Of course the Chaldeans also used names which were not passed on, and even the constellations which bore names we still use did not have the same extent that our constellations have.[4] Evidently the Chaldeans held the concept of the horizon as dividing the celestial sphere into two halves, for they noted the behavior of "opposite stars": when Aldebaran rises, Arcturus sets; when the Pleiades rise, the Scorpion sets, and so

---

[4] Establishing the similarities and differences is a separate, if small, discipline in the history of astronomy, which is called astrognosis.

forth. According to F. X. Kugler (quoted by Pannekoek), "There exists a list of stars all around the sky, with numbers added, which evidently stand for the consecutive distances." Because we know (from Greek authors) that water clocks were in use, Pannekoek concluded: "It seems safe to consider the numbers as differences in time of transit through the meridian . . . they may have been used to read in the sky the progress of the hours of the night."

Long-continued observation, not distracted by a search for omens, had taught the Chaldeans the planetary periods, which are rather long. To understand what they mean, the term "synodic period" must first be explained.

When we now ask, for any reason, "What is the period of Jupiter?" the answer is 11.86 years, meaning that Jupiter needs 11.86 earth years to complete one orbit around the sun. But when the earth was the self-evident center of the universe this period, also called "sidereal period," was meaningless. Then the question "What is Jupiter's period?" phrased in the prevailing language and terminology, meant something else; in fact it could have two different meanings. The more likely one was what we now call the "synodic period," the time that elapses between two oppositions. The synodic period of Jupiter is almost precisely 399 days.

Let us first see how this synodic period comes about. The term "opposition" means that Jupiter—or any planet—is occupying a position in the sky 180 degrees from the position of the sun, just like the "opposite stars" listed so carefully by the Chaldeans. We now know that this happens when the sun, the earth, and Jupiter form a straight line in space, with the earth between the sun and Jupiter. Both the earth and Jupiter move around the sun in the same direction, but the earth has a shorter orbit to travel and also a higher orbital velocity. Therefore, one day later, the three bodies no longer form a straight line; the earth has moved ahead and Jupiter has been left behind. If Jupiter did not move at all, the next opposition would take place one year after the first, when the earth has completed one orbit. But Jupiter has moved in the meantime, though slowly, and the earth needs another 34 days to catch up. Therefore a straight line will be formed again 399 days later.

The synodic periods for the five planets known to the Chaldeans are: Mercury, 115.9 days; Venus, 583.9 days;[5] Mars, 779.9 days; Jupiter, 399 days; Saturn, 378 days. But Jupiter, at the second opposition of this example, obviously shines from a different starry background than dur-

---

[5] Since Mercury and Venus have shorter orbital periods than the earth does, they make more than one revolution during the synodic period and then have to catch up with the earth.

ing the first opposition. The planetary period which the Chaldeans knew means the time interval between oppositions in which the planet was seen in the same constellation.

Pannekoek gives a table for the calculation of these periods:

Saturn	57 synodic periods =	2 revolutions	=59 years	+2 days	(− 6 days)
Jupiter	65	= 6	=71	−5	(− 0 days)
Jupiter	76	= 7	=83	+0	(−13 days or +17 days)
Mars	22	=25	=47	−7	(+ 2 days)
Mars	37	=42	=79	+4	(+ 7 days)
Venus	5	= 8	= 8	−2	(− 4 days)
Mercury	19	= 6	= 6	+8	(+14 days or −16 days)
Mercury	41	=13	=13	+2	(− 4 days)

The years are solar years; the number of days are the days to be added or subtracted for correction; the days in parenthesis are the days to be added or subtracted if the calculation were carried out in Babylonian years of 12 and 13 lunar months. (*A History of Astronomy,* pages 54-55.)

F. X. Kugler deciphered a damaged text from the Persian period which Pannekoek renders as follows:

. . . Dilbat [Venus] 8 years behind thee come back . . . 4 days thou shalt subtract . . . Gudu [Mercury] 6 years behind thee come back . . . the phenomena of Zalbatanu [Mars] 47 years . . . 12 days more . . . shalt thou observe . . . the phenomena of Sag-ush [Saturn] 59 years . . . come back day for day shalt thou observe . . . the phenomena of Kaksidi [Sirius] 27 years . . . come back day for day shalt thou observe . . .

The tablet does not say how these periods were calculated—probably by a mixture of actual observations and interpolations—but the planetary periods are the ones calculated by Pannekoek. The 27 years given for Sirius, however, fails to make sense, since Sirius is a fixed star, and Kugler thought that this may be advice to the computer (one might say somewhat as if a modern paper stated: "metric units," or: "use natural logarithms") in that it indicated that the calendar periods used were 8 + 19 years, 8-year periods alternating with 19-year periods. There is hardly any other explanation for the figure 27, though Pannekoek points out that no instance of such use is known.

Now what was the purpose of such tables which must have taken infinite patience to construct?

Again we have to remember that to the Chaldeans the earth stood still. If one asks now, "Where will Jupiter be on May 1?" there are also two answers. One would be: "So and so many degrees from the vernal equinox," which would tell the position of the planet in its orbit. The other could be: "In the constellation of Taurus at such and such a point." This is what is called the "ephemeris," the position in the sky as seen from the earth. The Chaldeans, of course, knew only the ephemeris. Now if the king wanted to know the ephemeris of the planets for the year 100 of the Seleucid Era, his astronomers would take the position of Saturn for the year 41 (100 − 59), the position of Jupiter for the year 17 (100 − 83), the position of Venus for the year 92 (100 − 8), and so forth, apply a few minor corrections, and present the king with an ephemeris which would agree with reality when the time came.

We do know that they actually computed in this manner. The angular measure which they used was called an *ammat* (subdivided into 24 *ubani*) which was the equivalent of 2½ of our degrees. Everything worked out beautifully and simply in their number system: the zodiac was divided into one dozen signs, each measuring one dozen *ammat* (= 30 degrees) and each *ammat* was two dozen *ubani*.

Another concern of the astronomers was, of course, the occurrence and prediction of eclipses. Just who noticed first that, if there is a total eclipse of the moon, the next one will take place 41 or 47 months later, is not known. The Chaldeans probably started out with such a rule of thumb but they ended up with a table which Pannekoek calls: ". . . an important document of Babylonian science. It is not, as are so many texts, a list partly of observations, partly of resulting predictions; it is a formulation of theory in the form of a table extending equally over past and future. It combines the multitude of former and later lunar eclipses in one condensed table, which, potentially, can be extended indefinitely in both directions. This representation of a large realm of phenomena in an abstract picture shows to what remarkable heights astronomical science had attained." [6]

It cannot be dated precisely, but since the Seleucid Era is used it must have been compiled after 280 B.C. During the three centuries between 280 B.C. and the time of Christ the Chaldean astronomers continued to make tables, attaining higher and higher stages of accuracy, as proved by a table for the planet Jupiter, reconstructed by Strassmaier and Kugler. Fragments of tables for other planets have also been found.

From that last period we even know the names of some of these astronomers, because they then took to beginning their tables with a

---

[6] The tablet, which is in the British Museum, was exhaustively described and discussed by J. N. Strassmaier and J. Epping in the *Zeitschrift für Assyriologie* (VIII, 1893, and X, 1895) under the title: *Ein babylonischer Saros-Canon*. The table is given in Pannekoek's *A History of Astronomy*, page 61.

formula such as "Computing table of Kidinnu for the years . . ." This Kidinnu appears in Pliny the Elder's *Natural History* as Cidenas. Strabo, whose life span probably ran from 63 B.C. to 24 A.D., mentions the names of Kidenas, Naburiannuos, and Soudines in his *Geography*. The first is, of course, Kidinnu, while the last is believed to be a Greek rendering of Anu-shé-shu-idinna, another name in the cuneiform tables.

With all their ability in observing and computing the Chaldeans never progressed beyond writing better and better ephemerides. They never developed an astronomical system, presumably because, primarily, they were performing a religious service. They had outgrown the omen hunting of the Assyrians, but their precise determination of astronomical events had the ultimate purpose of furnishing the proper time for religious services. Their calculations were a form of worship and they did not need to develop an astronomical system because their religion told them what the world was like.

Their astronomy did not end because of a specific political event such as a war or a siege. It just petered out; the last tables deciphered by Kugler dealt with the year 10 B.C., and later an astronomical table from 75 A.D. was found. After that, nothing.

If Chaldean astronomy was the first milestone along the path of the new science, Greek astronomy was the second. But before we can cross the Mediterranean to a country more familiar to us, both because of superior documentation and a better-known language, we have to look at Babylon's neighbors: Egypt and Israel.

In Egypt the political history may have been turbulent and difficult but the economic basis of the life of the nation was simple: it was the annual flooding of the Nile, which not only delivered water to the fields but also fertilized them because of the silt it deposited. The flooding of the river is an annual event, but it cannot be a punctual one, since it depends on the amount of snow accumulated in the mountains, its rate of melting, and other meteorological factors. A comparable event for our latitudes would be the first snow of winter. There is no doubt that it will snow and one knows roughly when to expect it, but the first snowfall does not necessarily occur on the seventh day of November. Likewise the Nile does not flood at a certain date.

In addition to fertilizing the fields, the Nile floods did two things: they forced the development of a central government (for flood regulation) very early in history, and they advanced the science of geometry for purposes of surveying areas. And though the interval between two floods may vary by several weeks, it seems to have pointed out to the Egyptians that the traditional year of 12 months of 30 days each was too short. They therefore added 5 days at the end of the twelfth month; we know them under the Greek name of *"epagomenes,"* which just means "added days." As far as the Egyptians were concerned, the result was a charming five-day festival, since somebody in authority had come to the pleasant conclusion that it would probably be unlucky to work during these days.

As we well know, 365 days is still too short, but the error of about one-quarter of one day would not soon be noticed in a land of almost continuous sunshine and with an economy based on irregular river floods. The error takes 120 years to build up to one month; if you were watching for the Nile floods they would seem to arrive later and later in the year. In Egypt, as elsewhere, the priests were in charge of the calendar and they did notice the discrepancy after enough time had gone by. But instead of revising the calendar they made a distinction between calendar rites, such as the celebration of the arrival of the new year, and the religious ceremonies which accompanied such agricultural activities as sowing after the flood had retreated. The calendar (including the 5 *epagomenes*) remained firm, let the agricultural rites fall when they might. One might say the Egyptians used two calendars simultaneously, a fictitious one for religious purposes and a real one for agriculture. The majority of the people not only did not care, they didn't even know.

The Egyptians, living under a normally cloudless sky from which the stars shone brilliantly, naturally evolved their own set of constellations.[7] Some of them were more or less the same as ours, though with different names (our Big Dipper is the "Bull," our Little Dipper the "Hippopotamus"), while others, like the "Crocodile" and the "Sparrow Hawk," are not. Just to make our life difficult—or so it seems—their tomb paintings of constellations show only pictures of the Crocodile or the Bull (or just the animal's foreleg) without much indication of which stars were used to make up the constellation.

The Egyptians did not try to construct tables like those of the Chaldeans. During the day they used sundials and for the night hours they had water clocks. Abstract thought seems to have been far from their minds. The only star to which they paid attention was Sothis (Sirius); it seems that Sirius, as observed from Memphis, the capital, once became visible in the morning twilight just above the eastern horizon when the river started to rise. But the interest in the appearance of

---

[7] A fair portion of *l'Astronomie Égyptienne* by Eugenios Marie Antoniadi (Paris, 1934) is devoted to the Egyptian constellations.

Sirius must have been purely symbolical. In the first place, the whole calendar was fictitious, so that it could not be used to predict the rising of the star. In the second place, even with a correct calendar, the appearance of Sirius on the morning horizon and the beginning of the flood could have agreed only by coincidence.

At a later date embroideries were added. Sirius, as compared with the Egyptian calendar, is one day "early" every four years; hence it would be four times 365 years, or 1460 years, before Sirius rose on the same date again. This interval was later called the "Sothic Period" and much ink was spent on speculations about the rites connected with it. It was all a later invention; the Egyptians did not use such a period.

Just about two centuries ago western Europe became interested in Egypt—as a by-product of Napoleon's campaign?—and in every literary salon there was discussion of its enormous temples, of the pyramids, the Sphinx, and the intriguing but totally nonlegible script traditionally referred to as hieroglyphics. Linguists, especially French linguists, began to wonder whether it might not be possible to decipher the hieroglyphics. Some early valiant attempts miscarried, until the famous Rosetta stone (found in 1799) provided a clue because it repeats the same decree in hieroglyphics, in demotic script, and in Greek.

But as the Europeans looked at the colossal stone structures and as they worked their way through the papyri which they were slowly learning to read, they began to notice the absence of something. Had there been no Egyptian astronomy? At first nobody was especially disturbed—papyri which were astronomical texts would be discovered sooner or later. But as time, and discoveries, went on and there still was no sign of Egyptian astronomy, speculation developed. Assuming that the priests had considered astronomical knowledge sacred, it was unlikely that it had been entrusted to a papyrus which anyone might find. Hence the logical conclusion was that the priests had hidden their astronomical knowledge in some manner.

But where and how?

John Taylor, bookseller and publisher in London, thought he had found the answer and put it down in a book, *The Great Pyramid, Why It Was Built and Who Built It,* which he published in 1859. The main idea was that the knowledge was hidden in plain sight, in a form which would mean nothing to those not initiated, but which would tell everything to those who were. The knowledge was hidden in those large and otherwise inexplicable structures, the pyramids, especially in one of them, the so-called Great Pyramid, also known as the pyramid of Cheops.[8]

This pyramid is located about six miles west of Cairo. Because other smaller pyramids were built near it at a later date the locality is now known as the "pyramid plateau." Why Khufu chose this site is not stated in any known inscriptions, but a few logical reasons quickly come to mind. The site is near enough Khufu's summer palace for him to have watched the construction. He probably did. Also, the area would be covered with water during the annual flood, so that the blocks of stone, mostly quarried nearby, could be floated to the site on rafts. Since the peasants were idle during the flood they could be pressed into service without loss to the national economy. Still another likely reason for Khufu's choice—stressed by Egyptian egyptologists—is that there seems to be a natural rocky outcropping at that point. This is now hidden by the pyramid itself, but its existence obviously saved a good deal of work when the nearly solid structure was built over and around it.

King Khufu built the pyramid as his tomb and monument, but since John Taylor had decided that it had been built to hide secrets he started looking for them. What, for example, did the height of the pyramid signify? Taking a statement about the pyramid's original height he concluded that it was 1/270,000 of the circumference of the earth. The only possible answer is "why not?" since a great many measurements are fractions of the earth's circumference. (I just "discovered" that the wingspan of the Boeing 720 jet passenger liner is one millionth of the equatorial circumference of the earth, which fact must have great significance.) Taylor himself must have felt that such a ratio did not carry much conviction; he continued looking. In England, in Taylor's time, a measure for wheat, called a Quarter, was in use. But there was no "whole" for this "quarter." Taylor found that the English measure was precisely one quarter of the cubic volume of the stone chest which had "mistakenly" been called the sarcophagus. He also discovered that the square of the height of the pyramid, compared to the area of one of its triangular faces, was a demonstration of the "golden section." This is the division of a straight line into two unequal parts in such a manner that the ratio of the shorter to the longer is the same as the ratio of

---

[8] This is the Greek version of the name; they pronounced it sounding the "ch" as a guttural. The Egyptian name of the ruler transliterates from the hieroglyphics as *Hwfw*, which—in order to pronounce it at all—is pronounced Khufu. As for the word "pyramid," the Egyptian term was *pir-em-us*, which actually meant the height of the pyramid. The Greeks adapted the word to their language as *pyramis*, using it for the structure as a whole. The next step was the formation of a plural: *pyramides*. The current word "pyramid" (which is the same in most western languages) is an artificial singular constructed from the Greek plural.

the longer to the whole. Mathematicians, Taylor wrote, credit Euclid with the discovery of the golden section, but here was a much older example.

Unfortunately Taylor found a disciple who actually was a scientist. He was Charles Piazzi Smyth, son of an English admiral and incidentally an uncle of Robert Stephenson Smyth Baden-Powell, the founder of the Boy Scouts. Charles Piazzi Smyth was born at Naples on January 3, 1819. Professor Giuseppe Piazzi, S. J., discoverer of the planetoid Ceres, who was his godfather, expressed the hope that the baby would grow up to be an astronomer. The baby did; he rose to be Astronomer Royal for Scotland, making very valuable contributions to the then new science of spectroscopy. But John Taylor convinced him that Khufu's pyramid was a place of concealed secrets, and the result was intellectual disaster.

Having far greater astronomical knowledge than Taylor and also much more practice in finding mathematical relationships, Smyth had little trouble in seeing things Taylor had overlooked. The book he wrote was entitled *Our Inheritance in the Great Pyramid*; it appeared in 1864 and ran to 600 pages. The main "secret" it disclosed was that the Egyptians had known how to "square the circle"; in the pyramid this was demonstrated by the fact that the bottom square was equal in area to a circle drawn with the height of the pyramid as its radius.[9] The base of the pyramid was 3055.24 feet long, according to the best measurement Smyth could find. Neither height nor slope angle could be measured directly. Originally the pyramid had been built of granite blocks which formed the steps we can see now. But the blocks had been covered with a casing of white limestone; when new the pyramid had smooth slopes and was blinding white under the desert sun. Herodotus saw it still that way, but later the limestone casing was removed for other building projects; pieces of the pyramid casing now form parts of mosques in the area.

Since the height could not be measured, Smyth had to approach the problem from the other end. The slope angle was somewhere near 52 degrees. Smyth found that it must have been 51°51'14.3", which produced a height of 486.256 feet. Therefore the ratio of height to circumference was 2π. That Smyth, after these mathematical manipulations, could say that he had "discovered" this ratio is incredible. In reality he had put it in. And he followed this method all the way through.

One side of the pyramid, at its base, measured 763.81 feet; dividing

---

[9] In fairness it should be mentioned that proof of the insolubility of this problem was still in the future. Ferdinand Lindemann published it in 1882, showing that π is a so-called transcendental number which cannot be constructed.

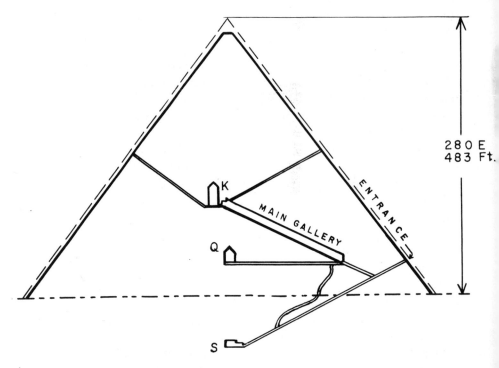

280 E
483 Ft.

Cross section through the Great Pyramid. The dotted line marks the now-missing limestone sheath. K is the king's burial chamber, Q the so-called (actually unused) Queen's chamber, and S an underground chamber

this figure by 365.2422 Smyth obtained a unit of length of a little more than 2 feet. He called this the "pyramid meter" and then proclaimed that the Egyptians, by making the base 365.2422 pyramid meters long, had shown that they knew the number of days in the year. Then he divided the pyramid meter into 25 parts to obtain the "pyramid inch." By a strange coincidence it was nearly the same as the English inch. But this was *not* a coincidence, according to Smyth; the pyramid inch had simply remained in use even though the carelessness of later artisans had shortened it by a small fraction. (Since this "proved" that the inch was sacred, a group of people in Boston, in 1879, started a movement for outlawing the "atheist metric system." The group had the support of President James Garfield.)

The pyramid inch led to many additional discoveries. Multiply it by 10^7 and you have the length of the polar axis of the earth—or you would have if the length were what Smyth thought it was. Express the height of the pyramid in pyramid inches and multiply this figure by 10^9

and you have the distance of the sun from the earth. The result is 91,840,000 miles, which is neither the maximum distance at aphelion, nor the minimum distance at perihelion, nor even the mean distance.

As for the sarcophagus, it was not only the original "whole" for the Quarter, it was more. Express its volume in cubed pyramid meters (5.7) and you have the specific gravity of the earth—too bad that the true figure happens to be 5.22. As for the whole volume of the pyramid, it gave, when expressed in cubic pyramid inches, the total number of all the people who have walked the earth since Creation.

I'll omit later discoveries made by other pyramidologists—such as that great events in history are indicated by cracks in the granite slabs forming the inclined tunnel called the "main gallery"—and restrict myself to the mathematics pertaining to astronomy. Even those who rejected Piazzi Smyth's manipulations had to admit that the slope angle, which could be measured, was close to the slope required for the golden section and also to that required for expressing π. Nobody could say that the Egyptians had *not* tried to do either of these things. But one also could not claim that they had.

The mystery was not solved until the German egyptologist Ludwig Borchardt did what Smyth should have done, namely, find out how the Egyptians of the time of Khufu measured distances and angles. Borchardt explained [10] that the unit of length was something he called the Egyptian ell, since it was similar to the later ell in length. Two types of ell were in use, the ordinary ell which was 6 palms long and the "royal ell" which was 7 palms long. Naturally it was the royal ell which was used for the king's tomb.

According to Borchardt one palm was 75 millimeters or just about 3 inches. But more important for the problem at hand was the way the Egyptians measured angles, or, in this case, a slope. Problems, with their answers, which are contained in the *Papyrus Rhind,* tell us how it was done. A slope was expressed like a step in a staircase, by giving the vertical height and the horizontal distance from the vertical (see diagram). The height, for purposes of calculation, was always taken to be 1 ell and the slope was expressed as the deviation from the vertical for 1 ell, say 5½ palms. In modern terms, a slope of 5½ palms is a 51° 50.6′ slope. And here you had an interesting coincidence:

[10] *Gegen die Zahlenmystik an der Grossen Pyramide von Giseh* (Against the Number Mysticism of the Great Pyramid at Giza. Berlin, 1923).

		SLOPE	
	FOR π	FOR 5½ PALMS	GOLDEN SECTION
slope angle	51° 51.2′	51° 50.6′	51° 49.6′
slope (Egyptian)	5.4979 P.	5.5000 P.	5.5032 P.
baseline for a height of 280 ells	439.82 E.	440 E.	440.24 E.

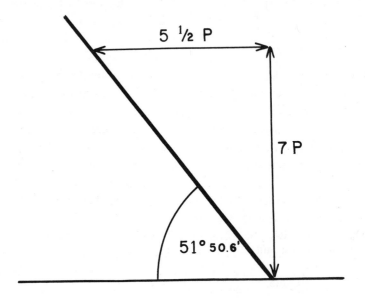

The way the builders of the Great Pyramid measured angles

It so happened that the 5½-palm slope produced an angle which could be interpreted as π or as the golden section. That the Egyptians did not try for it is shown in the same *Papyrus Rhind,* where it is stated that a square with a side of ⁸⁄₉ of a circle's diameter will have the same area as that circle. In our system this makes $\pi = 3.1604$ (larger than the correct value of 3.14159 . . .), so that a pyramid in which the Egyptians had tried to embody *their* value for π would have had a different slope.

Somebody might still argue that the Egyptians tried for the golden section, but there is no indication that they knew it.

After this excursion into silliness, we can turn to Babylon's other neighbor, Israel.

To the best of my knowledge no Jewish scholar has yet gone through the classical Jewish writings with a view of determining the astronomical knowledge (or beliefs) of the Jews in, say, 500 B.C. But the Italian astronomer Giovanni Virginio Schiaparelli, whose name will be encoun-

tered again and again in this book, published a work entitled *L'astronomia nell' Antico Testamento* in Milan in 1903. The title, of course,
means "Astronomy in the Old Testament," [11] and the main surprise for
the reader is that there is so little of it. But for the Jews of Old Testament times a reason can be found. The examples of Old Babylon, where
the lights in the sky were considered the seats of the gods (and by the
common man, no doubt, the gods themselves), and of Assyria, where
what I called proto-astrology (astrology from precedent rather than from
rules) dominated life, were "horrible examples" to the Jews. Zephaniah
(1:5) said that the Lord told him He would "cut off" all those "that
worship the host of heaven upon the housetops."

The one who was most violent in his expressions was Isaiah: "Let
now the astrologers, the star-gazers, the monthly prognosticators [of
the new moon], stand up, and save thee from these things that shall
come upon thee. Behold, they shall be as stubble; the fire. shall burn
them; they shall not deliver themselves from the power of the flame."
(47:13-14.)

Isaiah was so furious about the influences—and inroads?—of Assyrian
thought that he predicted the end of the starry sky itself: "And all the
host of heaven shall be dissolved, and the heavens shall be rolled together as a scroll; and all their host shall fall down, as the leaf falleth
off from the vine . . ." (34:4.)

With this attitude, which rejected the study of the sky as both "foreign" and "godless," astronomy could not develop among the Jews.
As Schiaparelli puts it: "Small wonder that astronomy among the He-
brews remained at about the level which, as we know, has been reached
by some non-literate peoples of the Americas and in Polynesia . . ."
The general picture of the world, as Schiaparelli traced it, was that of
a flattened sphere with a plane through its center. That plane was the
land and the surface of the waters, below was the abyss, above, the air
which supported the clouds. Apparently the top of this sphere was pictured as being transparent, for indications are that the sun and the
moon were thought to be above the upper part of the sphere.

The astronomical phenomena known to the Jews were mainly the sun
and the moon and the eclipses. Not knowing what caused the eclipses
they regarded them as omens of punishments to come: "the sun shall
be turned into darkness and the moon into blood, before the great and
the terrible day of the Lord come." (Joel 2:31.) As almost everybody

---

[11] It was translated into German in 1904 as *Die Astronomie im Alten Testament,* by the librarian Dr. Willy Lüdtke, who added notes, especially from a
German work by Eberhard Schrader about correlations between the Old Testament and cuneiform inscriptions. I have used this German translation.

knows, the eclipsed moon often looks dark red; therefore this line almost certainly refers to eclipses. It is quite possible that Joel did see an eclipse himself. Theodor von Oppolzer's *Kanon der Finsternisse* (a comprehensive list of eclipses from 1207 B.C. to 2163 A.D.) lists total eclipses visible from Palestine on August 15, 831 B.C.; April 2, 824 B.C.; and June 15, 763 B.C.; and also two annular eclipses, on March 2, 832 B.C., and October 6, 825 B.C.

Of the planets only two appear to be mentioned in the Old Testament. The reference in Isaiah (14:12) "How art thou fallen from heaven, oh Lucifer, son of the morning!" can only mean Venus as a morning star. The other planet is less certain; the verse in question is the one of Amos (5:26): "But yet have borne the tabernacle of your Moloch and Chiun your images, the star of your god . . ." The word rendered as Chiun in this translation can be read either as *Kijjûn* or as *Kêwan,* depending on which vowels are inserted into the vowel-less text. *Kêwan* was the name of the planet Saturn among the Syrians and also among the Persians, but Schiaparelli pointed out that a German expert had reasons to believe that the word, at the time of Amos, meant the planet Mars. Since Mars is much more conspicuous than Saturn, it seems a more likely choice.

Of the fixed stars and constellations only a very few are named and most of the references are in the Book of Job. The stars *kîmah* and *kesîl* (Job 38:31) are the Pleiades and (probably) Orion, while *ajish* (Job 38:32) must be the Hyades. Two other constellations are relatively easy to identify; a third mentioned in the same passage is a surprise. The verse is Job 37:9, which is usually translated as "out of the south cometh the whirlwind; and cold out of the north." But in the original the words "north" and "south" are the names of constellations. The northern one is either *mizrajim* or *mizrîm*; the first is the dual and the second the plural of the word *mizreh,* which means "winnowing shovel." The *mizrajim* are, therefore, the two winnowing shovels, the Big and the Little Dipper. "South" in the original is *chadrê thêman,* the "chambers of the South." We do not know all the stars which were considered to belong to the "chambers of the South," but we do know that among them were the "upper" stars of the Southern Cross, part of which then was visible above the horizon from Palestine.

Although Isaiah ranted against star-gazers, and in Job (38:5) the Lord asks, "Who has laid the measures thereof [of the earth], if thou knowest? or who hath stretched the line upon it?"—indicating that measuring the earth was a superhuman task—the simple fact remained that the Jews could not do without a calendar. And that calendar was a lunar calendar; even the word for month (*jerach*) is closely related to the word for moon (*jareach*), just as the two words are in English. As with their despised neighbors, the new month began when the crescent first became visible, and even the names of the months were quite like the Babylonian names. But it is interesting and significant that the Bible almost always just said, "the third month" or "the fifth month." Since these were purely lunar months, an extra month was needed from time to time; it was made to follow the twelfth month and, when named, was called *we-Adar,* literally "and Adar," meaning second Adar.

Though there can be no doubt that the first astronomers were the Chaldeans, during the latter part of their history, they were no longer the only ones. Greek thinkers had done much thinking and wondering of their own, and though they often used to refer to "the ancients," usually meaning the Chaldeans, their ideas certainly were not all based on Chaldean work. Just how much influence the Chaldeans actually had on the Greeks probably cannot be established at this late date.

One connecting link is known. A Chaldean whose name is known in the obviously Grecianized form of "Berossos" settled on the island of Cos around 280 B.C. Cos, the second largest of the Dodecanese Islands, thereby acquired the fame of being the seat of the first Chaldean school of astronomy in the Greek world. But it was the only one, for by the time Berossos took ship for Cos the astronomy of his predecessors was on the decline, while that of the Greeks was beginning to bear flower and fruit.

2

THE GREEK ASTRONOMERS

THE very fact that the science of the stars is called "astronomy" documents the important place which the Greeks held in the development of this field of knowledge. The word is derived from αστερ (aster) or αστρον (astron), meaning "star" and νόμος (nómos) meaning "law." There were two other linguistic possibilities: the second part of the word could have been γνῶσις (gnosis), meaning "knowledge," or else it could have been λογος (logos), which really means "instruction" but can be used to mean knowledge. In fact, these two possible words do exist. The first, astrognosis, is, as was mentioned in Chapter 1, the name of a subdivision in the history of astronomy (or, if you prefer, a branch of the history of mythology, since it relates to the names of constellations). The other word is astrology.

The words are the same in most languages, with a few small variations in spelling and pronunciation. During the last centuries the Germans made an attempt at translating the Greek-derived words, using *Sternkunde* for astronomy (the Dutch word is very similar) and *Sterndeutung* for astrology. But these German translations remained words one might use in writing; they did not penetrate normal speech. The Greek influence goes further.

The planets have that designation because of the Greek word πλανητης (planetes), meaning "wanderers," which, among the fixed stars, they are. Comets have their name because of the Greek word κομητης (kometes) which means "long-haired." Even the pole has a Greek name; the word "pole" comes from πολείν (polein), "to turn over" or "to turn around." And the word "zone" is just the Greek word for "belt."

Like other peoples, the Greeks evolved their own proto-astronomy. But while for all other ethnic groups (as, for example, the Polynesians, who are known to have had such factual lore), we have to guess at examples, for the Greeks we have an example in writing. It is contained in the work which one of my teachers invariably called "the only and ultimate epic," Homer's *Odyssey*. The lines in question probably date back to 600 B.C. and may be as early as 800 B.C. They are the ones called Kalypso's Sailing Instructions.

Keeping the raft to her course by the helm with the skill of a sailor,
Seated he steered (not for a moment did drowsiness fall on his eyelids),
Holding the Pleiads in view and the autumn-setting Boötes,
Holding moreover the Bear, that is called by the name of the Wagon.
(Ever she circles around and around on the watch for Orion,
Having alone of all stars no share in the baths of the ocean.)
Her—since thus had commanded the beautiful goddess Kalypso—
Voyaging over the ocean he steadily held on his left hand. . . .[1]

Since this means navigation on a northeasterly course and since Odysseus finally arrived in southwestern Spain, the origin of the voyage could only have been Madeira.[2]

Hesiod, who in all likelihood was Homer's contemporary, also transmitted bits of such knowledge:

Then when the stars of the Pleiads, the daughters of Atlas, are rising
Harvest begins, but the seeding takes place when they are setting.
(Lines 383–384)

which information is repeated in lines 614–617. And

But at the time when Orion and Sirius well in the midst of the heavens
Are standing, and Eos, she of the rosy fingers, is viewing Arcturus,
Perses, cut now the grapes and gather them into your houses.
(Lines 609–611)

As regards the early astronomy of the Greeks, there would probably be no special problems in following the trends of thought if one could only be certain what was actually said by the various men whose names are in all classical history books. "Berossos taught astronomy at Cos"— fine, but what did he teach? We don't know. "Pythagoras of Samos was the most prominent of the early philosophers"—possible, but we don't really know why, since none of his writings has been preserved. Generally speaking, we do not have the works of any Greek philosophers prior to Plato and Aristotle. We cannot even say that we know the opinions of the earlier philosophers from quotations in later works. We only know some of their opinions through such quotations and we have no way of judging whether the quotations are accurate, or, even if they

---

[1] Homer's *Odyssey*, H. B. Cotterill trans. (London: Harrap, 1911), V, 270–77.
[2] This was checked by Drs. Hennig and Erpelt in 1933 by very modern means; they set the projector of the Düsseldorf planetarium back to 800 B.C. and saw that the Bear (the Big Dipper) did not touch the horizon, hence had no share in "the baths of the ocean," and that the Pleiades and Boötes emerged from the same point in the east-northeast. See *Die Geographie des Homerischen Epos,* by Richard Hennig (Leipzig, 1934).

are accurate, whether the quoted opinion is typical of the man.[3] In addition to these difficulties, which historians accept as part of their lot, ancient writers also made simple mistakes, as is shown in the case of Thales of Miletus (624–547 B.C.), the earliest of the Ionian philosophers. What we really know about his opinions is that he thought the earth to be a disk floating on water; Aristotle quoted this opinion for the purpose of criticizing it. But Thales' fame as an early astronomer rests on the story told by Herodotus that he had predicted an eclipse of the sun.

"As the Medes and the Lydians were fighting," Herodotus wrote, "it happened that in the middle of the battle the day changed into night. And this change had been predicted to the Ionians by Thales of Miletus and he had given the year in which it took place." The battle was that of the River Halys and the year was 584 B.C. But the story of Thales' prediction must have been made up *ex post facto* by one of his admirers. Nobody at the time knew how to predict a solar eclipse. The Babylonians could predict lunar eclipses some time ahead because of their careful tabulations, but the prediction of a solar eclipse is more difficult by far and would have required much more extensive tabulations than were then available. Or else it would have required a knowledge of the true situation in space, which nobody had, especially not Thales.

The next philosopher usually mentioned after Thales is Anaximander (611–546 B.C.). For him, at least, we have quite a number of quotations, preserved mainly by Aëtios, Aristotle, and Hippolytos. Fortunately these quotations do not contradict one another. The earth, according to Anaximander, "has the shape of a cylinder with a height of one third of its diameter." All the heavenly bodies "are wheel-like [wheel-shaped— Anaximander had in mind the thick solid wooden wheels of his time] condensations of air, filled with fire, and with holes from which flames emanate." "The sun is a circle 28 times as large as the earth." "The moon is a circle 19 times as large as the earth . . . it has an inclined position like the sun and only one hole [for the flames]." The lunar phases were explained by Anaximander by the rotations of this wheel, the eclipses by a temporary blocking of the hole from which the flames emanate.

In the case of Anaximander's near contemporary Anaximenes (585–

[3] The existing quotations have been collected repeatedly. Specifically devoted to Greek astronomy are *Greek Astronomy* by Sir Thomas L. Heath (London, J. M. Dent & Sons, Ltd.; New York, E. P. Dutton & Co., 1932), which gives the English translations of the existing relevant passages, and *Antike Astronomie* by Professor Heinrich Balss (Munich, 1949), which gives the Greek and Latin originals on the left-hand pages with the German translations on the right-hand pages. Because of the easy opportunity to check the original which this work provides, most quotations in his chapter are based on Professor Balss's book.

526 B.C.), the quotations do contradict one another. According to Hippolytos, Anaximenes said that "there are also earthlike bodies in the region of the stars which circle with them," while Aëtios made Anaximenes say that "the stars are like nails" affixed to the sky.

For the great Pythagoras (probably 580–500 B.C.) the sources are even more uncertain—incidentally, Aristotle never ascribed a statement or an opinion to Pythagoras personally but always quoted "the Pythagoreans." Professor Balss quotes only two statements, both from Diogenes Laërtios: "It is furthermore reported that Pythagoras was the first to call the heavens *kosmos* and that he declared the earth to be a sphere, but Theophrastos said that Parmenides said so first and Zeno credits Hesiod." "And of him [Parmenides] it is believed that he was the first to see that the morning and evening stars are the same star . . . but others say that Pythagoras was the first." [4]

Parmenides of Elea is believed to have lived from 504 to 450 B.C. Probably the only safe statement that can be made is that the sphericity of the earth was recognized between 550 and 450 B.C. But even if the credit for the two statements quoted should go to Pythagoras, Parmenides alone is credited (by Plutarch) with a new and correct thought: "Moving around the earth, he [the moon] illuminates the nights with borrowed light." This thought was expanded by "the Pythagoreans"—particularly by Philolaus of Tarentum, who lived at about the same time as Parmenides—into the idea that even the sun radiated secondary light only. The final version of this purely philosophical concept was that of the Central Fire, called *hestia* ("hearth"), and the *antichthon* ("counter-earth"), which was introduced only to bring the total number of the heavenly bodies to ten. In this concept the *hestia* was in the center of the universe. The spherical earth revolved around the central fire, which remained invisible because the *antichthon* was between the two. The sun's rays were a reflection of the *hestia*, while the moon's light was a reflection of the sun's light.

Anaxagoras of Clazomenae (probably 500–428 B.C.) must also be mentioned. He still believed in Anaximander's wheel-shaped earth but clearly stated that the sun was a glowing mass while the moon consisted of soil. He had a clear mental picture for the reason of the moon's disappearance every month ("because it is in conjunction with the sun") and also explained the eclipses. As quoted by Hippolytos, he said that "the moon will be eclipsed when the earth, and sometimes the bodies below the moon, are in line between the moon and the sun; the sun

---

[4] The Chaldeans knew that fact too, but since their tablets are not dated as a rule, the question of the priority of this discovery will never be settled.

will be eclipsed when the moon, at the dark moon phase, is between the sun and the earth."

Much of the discussion about the nature of the sun and of the moon seems to have had the purpose of serving as a basis for further-ranging philosophical speculation about the "plurality of worlds" and the question of whether other worlds, if they existed, might be inhabited. The little that is known about these discussions is reported in Chapter 21 as an introduction to the modern concepts of life on other worlds. One philosopher who took a very positive attitude on that point was Democritus the Abderite, who lived in the late fifth and early fourth centuries B.C. Here it is only necessary to mention that Democritus was the earliest philosopher known to have given the correct explanation of the Milky Way. Aëtios quotes him as having said that the *Via lactea* (the later Roman term), "consists of very many small stars, closely huddled together which, by their proximity, increase their light."

Socrates is one more of the Greek philosophers whose own writings have not survived into our time, but his philosophy has been preserved by his disciple Plato (whose original name was Aristokles). Plato, as disciple of Socrates and teacher of Aristotle, formed a most important link. And the writings of Plato have survived, much as this fact may be deplored occasionally by college students.

Socrates' attitude toward astronomical studies was, to us, not a little surprising. As reported by Xenophon,[5] it was highly "unphilosophical" and strictly utilitarian. The paragraph describing this attitude is hardly ever quoted, presumably to avoid darkening an illustrious name; it reads:

Socrates recommended the study of astronomy, but only for the purpose of telling the time of the night, of the months, and of the year, so that during travels on land or on water, or while standing watch or performing any other chores that are conducted at night, one might distinguish the times of the phenomena mentioned. This could easily be learned from hunters who hunt at night, from helmsmen and others who pay attention to such knowledge. But he warned against continuing astronomical studies to the point of becoming acquainted with those bodies which change their positions among the others, the knowledge of the planets and stars which appear only from time to time; or to spend time in investigations of their distance from the earth, or their movements and the causes of their movements. He very strongly warned against this for, as he said, he could see no value in it. Though he himself was acquainted with it he felt that this could use up a man's whole life and thereby prevent him from doing many useful things.

Plato evidently changed the master's attitude in the *Republic*, for when Glaukon says that astronomy is a useful science for agriculture,

[5] *Memorabilia* IV; 7, 4.

navigation, and warfare, Plato makes "Socrates" answer: "You are naive! Are you afraid of the multitude which might think that you recommend useless knowledge?" In the last chapter of the *Republic,* Plato pays a great deal of attention to the motion of the planets. In Plato's description of what the souls saw in heaven, the outermost whorl, called the first, is the starry sphere. It shines in many colors. "The seventh shines in the brightest light [the sun]; the eighth shines by the reflection from the seventh [the moon]; the second [Saturn] and the fifth [Mercury] resemble each other and are of a darker yellow than the others; the third has the whitest color [Jupiter]; the fourth is reddish [Mars], while the sixth [Venus] has the brightest white after the third." This passage is obviously a description of the solar system as then imagined, but additional passages do not make any astronomical sense, in spite of much playing with secondary and supposedly extended meanings of the words used. One can only agree with Sir Thomas L. Heath: "The attempt to translate the details of the poetic imagery into a self-consistent picture of physical facts is hopeless."

Even though Plato's original writings are available, the opinions expressed are not always clear. The book *Timaios* contains a sentence which was to be fought over for centuries. "The earth, our foster mother, packed round the axis which stretches through the universe, became the guardian and artisan of night and day, as the first and most venerable of the gods created within the heaven." Calling the earth the "guardian and artisan of night and day" [6] sounds suspiciously as if it was the earth which caused night and day; in other words, as if Plato had the diurnal rotation in mind.

Plutarch wondered about this too: "Did he [Plato] ascribe a motion to the earth as he ascribed motions to the sun, the moon, and the five planets which he called the instruments of time because of their turnings, and is it necessary to interpret the sentence 'the earth packed round the axis of the universe . . .' as meaning in rotation around itself, as Aristarchos and Seleukos later did, the first one calling it a hypothesis and the other one considering it a proven fact? Theophrastus adds to his report the short remark that Plato, in his later years, regretted having given the earth the place in the center of the universe which it does not deserve." All one can say now is that *if* Plato had a diurnal rotation in mind he was correct.

What Plato had said poetically Eudoxos of Knidos expressed mathematically. Eudoxos, who lived from 408 to 355 B.C., not only tried to

---

[6] The original reads: *phylaka kai demiurgon nyktós te kai heméras.* . . .

improve the Greek calendar—the term "tried" is necessary because, although his mathematics was correct, there is no evidence that anybody used his suggestions—but also produced a model of the various crystal spheres carrying the planets which, after some changes, dominated thinking for many centuries. He also named a number of conspicuous stars and compared their relative brightness. One cause of Eudoxos's future influence is something he did not do himself. His work was simply entitled *Phainómena*, and about a century later one Aratos of Soloi used both the material *and* the title for an astronomical poem which was repeatedly translated into Latin—by Cicero among others—and in that form survived into and through the Middle Ages. Even the illustrations in some of the medieval manuscripts cause experts who have examined them to suspect strongly that they, as well as the text, are of classical origin.

Modern astronomers, including G. V. Schiaparelli,[7] who examined the "spheres of Eudoxos," found that his model represents the motions of Saturn and Jupiter perfectly (as far as naked-eye observation is concerned) but cannot account for the motions of Mars and Venus. Schiaparelli had to take the information from some commentaries on Aristotle by Simplikios (often referred to as Simplicius, the Latin form of his name), who wrote during the fifth century A.D. There the periods of the revolutions of Saturn, Jupiter, and Mars are given as 30 years, 12 years, and 2 years, respectively, while 13 months is used for the synodic periods of both Jupiter and Saturn. Presumably Eudoxos could have devised a better system if he had had better measurements available. As it was, he knew about the motions described by the planets but had only very rough approximations of the periods involved.

The next important name is that of Plato's disciple Aristotle, who lived from 384 to 322 B.C., tutored Alexander the Great, taught in Athens as head of the Peripatetic School, and tried—like Alexander von Humboldt twenty-one centuries later—to know everything. His works range from *Rhetoric* and *Politics*, via *Parts of Animals* and *On Plants*, to *Metaphysics*. Aristotle's astronomical thoughts are contained mainly in his *On the Heavens*, but there are also scattered references in his *Metaphysics* and elsewhere. His goal was, of course, to produce a complete picture of the universe—one which explained everything, and left nothing out; which conformed with his teacher's idea that the celestial bodies are at least semidivine and therefore must move in circles since anything less perfect than a circle would not be fitting; and which, last

[7] In his *I precursori di Copernico nell' antichità* (The Forerunners of Copernicus in Antiquity), published in Milan in 1873. Most unfortunately, this very interesting work has never been translated into English.

but not least, clobbered the ideas of the Pythagoreans at every turn.

In his early works Aristotle followed Plato closely, but as his age, experience, and knowledge increased he drew away and became Plato's successor rather than his disciple. He became Plato's "successor" in another sense, too, at a much later date. During the first millennium after Christ, the words "The Philosopher" meant Plato; subsequently they meant Aristotle. The later Middle Ages indulged in a kind of Aristotle cult; if a fact could not be found in his works, that fact obviously did not exist. And universities in Europe, before installing anyone as a professor, made him swear an oath that he agreed with the views of Aristotle "and especially with his view on the nature of the comets." This long and naturally sterile period of "Aristotaliarism" caused many later condemnations of Aristotle's teachings, which were both ill-tempered and fully justified. But for his own time Aristotle took a decidedly long step forward.

To Plato the "real" world consisted of ideas, and the visible and tangible world was merely a more or less deceptive apparition of the "real" world; to Aristotle the world of visible phenomena was the real world, with ideas as the essence of these phenomena. The purpose of philosophy was still to recognize the ideas, but in order to do so one had to know everything about the visible phenomena and this knowledge had to be as precise as it could be made. Therefore he urged careful observation and description—and even some experimentation; he himself dissected the bodies of marine creatures. So far one can only applaud, but Aristotle's fundamental mistake was to underestimate the magnitude of the task and to conclude that he personally knew enough to draw conclusions. The picture of the universe at which he arrived was most harmonious and, in a way, logical; the fundamental assumption being that the universe must be perfect and since there is only one perfect body, namely the sphere, it has to be spherical.

The four "elements"—earth, water, air, and fire—have "natural" movements, downward for earth and water, upward for air and fire. Aristotle was careful to explain something which must still be said even now in lectures on space travel—that "upward" means away from the center and "downward" means toward the center. The center, of course, is the earth, consisting of earth and water and being spherical in shape. The air is the next layer, then the fire, and high up, where air and fire are mixed, the mixture is sometimes ignited and appears in the shape of meteors and of comets. Though the earth is not very large it is heavy and therefore at rest. The celestial bodies, which are made of a fifth element more perfect than the earthly four, are spherical in shape and move on crystalline spheres. The universe as a whole is not only spherical but also finite because it cannot be infinite. If it were, one of the elements would have to be infinite, which means that there could then be no room for the other elements. Moreover the universe must be finite since an infinite circle cannot exist. And there are no changes in the universe; all the changes that have been observed, all the changes there can be, take place inside the sphere of the moon where the four earthly elements can be found.

Let us conclude the discussion of Aristotle with a direct quotation—one of his many unkind remarks about the Pythagoreans:

. . . the statement that the motion of the celestial bodies causes a musical harmony . . . is quite ingenious but fails to be the truth. To some thinkers it seems to be a necessary consequence that the motion of such large bodies must produce a noise, since this is true of bodies moving on earth even though they have a far lesser volume and do not move at such enormous velocities. But where the sun and the moon, and a multitude of enormous bodies, move with such velocities, a noise with a volume beyond comprehension must be produced. This they assume and they also assume that the velocities because of the varying distances represent the relationships of a musical harmony. . . . Since it seems incredible that we do not hear this sound they explain that we are not conscious of it because we hear it from the moment we are born. . . .

Aristotle's contemporary, Heraklides of Pontus (388–315 B.C.), is said to have been another disciple of Plato and seems to have written about as voluminously as Aristotle, but none of his writings have survived. The same Simplikios who furnished a description of the spheres of Eudoxos says about Heraklides at one point, "by supposing that the earth is at the center and moves in a circle [the meaning is "rotates"] and the heaven is at rest, he thought to save the phenomena." The term "to save the phenomena" is a figure of speech meaning to account, geometrically, for the observed positions and movements. Heraklides evidently accounted for the phenomena by having the earth turn on its axis and the sphere with the fixed stars remain at rest.

Heraklides also proposed something else which we know to be correct. The prevailing idea all along had been that the celestial bodies moved along spheres. To some, like Eudoxos, these spheres were mere mathematical abstractions, while to others, like Aristotle, they were real. But the motion along a sphere did not satisfy observations; hence combinations of spheres had to be imagined. When drawn on a piece of slate, or on a piece of papyrus or whatever happened to be at hand, the spheres naturally turned into circles and the big circle was later called the *deferent*. The smaller circle on the bigger one was called the epicycle. In order to make everything perfect, the actually visible celestial body had to move with a uniform velocity along the epicycle, while the center of the epicycle moved with a uniform velocity along the deferent. This nicely "saved the phenomena" of Jupiter and Saturn and could be made, with some difficulty, to work for Mars. But it never worked with Mercury and Venus, and Aristotle wisely did not talk about them. Venus and Mercury appeared to the right and left of the sun and it was difficult even to decide where the spheres of the two should be. Some mathematical philosophers, or philosophizing mathematicians, put them beyond the sun, so that, counting from the earth outward, the moon came first, the sun next, then Mercury, and farther out Venus. Others felt they came closer to an explanation with the sequence Moon, Mercury, Venus, Sun (and then Mars and the outer planets). Heraklides solved the difficulty by proposing that the sun moved directly along the main circles while Mercury and Venus moved on epicycles *around the sun* as the center.

And then came Aristarchos of Samos.

We are not too lucky as regards Aristarchos. His work containing the main idea in which we are interested has not been preserved directly. In fact only one of his works, entitled "On the Sizes and Distances of the Sun and the Moon"[8], survived by being part of a collection of short writings on astronomy and related themes which was generally referred to as the *Small Composition* and fortunately often copied, both in the original Greek and in Arabic. The *Small Composition* contained two works by Euclid, two by Autolycus, three by Theodosius, and one each by Hypsikles and Aristarchos. The work will be discussed soon, but Aristarchos' main idea has to come first.

Probably the best second-hand source for the lost book of Aristarchos—who, incidentally, died in 230 B.C. at the age of eighty—is the famous *Psammites* or "Sand-Reckoner" of Archimedes:

But Aristarchos of Samos brought out a book consisting of certain hypotheses, in which the premises lead to the conclusion that the universe is many times greater than that now so called. His hypotheses are that the fixed stars and the sun remain motionless, that the earth revolves about the sun in the circumference of a circle, the sun lying in the middle of the orbit, and that the sphere of the fixed stars, situated about the same center as the sun, is

---

[8] The Greek text was printed for the first time in Oxford in 1688, edited by John Wallis. It had been preceded by two Latin translations, one by Georgius Valla (1488) and one by Federico Commandino (1572). Sir Thomas L. Heath, in his *Aristarchus of Samos, the Ancient Copernicus*, (Oxford: Clarendon Press, 1913) also gives the Greek text with an English translation. A German translation by A. Nokk was published in Freiburg im Breisgau in 1854, a French translation by Comte de Fortia d'Urban in Paris in 1823.

so great that the circle in which he supposes the earth to revolve bears such a proportion to the distance of the fixed stars as the center of the sphere bears to its surface.

Now it is easy to see that this is impossible; for, since the center of the sphere has no magnitude, we cannot conceive it to bear any ratio whatever to the surface of the sphere. We must, therefore, take Aristarchos to mean this: since we conceive the earth to be, as it were, the center of the Universe, the ratio which the earth bears to what we describe as the "universe" is the same as the ratio which the sphere containing the circle in which he supposes the earth to revolve bears to the sphere of the fixed stars. (Translation, Sir Thomas L. Heath, in *Greek Astronomy*)

Plutarch, in his *On the Face in the Moon,* is another witness to Aristarchos's anticipation of Copernicus; he has one of his disputants say: "Only do not, my good fellow, enter an action against me for impiety in the style of Kleanthes, who thought it was the duty of the Greeks to indict Aristarchos of Samos on the charge of impiety for putting in motion the Hearth of the Universe, this being the effect of his attempt to save the phenomena by supposing the heaven to remain at rest, and the earth to revolve in an oblique circle, while it rotates, at the same time, about its own axis."

Here we have the clearest possible evidence for a modern concept in antiquity: the earth rotates on its axis while moving around the sun, and the term "oblique circle" used by Plutarch obviously refers to the inclination of the earth's orbit to the earth's equator. It would be interesting to know how far Aristarchos went. Evidently he also had Mercury and Venus revolving around the sun as Heraklides had done before him. And to "save the phenomena" for the outer planets he must have arranged them in the modern order. That much can be taken for granted. But did he have the courage to do away with the epicycles? We don't know. An ancient manuscript copy of his book may turn up somewhere—Plutarch, who died in 120 A.D., presumably saw one—and recent experience with the Dead Sea Scrolls makes one hopeful of similar finds elsewhere.

The book we do have, the one preserved in the *Small Composition,* is a carefully written geometrical text. Sir Thomas Heath says about the style that it is "thoroughly classical, as befits an able geometer intermediate in date between Euclid and Archimedes, and his demonstrations are worked out with the same rigor as those of his predecessor and successor." It begins with a number of statements, called "hypotheses," which either have to be accepted (i.e., "The moon receives its light from the sun" and "The earth is in the center of the sphere of the moon"—we would say in the center of its orbit), or which can be proved (i.e., "When the moon appears halved the great circle which divides the dark and the bright portions of the moon [the "terminator" of later terminology] is in the direction of our eye"), or which could be measured by observation. In the last category is Hypothesis No. 6: "The moon subtends one fifteenth part of a sign of the zodiac." Since one sign of the zodiac traditionally measures 30 degrees this would make the apparent diameter of the moon 2 degrees, and that of the sun the same, since Aristarchos stated that they have the same apparent diameter. Nobody has advanced a convincing explanation of how this error crept in; my personal belief is that the book is the work of a fairly young man who in this case repeated what somebody else had told him. It was *not,* as one might suspect, a "traditional figure," for it is found nowhere else.

In any event he corrected it himself at a later date, for Archimedes, in *Psammites,* credits him with the discovery that the apparent diameter of the sun is about $\frac{1}{720}$ of the zodiac, or ½ degree, which is very close to the true value.

Aristarchos's method is based on the fact that earth, sun, and moon must form a triangle in space with one angle of 90 degrees at the moon, when the moon appears halved to us. The sharpest angle of this triangle, the one at the sun, is given as 3 degrees. This figure is a heavy over-estimate and we don't know where Aristarchos got it. Pannekoek, in discussing this, says: "These Greek scholars were mathematicians rather than astronomers; the celestial bodies just happened to be the objects of their geometrical propositions. Hence the astronomical quantities were treated somewhat superficially, their precise value did not matter; ingenuity was exhibited in the solution of the geometrical problem." [9]

The 3-degree angle at the sun is another thing that makes me assume that we are dealing with the work of a young man. He probably started out, as Pannekoek suggested, as a geometer, interested in the geometrical problem. Later on he apparently began to check the figures he had been given by others. As we have seen, he revised the figure for the apparent diameter of the sun (which applies to the moon, too) and he may have recalculated his earlier work, then finding the long distances mentioned by Archimedes and revising the whole concept of the "universe" as a result of his new figures.

But even his first work broke ground, and it spurred others on to do additional work. Aristarchos had shown that the distances *could* be measured, and others went ahead.

[9] *A History of Astronomy,* op. cit.

The Size and Distance of Sun and Moon
(The figures are in earth diameters)

	MOON		SUN	
	DISTANCE	DIAMETER	DISTANCE	DIAMETER
Aristarchos of Samos (310–230 B.C.)	9½	⁹⁄₂₅ = 0.36	180	6¾
Hipparchos of Nicaea (162?–126? B.C.)	33⅔	⅓ = 0.33	1245	12⅓
Posidonios of Rhodes (135–51 B.C.)	26⅕	³⁄₁₉ = 0.157	6545	39¼
Ptolemy (Claudius Ptolemaios) (c. 100–160 A.D.)	29½	⁵⁄₁₇ = 0.29	605	5½
Modern	30.2	0.27	11,726	108.9

(Sir Thomas Heath, op. cit.)

But the concept of the moving earth was still too much for the third century B.C. to accept. About a century after Aristarchos one Seleukos "the Babylonian" is mentioned as having taught what we now call the Copernican theory, but thereafter nothing is heard of it until Copernicus's own time.

However, it is interesting that the designation "the Babylonian" should crop up again in the second century B.C. Just as, in earlier times, the Chaldeans and the Babylonians had undergone a cultural merger, in the centuries preceding the time of Christ, the Greeks and the peoples of the Near East had merged culturally. Because of the conquests of Alexander, the Persian Empire and other parts of western Asia had become accessible and "his" city, Alexandria, capital of Greek-ruled Egypt, became in every respect the capital of the western world, in terms of commerce as well as literature and science. The main interest was in philology, medicine probably ranked next, and after medicine, astronomy, in which Chaldean tables and Greek geometry united. The government was firmly in the hands of the long line of the Ptolemies.[10]

During this "Hellenistic Period" the "Alexandrian school" of astronomy came into being. Two of the earliest of these astronomers, from the period 296–272 B.C., were Aristyllus and Timocharis, who were mentioned by Ptolemy. But the first man of this school to do something novel was a geographer. He was Eratosthenes, born around 270 B.C. at Cyrene in Africa and called to Alexandria by Ptolemy Euergetes, to become one of the first directors of the famous library there.

Eratosthenes was the first to estimate accurately the size of the earth.

[10] The astronomer Ptolemy, the Ptolemaios of the Greeks and Claudius Ptolemaeus of the Romans, was almost certainly *not* related to the Egyptian royal house; the name seems to have been fairly common.

His method was as ingenious as it was simple. To the south of Alexandria was the town of Syene, the modern Aswan, 5000 stadia away, according to the royal messengers. At Syene there was a deep well and on the longest day of the year the midday sun's rays illuminated the bottom of the well, which meant that the sun was vertically over Syene. But at noon on the same day in Alexandria the sun still cast a shadow. By measuring the length of that shadow Eratosthenes could easily calculate that the distance from Alexandria to Syene was $\frac{1}{50}$ of the total circumference of the earth. Hence the circumference was 50 times 5000 or 250,000 stadia.

It was a calculation full of minor mistakes. As we now know, Aswan is not due south of Alexandria, nor is it precisely under the Tropic of Cancer; hence the sun is not precisely overhead at Aswan at noon on the day of the summer solstice. Moreover, the figure of 5000 stadia given by the King's runners was of course a round figure. But these various minor mistakes happened to cancel each other, for if we use the probable value of 515 feet for the stadion used by Eratosthenes we find that he came astonishingly close—128,750,000 feet versus the simplified modern value of 131,294,000 feet (obtained by considering the earth a sphere instead of a spheroid and using the mean of polar and equatorial diameters). The Stoic philosopher Posidonios, mentioned in the table of classical determinations of solar and lunar distances, repeated the experiment in about 100 B.C., using the bright star Canopus which would be 7½ degrees above the horizon in Alexandria while it was at the horizon at Rhodes. His finding was 240,000 stadia, quite good considering that the distance from Rhodes to Alexandria is not the 5000 stadia that he assumed. Also we do not know what allowance, if any, he made for the refraction of the starlight in our atmosphere.

The next great name in the history of Greek astronomy is that of Hipparchos, who also worked mainly on the island of Rhodes. Most of what we know of his work was preserved by Ptolemy. In consequence, the system of the world with the earth in its center, which Aristotle advocated so strongly, is now generally spoken of as the Ptolemaic System. It would be simpler to call this the geocentric system, but if any man's name has to be attached to it, it should be that of Hipparchos, since he actually developed the theory to its highest form; Ptolemy merely perpetuated it.

The three treatises of Hipparchos, mentioned by Ptolemy, but not directly known, were entitled *On the Length of the Year, On Intercalation of Months and Days,* and *On the Change of the Solstices and Equinoxes*, and they give a good idea of the work in which Hipparchos

was mainly engaged. It was calendar work for the most part. He rede-
termined the lunar period as 29 days, 12 hours, 44 minutes, and 2.5
seconds; about one second too short. The length of the year, according
to Hipparchos, was "365¼ day diminished by nearly $\frac{1}{300}$ of a day."
He apparently was troubled by the realization that his year and the
Babylonian year did not agree and tried to find an explanation. It
turned out to be his greatest discovery. A year could either be the
return to (the position of) a star. Or it could be the return to the
equinoctial point. Hipparchos, to quote Ptolemy's description, "by careful comparison of observed lunar eclipses of his own time with others
which had been observed by Timocharis in earlier times, arrived at the
result that in his own time Spica preceded the autumn equinox by
6 degrees and in Timocharis' time by 8 degrees." It was the discovery
of what is known as the precession of the equinoxes, the important
point of the discovery being that Hipparchos recognized it as a continuous process and said so.

During the last eighty years, when cuneiform texts were deciphered,
it was found that the Chaldeans at different times used slightly different
longitudes as the zero point, and it was concluded that the precession
of the equinoxes (which should more properly be called the retrogres-
sion of the equinoctial points) was known to them. If this were the
case, Ptolemy, who was much closer to them in time than we are, would
probably have said so, but he gives all the credit to Hipparchos. The
Chaldeans probably noticed that their tables did not quite agree with
reality and might have been "shopping around" for a zero point which
worked. But they never realized that the equinoctial points moved
always in the same direction; if they had, there would have been no
need for the trial-and-error method in which they apparently indulged.

Among other activities of Hipparchos were his utilization of an eclipse
(the one in 129 B.C. is the most probable one) for determining the
distance of the moon, the making of the first known catalogue of fixed
stars, and his work on the epicycle theory, the principle of which has
already been explained. But while Hipparchos had no problems as
regards the geometrical demonstrations, he did not have enough observations to establish the values properly. At a later date some of the
difficulties of the epicycle theory were removed by assuming that, while
the earth was obviously and indubitably in the center of the universe,
the center of the main circles, the deferents, might not coincide with the
center of the earth. Since we know the work of Hipparchos mainly
through Ptolemy it is not quite certain that this idea originated with
him. There is some reason to think it did, but the question cannot be
settled definitely with the historical material now available.

There has been a great deal of speculation about what kind of instruments were available to a man like Hipparchos. That the astronomers of his time sighted along a staff of some kind was obvious, but did they have graduated circles? The accuracy they achieved very strongly suggests the existence of graduated circles; in fact it is impossible to see how they could have done without them. But if literary documentation is the criterion, we face a vacuum.

The Greek astronomers excelled in putting down their geometrical operations with every sign of great—and justified—pride in their ingenuity. But they did not waste time and writing materials on an explanation of their methods. Possibly there were such writings which have been lost because later copyists did not want to waste *their* time recording obsolete methods, but I doubt it, since later astronomers, with superior instruments, would happily have pointed out how their equipment for observing surpassed that of Timocharis or Aristarchos. Another argument, advanced by some writers of energetic imagination, is that the methods were secrets available only to initiates. This idea is equally invalid—there were hardly enough astronomers to form any sort of tight guild, and, besides, in those days the written word itself was available only to "initiates." The most probable explanation is that the methods were so well known that writing them down was considered unnecessary.

We now have an example of the sort of thing the Greeks did *not* write down. It is also an example of knowledge that was within reach and remained "undiscovered."

This example is the Antikythera machine. It takes its name from the tiny island of Antikythera, thus named because it is below Kythera (Cythera) in the south of the Peleponnesus. In 1900, Greek sponge divers, in order to escape a storm, anchored their boat off Antikythera. Having to wait, they looked around, and since they were divers their looking around extended below the water line. And they discovered an ancient wreck, loaded with bronze and marble statues. It was established later that the vessel must have been wrecked between 75 and 55 B.C., on a journey which might have started on Cos and probably would have ended in Rome.

The art treasures stored aboard the ancient vessel were recovered. Of course two thousand years of immersion in salt water had done a good deal of harm; the bronze objects had corroded; the surfaces of the marble statues were covered with marine organisms. As art experts were cleaning up the statues, one lump of corrosion split in drying out. It was immediately evident that this shapeless lump was more important than the statues of gods and goddesses. A bronze plate showed, with toothed gears and graduated circles adhering to it. The bronze plate had been inscribed but only a few words and letters here and there remained legible. What could be read indicated some connection with astronomy. Some tentative reports were published in archaeological journals but there the matter rested.

A few years ago Derek J. de Solla Price of Princeton University wrote to the director of the National Archeological Museum in Athens, requesting a set of photographs of the "Antikythera device." The fragments had been cleaned up a good deal in the meantime, but the photographs were not enough for an attempt at reconstruction. Aided by a grant from the American Philosophical Society, de Solla Price went to Athens where he and the epigrapher George Stamires succeeded in deciphering the inscriptions. Every little fragment was photographed and sketched and measured several times over, and then de Solla Price returned to Princeton.

"Little by little," he reported,[11] "the pieces fitted together until there resulted a fair idea of the nature and purpose of the machine and of the main character of the inscriptions with which it was covered. The original Antikythera mechanism must have born a remarkable resemblance to a good modern mechanical clock. It consisted of a wooden frame that supported metal plates, front and back, each plate having quite complicated dials with pointers moving around them. The whole device was about as large as a thick folio encyclopedic volume. Inside the box formed by frame and plates was a mechanism of gear wheels, some twenty of them at least, arranged in a nonobvious way and including differential gears and a crown wheel, the whole lot being mounted on an internal bronze plate. A shaft ran into the box from the side and, when this was turned, all the pointers moved over their dials at various speeds. The dial plates were protected by bronze doors hinged to them, and dials and doors carried the long inscriptions that described how to operate the machine."

From one of the inscriptions it could be deduced that the machine had been built in 82 B.C., had been used for two years, and had been repaired twice during that time. The find of the Antikythera machine changes a good many prevalent ideas about classical Greece. Simply for lack of written evidence it had been assumed that while the Greeks were masters of literature, of some arts like sculpture, of massive architecture, and of geometry, they had lacked mechanical arts almost completely. The latter assumption had been rather weak all along, because of the elaborateness of some Greek armor and the high ingenuity shown

[11] In *Natural History,* March 1962.

in such weapons as the stone-throwing *palintonon* and the dart-shooting *gastrophetes* ("belly gun"; it was cocked by leaning on it), but until the Antikythera machine was found there had been no proof of Greek mechanical ability. Since nobody had written about graduated circles or the more complicated kinds of gears, they were assumed not to exist. "Is it not possible," asks de Solla Price, "that, just as today's artists do not customarily paint electrons and nuclear symbols or the design of automobile engines, the Greek writers did not have the tradition of writing about their machines and sciences unless such writings could constitute a monument of thought?"

The Antikythera machine clearly proves the existence of a tradition in mechanics—it is so complicated that it cannot possibly have been the first or even "early." But what did it do? To quote de Solla Price once more: "It appears that this was, indeed, a computing machine that could work out and exhibit the motions of the sun and moon and probably also the planets. Exactly how it did this is not clear, but the evidence thus far suggests that it was quite different from all other planetary models. It was not like the more familiar planetarium or orrery, which shows the planets moving at their various speeds, but much more like a mechanization of the purely arithmetical Babylonian methods. One just read the dials in accordance with the instructions, and legends on the dials indicated which phenomena would occur at any given time."

The Antikythera machine, then, was a tabulation expressed in gear ratios; one might call it an early mechanical slide rule, if the term "slide rule" is not used too narrowly. One may suspect that the main users of this and similar devices were not the astronomers who wondered about the laws of motion and who were forever trying to make their tables more accurate, but astrologers who wanted to know quickly what the aspects of the heavens had been (or would be) at a given time. The astrologers also did not need very high accuracy, as no plotting politician or worried merchant cared about the precision of the arithmetical procedure if the prediction was favorable.

With Ptolemy, Greek astronomy reached its climax—and virtually its end. Arab sources, written centuries later, claim that Ptolemy died at the age of seventy-eight, and even describe his appearance. Historians discard these statements, not because they are incredible but because they cannot in any way be proved. What we definitely know about Ptolemy is that he lived in Alexandria and observed from 127 A.D. to 141 A.D.

Ptolemy deserves praise for two things. Without his work the work of Hipparchos might be, not completely lost, but far more fragmentary, and without his example of painstaking work his Arab successors might not have been stimulated to be so painstaking in an effort to improve upon his observations. But as a thinker about astronomical phenomena he showed himself to be as reactionary as possible. His arguments that the earth must be the center of the universe and unmoving are straight out of Aristotle, and he would not even concede the rotation of the earth. "Certain thinkers . . . [believe] that no evidence can be brought against them if they suggest for the sake of argument that the heaven is motionless, but that the earth rotates about one and the same axis from west to east, completing one revolution approximately every day. . . . These persons forget, however, that while, so far as appearances in the stellar world are concerned, there might perhaps be no objection to this theory in the simpler form, yet, to judge by the conditions affecting ourselves and those in the air about us, such a hypothesis must be seen to be quite ridiculous."

After a number of long and rambling sentences about the motion of "rarefied things" and of "earthy things," Ptolemy proceeded to describe how things would be if the earth rotated: "Clouds and any of the things that fly or can be thrown could never be seen traveling toward the east, because the earth would always be anticipating them all and forestalling their motions toward the east." If somebody were to suggest as an apology for Ptolemy that the concept of inertia had not yet been formulated in his time, this apology would miss the mark about as far as Ptolemy's own statements do. The question is one of relative motion and Ptolemy could easily have found out how things really work by having spears thrown from standing and from moving chariots.

But while Ptolemy strained all resources of rhetoric and argumentation to keep the earth unmoving in every respect, he exerted the utmost geometrical ingenuity to develop the epicycles of Aristarchos into a system that might agree with reality. Some historians, incidentally, doubt that Ptolemy personally conducted astronomical observations. His own work is silent on this point; in fact he says nothing at all about methodology but just states "it was found." It is quite possible that he was a pure theorist. Although he insisted on motions along circles and on uniform velocity of these motions, the actual motion of the moon caused him to make an interesting assumption: the epicycle on which the moon traveled, moved along the deferent (which Ptolemy invariably called the "excenter") at a uniform rate, but uniform with respect to the earth, not with respect to the center of the deferent. This, of course, is not a uniform motion. Ptolemy here paid lip service to tradition but subtly changed things around in such a way that they worked out properly. "I do not profess," he said in the introduction to his work, "to be able to account for all the motions at the same time; but I shall show that each by itself is well explained by its proper hypothesis."

Ptolemy's work bore the title *Megale Syntaxis,* the "Great Collection," and comprised Hipparchos's catalogue of fixed stars (with some additions and an erroneous correction) and the reworked epicycle theory.

Virtually every historian of astronomy during the last two centuries has displayed a marked impatience with Ptolemy; the attitude might be expressed by the sentence "Why didn't he open his eyes?" I'll quote only one example, from J. L. E. Dreyer: [12]

"To the modern mind, accustomed to the heliocentric idea, it is difficult to understand why it did not occur to a mathematician like Ptolemy to deprive all the outer planets of their epicycles, which were nothing but reproductions of the earth's annual orbit transferred to each of these planets, and also to deprive Mercury and Venus of their deferents and place the centers of their epicycles in the sun, as Heraklides had done."

Occasionally one gets the feeling that Ptolemy did not want to make a decision, as he insists quite often that he is only interested in "saving the phenomena"—in showing how the motions can be represented geometrically. But Ptolemy's was the last of the great Greek works, which survived partly because it was the last and partly because of a series of circumstances that will be recounted in the next chapter. To quote Dreyer once more:

"Although the system of Ptolemy . . . did not profess to give a correct picture of the actual system of the world, it would have been impossible to omit a description of it from our review of the cosmical systems, chiefly on account of its enormous historical importance. For more than fourteen hundred years it remained the Alpha and Omega of theoretical astronomy, and whatever views were held as to the constitution of the world, Ptolemy's system was almost universally accepted as the foundation of astronomical science."

At the beginning of the current century, it seemed for a while as if

[12] *A History of Astronomy from Thales to Kepler* (New York: Dover Publications, 1953). The first edition of this work, published by the Cambridge University Press in 1905, had the title *A History of the Planetary Systems from Thales to Kepler.*

an important work of Greek origin had simply been overlooked. Not a work on astronomy, but one with a very strong astronomical background; moreover, a very well-known work indeed—namely the Book of Revelation.

The story is as follows: after the assassination of Czar Alexander Nikolayevitch (Alexander II) in 1881, the Russian secret police rounded up not only the Nihilists who were responsible for the assassination but hundreds of intellectuals who had engaged in what the police called socialist activities. Among these was Nikolai Morozov. Being a "political prisoner," he had certain privileges; he was not forced to work, he was permitted to read (of course the books were censored before they were made available), and he could request writing materials. In the year following his arrest, Morozov, reading the New Testament, was suddenly struck with the idea that the names of various constellations were mentioned in the Book of Revelation. The more he read, the more he found. "A woman clothed with the sun and the moon under her feet" (12:1); was this a reference to the constellation Virgo? And did the "sharp sickle" (14:14) mean the crescent of the moon? Morozov requested several scientific books, among them the works of Sir Isaac Newton. The request was granted, though incompletely and with considerable delay, and during the years to come Morozov occupied himself with reading, calculating, and writing.

Early in 1906 he was finally released—after an imprisonment of nearly 25 years—and the book he had written in prison was published in 1907. It bore the title *The Revelation in Thunder and Storm* and was a sensational success. The first printing of 6000 copies was sold within a month; a second printing of 10,000 copies appeared immediately afterward. A German edition in 1912 had a long introduction by Professor Arthur Drews, a historian especially known for researches into early Christian and pre-Christian mythology.

Morozov was not concerned with theological interpretations of Revelation; he had something different in mind. The author of Revelation called himself John and stated that he "was in the isle that is called Patmos" (1:9); he also said that he was commanded to "write the things which thou hast seen" (1:19). Morozov concluded that, obeying this command, John had described the sky as it looked from Patmos in the evening after the late afternoon thunderstorm during which John saw his vision. In that case, the description of the sky might furnish a clue as to the date of the vision, and the date in turn might provide a clue to the identity of John.

The astronomical clues seemed perfectly clear to Morozov. "There were seven lamps of fire burning before the throne" (4:5). The constellation of Cassiopeia, which looks like a poorly drawn W, has been occasionally called "Queen's Throne" or just "Throne." If by the word "throne," John meant this constellation, there could be little doubt that the seven lamps were the seven bright stars of the Big Dipper. Logically, then, the "four beasts," of which the first "was like a lion, and the second beast like a calf, and the third beast had a face as a man and the fourth beast was like a flying eagle" (4:7) were the constellations Leo, Taurus, Aquarius, and Pegasus.

If the four beasts were astronomical symbols, the four horsemen were likely to be the same. "And I saw . . . a white horse and he that sat on him had a bow . . . and he went forth conquering" (6:2); the bow suggested the constellation Sagittarius and the white horse might be a planet (planets move, as do horses). A white planet had to be Venus or Jupiter, but "conquering" suggested maleness; therefore the sentence must mean that Jupiter was in Sagittarius. "And there went out another horse that was red . . . and there was given unto him a great sword" (6:4). The great sword indicated Perseus and the only red planet is Mars; hence Mars was below the constellation of Perseus. The "pale horse" (6:8) was obviously Saturn, while the "black horse" ("and he that sat on him had a pair of balances in his hand," 6:5) must mean that Mercury was in the constellation Libra. The reference (12:1) to the "woman clothed with the sun . . ." meant that the moon was under the constellation Virgo and the sun above it.

To find the desired date, Morozov looked for a time when Jupiter was in Sagittarius, Mercury in Libra, Mars near Perseus, and the moon under Virgo's feet. He found that the planets had these positions in the fall of 395 A.D. (After his release he had his own calculations verified by two astronomers of the Pulkovo Observatory, Drs. Liapin and Kamensky.) Then he saw one more clue: ". . . there was a great earthquake and the sun became black as sackcloth of hair, and the moon became as blood" (6:12), which can only describe an eclipse of the sun. By calculating the position of the moon, he found that an eclipse had taken place in the late afternoon of September 30, 395 A.D.

This being the date of the vision, who could "John" be? Well, John Chrysostom, one of the fathers of the Greek church, was born in 345 A.D., baptized in 369, became bishop of Constantinople in 398, and died in 407. Morozov believed that he had established the authorship of Revelation and the precise date of the vision. The book had obviously been written immediately afterward.

At first everybody was very much impressed. The first doubters were

Russian priests, as this late date did not agree with their church chronology. Moreover, if John Chrysostom had been the author, why hadn't
he said so in one of his other works? The next doubter was Professor
Arthur Drews, who wrote the introduction to the German edition of
Morozov's book. He pointed out that Revelation is often mentioned by
older Christian writers and that its early existence is well attested,[13]
but suggested that the older authors "might have had a different Revelation under the name of John, which was only reworked by Chrysostom
and then included in the New Testament by St. Jerome, while the original
text was lost."

The last word obviously had to be spoken by an astronomer. The
two Russian astronomers had only calculated the positions of four planets for 395 A.D., without taking any stand on their historical significance.

Morozov's book had never been translated into English; in 1940
Michael S. Kissell tried to remedy this oversight with two long articles
published in *Popular Astronomy* in December 1940 and January 1941.
Dr. N.T. Bobrovnikoff, replying to these articles in the May 1941 issue,
showed that Morosov's explanation had been an entirely artificial construction.

The main artificiality consists in equating the "black horse" with
Mercury. The Greek word used is *mélas,* which means "black" and black
only. Morozov wanted to make out that it also means "inconspicuous"
and would, therefore, apply to Mercury. But the word has never been
used by anybody in that sense; besides, Mercury, in a clear sky, is not
inconspicuous. But the word "black," strange as it may seem, was
sometimes used for Saturn. "Now," Bobrovnikoff wrote, "if the apoc-
alyptic horses really were planets, we should identify them as follows:
the black horse with Saturn, the red one with Mars, the white one with
Venus, and the pale one with Mercury. Morozov's scheme, therefore,
falls to pieces. But why should the horses be identified with the planets?
I do not believe there is a single instance in ancient literature to allow
this interpretation. The planets were *prósopa,* that is, faces of persons,
which might ride horses, but not vice versa."

As to the eclipse of the sun, Morozov himself had to admit that this
eclipse of 395 had not been visible from Patmos. Bobrovnikoff added
that the statement "the moon became as blood" is more descriptive of
a lunar eclipse, and it is impossible for a lunar and a solar eclipse to
occur on the same day. Morozov also admitted that Mars was below
the horizon for Patmos on that day. This fact alone should have deterred

[13] Justin refers to Revelation in 135 A.D. as a "recognized Christian book" and
identifies the author with the Apostle John. Another important early source is
Irenaeus, Bishop of Lyons, who died in about 220 A.D.

him from going on, since the basic assumption was that "John" described the sky as he saw it. Bobrovnikoff wrote:

Any exact assignment of the planets to the constellations (such as the moon at Virgo's feet) is hopeless. Modern constellations are not always the same as the ancient ones, and too little is known of their evolution to be sure of anything. Neither the position of the figures nor their extent has been invariable. Taking Virgo again as an example, we find it pictured with the head toward Leo on the early Roman planisphere of Geruvigus, with the head toward Scorpio in the Babylonian zodiac, with the head toward the celestial pole in the Egyptian zodiac of Dendera, and with the head away from the pole in another Egyptian zodiac described by Daressy. Therefore, the expression "the moon at Virgo's feet" is rather meaningless unless we establish the system of the zodiac used. Nor is there much certainty about the attributes of the figures representing the constellations. Virgo, again, although always preserving the semblance of a woman (a mermaid in the Babylonian zodiac!) was pictured with wings or without wings, as Astraea, Irene, Isis, etc. Although she always has an ear of corn [14] in her left hand. in her right hand she has had an olive branch, a palm branch, a child, or even a sword. Remembering that Orion also has a sword and that Hercules was sometimes represented with a sword instead of the familiar club, the assertion of Morozov that Perseus is the only constellation with a sword seems a slight overstatement. That was his justification for putting Mars in Aries, "under Perseus". No matter where you put Mars, it is always possible to find a nearby constellation with a sword.

In addition, Mars in Libra, though astronomically correct for that year, may be mythologically wrong. For a long time Libra was not considered a separate constellation; the stars forming it were designated as the pincers of the scorpion.

Another pertinent fact is that classical philologists say that the Greek of Revelation is quite unusual, in fact unique; it is the Greek of a man who writes Greek but thinks in Hebrew or in Aramaic. This would fit the Apostle John but would be a sheer impossibility for John Chrysostom.

Morozov had done to Revelation what Piazzi Smyth had done to the pyramid of Khufu: he had put in the information as he went along. There may be overlooked Greek sources of astronomical information, but Revelation is not one of them.

---

[14] Not maize, of course, but wheat or barley.

3

FROM PLINY THE ELDER TO
IOHANNES DE SACROBOSCO

G AIUS Plinius Secundus, the Roman scholar, usually referred to as Pliny the Elder to distinguish him readily from his nephew Gaius Plinius Caecilius Secundus, died in 79 A.D., suffocated by the fumes from Mount Vesuvius, which he had approached too closely to observe the eruption.

Iohannes de Sacrobosco (John of Holywood, but possibly John of Halifax) the English mathematician, cannot be dated with such accuracy. He was a professor in Paris and lived and probably died there. We know that he was a contemporary of Abbot Alexander Neckam (1157–1217), though he probably lived a decade or so beyond the date of Neckam's death.

The use of these two names in the title of this chapter has two purposes. One is simply to establish the time span involved; the other is to indicate that during that interval learning, what there was of it, had moved north of the Alps.

But the same twelve hundred years might also be called the "interregnum." It was the interval between one era of thought and the next. That does not mean, of course, that nothing happened during these twelve hundred years. Of course things were going on, but no real progress was made. It is true that the lifetime of Ptolemy falls into this period—but only chronologically; he could be described as a late offshoot of an earlier era. One might even argue that Ptolemy's dogmatic adherence to the view of that earlier era contributed heavily to the sterility of the "interregnum."

As for Pliny the Elder, he did us an enormous service in having compiled his *Natural History*, which has been serving scholars ever since to establish what was known in his time. But Pliny was essentially a compiler, even though quite often, in the course of relating what he had read in the works of others, he added some personal information. In the astronomical section he had nothing to add; he repeats Aristotle's views, mentions those of a few others, and then goes on to the next topic.

Since by the time of Christ Rome had become the political and financial center of the western world it is not too surprising that Greek names begin to show up among the Romans. One of them, Cleomedes, a contemporary of Emperor Augustus, wrote a manual of astronomy which preserved for us the details of Eratosthenes' measurement of the earth. Cleomedes was also the first to explain how it was possible that the sun and the eclipsed moon could be seen simultaneously at opposite points of the horizon, as he knew about the refraction of light in the atmosphere and especially near the horizon. In about 10 A.D. one Manilius wrote a poem about the stars and in 92 A.D. one Menelaus (also a Greek name in Latin spelling) made observations from Rome of so-called occultations—the covering of a star or planet by the lunar disk—which were utilized by Ptolemy. And only a few years later followed Plutarch's *On the Face in the Moon* (though written in Greek, it is usually quoted by its Latin title *De Facie in Orbe Lunae*) in which the moon is described as an earthlike body, with mountains and valleys, plains and streams.

Aristotle's statement that all the "earthy substances" had to come together in the center of the universe did not worry Plutarch at all: "The moon is secure [from falling to the earth] by its own motion and the great velocity of its travel, just as something that is put into a sling is prevented by its [circular] motion from falling down." We cannot date the book, but it is known that Plutarch died in 120 A.D.

Just as Plutarch exhibited remarkably clear thinking in the case of the moon, Lucius Annaeus Seneca—a contemporary of Pliny—was the first classical writer whose ideas about comets approached reality (see Chapter 7). But these promising beginnings did not lead anywhere; even an abstract thinker is not as independent of his surroundings as he would like (and sometimes pretends) to be. The power of the Roman Empire began to decline, for a great diversity of reasons. The factor of the intrusion of the Christian religion has probably been exaggerated; the exhaustion of the Spanish mines, which led to the gradual disappearance of trustworthy gold and silver coins, might be at least as important. Also there were reverses in war and, beginning in 188 A.D., a violent outbreak of the plague. Then came invasions by tribes from north of the Alps.

It is only logical that the astronomical writings from the third century on no longer attempted to add to the science and to improve the art, but were quite conscious efforts to save what existed. Pappos, a mathematician of the third century A.D. wrote a commentary on the work of Ptolemy, as did Theon of Alexandria a century later. A still later com-

mentator was Simplikios or Simplicius, who has already been mentioned. He stated in his commentary that one Ammonius of Alexandria
had been his teacher. Simplikios himself was expelled by the Byzantine
Church in 529 A.D. and found refuge in Persia.

But we have to go back to Theon of Alexandria for a moment because
he was the first to mention a strange idea that was to have some influence later on. Hipparchos had discovered that the solstitial point and
a given constellation, if they coincided at one time, slowly began to
draw apart, and Ptolemy, by comparing observations, had accepted the
convenient value of 1 degree per century for what we now call the precession of the equinoxes. So far things were reasonably clear except
that the amount of the precession had to be determined more accurately.
But Theon came up with something new, claiming that it was something old:

"According to certain opinions ancient astrologers believe that from
a certain epoch the solstitial signs have a motion of 8 degrees in the
order of the signs, *after which they go back the same amount*; but
Ptolemy is not of this opinion, for without letting this motion enter into
the calculations, these when made by the tables are always in accord
with the observed places. Therefore we also advise not to use this correction; still we shall explain it. Assuming that 128 years before the
reign of Augustus the greatest movement, which is 8 degrees, having
taken place forward, the stars began to move back; to the 128 years
elapsed before Augustus we add 313 years to Diocletian and 77 years
since his time, and of the sum (518 years) we take the eightieth part,
because in 80 years the motion amounts to 1 degree. The quotient
(6° 28′ 30″) subtracted from 8 degrees will give the quantity by which
the solstitial points will be more advanced than by the tables."

This correction, which Theon said should not be used, poses an interesting problem. The figure used (45 seconds per year, or 1¼ degrees
per century, or 1 degree in 80 years) is the value for the precession of
the equinoxes deduced by Hipparchos; hence the idea of a regular
swinging back and forth of the starry sky, or of the zodiac only, is
somehow connected with Hipparchos. The fact that Theon called the
advocates of this idea *"palaioi"* (the ancients) must not be taken too
seriously; since his commentary was about Ptolemy he probably considered everything preceding Ptolemy as "ancient."

But why was the swing of what later came to be called the "trepidation of the equinoxes" 8 degrees of arc, which, at the assumed rate,
led to a period of 640 years and why did they pick the year 158 B.C.
as one of the years when a change of direction took place? There is

no definite evidence, not even evidence that somebody made a mistake at a certain time, so that some guesswork has to be called in to help. J. L. E. Dreyer [1] advanced the following hypothesis:

The year is probably that in which they supposed the astronomical work of Hipparchos to have commenced, and the only way in which a change of 8° in the equinoxes and solstices can be connected with Hipparchos, is his having finally placed the beginnings of the signs of Aries, Cancer, Libra (claws of Scorpion), and Capricornus at the equinoxes and solstices, as Aratus had done, while Eudoxos and others placed these points in the middle of those signs or at the eighth degree. . . . Possibly some ignorant writer by a misunderstanding concluded from this discrepancy that the equinoxes oscillated backwards and forwards, and thus started the theory of the variability of precession which, owing to the low state, or rather non-existence, of practical astronomy for many centuries after Ptolemy, took firm root, spread to India and among the Arabs, and was not finally swept aside until Tycho Brahe appeared on the scene.

The Hindus apparently never succeeded in starting an astronomical science of their own. In earlier days they took over the "lunar stations" from the Babylonians; at a later date, under the Gupta dynasty of Hindustan (400–650 A.D.), there appeared a literature of astronomical and mathematical writings collectively called "Siddhantas." One of the authors of these Siddhantas was Brahmagupta; another was Aryabhata who divided the zodiac into twelve signs. The signs were represented by the same procession of animals, etc., which populated the Greek zodiac; even the names are translations of the corresponding Greek words. Aryabhata also taught that the earth revolved on its axis. According to Professor Benoy Kumar Sakar [2] the Hindu scientist Varahamihira (505–587 A.D.) candidly acknowledged this borrowing. He stated that the science of astronomy was "well established" among the "barbarian Yavanas"—the Hindu form of the word "Ionians," meaning Greeks. (The Greeks, if they had known about it, would have greatly resented the application of the term "barbarians" to themselves; they considered it their privilege to use this term for non-Greeks.)

The carriers of the astronomical information had been largely Nestorian Christians who (like Simplikios) had been expelled by the Byzantine Church and had fled to Persia and points east.

A few hundred years later this Greek, or rather Alexandrine, science returned to the West via a new nation: the Arabs. Shortly after 600 A.D. the Arab tribes, united by Mohammed's religion, had started out on a

---

[1] *A History of Astronomy from Thales to Kepler, op. cit.,* pages 204-205.
[2] *Hindu Achievements in Exact Science* (London: Longmans, Green & Co., 1918). Professor Sarkar, of the Indian National Council of Education, admits that the Hindus did not originate an astronomy of their own.

war of conquest, first concentrating on two provinces of the Byzantine Empire, Egypt and Syria. Alexandria itself was taken—and largely destroyed—in 640 A.D. Then the Arabs proceeded to Mesopotamia in the east and expanded along the Mediterranean shore in the west. It would be wrong to say that, after having conquered, they settled down, since they never really did. Their uniting bond was the new religion— Islam—which made them present a united front against any non-Islamic nation but did very little to prevent them from squabbling among themselves. Politically they consisted of a collection of caliphates and sultanates which did not love one another on principle. But they did prosper, apparently mainly through pride in individual workmanship, and in due time they became receptive to science. As regards astronomical thought they had the advantage of having no religious handicap whatever, for their holy book, the Koran, said nothing about the shape of the earth or the nature of the moon.

In 773 A.D. Caliph al-Mansur granted an audience to a traveler from India who told the caliph that he, like his colleagues in the east, could predict eclipses and knew the stars. The caliph ordered the translation of some Indian books brought by the stranger. And the Arab scribes and learned men who presumably sat down with the traveler to make the translation learned something new which the Indians had invented. It is termed "positional notation", meaning that a digit, say 5, in the right-hand column means "5," but that the same digit, 5, if it appears one column to the left means 50. To indicate empty columns, to the right of the digit which determined the value, a special symbol was used, namely the zero. Since this system which eliminated the obvious difficulties of manipulating xxxiv + xvii + ic, reached the Christian world via the Arabs, the numerals are referred to as "Arabic numerals" to this day. The man who, early in the ninth century, produced the first astronomical tables in Arabic, using this new system of notation, was Muhammad ibn-Mûsâ al-Khwârizmî.

Once the Arabs had realized that some kinds of knowledge could be acquired from foreign books they indulged in an orgy of translating. Nestorian Christians had preserved and handed down Syrian translations of Greek manuscripts, which were now translated into Arabic. Caliph Harun al Rashid ordered the purchase of Greek books; his son and successor Caliph al-Ma'mûn, upon conclusion of a peace treaty with the Byzantine Emperor, stipulated in a clause of the treaty that so and so many Greek manuscripts were to be handed over to him. Among the manuscripts acquired by al-Ma'mûn, who reigned from 813 to 833, was a copy of Ptolemy's *Megiste Syntaxis,* which then became known as the *Almagest*. But the Arabs did not just translate; they checked. Caliph al-Ma'mûn, upon reading about the determination of the size of the earth, ordered a check. It was carried out as follows: two parties assembled at one point, having first carefully measured the height of some stars at that point. Then the two parties separated, one going due north and the other due south, and measuring the distances they traveled. While traveling they observed the displacement of the stars and stopped when the displacement was 1 degree; that is, as soon as the southbound party had traveled one degree of latitude to the south and the northbound party one degree of latitude to the north.

One degree of latitude, they found, corresponded to 56⅔ Arabic miles, a result that is in reasonable agreement with the one obtained by Eratosthenes.

By preserving and expanding the work of the Greeks, the Arabs became the most important source of classical science, especially classical astronomy, for the Europeans at a later date. But the Europeans used Latin as their international written language, and consequently most of the Arab names were Latinized to such an extent that they are barely recognizable. Thus al-Farghâni, who wrote a commentary on Ptolemy, became Alfraganus; abu-Ma'shar Ja'far turned into Albumazar; while Muhammad ibn Jâbir ibn Sinân abu-Abdullâh al-Battânî became Albategnius, and Ibn al-Zarqâla, Arzachel. Occasionally an Arabic name was preserved unchanged; for example, Abd al-Rahmân ibn-'Umar happened to be known as al-Sûfî, meaning "The Wise," and he appeared in later European literature as Alsufi or Alssufi.

Now for their work: Albumazar wrote a book on the astrological meanings of the constellations and the planets, and the positions of the planets in the various signs. It was a genuine and on the whole successful attempt to gather together the incredibly scattered references to "meanings," and consequently it became a kind of standard work. If you insisted on prophecy, Albumazar had laid down both tradition and "principles." The book even became one of the incunabula; it was printed in Augsburg in 1486.

While Albumazar had tried to bring some order to the system of "meanings," Thâbit ibn-Qurra (826-901) busied himself with theory. He tried to reconcile the "trepidation" of Theon of Alexandria with the value for the precession established by Ptolemy. "Tobit," as he was called in Europe, came to the conclusion that the older idea of the back-and-forth movement had been wrong, that Ptolemy's precession was variable and accompanied by an oscillation of the equinoxes. He thought that all the measurements could be accounted for by assuming that the zero point of the ecliptic describes a small circle of 4-degree radius in 4000 years. "This theory," wrote Pannekoek, "was accepted throughout the Middle Ages and, because of its complicated character, has given much difficulty to astronomers." It hardly need be added that the complication was unnecessary.

The greatest or, at least, the most famous of the Arab astronomers was Albategnius, who was a kind of counterpart of Ptolemy, except that he is known to have made very numerous observations himself. His main observational work took place in the town of Rakka from 877 to 919—he died in 928 A.D.—and he reworked Ptolemy's star catalogue with many corrections. He also invented new methods of computing—for example, a method of computing spherical triangles. But his reworked tables, based on Ptolemy's system with all its extra complications, proved somewhat too difficult for quick calculations, and the Moslem astronomers in Spain preferred Al-Khwârizmî's older and easier tables, which they reworked for the meridian of Cordoba. While Albategnius and others were mainly concerned with the positions of the fixed stars, Alsufi checked the traditional catalogues in another way: he observed for the purpose of correcting the magnitudes originally assigned to the stars by Hipparchos.

With all this activity by Arabian astronomers, something crept into the star charts which has remained there to this day—Arabian star names. They sound impressive—though most of the time nobody is even reasonably sure of their proper pronunciation—but they are another unnecessary complication. However, the blame should not rest on the Arabs, but on the earlier Greeks. The Arabic star names are rarely Arabic; most of them are Arabic translations or equivalents of the Greek names. If somebody among the Greeks had had the idea of numbering the stars in a constellation in descending order of brightness, much confusion would have been avoided. But the idea of calling the brightest star in a constellation "No. 1," or "alpha," which seems so obvious to us, just did not occur to them. Even then, of course, there would still be some problems, since some stars at the border of one constellation might get shifted to the neighboring one, but in general life would be simpler if Hipparchos or Aristarchos of Samos had thought of such a system.

There is a sizeable amount of literature about the Arabic names,[3]

[3] Of the many works I'll mention only: Giovanni Virginio Schiaparelli's *Vocabulista in Arabico* (Florence, 1871), H. Lammens' *Remarques sur les mots français dérivés de l'arabe* (Beyrouth, 1890), L. Ideler's *Untersuchungen über den Ursprung und die Bedeutungen der Sternnamen* (Researches about the origins and the meanings of star names. Berlin, 1809). Abd-el Hamid Samaha's *The Arabic*

but for our purposes a number of typical examples will do. Every amateur astronomer who points out Algol and Aldebaran to his less-learned friends is indubitably convinced that he is using genuine Arabic words. Well, in a way he is, but only in a way. Algol (Beta Persei) was described by Ptolemy as the "head of the gorgon"; the Arabs, having in their own mythology a female demon, Gûl, translated almost literally *ra's al-gûl*, head of the Gûl. Though the words are Arabic, the name is a translation from the Greek, later shortened. Aldebaran (Alpha Tauri) is a very similar case. The star's complicated Greek definition was translated into an equally complicated Arabic one in which the term *ad-dabarân* occurs, meaning "to follow," so that "Aldebaran" signifies "he who follows [the Pleiades]." Alkor—the small star next to Mizar in the Big Dipper—may also sound quite Arabic, but it isn't. Ptolemy did not list this star at all. It was listed by the Arabs, under various names, "but," Paul Kunitzsch points out, "there is no form [of any of these names] which has even the faintest similarity to 'Alkor.' " The name was a late addition to European star charts. As for its neighbor Mizar, that name is old (and not Arabic) but was used for several different stars; it was fixed on Zeta Ursae Majoris by the German astronomer Johann Elert Bode late in the eighteenth century.

As a final example let us take Alpha Orionis, which appears on charts as Beteigeuze, Betelgeuse, and three or four other variations. The Arabic term seems to have been *mankib al-gawzâ* (meaning "shoulder of Orion"); later, weird and meaningless forms like "yed elgeuze" and "Bedelgeize" began to appear. Somebody suspected that the Arabic word might have been *bât al-gawzâ;* unfortunately there was no Arabic word *bât.* It was Christian Ludwig Ideler who found the true explanation: some Arabs had called the star the "hand" of Orion, in Arabic *yad al-gawzâ.* As "y" and "b" in Arabic script differ by only one dot, *bad al-gawzâ* (in itself meaningless) originated from a miswriting or a misreading. This was then transcribed into Betelgeuze (it should at least have been Bedelgueze), and to confound the confusion the first edition of Bayer's catalogue (1720), by a simple misprint made Betelgeuze into Beteigeuze, which is still the preferred form on star charts of German origin.

Just as the Arabs had started looking for science and wisdom in Greek manuscripts beginning around 800 A.D., the Christians, two cen-

---

Names of the Stars (Bulletin No. 39, Helouan observatory, Cairo, 1944). I have taken my examples from *Arabische Sternnamen in Europa* (Arabic Star Names in Europe) by Paul Kunitzsch (Wiesbaden, 1959), because it is the most recent work and Dr. Kunitzsch, who lives in Cairo, had the assistance of native scholars.

turies later, began to peruse Arabic books. The place of interchange was now Spain, and some of the Christian seekers after knowledge happened to be there, as was Alfonso X, king of Castile, after the Castilian Christians had won the plains of Andalusia and the cities of Cordoba and Sevilla from the Moslems. Alfonso assembled a group of learned men, under the leadership of a Jewish scholar, Isaac ben Said, to construct and calculate a new set of tables. These were finished in 1252 and are still known as the "Alfonsine Tables." Alfonso himself was very much interested in this work; he is the man who, after listening to a dissertation on deferents, epicycles, off-center motions, etc., exclaimed that if the Lord had asked his advice he would have made the universe less complicated.

Earlier, Pope Sylvester (who died in 1004), before he was elected Pope, had inquired about books on astrology in Barcelona. A century after Sylvester, Athelhard of Bath went to Spain to study Arabic science, as did Gerard of Cremona, who went to Toledo looking for a copy of the *Almagest*. By the time Gerard of Cremona died, in 1187, universities had been founded in Paris, Bologna, and Oxford. Sometimes friction developed between the universities and local bishops, and sometimes that friction was justified. The eager searchers were not content with the *Almagest* alone, but also imported the philosophy of Ibn Sînâ (Avicenna, mainly celebrated as a physician), which certainly was not Christian. They imported the speculations of al-Bitrûjî (Alpetragius), who had no use for Ptolemy's epicycles, and of Muhammad ibn-Rushd (Averroës), who was a pantheist. The bishops, who tried to interfere, failed to write down their thoughts; it is quite possible that they were surprised that a non-Christian literature existed at all. Once that surprise had worn off the general attitude seems to have been that, since there were things to be learned, first translate and learn; assimilation into Christian dogma would follow in time.

The *Sphere* of Iohannes de Sacrobosco falls at the end of the period of translation. His main sources were Ptolemy's work, of course, and some of the writings of Alfraganus and Albategnius, always conscientiously credited when quoted or paraphrased. Later critics have said often and loudly that the *Sphere* was "merely a compilation"; that it contained nothing new to advance the science of astronomy. Though such criticism is factually justified, it missed the point. Sacrobosco was writing, not what we would now call a "research paper," but a textbook for use in the new universities. It was also used by the monastic orders.

The book consists of four chapters, with a short introduction which reads:

The treatise on the sphere we divide into four chapters, telling, first, what a sphere is, what its center is, what the axis of a sphere is, what the pole of the world is, how many spheres there are, and what the shape of the world is. In the second [chapter] we give information concerning the circles of which this material sphere is composed and that supercelestial one, of which this is the image, is understood to be composed. In the third we talk about the rising and setting of the signs, and the diversity of days and nights which happens to those inhabiting diverse localities, and the division into climes. In the fourth the matter concerns the circles and motions of the planets, and the causes of eclipses.[4]

In a present-day course labeled "Introductory Astronomy" this information would be imparted in the first three or four sessions, but at the time of Sacrobosco it constituted a full course in astronomy for the students at a university. Printed as a modern book, the whole *Sphere* would only make about twenty-six pages, not counting any diagrams or illustrations that might be inserted.

The first chapter establishes the picture of the world as envisioned by Aristotle and amplified by Ptolemy, with a spherical but immobile earth. The size of the earth is given according to Eratosthenes. The second chapter explains the meanings of the "circles": the equator, the zodiac, the meridian, the horizon, the arctic and antarctic circles, and the tropics; it concludes:

That zone which lies between the tropics is said to be uninhabitable because of the heat of the sun, which ever courses between the tropics. Similarly, the zone of earth directly beneath it is said to be uninhabitable because of the fervor of the sun, which ever courses above it. But those two zones which are described by the Arctic circle and the Antarctic circle about the poles of the world are uninhabitable because of too great cold, since the sun is far removed from them. The same is to be understood of the zones of earth directly beneath them. But those two zones of which one is between the summer tropic and the Arctic circle and the other between the winter tropic and the Antarctic circle are habitable and tempered from the heat of the torrid zone between the tropics and from the cold of the extreme zones which lie about the poles. The same is to be understood of the stretches of earth directly beneath them.

These "zones" (celestial and terrestrial) are subdivided in the third chapter into "climes," or rather the temperate zone is. A condensed description runs as follows:

The middle of the first clime is where the length of the longest day

---

[4] From *The Sphere of Sacrobosco and Its Commentators* by Lynn Thorndike (Chicago: University of Chicago Press, 1949). This book consists of an Introduction, the Latin text of the *Sphere,* an English translation of the *Sphere,* the Latin text of the Commentary of Robertus Anglicus, an English translation of this Commentary, and the Latin texts of the commentaries by Michael Scot and by Cecco d'Ascoli, plus excerpts from several minor commentaries.

is 13 hours and the pole is elevated below the horizon 16 degrees and is called the "clime of Meroe." The middle of the second clime is where the longest day is 13½ hours and the elevation of the pole is 24¼ degrees and is called the "clime of Syene." The third clime is that of Alexandria, with the longest day of 14 hours and the elevation of the pole 30¾ degrees; the fourth is the "clime of Rhodes," with a longest day of 14½ hours and the elevation of the pole 36⅖ degrees; the fifth is the "clime of Rome" with a longest day of 15 hours and with an elevation of the pole of 41⅓ degrees. The "clime of Boristhenes," the sixth, has a longest day of 15½ hours and an elevation of the pole of 45 ⅖ degrees. The seventh clime, that of "Ripheon," has a longest day of 16 hours and a polar elevation of 50½ degrees. "Beyond the end of this seventh clime there may be a number of islands and human habitations, yet whatever there is, since living conditions are bad, is not reckoned as a clime."

The fourth chapter is very short, only two printed pages, but it contains explanations of the eclipses:

Since the sun is larger than the earth, it is necessary that half the sphere of earth be always illuminated by the sun and that the shadow of earth, extended into the air like a cone, diminish in circumference until it ends in the plane of the circle of the signs inseparable from the nadir of the sun. The nadir is a point in the firmament directly opposite to the sun. Hence, when the moon at full is in the head or tail of the dragon beneath the nadir of the sun, then the earth is interposed between sun and moon, and the cone of the earth's shadow falls on the body of the moon. . . . But, since in every opposition—that is, at full moon—the moon is not in the head or tail of the dragon or beneath the nadir of the sun, it is not necessary that the moon suffer eclipse at every full moon.

Similarly, the sun is eclipsed when the body of the moon is interposed between our sight and the body of the sun. Hence it will obscure the brightness of the sun for us, and so the sun will suffer eclipse—not that it ceases to shine but that it fails us because of the interposition of the moon. . . .

Iohannes de Sacrobosco's *Sphere* was followed very soon by a similar but shorter and less meticulous *De sphaera* by Robert Grosseteste, who was the first rector of the Franciscans at Oxford in 1224. The date of his birth is not known; he died in 1253. Though it was believed for many years that Grosseteste's *De sphaera* came first (medieval manuscripts usually contain both Grosseteste's and Sacrobosco's "spheres"), Thorndike has shown that Sacrobosco's must be the earlier work. But while Grosseteste had probably read Sacrobosco's *Sphere,* his work contains a number of statements that cannot be found in it, and so must be considered an independent work, though heavily influenced by Sacrobosco's.

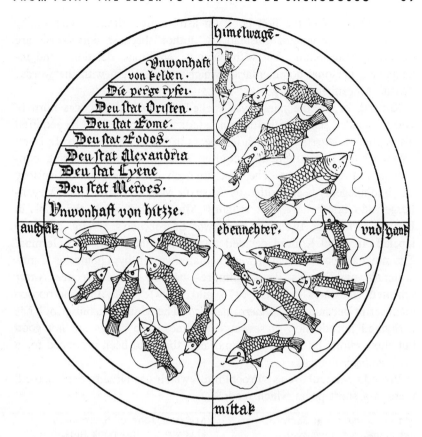

The climes of the earth, as shown in Konrad von Megenberg's *Sphaera teutsch*. The word *himelwagē* at the top means "heavenly wain"; here, in reference to Polaris in the Little Dipper, it stands for north. The word *mittak* at the bottom means "midday" (noon) and stands for south; the words *aufgāk* and *vnd'gank*, meaning "sunrise" and "sunset," stand for east and west

There followed a rash of commentaries, the most important being that of Robert Anglicus and one ascribed to Michael Scot. Then there was one by Cecco d'Ascoli and another "sphere" by John Peckham, and at least four commentaries with no stated author. Thorndike mentions a Munich manuscript containing a short Latin tract, "Questions on the Sphere of Iohannes de Sacrobosco," by "Conrad de Monte Puellarum," dated 1346. Thorndike identifies the author as canon at Ratisbon, and concludes that these "Questions" were a youthful work. All this is correct, but it does not go far enough.

"Conrad de Monte Puellarum" was Konrad von Megenberg, who, later in his life, became important as the originator of the first book on

natural history and the first book on astronomy written in German.[5])
I had to say "originator" instead of "author" because both works are
essentially translations, but with changes, additions, deletions, and in-
terspersed personal commentaries which always begin with the words:
"I, the Megenberger, say . . . "

Konrad, or, as the name was spelled then, Chuonrat, was born in
1309, attended school in Erfurt, and studied in Paris, where he acquired
his degree of *Magister*. After a few years in Vienna he went to Ratisbon
(Regensburg), and there he acquired a large Latin manuscript, consisting of twenty books. The first nineteen dealt with natural history
and had allegedly been written by Albertus Magnus ("But I, the Megenberger, do not believe that magnus Albertus has made the book in
Latin"), while the twentieth book was Sacrobosco's *Sphere,* correctly
labeled. In 1349 Konrad decided to translate the whole into German.
The nineteen books—which were actually written by Thomasius Canti-
pratensis or Thomas de Cantimpré—became his *Puch der Natur*
(printed six times between 1475 and 1499), while the Sacrobosco
manuscript became the *Sphaera, deutsch.* The Munich manuscript [6] has
a rhymed introduction of seventy-four lines. The verses are not good
but show effort; by now they sound as if they had been produced for a
Meistersinger contest.

Preceding Sacrobosco's "Proëmium," which has already been quoted,
there is a short poem which reads:

Maister Johans von Sacro-Bosco	Magister John of Sacrobosco
het getiht daz puch also.	Has written this book thus.
In latin ist ez gesezzen.	In Latin it has its setting.
So han ich maister Chuonrat von Megenberch	I, now, magister Konrad of Megen-berg,
ez ze deutsch gemezzen.	Have put it in German measure.

The remainder is more or less a straight translation, with some remarks and explanations interpolated and some short lists (such as the
signs of the zodiac) rendered into verse, presumably to make them
easier to memorize.

Several centuries were still to elapse between Sacrobosco's *Sphere*
and the rebirth of astronomy, but the *Sphere,* by being a simple and
short manual of elementary astronomical instruction, marked the first
step.

[5] If anybody wonders how "Megenberg" can turn into "Monte Puellarum," I
can only say that this was Konrad's own translation. Though his Latin was fluent,
he simply delighted in what might be termed forced translations; for example,
he rendered the word crocodile as *Kutschdrill* in German. "Megenberg" is a place
name (location unknown); for purposes of translation Konrad changed it into
Maidenberg, hence *Monte Puellarum.*

[6] Published in Berlin in 1912 by Otto Matthaei under the title *Konrads von
Megenberg Deutsche Sphaera.*

4

DE REVOLUTIONIBUS ORBIUM COELESTICUM -- COPERNICUS

T H E last commentary on Sacrobosco's *Sphere* was published in Rome in 1570, about 350 years after the first manuscript copies were made. Its author was a professor of mathematics, Father Christopher Clavius, S. J. (1538–1612); his family name had originally been Schlüssel, also meaning "key," and the original spelling of his first name was probably Christoffel. He is famous as the leading astronomer of the commission for calendar reform under Pope Gregory XIII.

The commentary by Father Clavius was about five times as long as the book commented upon, and with good reason. In a little over a hundred years before this commentary was written, more innovations had occurred than in any other previous century. To begin with, at Mainz in Germany one Johann Gensfleisch Gutenberg had started printing books, and on the Atlantic Ocean off the coast of Africa Portuguese ship captains had crossed the equator. The importance of printing needs no elaboration, but the crossing of the equator had changed a lot of ideas. Even at the equator the heat had not been so intense that the sea turned into a jelly. Nor had the rays of the sun been powerful enough to set the wooden ship afire.[1] Moreover the equatorial lands were inhabited, against all beliefs and expectations. The "seven climes" listed since antiquity, did not have to be abandoned; others now had to be added.

In 1492 Christopher Columbus (originally Christoforo Colombo, though he himself used the Spanish form Christóbal Colón) had reached what turned out to be a new continent, a fact which was of astronomical interest, too, since it was one more indication in favor of Eratosthenes' measurement of the size of the earth.

On October 31, 1517, one Martin Luther had nailed ninety-five theses on the heavy oaken door of the church of Wittenberg, Germany.

And on February 19, 1473, Nicolaus Copernicus had been born in a

---

[1] These ideas had actually been taught, but for many centuries nobody had taught that the earth was flat. That Columbus had to fight this belief is a myth of recent vintage.

township on the Vistula, called Thorn by the Germans and Torun by
the Poles.

Among them, the captains from Portugal, the inventor from Mainz,
the navigator from Genoa, the religious reformer from Eisleben, and the
astronomer from Thorn had made a new heaven and a new earth.

Some of the astronomical events leading up to Copernicus's work
must first be mentioned. One that did not have any direct influence on
subsequent events, but which falls into the period between Sacrobosco
and Copernicus, was the star catalogue of Ulugh Beg. Ulugh Beg, who
was one of the grandsons of the Mongol warrior-king Tamerlane,
founded an observatory at Samarkand, with all the equipment of the
period. One of the instruments was a masonry quadrant with a radius
of 60 feet, with the main purpose of measuring the elevation of the sun
accurately. The observations of the stars made by Ulugh Beg between
1420 and 1437 resulted in the only star catalogue not based on Hipparchos's catalogue, as given in the *Almagest*. It was a completely
independent work, which became known to the western world in 1665
when it was printed at Oxford. But by that time it was only a historical
document, as better catalogues had been made in Europe in the meantime.

Of more direct influence was what might be called the Viennese
school, which began in 1383 when the University of Vienna persuaded
Heinrich von Langenstein to leave his post at the University of Paris
and come to Vienna. Heinrich von Langenstein was a mathematician
and it can be taken for granted that one of his trunks contained a copy
of Sacrobosco's *Sphere*. He is chiefly remembered because one of his
pupils was Johannes von Gmunden (so called because he had been born
in Gmunden am Traunsee in Austria), who began to study at the
University of Vienna in 1400 and stayed on to become the university's
first professor exclusively for mathematics and astronomy. The "mathematician" of a university, at that time, usually taught other things too,
such as Hebrew or theology; Johannes von Gmunden, though he had
been ordained a priest in 1417 and had even been active in the parish
of the small village of Laa for a while, restricted his teaching to astronomy (Ptolemy, of course) and mathematics. Among his works were a
revision of the Alfonsine tables and the first two city maps to be drawn
to scale, the maps of Vienna and of Pressburg.

When Johannes von Gmunden died in 1442 the university had another bright pupil, not quite twenty years old, who was born in Peuerbach (or Purbach) in Austria and who consequently called himself
Georg von Peuerbach. After traveling in Germany, France, and northern

Italy, Georg von Peuerbach was made Court Astronomer by King Ladislaus of Hungary in 1454; during the same year he became a professor in Vienna. For his astronomical lectures Georg von Peuerbach followed the example of Johannes von Gmunden and taught Ptolemy's theory of epicycles. But he went one step further—or backward, as we look at things—for, in his *Theoricae planetarum,* he inserted sold crystal spheres between the regions of each of the planets. His introduction of the trigonometric ratio sine to western mathematics was a far superior step; he computed a table of sines (at intervals of 10 minutes of arc) and also computed the *Tabulae eclipsicum.*

Georg von Peuerbach would be less well known today if he had not attracted a pupil from Germany who later became his friend and collaborator. This was Regiomontanus (real name Johann Müller),[2] who was only thirteen years younger than his teacher. When Peuerbach died in 1461 at the relatively early age of thirty-eight, his scientific heritage fell to Regiomontanus, who completed some of his friend's unfinished work, especially the sine table. Regiomontanus left Vienna soon after Peuerbach's death and went to Italy for a number of years. In 1468 he was called to the court of the King Matthias Corvinus of Hungary, but in 1471 he moved to Nuremberg. One of the rich patricians of that city, Bernhard Walther, had offered him a house, an instrument workshop, an observatory, and—what Regiomantanus wanted most—a printing press. Regiomontanus felt strongly that knowledge, in order to be valuable, had to be disseminated, and that the newly invented printing press provided the means.

One of the first things he printed was his late friend's *Theoricae planetarum.* The sine tables came next; they presented some difficulties. Printers by that time had successfully managed books as big as the Bible, but no compositor had ever been called upon to set columns of figures. Regiomontanus had to invent new printing forms, and did so successfully. He had a large publishing program, over twenty different titles, some of which were to be Latin translations of Greek scientific writings. Among the works planned was a Latin translation of all Ptolemy's writings.

But while he was planning his publishing program, he had another problem on his mind. The ancient corrections for the calendar, introduced by Julius Caesar,[3] had proved insufficient. The full moon of the

[2] His Latin name is a translation of Königsberg, the name of the city in Franconia near which he was born in 1456. This is not the Königsberg of Immanuel Kant and Friedrich Wilhelm Bessel; that one is in East Prussia.

[3] In 46 B.C. The need for reform was then so urgent that several months had to be dropped and Caesar's enemies were quick to call this year the "Year of Confusion." Caesar's friends, however, insisted that it was the *last* year of confusion.

Regiomontanus, from a woodcut in the library of the University of Vienna

calendar and the full moon that could be seen in the sky disagreed by three full days and the discrepancy was even worse with the vernal equinox, both numerically and for religious reasons. The New Testament said that Christ had risen from the dead on the Sunday after the Sabbath (Saturday) following Passover which fell at the full moon on the fifteenth of the month of Nisan. The commemorative festival, Easter, therefore was determined by the Sunday following the first full moon after the vernal equinox. But since the calendar had not been corrected for so long, the vernal equinox had moved from its normal date of March 21 to March 11.

Hence, unless calendar reform was carried through soon, Easter Sunday might occur about a month too early. What was worse, the church would know that the date was wrong, without being able to do anything about it but to keep quiet. It could not violate its own tradition and rules. Pope Sixtus IV (he was Pope 1471–1484) was well aware of the urgency and severity of the matter and called Regiomontanus to Rome in 1475 to advise not only on the necessary shift in dates, a relatively simple matter, but also on new formulas for calculating the calendar so that this situation would not be repeated. But in the following year there was another outbreak of the plague in Rome, and Regiomontanus, only forty years old at the time, became one of its victims. The Pope himself escaped the disease, but his plans for calendar reform died with the man who was to have been his chief adviser.

The large publishing program Regiomontanus had in mind also collapsed. But his observing program was carried on by the man who had lured him to Nuremberg, Bernhard Walther. Walther, who had learned astronomical observing from Regiomontanus, at first probably just from curiosity, became sufficiently interested to start work on his own. From the death of Regiomontanus until his own death in 1504 he carried through a long series of systematic observations, the first of such length in western Europe. This work was utilized by Tycho Brahe and Johannes Kepler a full century later.

As for the reform of the calendar, that also took place about a century later, and a rather amusing difficulty had to be overcome. The Pope's astronomical commission, headed by Christopher Clavius, the commentator on Sacrobosco, had no great problem in tracing the mistakes that had been made in the time of Julius Caesar. But the new formula, whatever it was, had to be simple enough to be used by any reasonably educated person. The Vatican, for its own use, could tolerate any amount of mathematical difficulty; there were astronomers and mathematicians in Rome. But how about a missionary who might be away from civilization for years, who might in fact be marooned for life? He had to have a formula which he could not only handle himself but easily memorize and teach to others. The astronomical commission received help from an unexpected quarter; one of the Vatican librarians had thought up such a simple formula. His name was Aloysius Giglio (Latinized into Lilius) and, though he was dead by the time the commission met, he had instructed his brother to pass it on. It was the now well-known rule that every fourth year is a leap year *except* century years, such as 1700, 1800, and 1900; *if* the century year is a multiple of 400 it becomes a leap year. This has the result that three leap years are omitted in four centuries, which is a correction fully sufficient for all ordinary purposes.

The Council of Trent authorized the change; Father Clavius wrote a book about the reasons, the principles involved, and so forth, and Pope Gregory XIII issued a papal bull directed to all princes and the ruling bodies of republics, which were mostly city states. Unfortunately the bull "ordered" the princes to use the corrected calendar, but by 1582, when the bull was issued, many princes were Protestants who disregarded a papal "order." The Russian church did too; in fact the Bolshevik revolution was required in order to introduce Pope Gregory's calendar into Russia. In the meantime the various Protestant countries had one by one accepted it, not for religious but for mercantile and military reasons.

As the preceding discussion shows, Nicholas Copernicus was born into a Europe where astronomical activities not only existed but had a fairly long tradition.

His father had the same first name, Nicolaus (Polish: Mikolaj) as his famous son and he is known to have moved to Thorn from Kraków about 1458. Young Nicolaus grew up in Thorn and, when he was old enough, attended the parochial school at St. John's Church. When his father died (in 1483) the boy was only ten years old and needed an official guardian. His maternal uncle Lucas Watzelrode— later bishop of the Ermland—became his guardian and saw to it that the boy prepared himself for higher studies. There is no record of where he did so, but the likely place was the Cathedral School in the nearby town of Wloclawek. In 1491 Nicolaus was enrolled at the University of Kraków, where he studied for four years. The university had had an excellent teacher of mathematics and theology in the person of Albert Brudzewski (Albertus Blar). By the time young Copernicus arrived in Kraków, Brudzewski was no longer active as a teacher (he died in 1497), but his direct pupils taught and Copernicus might have met the great professor in person. In any event, after finishing in Kraków, Copernicus went to Italy to study astronomy under Domenico Maria di Novara, professor of astronomy and of mathematics in Bologna.

The real reason for the trip to Italy had not been to study astronomy under di Novara. Uncle Watzelrode had sent the young man to study canon law, and had even exerted some influence at home to get Copernicus elected Canon of the Ermland,[4] which gave him an independent income. Copernicus stayed in Italy until 1503; during that time he went to Rome, where he lectured—presumably to beginners in the field— on mathematics and astronomy, then to the University of Padua, where he studied medicine, and finally to Ferrara, where he obtained a doctor's degree in canon law. It can be seen that he returned to his uncle as a man of many accomplishments.

As Stephen P. Mizwa, the secretary of the Kosciuszko Foundation, put it in 1943, he was "a churchman by the wish of his guardian uncle and by vocation, an artist for relaxation, a physician by training and predilection, an economist by accident,[5] a statesman and a soldier by

---

[4] A canon of that time was a churchman, but not an ordained priest, a distinction often neglected later even by Polish Catholic writers.

[5] At one point in Copernicus's career, the King of Poland, Sigismund I, requested that he take part in a currency reform. Copernicus, on that occasion, coined a statement which economists now call Gresham's Law, namely that the existence of bad money drives good money out of circulation (mainly into hiding). It is interesting that astronomers were repeatedly entrusted with monetary problems; it happened earlier to Nicol Oresme in France, and later Sir Isaac Newton was appointed Master of the Royal Mint.

necessity, and a scientist by the Grace of God and by sheer love of the truth for truth's sake."

Lucas Watzelrode made Copernicus go to Heilsberg in the Ermland where he resided; it is very probable that he considered his nephew his logical successor and intended to ease him into his bishop's seat gradually. The situation was complicated, to say the least. The diocese of the Ermland was about one-third of the area later called East Prussia. The other two-thirds was ruled by the Order of the Teutonic Knights, which, at that period, has to be considered mainly as a business organization, in spite of its feudal titles and parade armor. The Teutonic Knights had had reverses, but their main financial asset was the East Prussian area—the amber coast. They intended to hang on. They also intended to swallow up the Ermland of Bishop Watzelrode, since it was an enclave in their own territory. Bishop Watzelrode could hold out against the Knights only by superb politics; he saw to it that his relations with the King of Poland were good, even though, at one time, the King had opposed his consecration as a bishop.

The result of this situation was that Copernicus, whom we think of primarily as an astronomer, was for years occupied with anything but astronomy. He was his uncle's right hand; he wrote long memorabilia in Latin to the King of Poland, in one of which the Knights are called *latrones* (robbers), which to this day is a term applied to competitors He practiced medicine; in fact among his contemporaries he was best known as a doctor. He probably did make astronomical observations in his spare time but his instruments were not the best then available; his younger contemporary Peter Apian (real name Bienevitz) had better instruments. Also in his spare time, he read any available works of the Greek astronomers—he had studied Greek in Italy.

In 1512 Copernicus had to accompany his uncle to Kraków, for the wedding ceremonies of King Sigismund. On the way back to Heilsberg the stern churchman and astute politician fell sick. The nearest town was Thorn, where he had been born, and he died in the city of his birth on March 29, 1512. Copernicus was free. He probably accompanied his uncle's body to Frauenburg, where the bishop was buried in the Cathedral. Copernicus was appointed Canon of Frauenburg Cathedral. On June 5, 1212, he observed an opposition of the planet Mars from Frauenburg.

One of Copernicus's three astronomical works, the *Commentariolus* (Little Commentary), is now believed to have been written in 1512 or 1513, though probably not in the form in which it was later published. The known facts about this work, like virtually all the facts about Copernicus's life are quite meager. A historian in Kraków, whose name is given as Mathias von Miechow in German sources, utilized the first day of May 1514 to make a list of the books and manuscripts in his possession. One of the items reads: *Item sexternus Theorice asserentis terram moveri, Solem vero quiescere* (Item: a tablet about a theory asserting that the earth moves, the sun being at rest). The name of Copernicus is not mentioned, but it would be too much to be asked to assume that somebody else with connections and friends in Kraków had conceived this theory at that time.

But the time had not yet come when Copernicus, after routine duties as a canon, would be able to devote most of his spare time to astronomy. For a while his church duties were quite strenuous, partly because of what would now be called a jurisdictional dispute, partly because of political events. The most pressing question on the local scene was, of course, who was to succeed Watzelrode as bishop. The King of Poland claimed the right to appoint the bishop of the Ermland, and he had the backing of the Pope, but the Ermlanders insisted on choosing one of their own brethren. The King finally gave in and Fabian von Lossainen was elected bishop. The terms of the compromise were that, in the future, the Ermlanders would submit a list of names to the King. From this list he would pick four which were acceptable to him, and one of these four was then chosen by the Ermlanders. Copernicus's name was once on that list, but he never became a bishop.

However, he was one of the two canons whom Fabian von Lossainen, who was sick at the time, sent to negotiate a peace between the Grand Master of the Teutonic Knights and the King of Poland. The peace negotiations failed in 1519, and in 1520 Copernicus was prepared to defend Allenstein Castle against the Knights if it should be attacked. It wasn't, and in 1521 the two years' war, during which not a single real battle had been fought, ended in an armistice. The armistice, in turn, ended when the Grand Master of the Knights agreed to accept the title of Duke, getting East Prussia for doing homage to the King of Poland. Soon after, the new duke turned Protestant, an action which, strange as it may sound, stabilized the political scene for quite some time.

Copernicus's second astronomical work originated in that period. It is the so-called "Letter Against Werner," written as an actual letter to Bernard Wapowski, Canon at Kraków. For once we don't have to wonder precisely when it was written; it is dated "Frauenburg, June 3, 1524." [6] The "Werner" of the title was the Nuremberg mathematician

[6] The "Letter Against Werner" is one of the *Three Copernican Treatises* in the book of that title, the other two being the *Commentariolus* and the *Narratio Prima*

Johannes Werner, who, in 1522, published a collection of mathematical and astronomical papers. Wapowski had sent a copy of the book to Copernicus requesting his opinion on the chapter about "the motion of the eighth sphere," containing the fixed stars. Copernicus seems to have needed some urging to state his opinion, but when he did, it was devastating. The "Letter" was copied often—Tycho Brahe had a copy—but it was not printed until Jan Baranowski appended it to the 1854 edition of Copernicus's main work, which was published in Warsaw.

The *Commentariolus* also existed only in manuscript form for centuries, the first publication (of the Vienna copy) was in 1878 by Maximilian Curtze. Then another copy was found in 1881 in Stockholm and promptly printed; the two manuscripts together permitted the reconstruction of the original text which naturally had suffered in copying.

After a short introduction, in which Copernicus pointed out that all the ancient attempts to explain the motions by concentric circles or spheres could not produce a complete agreement between theory and reality, he made seven statements still very much worth quoting:

I. *Omnium orbium coelesticum sive sphaerarum unum centrum non esse.*

1. All the celestial circles or spheres do not have just one [common] center.

II. *Centrum terrae non esse centrum mundi, sed tantem gravitatis et orbis Lunaris.*

2. The center of the earth is not the center of the universe but only of gravity and of the lunar orbit.

III. *Omnis orbes ambire Solem, tanquam in medio omnium existentem, ideoque circa Solem esse centrum mundi.*

3. All the spheres revolve around the sun, as if it were in the middle of everything, so that the center of the world is near the sun.

IV. *Minorum esse comparationem distantiarum Solis et terrae ad altitudinem firmamenti, quam semidimetientis terrae ad distantium Solis, adeo ut sit ad summitatem firmamenti insensibilis.*

4. The ratio of the earth's distance from the sun compared to the height of the firmament is so much smaller than the ratio of the earth's semi-diameter to the distance from the sun that the distance to the sun is imperceptible when compared to the height of the firmament.

---

of Rhaeticus, translated by Edward Rosen. The second edition (New York: Dover Publications, 1959) also contains an annotated Copernicus bibliography, covering the years 1939-1958. A similar German work which unfortunately has not become well known, even in Germany, is *Nikolaus Kopernikus: Erster Entwurf seines Weltsystems* (First Sketch of His System of the World) by Fritz Rossmann, published in Munich in 1948 under Military Government Information Control. It contains the *Commentariolus*, Latin and German in parallel columns; Aristotle's *Peri ouranoy*, chapters XIII and XIV, Greek original and German translation by Johannes Kepler in parallel columns; plus Kepler's commentary as he wrote it, with no modernization of style and spelling.

V. *Quicquid ex motu apparet in firmamento, non esse ex parte ipsius, sed terrae. Terra igitur cum proximis elementis motu diurno tota convertibur in polis suis invariabilibus firmamento immobili permanente ac ultimo coelo.*

5. The motions appearing in the firmament are not its motions but those of the earth. The earth with its adjacent elements [meaning air and water] performs a daily rotation around its fixed poles while the firmament remains immobile as the highest heaven.

VI. *Quicquid nobis ex motibus circa Solem apparet, non esse occasione ipsius, sed telluris et nostri orbis, cum quo circa Solem volvimur ceu aliquo alio sidere, sicque terram pluribus motibus ferri.*

6. The motions of the sun are not its motions but the motion of the earth and our sphere with which we revolve around the sun just as any other planet does; so the earth is carried along by several motions.

VII. *Quod apparet in erraticis retrocessio ac progressus, non esse ex parte ipsarum sed telluris. Huius igitur solius motus tot apparentibus in coelo diversitatibus sufficit.*

7. What appears to us as retrograde and forward motion [of the planets] is not their own but that of the earth. The earth's motion alone, therefore, is sufficient explanation for many different phenomena in the heavens.

These seven assertions are the core of what has later been called the "Copernican Revolution"—that most of the motions in the sky are only apparent because we ourselves are moving. In his *Commentariolus* Copernicus also gave the order of the spheres:

Summus est stellarum fixarum immobilis et omnia continens et locans, sub eo Saturnus, quem sequitur Iupiter, hunc Martius, subest huic orbis, in quo nos circumferimur, deinde Venerius, ultimus Mercurialis. Orbis autem Lunae circa centrum terrae vertitur. . . .

The highest is the sphere of the fixed stars, immobile, containing and fixing location for everything. Below it is Saturn, followed by Jupiter, then Mars, below it the sphere in which we move, then Venus and finally Mercury. The lunar sphere revolves around the center of the earth. . . .

These opening pages of the *Commentariolus* sound so "modern" that a reader of today who proceeds further suddenly feels something quite close to disappointment. This "modern" concept is darkened by the persisting epicycles. Copernicus, for all his undisputed daring, could not dispense with the perfect (meaning "uniform") motion along the only perfect curve there is, the circle. But since the observed motions, even with the understanding that they are observed from a moving body, fail to conform to this concept, Copernicus has epicycles running on epicycles. Moreover, the center of the first epicycle seems to perform a straight-line motion, going back and forth, but this "imperfect" motion

Nicholas Copernicus. This picture was originally part of a manuscript of Copernicus's work owned by Rhaeticus and is generally believed to be a self-portrait

fortunately could be explained by assuming the center of the first epicycle to move *simultaneously* on two more circles. In the case of Mercury, Copernicus had to explain the observed motion in the manner just mentioned. The main circle, the deferent, is centered in the sun. Motion on two *"orbiculi"* moved the center of the first epicycle back and forth, and the planet itself moves on the second epicycle, the center of which moves on the first epicycle.

The concluding lines of the *Commentariolus,* as translated by Professor Edward Rosen, are: "Then Mercury runs on seven circles in all; Venus on five; the earth on three, and round it the moon on four; finally Mars, Jupiter, and Saturn on five each. Altogether, therefore, thirty-four circles suffice to explain the entire structure of the universe and the entire ballet of the planets."

Even though the work was not printed, it evidently became known to people interested in the subject. Johannes Albertus Widmanstadt, secretary to Pope Clement VII, noted that in 1533 the Pope had requested him to explain the ideas of Copernicus to him. Likewise, in

1536, Nicolaus Cardinal Schönberg in Capua wrote to Copernicus requesting additional explanations and tables. The reply of Copernicus later formed a part of the introduction to his main work. But the interest was not confined to members of his own church; in fact the man who was to become most influential in the dissemination of the new idea was a Protestant. He was Georg Joachim, called Rhaeticus, who became professor of mathematics at the University of Wittenberg in 1536. (His birthplace was Feldkirch in the ancient Roman province of Rhaetia; his birth date was February 16, 1514.) Rhaeticus had heard of the new system and wanted to know more. And since Copernicus had not yet committed any work to print, Rhaeticus decided to find out at the source; in the spring of 1539 he traveled from Wittenberg to Frauenburg to call on Copernicus.

This decision required some courage. The Catholic church of the Ermland, surrounded by the territory of the Knights who had turned Protestant, was probably more anti-Lutheran in feeling than any diocese in Italy. Moreover, Rhaeticus came from Wittenberg itself and to the Ermlanders anybody from Wittenberg was suspected of being a personal emissary of Martin Luther. But Copernicus received Rhaeticus most cordially. This cordial reception may account for the well-attested fact that Copernicus thereafter lived quite isolated from his brethren. That Rhaeticus was also received by Duke Albert, the former Grand Master of the Knights, probably made the situation somewhat worse. But neither Copernicus nor Rhaeticus seemed to care; Copernicus was Rhaeticus's host for more than two years. Rhaeticus, being a mathematician, had no difficulty in understanding Copernicus, and helped him with the formulation of the main work then in progress. Rhaeticus also traveled and drew the first map of East Prussia, which unfortunately is lost, as are two books which he wrote during that period. One was a book proving that the heliocentric system of the world did not contradict Scripture, which would be interesting to read. The other was a biography of Copernicus, for which any historian would pay almost any price.

Another book that Rhaeticus wrote—a letter covering sixty-six folio pages of print—has survived. It is called the *Narratio Prima* (First Account) and was officially addressed to Rhaeticus's teacher Johannes Schöner; it was first printed in Danzig in 1540.

Rhaeticus stated in this account that a *Narratio Secunda* would follow. It was never written, perhaps because it was not needed. The "First Account" was reprinted in Basel in 1541; there was much demand for it because by then most learned men had heard of the "new theory" and there was nothing in print about it except Rhaeticus's

Account. The success of the *Narratio Prima* also seems to have convinced Copernicus that it was time to bring out his own major work; another incentive may have been the fact that he was nearing seventy.

For his main work Copernicus chose the title *De revolutionibus orbium coelesticum,* which is almost impossible to translate. The linguistic aspect is easy; it means "On the Revolutions of the Celestial Orbs." The difficulty is that Copernicus did not follow a strict terminology, neither anybody else's nor his own. The word "orb" especially was used with more than one meaning. In the *Commentariolus* a planet is called *sidus* or *corpus;* in the *Revolutionibus* he also calls planets *planeta, sidus errans, stella errans,* and even *globus;* the variety of terms in itself indicates the length of time Copernicus worked on the book. But he never uses *orbis* to mean "planet," though it can mean "great circle." Copernicus used the terms *orbis, sphaera,* and *circulus* interchangeably and at no point does he say that his spheres are, or are not, real. One might say that *orbis* has roughly the meaning of our word "orbit," but apparently with the additional concept that it is the "orbit" which moves, carrying the planet along.

De Revolutionibus is subdivided into six "books," or sections, the first about the arrangement of the solar system, the second containing a newly arranged star catalogue, the third about the precession, the fourth about the motion of the moon, and the last two about the motions of the planets. Rhaeticus supervised the printing of the typographically difficult portions of the book, which was done in Nuremberg. He left there, however, before the printing was finished, and requested Andreas Osiander to see the book through the press. Osiander was a skilled mathematician and a well-known Lutheran theologian and he found it necessary to urge caution. On April 20, 1541, he wrote to Copernicus: "I have always felt about hypotheses that they are not articles of faith but the basis of computation; so that even if they are false it does not matter, provided that they reproduce exactly the phenomena of the motions. For if we follow the hypotheses of Ptolemy, who will inform us whether the unequal motion of the sun occurs on account of an epicycle or on account of the eccentricity, since either arrangement can explain the phenomena? It would therefore appear to be desirable for you to touch upon this matter somewhat in your Introduction." On the same day he wrote to Rhaeticus, who was with Copernicus: "The peripatetics and theologians will be readily placated if they hear that there can be different hypotheses for the same apparent motions. . . ." He went on to say that if the possible opponents can be convinced that one man may devise a better hypothesis than another man, then the man

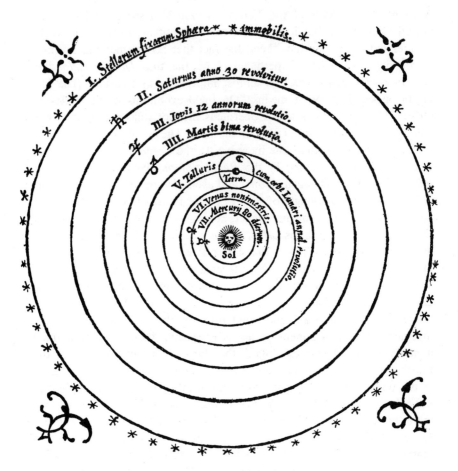

Copernicus's picture of the solar system, from his main work
De Revolutionibus Orbium Coelesticum

who has devised the most convenient hypothesis is to be congratulated.
"In this way they will be diverted from stern defense and attracted by
the charm of inquiry; first their antagonism will disappear, then they
will seek the truth in vain by their own devices, and go over to the
opinion of the author."

Copernicus would have none of this; these were his opinions and he
was going to publish them openly. But Osiander, who after all was not
completely wrong, was supervising the printing, and *De Revolutionibus,*
when it appeared, lacked the introduction by Copernicus but had a
preface presenting the whole as a new hypothesis. Osiander had written
the preface, but, since it was unsigned, it was believed to be by
Copernicus.

Copernicus's friend Tiedemann Giese, bishop of Kulm, reported that Copernicus received the first copy of his book literally on his deathbed. It is said that he was only partly conscious and could not see his book but could only feel it. He died on May 24, 1543.

Since the biography written by Rhaeticus, who knew him well, is lost, there is no real biography of Copernicus; there are only books containing such biographical material as could be assembled later.[7]

While the "First Account" of Rhaeticus had sold quickly, the main work of Copernicus was received without enthusiasm. One obvious but often overlooked reason is that it was simply too difficult for most people, even educated people, who could read Latin without hesitation. To a historian, for instance, this was one more book full of tables and mathematics; that its author presented a new hypothesis did not impress him. Osiander's well-meant preface worked in both directions. The emphasis on the word "hypothesis," as Osiander had expected, kept the theologians from attacking it; the book was not inserted into the *Index librorum prohibitorum* (the Index of Forbidden Books) until 1616 (and was removed in 1835). On the other hand, only a very few people became excited about it, most of them more than fifty years later.

The Catholics, with whom Osiander had been mainly concerned, did not attack it for some time. And the Protestants were not enchanted by it. Martin Luther himself said, during one of his Table Talks, *"der Narr will die gantze Kunst Astronomiae umkehren"* ("the fool wants to overturn [or "invert"] the whole art of astronomy"), which, considering Luther's personality, can be construed either as a wholesale rejection or as a jocular aside on something in which Luther's interest was slight. Luther's friend Philippus Melanchthon (real name Schwarzert) made a similar reference: *"ille Sarmaticus Astronomus qui movet terram et figit Solem"* ("that Sarmatian astronomer who moves the earth and stops

[7] The first Copernicus biography was written by a Frenchman, Pierre Gassendi, about a hundred years later. The only two books in English are both by Angus Armitage of the University College, London. The first was entitled *Sun, Stand Thou Still* (New York: Henry Schuman, 1947); the second, called by its author "an outgrowth of the first," is *Copernicus, the Founder of Modern Astronomy* (New York and London: Thomas Yoseloff, 1957). The main work by a Polish scholar is Ludwik A. Birkenmajer's *Mikolaj Kopernik—Studya nad Pracami Kopernika oraz Materyaly Biograficzne* (Studies on the Writings of Copernicus and Biographical Materials) of which Part I, comprising 711 pages in quarto, appeared in Kraków in 1900, Part II in 1924. Of the German literature Max Caspar's *Kopernikus und Kepler* (Berlin, 1943) gives a clear and condensed version of the thought processes of both men, as far as their astronomical work is concerned, while Ernst Zinner's *Entstehung und Ausbreitung der Coppernicanischen Lehre* (The Origin and Dissemination of the Teachings of Copernicus) contains a very extensive Copernicus bibliography. This was printed as a "Transaction" (*Sitzungsbericht*) of the *Physikalisch-Medizinische Societät* at Erlangen. It is volume 74 of the Transactions, 1943.

the sun"); Melanchthon was also not particularly interested in astronomy.

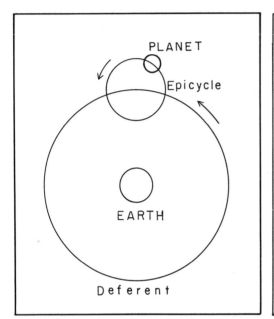
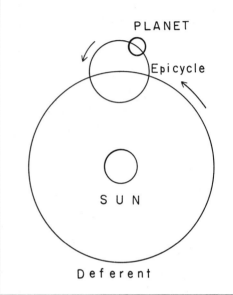

The concepts of Ptolemy and Copernicus (simplified), showing that earth and sun changed places without fundamental changes in the mechanism

Looking backward, it must be said that Copernicus's work *was* a hypothesis, with its double epicycles and additional *"orbiculi."* Copernicus had the proper arrangement, but otherwise he merely "saved the phenomena." The Copernican system became "the truth" after Johannes Kepler had modified it, not before.

One more thing must be discussed, although a lot of printer's ink has been wasted on it already. But for that very reason, the chapter would be incomplete without this discussion. This is the question, bitterly contested for more than a hundred years between Poles and Germans, of whether Copernicus was a Pole or a German. On extraneous facts the Germans make out quite well. The name Copernicus is of course the Latinized version; the commonest un-Latinized form is Koppernigk. It is in all probability derived from that of the village of Köppernik near Neisse in Silesia; the name indicates that the inhabitants of that village at some time had something to do with copper, either as traders, or as artisans. The spelling of both village and family name is a point heavily stressed by German authors. The Slavonic languages sometimes produce weird-looking combinations of letters, like the name of the composer Franz Drdla (Czech), or Kosciuszko, for that matter, but they don't double consonants. Another point on which the Germans score is the fact that, although Copernicus, both as a churchman and as a scientist, was accustomed to write in Latin, there are a few private letters written in German, but no letters in Polish.

On the other hand Copernicus, all his life, behaved as a Polish churchman. He attended the wedding of the King of Poland as a Pole, he negotiated for the King of Poland—though second-hand—with the Grand Master of the Teutonic Knights. He was ready to defend Allenstein Castle against the Knights.

Both sides have injected some silliness into what could have been a serious (and peaceful) discussion. One German writer insisted that the fact that Copernicus had his chief work printed in Nuremberg proved his sympathies and, by inference, his ancestry. Why should he have rejected the services of Rhaeticus? A man like Rhaeticus might have been a Scotsman and the work therefore printed in Edinburgh, which would not even make Copernicus a sympathizer to the Scottish cause. On the other side, the nineteenth-century Polish artist Wojciech Gerson painted a view of Copernicus lecturing in Rome in 1500. In the audience of the so far completely undistinguished young man can be seen Pope Alexander VI, Leonardo da Vinci, and Copernicus's teacher Domenico Maria di Novara, the last being the only one who could conceivably have been interested. A Polish writer considered the fact that Copernicus remained a Catholic as a proof of his being Polish, as if there were not many thousands of German Catholics to this day.

If Rhaeticus had asked that question of Copernicus, the answer might well have been that Copernicus considered himself an Ermlander, a member of a group mainly German in origin (as witness the place names) but politically tied up with Poland.

Discussing the nationality of Copernicus in terms of present-day nationalities makes no sense, since the situation was different in his time.[8] Of course his actions were those of a Polish churchman. That was his profession.

---

[8] I cannot help being reminded of a statement ascribed to Albert Einstein: "If my theory is proved right the Germans will say I am a German and the French will acclaim me as a citizen of the world. If I am proved wrong the French will say that I was a German and the Germans will say that I was a Jew." At the time Einstein was a citizen of the United States.

5

THE INVENTION
OF THE TELESCOPE AND THE
"NEW ASTRONOMY"

T H E Portuguese and, somewhat later, the Spanish captains who sailed southward along the coast of Africa and finally around its southern tip made not only geographical discoveries but astronomical ones. Their geographical findings quite often disagreed with the map drawn by Ptolemy, and they entered their corrections, writing politely, "with Ptolemy's permission." Their astronomical discoveries consisted in seeing and noting the southern constellations which were not visible even from the southern shore of the Mediterranean. They did not write "with Ptolemy's permission" in these cases only because they had not read the *Almagest*.

It is not always known which captain or navigator was the first to notice a particular bright star of the southern sky, since not everybody kept a diary and the diaries which were kept did not always survive. The two aggregations of stars known as the "Magellanic Clouds"—actually satellite galaxies—though they are named after Fernando de Magalhães (Magellan), had been noticed before his time, but we do not know who saw them first. Sometimes there are uncertainties due to poor descriptions, which often sprang from a curious belief then prevalent—the navigators seem to have expected the constellation of the southern sky to be counterparts of the northern constellations.

Alvise de Cadamosto, the discoverer of the Cape Verde islands, therefore wrote, when his ship was anchored at the mouth of the Gambia River in 1454: "Since I still see the north polar star I cannot yet perceive the southern pole star itself, but the constellation I behold in the south is the Southern Wain." As there is no southern pole star and no Southern equivalent of the Big Dipper, Cadamosto constructed a constellation of his own by combining the four main stars of the Southern Cross with other nearby bright stars, most probably *alpha* and *beta Centauri*. But since people like to ascribe a discovery to somebody, Cadamosto is usually listed as the "discoverer" of the Southern Cross, though he was not the first to see these stars and did not consider them a constellation by themselves.

The Southern Cross later caused a number of detailed discussions, because of a passage in Dante's *Divina Commedia*:

Jo nu volsi a man destra, e posi mente	At right, in the direction of the southern pole,
All' altro polo, e vidi quattro stelle	I saw the lights of a quadruple star
Non viste mal fuor ch'alla prima gente,	Which Eve and Adam only were to see.
Goder pareva il ciel di lor fiammelle.	The heavens gloried in its radiation.
O settentrional vedovo sito	O you poor widowed barren North,
Poi che private se' di mirar quelle!	You never see the marvel of this constellation!

(*Purgatorio,* lines 22–27)

Amerigo Vespucci, who called the Southern Cross the "rhombus" (actually a much better name) was the first to identify Dante's *quattro stelle* with his "rhombus," but it was only much later that somebody realized that the *Purgatorio* had been written in about 1318, long before any Western navigator had pushed south far enough to see the constellation as a whole. By that time it could also be shown that the constellation had been visible from Mesopotamia a few thousand years before Dante—it was mentioned in Chapter 1 that at least some of the stars of the Southern Cross appear under the name of "chambers of the south" in the Book of Job—so that Dante's statement that the *prima gente,* the "first people," had seen it was factually correct. It seemed incredible that an Italian poet—who hardly traveled at all—could have had factual knowledge of the existence of this constellation or been acquainted with such an astronomical detail as its former visibility from Mesopotamia. Was this all an incredible coincidence, or did a great poet have "mystic vision"?

Even completely rejecting the concept of "mystic vision," the problem was interesting enough to entice Alexander von Humboldt to devote a special study to it.[1]

Dante's source for the existence of the *quattro stelle* was no doubt Arabic, though we don't know which of the possible sources he used.

One possibility is a globe of the sky, showing the Southern Cross, which was made in Egypt by Caïssar ben Abucassan just about a century before Dante wrote these lines. Another such globe, which used to

[1] In his *Examen critique de l'histoire de la géographie* (vol. IV, p. 319ff., Paris, 1836). Later discussions of the same problem can be found in *Historie de Dante Alighieri* by François Artaud de Montor (Paris, 1841) and in *Terrae Incognitae,* by Dr. Richard Hennig (Leyden, 1938), vol. III, p. 148ff.

be in the Dresden Museum, was made in 1279, when Dante was a young man. While there is no way of proving that either these particular globes was ever taken to Italy, the fact that there were two of them indicates that there probably were more. Dante might have even seen, or at least been told about, what may well be called the first planetarium. When Emperor Friedrich II of Hohenstaufen, the son of Friedrich Barbarossa, returned to Italy in 1229 from the Fifth Crusade, he brought with him a very unusual Arabic tent. It is described as having had a cupola-shaped roof showing the constellations and a hidden clockwork that made the stars, or more likely the whole roof, move. Two centuries ago the story of the "astronomical tent" was disbelieved, but now that we know of the Antikythera machine, it appears eminently probable.

Dante, therefore, could have known of the existence of the constellation, which, since his sources were not Christian, was not called a cross.[2] A few lines later he states that "the Wain had disappeared," which is not surprising either. Northerners have always complained when they were brought to places where they could not see that most reliable of all constellations. The soldiers of Alexander the Great were perturbed by this fact, and Pliny the Elder consistently made a point of mentioning that the Wain could not be seen from this or that place. The fact that the North Star is not visible from Sumatra is the only astronomical reference in all of Marco Polo's writings. The only mystery to remain is the reference to the former visibility of the Southern Cross from Mesopotamia. In all probability this is a poetic allusion that just happens to be right. The concept that all of the sky could be seen from Paradise (while it was on earth) is not hard to understand.

The unknown Arabic artisan who constructed the "astronomical tent" had been forced by necessity to attach all his stars to one curved surface, thus re-creating Aristotle's idea that the stars are attached to a crystal sphere. In reality this concept was no longer held at that time, especially not among the Arabs who had arrived at the belief that a brighter star was brighter because it was closer to us. The original crystal sphere which held all stars at the same distance from the earth was replaced by an area of considerable depth. This was one of the instances in which Mohammedans and Christians agreed. Saint Augustine, in his *Commentary on Genesis,* had also stated that some stars were closer to the earth than others. The general assumption, in both Mohammedan and Christian camps, apparently was that all the fixed

---

[2] The first known use of this name is in a letter written January 6, 1515, by Andrea Corsali, in which the constellation is called the "wonderful cross."

stars were of equal brightness and size, so that the visible differences in brightness could only be accounted for by assuming different distances.

Father Clavius, in his 1570 commentary on Sacrobosco's *Sphere,* agreed wholeheartedly. The stars are called fixed because they do not change position relative to one another and relative to the earth. Their distance from the earth also remains constant but not all of them are at the same distance. Clavius even gave a figure: he computed the "depth of the eighth sphere" as 65,357,500 miles. The faintest visible star, then, might be as much as 65 million miles farther away from us than the brightest visible star. And since Scripture said that the stars are "innumerable," Father Clavius could go on to suggest that there might be invisible stars, possibly as many as 10,000 in each of the constellations, which traditionally numbered forty-eight.

In 1570, then, the restricted little universe of Aristotle had grown, even among the non-Copernicans, to a sphere hundreds of thousands of miles in diameter, containing about half a million stars.

Only two years later an unusual event occurred: a new star flamed up in the constellation of Cassiopeia. For weeks it surpassed even Venus in brightness; then it began to fade. Sixteen months after the appearance of the new star the point in the sky where it had been shining so brightly was empty again, at least to the naked eye.

Since our habits of thought are so different from those of educated men of the sixteenth century a forcible act of reorientation is required to understand the impact of this happening. We are used to the thought of "new" stars, that is, stars which suddenly brighten into incredible brilliance for a period of weeks or months. For example, we may say that there is a "nova" in this or that constellation, which is a hundred thousand, or five hundred thousand, times as bright as it was before. A century ago astronomers thought that such a nova was the result of the collision between two stars, possibly dark stars. Now we have knowledge of nuclear energy (see Chapter 20) and our explanation is a different one, but nobody is very much surprised; it is merely an interesting phenomenon. Of course every astronomer would love to see a supernova which is what the new star of 1572 was, if only because they are rare. A supernova happens in a galaxy only two or three times every thousand years and is a fantastic spectacle: for several weeks it will be brighter than all the thousands of millions of other stars in its galaxy taken together.

We are just as much impressed by a supernova as were the people of the sixteenth century, but we are impressed in an entirely different manner. To the astronomers of that day the earth was still the center of the universe. Even the few who, with Copernicus, accepted a moving earth, were still in the habit of considering the earth on the one hand and everything else on the other. "Everything else" might be much bigger in physical size, but the earth was more important. The astronomers of the sixteenth century still were all astrologers too, firmly convinced that events in the sky influenced or at least predicted events on earth. The appearance of a star which, as far as anyone could tell, simply had not been there before was a unique event. Therefore it had to have a unique meaning. But since it had not happened before—or so it was thought—the astrological rules gave no guidance.

This aspect of their problem might be called astrological uncertainty. The other aspect was the inevitable collapse of whatever remained of Aristotle's philosophy. Aristotle had asserted the unchangeability of the firmament and had built all his reasoning on this fundamental assumption. This concept had also been his reason for placing comets and meteors in the atmosphere where changes were philosophically permissible. But now there had been a change in the sky, and it had not been a change vouched for by a few men, whose word could be doubted, but one which everybody had seen.

This particular supernova was later often called "Tycho's Star" because among the many people who had observed it was a twenty-six-year-old gentleman from Denmark by the name of Tycho Brahe.

Tycho Brahe had been born on December 14, 1546, as one of a pair of twins. The other twin was either stillborn or died very soon after birth; family chronicles, in those days, did not go in for fine medical distinctions. The surviving twin was christened Tyge and was very soon abducted by his rich, but childless and lonely, Uncle Jørgen. The inevitable family row was of major proportions but was ameliorated a year later by the birth of another son to Tyge's father Otto, and the two brothers agreed finally that Tyge would be brought up by Uncle Jørgen and Aunt Inger. In due course Tyge went to the University of Copenhagen where he learned Latin—and began to sign his name as Tycho—and after that Uncle Jørgen sent him to the University of Leipzig, where he was to study jurisprudence.

Tycho was only sixteen at the time and his uncle decided that he needed a traveling companion and guardian, or, as they called it, a *Hovmester*. (The actual meaning of the word is approximately "master of ceremonies.") Another student, some four years older than Tycho, named Anders Sørensen Vedel, was chosen for this post. Vedel was to introduce Tycho, to guard him physically if necessary, to handle the money, and to see to it that Tycho pursued his studies. There was no *prohibitus est* as regards some amusement; but there was a prohibition concerning "useless studies," for Tycho had exhibited a dangerous interest in science. While he was studying at Copenhagen there had been a predicted eclipse of the sun, on August 21, 1560. Afterward Tycho had pestered his professors for weeks with astronomical questions, causing them some uneasiness. The theologian of the faculty no doubt knew all the pros and cons concerning the proper translations of some of the more difficult passages in the Bible, and the historian no doubt knew his history; both could speak Latin as well as their native tongue; but the mechanism of a solar eclipse was as mysterious to them as it was to Tycho. One of his professors, in despair, had finally suggested that Tycho buy a copy of the printed Latin translation of the *Algamest* (published in 1555) and Tycho had done so, spending two big silver coins—*Joachimsthalers* [3]—for the book. Uncle Jørgen did not mind the expense so much, but astronomy (which he, of course, thought of as astrology) was of no use to a nobleman and future landowner. Law was another matter; a rich nobleman was bound to have property disputes with other noblemen and possibly even with the king. Hence the instruction to Vedel to see to it that Tycho studied law.

Vedel did, partly because these were his instructions and partly because he agreed with Jørgen Brahe. Vedel was an industrious, intelligent, and even versatile man, but his interests were history and folklore. On the other hand, after Tycho had done a day's work at the university studying law, Vedel let him look at the stars at night. And when Tycho said he would like to take some courses in mathematics, Vedel agreed that mathematics might be considered a useful science, even though it did not bear much relationship to law. He added that Tycho should remember that the mathematician of the University of Copenhagen, Ejler Hansen, had become insane because he had thought too much about mathematical problems.

Tycho Brahe probably promised meekly that he would not think about mathematics to the point of insanity and then went to the two mathematics professors, Bartholomaeus Scultetus (real name Schultz) and Valentin Thau, and told them his problem. Both were sympathetic and drew up a list of mathematical works which he should read first. Tycho Brahe must have made very interesting excuses for needing extra *Joachimsthalers,* but he got them out of Vedel and bought not only the mathematical books but also two astronomical tables, the *Ephemerides*

[3] A large silver coin then in international circulation. The name was derived from the location of the silver mine, in "Joachim's Valley" (German: *Joachimsthal*) in Bohemia. Later all coins of that size came to be known as *Thalers,* and still later the word was Anglicized into "dollar."

of Stadius and the *Tabulae Bergensis*. Then he started to observe, with instruments provided by Scultetus. And within a few months he had to admit that the tables did not agree with reality. The stars and the planets did not assume their predicted positions at the right time. The *Tabulae Bergensis* were several days off; the *Alfonsine Tables,* which by that time he had also bought, were in error by about a month.

In 1565 a letter arrived from Jørgen Brahe, requesting both young men to come home. Both were pleased, though for different reasons. Tycho Brahe was happy to be released from further lectures and symposia on law; Vedel was glad that he did not have to write to Jørgen Brahe about Tycho's star-gazing and obvious neglect of his official studies. And shortly after their return Jørgen Brahe died of pneumonia. Unlike Copernicus, Tycho Brahe was not relieved by the death of his uncle but mourned him deeply and sincerely. Thinking about his scientific problems he approached another uncle, his mother's brother Steen Bille, for advice. The advice he got was good and to the point: spend a year or so in becoming acquainted with or straightening out the property he had just inherited, then go to Copenhagen to be presented at court, and then go back to Germany for study. Tycho Brahe did precisely that.

But in Germany a misfortune befell him.

At Rostock, not at all far from home, he met another young Danish nobleman named Manderup Parsbjerg, and at a party at the home of Professor Bachmeister the two young men started a violent quarrel about a mathematical problem! They had to be separated forcibly, but unfortunately they met again a week later at a Christmas party where beer and wine increased their fervor. They left the house, drew their swords, and began a duel. Nobody was killed, but Tycho Brahe's nose was cut off.

Tycho had a silver nose made, painted so as to look real, but he felt himself permanently disfigured. This is believed to be the reason that he later married a commoner instead of a lady of the court. In any case the accident did not improve his disposition, which had been difficult to begin with, and which has been described as "a combination of the irritability of a genius and the haughtiness of a nobleman of the period." After another short stay at home he went to Augsburg, which was one of the two cities in Germany (the other was Nuremberg) where the most skilled artisans could be hired. He ordered two instruments, enormous for their time—one a quadrant for measuring the altitude of stars, the other a sextant for measuring the angular distances between stars. Then he had a 5-foot globe made; on this globe he intended to enter the positions of the stars, after he himself had measured those positions.[4] Tycho began observing at once, at Augsburg, as soon as the first instrument, the quadrant, was ready. It was placed on the grounds of the country seat of Paul Hainzel, alderman of Augsburg, at Göppingen, about a mile outside the city.

In 1571 Tycho Brahe had to return home again, this time to his father's deathbed. He stayed on in Denmark for a while—Uncle Steen Bille tempted him with a chemical laboratory. If by good luck (nothing else could have done it at that time) he had made a discovery or two in the field of chemistry, Tycho Brahe might now be celebrated as one of the early chemists, with a passing reference to the fact that for some time in his youth he was greatly interested in astronomy. But he didn't, and in the evening of November 11, 1572, as he walked from the laboratory to the main buildings, he saw the new star. In great excitement he called to loitering servants, stopped peasants on their way home from the fields, and, pointing at the sky, asked them what they saw. They all agreed that it was a very brilliant star, none of them, of course, having the faintest idea whether or not it had been there before.

Using his large Augsburg sextant Tycho Brahe measured the distance of the new star from the known stars of Cassiopeia. The next day he found that it was visible even in the daylight sky (this is the main reason for classifying it as a supernova). His life now revolved around the star. The chemical laboratory was forgotten; astronomy had won its final victory as far as his intellectual interests were concerned.

But now there was a new dilemma. He had observed the star and he was convinced that he had observed it better than any other man had because of his large and also very expensive instruments. Should he now write about it? Was it proper for a nobleman to write a book? He wrote a long letter about the star to Johannes Pratensis at the University of Copenhagen, asking also whether he should publish his observations. Pratensis wrote back, urging him to do so. So did Charles Dancey, the French envoy. So did Peder Oxe, the Master of the Royal Court, who said, "There is no reason why a nobleman should hesitate to publish what he has in mind, particularly if he is disseminating useful information."

Peder Oxe's letter probably was the decisive one: this was the voice of the court. Tycho Brahe's *De nova stella* (On the New Star), a large-

---

[4] The big globe, after first being sent to the island of Hveen, then to Prague, and then having disappeared for a while, was finally brought to Copenhagen and placed on top of the Round Tower of the University, where it unfortunately burned up in 1728.

sized book of 52 pages, was printed in 1573 in Copenhagen. Much of its contents was astrological: "The star was at first like Venus and Jupiter and its immediate effects will therefore be pleasant, but since it became like Mars, there will next come a period of wars, seditions, captivity, death of princes, and destruction of cities, together with dryness and fiery meteors in the air, pestilence and venomous snakes. Lastly the star became like Saturn, and there will therefore finally come a time of want, death, and imprisonment and all kinds of sad things."

The astronomical information, which is what interests us, consisted of a precisely measured position, the statement of the star's visibility in the daytime, and statements about its brightness, from which an approximate curve of its luminosity can be drawn. To Tycho it was of paramount importance that he had been able to prove that it was a fixed star where one had never been seen before.

In the following year Tycho Brahe lectured on mathematics, its history and applications (including astrology), at the University of Copenhagen on special invitation by King Frederik II, who also pledged his royal word that it was not below the dignity of a nobleman to lecture. As soon as the course was completed, Tycho Brahe began to travel again, looking for a place where he could settle down for his life's work. His first stop of any length of time was at Cassel, where Wilhelm IV, landgrave of Hessen-Cassel, had his own observatory. Tycho Brahe stayed for a week, during which he and his host discussed astronomy during the day and observed at night. Then he went to Frankfurt, timing his arrival to coincide with the Book Fair. The next stop was Augsburg, then a short sojourn to Italy, then back to Augsburg—how far had they progressed with the construction of his great globe?—and then to Regensburg.

In Regensburg he was present at the coronation of Rudolf II of Habsburg [5] as Emperor of the Holy Roman Empire and made the acquaintance of the emperor's chief physician. Tadéaž Hájek (Hagecius), who was an avid astronomer. Also he bought a manuscript copy of Rhaeticus's *Narratio prima*. Then he went home.

While Tycho was still traveling in Germany, Landgrave Wilhelm IV had written a letter to the king of Denmark, Frederik II. The landgrave, who had been very much impressed with Tycho, had learned of his idea of settling in Germany, probably in Augsburg, where he had so many friends. The landgrave wrote to the king as one father of a country to another. "Your Majesty must on no account permit Tycho

---

[5] Commonly misspelled Hapsburg. The name is, however, derived from *Habichtsburg*. Hawk's Castle.

to leave, for Denmark would lose its greatest ornament. . . ." Frederik was in full agreement, on several counts. The landgrave was right in principle—it was the duty of a prince to keep the famous and learned men of his country close to him. In addition the king was himself interested in scientific matters. And finally he liked Tycho Brahe personally, in spite of his having married a servant girl.

When Tycho Brahe, in his home, woke up on February 16, 1576, a distant relative was waiting for him, but not to make a family call. He was there as a royal messenger, bringing a letter from the king. The king said in this letter that he had heard that Tycho wanted to go to

Tycho Brahe

Germany for scientific companionship, but it seemed to the king that the same thing could be accomplished if Tycho stayed in Denmark and invited learned Germans to come to him. Looking out of a window at Elsinore, which was then being built, he, the king, had seen the island of Hveen, which did not belong to anybody and which seemed to him a fine place to build an observatory. If Tycho wanted it, he, the king, would give the island to him. True, it did not produce any revenue but the royal treasurer could make up for that. The treasurer would also provide the money for buildings on the island.

The same day a letter from Pratensis arrived. Tycho's friend had heard of the king's offer—there seem to have been no secrets in those days—and he urged Tycho to hurry to the king's designated hunting lodge, because His Majesty preferred to have things done quickly.

Tycho took the advice. On February 18, just two days after the messenger's arrival, he received a grant of "400 good old dalers" and then went to inspect the island of Hveen. The grant of the island read:

We, Frederik II . . . , make known to all men, that We of our special favor and grace have conferred and granted in fee, and now by this open letter confer and grant in fee, to Our beloved Tyge Brahe, Otto's son, of Knud-strup, Our man and servant, Our land of Hveen, with all Our and the Crown's tenants and servants who live thereon, with all rents and duties that come therefrom, and We and the Crown give it to him to have, enjoy, use and hold, quit and free, without any rent, all the days of his life, and so long as he lives and likes to continue and follow his *studia mathematices,* but he shall keep the tenants who live there under law and right, and injure none of them contrary to the law or by any new impost or other unusual tax, and in all ways be faithful to Us and the Kingdom, and attend to Our welfare in every way and guard against and prevent danger to the kingdom.
Actum Fredriksborg, the 23rd of May, Anno 1576
Frederik

On Hveen, Tyge Brahe, Otto's son, of Knudstrup, built *Uraniborg,* "the Castle of the Heavens." Naturally it was begun with the laying of a cornerstone, which was a block of porphyry, even though the building was to be of red brick. Charles Dancey, the French Ambassador, had provided the cornerstone, with an inscription identifying him as Carolus Danzaeus Aquitanus, R.G.I.D.L. (The initials stand for *Regis Gal-liarum in Dania Legatus.* The King of the Gauls' Envoy to Denmark.) When finished, Uraniborg looked a bit too elaborate and had a pronounced Flemish appearance, due no doubt to the fact that the two architects who built it (in succession) were named Jan van Paschen and Jan van Stenwickel. But the general design was Tycho's own—a square building measuring 49 feet on one side, with two semicircular bays, 18 feet in diameter, attached to the northern and southern façades. The highest point was about 37 feet above the ground. The basement was mainly a chemical laboratory with furnaces for making colored glass, and the astronomical part was above ground. As an observatory of pretelescopic times it was complete. Uraniborg was also complete as a nobleman's home. It had—no royal palace could boast such luxury—running water in every room. It had four guestrooms. It even had a jail.

Tycho Brahe never forgot the incredulous astonishment of his Prague days when his observations and his expensive tables did not agree. What had been wrong with everybody, he decided, was that they had been careless. Or their eyesight was not good enough. Or their instruments for measuring angles had been too small or poorly built. What was needed was accuracy. Hence the very large and expensive instruments, hence endless repetition of every measurement. It is significant that Tycho Brahe's later collaborator and friend Johannes Kepler, when he found a discrepancy between his calculation and Tycho's measurements, decided that his mathematics were at fault. The discrepancy amounted to one quarter of the diameter of the full moon.

Before Uraniborg was even completed—the building itself was finished in November 1580; the instruments and furnishings were in place a year later—Tycho Brahe witnessed another unusual celestial spectacle: the great comet of 1577 which was the occasion for his second book (see Chapter 7).

At one point Tycho Brahe had told the king that he needed isolation for his work and that he had to be undisturbed. Either Tycho's concept of "isolation" was an unusual one, or else it could not be achieved. When he measured the altitude of a star with his great quadrant he had one or two assistants, or pupils, help him. A third would sit nearby at a writing desk and note down the figures which Tycho shouted at him. In addition to assistants and pupils, Uraniborg was overrun with artisans and craftsmen, most of them German or Dutch, with Danish country folk tending the garden and Danish serving girls swarming in the kitchen. Tycho Brahe's king was known to fuss about the most trivial details (why had his French bootmaker taken a few days off?) and Tycho was a loyal subject in that respect too. He too fussed about everything every waking moment, but then would forget to obey his king's order to have the lantern in the lighthouse lit. At one point Tycho decided that he had too many assistants around, which problem he solved by building another smaller observatory, *Stjerneborg,* "Star Castle," for them. Hveen was supposed to be a quiet place to study the sky, but it had turned into a principality, which differed from others mainly in the fact that its lord—the men around Tycho called him Junker Tyge—chased star positions instead of stags or women.

Beginning about 1582 Tycho Brahe felt that his numerous observations of the planets should give him a clue as to the construction of the solar system. Of course he had read not only the *Narratio prima* by Rhaeticus but also Copernicus's own work. In fact a portrait of Copernicus hung in Stjerneborg alongside portraits of the classical astronomers to inspire Tycho's assistants. But he did not think that Copernicus was right, only partly right.

The great comet of 1585 interrupted his thoughts for a while, but then he returned to his measurements, bellowing for greater and still greater accuracy. In between he developed his own hypothesis, which has often been called a mixture of Ptolemy and Copernicus. It has also been called "Tycho's Folly." It certainly seems to be a mixture, but it was not meant to be one; Tycho thought his scheme could, and in time would, "save the phenomena" better than any other. This is his model of the universe: The earth was immobile in the center of the universe with the moon orbiting the earth at a fairly near distance while the sun described a much larger orbit around the earth. The planets Mercury and Venus orbited around the sun at distances smaller than the distance between the earth and the sun. The planets Mars, Jupiter, and Saturn also orbited the sun, but in orbits with a longer radius than the distance between the earth and the sun so that they could appear on one side of the earth while the sun was on the other side. The earth's center was also the center of the sphere of the fixed stars, which revolved once every 24 hours. Whether Tycho assigned a depth to this sphere, as did Clavius and most others, or whether he considered all stars to be equidistant from earth, is not stated explicitly.

Tycho Brahe's system looks strange to us mainly because we know it to be wrong. Actually it was a very interesting idea. Considering that the true distances in the solar system (except for that of the moon) were not known and that nobody in pretelescopic times could have any idea about the sizes of the planets, and considering especially that the rival Copernican system was not the one we now call by that name but the one Copernicus wrote, it is quite understandable that Tycho could think he had found the answer. We don't even have to take his own personality into account.

King Frederik II died in 1588 while his son Christian was still a minor, so that a regency had to be established. It was a regency of noblemen, of course, most of whom did not like Tycho Brahe. They could do nothing against him as "Lord of Knudstrup and of Hveen," the first being his by inheritance and the latter a royal lifetime grant. But they could curtail his income from other sources. They could annoy him by delegations of investigators and by court cases; excuses were

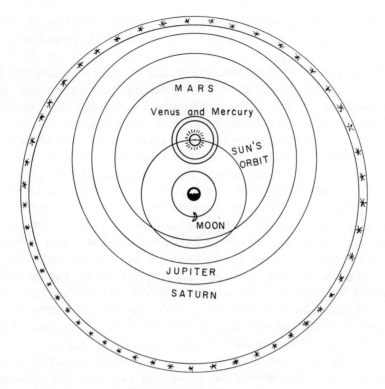

Tycho's concept of the solar system

easy to find because Tycho had neglected many things he had promised
to do. In the spring of 1597 Tycho Brahe left Denmark and went to
Wandsbeck in North Germany. From there he wrote a long and com-
plaining letter to the new king, Christian IV. It has been said that if
Tycho wanted to annoy the king with a letter it could not have been
better phrased for the purpose. The king answered sharply; if Tycho
still wanted to return to Denmark it would have been under circumstances he would have found humiliating.

He had to look for another patron. He wrote to his friend Hagecius,
Emperor Rudolf's physician. At the same time he wrote a book about
the instruments he had used at Hveen; lavish presentation copies were
sent to Rudolf II and for good measure to Christian IV too. The reply
from Hagecius came soon. The emperor would be pleased to have Tycho
Brahe serve him as a mathematician, but Hagecius recommended a
delay, as the plague was rampant in Prague.

The disease ran its course, as it always did, and in 1599 Tycho
arrived in Prague. The emperor, who was interested in astronomy,

astrology, alchemy, natural history, magic, art, and literature (in short, in everything except politics and ruling his empire), granted him an audience at once, promised him a fantastic salary, and provided him with temporary quarters. Some weeks later, when Tycho said that he needed an unobstructed horizon for observing, the emperor told him to select one of three castles in the vicinity, and Tycho chose Benatky Castle, situated on a hill some twenty miles from Prague.

A year later he was joined there by a young and overworked German mathematician, Johannes Kepler. Tycho had invited him in the most cordial terms, but when Kepler came he treated him as a "young man".[6] Kepler finally went to a Baron Hoffman in Prague to whom he told the whole story. Hoffman intervened. Tycho apparently was sincerely sorry, and the two continued to work together. Their new star chart progressed far enough for them to request a joint audience with the emperor, at which they suggested that the new tables should be called the *Rudolphine Tables*. The emperor agreed, but the tables bearing his name were not actually published until 1627.

On October 24, 1601, only two years after his arrival in Prague, Tycho Brahe died. He had been sick for only eleven days. The cause of his death was probably a ruptured bladder. While Tycho was on his death-bed, Kepler kept him company. Tycho bequeathed to Kepler all the thousands and thousands of meticulous observations he had made and asked him to do just two things in his memory: to finish the *Rudolphine Tables* as quickly as possible, and then to work out his, Tycho's, system of the world in detail.

Tycho Brahe was the most celebrated astronomer of his time, yet his name is not attached to any method or discovery. And if students now ask what he accomplished there is no short answer that can be given. He observed and measured and did both more patiently and more accurately than any man before him. As regards specific points, he proved that a bright comet was several times as far away from the earth as the moon is, hence that comets were astronomical and not meteorological phenomena. He proved that the star of 1572 was a fixed star, hence that changes go on in the far-away "sphere" of the fixed stars. He determined the precession of the equinoxes to be 51 seconds of arc per year and showed it to be continuous; in short, he killed the "trepidation of the equinoxes." He produced perfect positions for 777 stars, but he did not finish his catalogue. Some biographers have said

---

6 Kepler wrote to a friend: "I have found everything insecure. Tycho is a man with whom no one can live without exposing himself to the greatest indignities. The pay is splendid, but one can extract only half of it."

that this was because he died rather suddenly at the age of only fifty-five years, but he probably would not have finished it if he had lived twenty years longer; he was forever rechecking and adding.

His real contribution was providing a large amount of absolutely reliable material for others with a more theoretical turn of mind.

As regards his deathbed requests, Kepler did finish the *Rudolphine Tables*. But he did not work out Tycho Brahe's system of the universe. He did something better: he became the intellectual successor and "completer" of Nicolaus Copernicus.

Like Copernicus, and also like Tycho Brahe, Johannes Kepler came from a family in which academic and intellectual activities were not taken for granted. He was born on December 27, 1571, in the small city of Weil, a free city inside the dukedom of Württemberg.[7] His father was an unimportant military adventurer, his mother a shrewish but apparently bright busybody, who, at a later date, was even accused of witchcraft. One generation further back Kepler's ancestors were more respectable: his father's father had been Burgomaster of Weil and his mother's father the innkeeper of the nearby Eltingen. After doing very well in the local school Kepler went to a school for theologians which was supported by the duke of Württemberg for the sons of "poor and pious people." Though Kepler's father only half qualified—by being poor—the son's good marks opened the door for him. The theological studies began with languages (Latin, Greek, and Hebrew), classical literature, and so forth, with philosophy requested, and mathematics permitted, somewhere along the way. On August 10, 1591, when he was not quite twenty, Kepler received the degree of *Magister*.

This did not yet make him a Protestant theologian, being only the required preliminary for higher theological studies. These Kepler pursued at the University of Tübingen. But the university had an unusually able professor of mathematics and astronomy, Michael Mästlin. When Mästlin—who intended to keep his professorship—lectured on why Ptolemy was right and Copernicus wrong, Kepler was enchanted and sided with Copernicus. Though Kepler's parents had hardly been respectable people, they had, unwittingly perhaps, stimulated their first-born's imagination. In 1577 the mother had taken the six-year-old boy outside the city wall to view the great comet. And in 1580 the father had walked out into the fields with his son to watch a predicted eclipse of the moon.

But in spite of his interest in astronomy Kepler still pictured himself

---

[7] The current name of the city is Weil der Stadt.

as a future Lutheran pastor, and when the authorities of the Protestant
Boys' School at Graz, wrote to inquire for a promising magister from
Württemberg to teach mathematics, he had no idea that this might concern him. His professors, however, urged him to take the position, and
the duke, who had paid for his education, graciously gave him permission to leave his country. And in March 1594 Kepler was on his way
to Graz, maintaining both scientific and personal correspondence with
Professor Mästlin, among whose other correspondents was the Lord of
Hveen, Tycho Brahe.

While Magister Johannes Kepler was teaching mathematics and the
rudiments of astronomy to the "Upper School" at a salary of 150
guilders per year (50 less than his predecessor had received, since he
was a beginner), he began to think about the solar system, always with
the assumption that Copernicus was correct. One of the great advantages of the Copernican system was that the relative distances of the
planets from the sun could be calculated from their orbital periods. Not
the true distances, since the key factor, the distance from the earth to
the sun, had not been properly established. But a general idea of their
relationship could be established, and Kepler wondered why it was this
relationship and not any other one. This was one of his two main problems; the other was why the earth had a moon and the other planets
did not.

On July 19, 1595 (Kepler recorded the date so that it would not
be forgotten), he found his solution. If two of the eight spheres of
Copernicus were neglected—those of the fixed stars and of the moon—
there were six spheres belonging to the planets. These had a certain
numerical relationship. Were there, among the infinite number of possible figures, five which were in some way special? As soon as Kepler
had formulated his question in this way, he could think of five such
figures, the five regular solids of geometry, beginning with the tetrahedron, the triangular pyramid with four congruent surfaces, and ending
with the icosahedron which has twenty congruent surfaces. Since Kepler
was writing in German at this particular moment, he used German
designations, calling the tetrahedron the "four-planer," the cube the
"six-planer," etc., and continued:

"The orbit of the earth is the measure of all others. Around the
earth's orbit I construct a twelve-planer; the sphere around its corners
will be that of Mars. Around this sphere I construct a four-planer; the
sphere touching its corners is that of Jupiter, around which I construct
a cube, and the sphere touching its corners is that of Saturn. Then I
construct a twenty-planer inside the earth's orbit; the sphere inside that

is Venus. Inside the orbit of Venus I put an eight-planer, the sphere inside of that is Mercury. There we have the reason for the number of the planets."

Apparently he conceived this whole scheme by visualizing the bodies inside one another. Only after the scheme was ready in his head did he begin calculating to see whether the Copernican proportions of the planetary distances fitted his concept. He found that the Copernican figures and his geometrical construction did agree, if only approximately. He wrote to Mästlin, who was intrigued, if cautious.

In February 1596 Kepler was granted a short leave of absence to visit his grandparents who were ailing. He took the opportunity to visit Mästlin, who had agreed to supervise the printing of the book in which Kepler announced his discovery. Mästlin defended Kepler's idea in a memorandum to the ruling body of the University of Tübingen as "most ingenious, worthy of publication, and absolutely new," adding that, if proved correct, it would make the calculation of planetary orbits much easier. It would no longer be necessary to observe first and then calculate from the observations; knowing the principle involved one could calculate from the geometrical construction of the universe.

Mästlin did supervise the printing and reported to Kepler that he went to the printshop every day, sometimes two or three times per day. Kepler replied with enthusiastic words of gratitude, writing: "If you wish to compare my work to Minerva, I am Jupiter who carried it in his head. But if you had not, like Vulcan, performed midwifery with an axe it would never have been born." In 1597 Kepler received the finished book, which is usually referred to as the *Mysterium Cosmographicum*,[8] sometimes as the *Prodromus*. The reception of the book was most interesting. One Professor Johannes Praetorius said that all this was quibbling and hair-splitting and had nothing to do with astronomy, which was a practical science. But Professor Limnaeus in Jena was enthusiastic, stating that it was high time that the old and honorable art of Platonic philosophizing was revived. A professor in Padua by the name of Galileo Galilei wrote a few polite lines saying that so far he had only had time to read the introduction but was looking forward to reading the whole. It is by no means certain that he ever did read it.

Tycho Brahe had just left Denmark when the *Prodromus* appeared, but the copy which Kepler sent to him reached him in North Germany. He read it at once and wrote a long letter to Kepler, praising his

[8] The full title read: *Prodromus Dissertationum Cosmographicarum continens Mysterium Cosmographicum de admirabili Proportione Orbium Coelesticum deque Causis Coelorum numeri, magnitudinis, motuumque periodicorum genuinis et propriis, demonstratum per quinque regularia corpora Geometrica.*

ingenuity and his mathematical skill, but not agreeing as to the validity of the conclusions. The letter was very carefully worded, but most historians of the period have come to the same conclusion: Tycho did not agree at all (he said so in a letter to Mästlin), but he recognized the talent and did not want to antagonize Kepler because here was a possible—and capable—assistant.

Another copy of the *Prodromus* went to a man who, under the name of Reymarus Ursus, served as Imperial Mathematician in Prague. Originally a swineherder (!) this North German, whose real name was Nicolaus Reymers, had assisted in a local survey of property lines, discovered that he had mathematical talent, advanced to what would now be called an associate professorship at the University in Strassbourg, had then been appointed professor of mathematics in Prague, and had finally become Imperial Mathematician. To accompany his book, Kepler wrote a letter to Ursus, referring to him as the greatest living mathematician. As bad luck would have it, Ursus had published a theory about the solar system which was much the same as Tycho Brahe's, with the very important difference that Ursus' system left the fixed stars immobile and had the earth turn on its axis, while in Tycho's system the earth did not rotate.

Ursus's book, entitled *Fundamentum astronomicum,* was published in Strassbourg in 1588. Tycho Brahe read it and immediately "the bear of Prague," as he called Ursus, became his archenemy, so to speak, the focal point of all the troubles, major and minor, real and imaginary, that beset him. He published a violent attack on Ursus, stating that he had conceived his system in 1582 while Ursus himself admitted that he had "thought of" his in 1586. Ursus eventually replied to Tycho, in terms which today would be considered unprintable, and, to show his reputation as a mathematician, he included Kepler's letter (to which he had not bothered to reply) in this book, which appeared in 1597, the same year as Kepler's *Prodromus*. Tycho, needless to say, was annoyed. Kepler apologized with much tact and talent. But Tycho never forgot completely and two years later, when he was paying Kepler's salary, he assigned him the duty of writing another attack on Ursus. Fortunately Ursus died, in 1600, before the attack was finished. Tycho, at least, had the satisfaction of having survived his "vile and lying archenemy, the Bear."

One year later he too was dead, and Kepler immediately became his successor. Only two days after Tycho Brahe's death the Imperial Councillor Johannes Barvetius (Barwitz) called on Kepler to tell him that the emperor wished him to take care of Tycho's instruments and to complete the work they had been carrying on jointly. If Kepler accepted, as was the Emperor's and everyone else's wish, he was to submit a petition for a salary. Kepler accepted and, advised by friends, did not ask for a specific sum but humbly suggested that the emperor decree the amount. On October 1, 1601, Rudolf II appointed Johannes Kepler Imperial Mathematician with an annual salary of 500 guilders. Tycho Brahe had received 3000 guilders annually, but this had been a most exceptional sum for the time. The amount granted to Kepler was considered "good," and Kepler himself probably thought so too. That he would have trouble collecting it he did not then know. It was explained to him that the emperor would have to pay for Tycho Brahe's manuscripts. Tycho's heirs had petitioned the court, pointing out that the fief on Hveen had expired with Tycho's death—King Christian IV later gave the island to his mistress Karen Andersdatter—and their inheritance consisted of the manuscripts only.

Kepler was told to go on with his work, that the claims would be settled. What was really done was, first, to deny that Tycho's children were legitimate. Finally, on May 23, 1614, the Emperor Mathias, successor of Rudolf II, acknowledged the debt of "15,000 good silver thalers" to the survivors, but all that was ever actually paid was 1000 thalers on one occasion and 2000 on another.

Kepler's first activity was to prepare an edition of Tycho Brahe's Collected Works [9]; then he proceeded to work of his own. Observation did not play much of a role in his work schedule. Kepler described his eyesight as "dull" (he probably had myopia), and since his health was frail he could not spend wakeful nights and take care of his daytime obligations too.

But one event he did observe carefully—the appearance of another "new star", a supernova which appeared in the lower part of the constellation Ophiuchus in 1604.

The nova or supernova of 1604 happened to come at a time which many educated people considered critical. They thought so for a purely astrological reason, but that, in those days, was considered a serious

---

[9] The publishing history of Tycho Brahe's work is somewhat confused, mainly because Tycho had planned a complete edition of his works (under the title *Astronomiae instauratae progymnasmata*) in several volumes but had Volume II printed first in his printshop at Uraniborg. This volume, entitled *De mundi aetherii recentioribus phaenomenis,* bore the date of 1588, and contained Tycho's Latin work on the comet of 1577 (he also wrote a German work about it; see Chapter 7), remarks on the new star of 1572, an explanation of his methods of measuring stellar positions, etc. Volume I, assembled by Kepler, contained a reprint of *De nova stella* (first published in 1573), Tycho's catalogue of 777 stars (Kepler added 228), etc. Kepler's edition, though titled *Opera omnia,* is far from complete. The complete edition, under the same title, was edited by J.L.E. Dreyer and published by the Danish Literary Society in fifteen volumes between 1913 and 1929.

reason. It was astrological custom to take the signs of the zodiac in groups of three, each one representing one of Aristotle's "elements." The signs I, V, and IX formed the "fiery triangle"; signs II, VI, and X, the "earthy triangle"; signs III, VII, and XI, the "airy triangle"; and signs IV, VIII, and XII, the "watery triangle." As can be easily guessed, the fiery triangle was the most important. The other phenomenon that we must understand is the Great Conjunction, which meant that Jupiter and Saturn were close to each other in the sky as seen from the earth. Of course the Great Conjunction takes place in one of the signs of the zodiac, hence in one of the triangles. Now it happens that the time interval between two such conjunctions is twenty years, in round figures, and the places of two successive conjunctions are about 117 degrees apart. Hence the second Great Conjunction, though in another sign, is in the same triangle; in fact, ten conjunctions in a row remain in the same triangle. Or, again in round figures, ten consecutive conjunctions, covering 200 years, will be in one triangle, the next ten in the next triangle, and so on, until the first triangle, the fiery one, again contains the Great Conjunction. A new cycle began late in 1603, and many astrologers wrote many pamphlets about the event and its significance. Charlemagne had been born about 800 years before, and he had been born about 800 years after Christ. What would happen now?

During the early morning hours of October 11, 1604, one of the officials of the Imperial Court called on Kepler. He explained that he kept a diary on meteorological events. The previous night had been quite cloudy, but after dark he had seen through a rift in the clouds a star he had never seen before. Kepler thanked the man, but did not believe him. For about a week the sky over Prague remained cloudy, but October 17 was clear, and Kepler saw four bright "stars." They were Jupiter and Saturn in Great Conjunction, plus Mars, which also happened to be in that area of the sky, and the new star, as bright as Jupiter but scintillating in all the colors of the rainbow.

Kepler observed the star as it gradually faded and delivered "citizens'" lectures about it. He stressed the fact that it was a fixed star and also that Aristotle had been wrong in saying that there were no changes in the starry sky. This new star obviously had originated by the condensation of celestial matter. That it had been ignited by the conjunction of the planets was nonsense, but it was also nonsense to think that the time and place of the appearance of the new star was just a coincidence. It appeared then and there by the will of God, presumably to indicate His will. In his book *De Stella Nova,* which appeared in 1606 and was dedicated to the emperor, Kepler repeated his reasoning. Since he had arrived at the point of considering the new star God's will and a sign, he naturally had to say what it *might* mean. We don't know what he said in his lectures, but the book contains a fine collection of "if," "but others say," and similar phrases. At the beginning of the book he compared himself to "a stubborn beast of burden which resists and resists until beatings and curses finally force it to put its foot into the puddle."

He simply repeated what others had said: that the world would burn up, that all Europeans would move to America, that the Realm of the Turk would be destroyed, that Europe would change profoundly under a new ruler (*Nova stella, novus rex*—New star, a new king), and so forth, none of which prophecies he himself believed. The Bavarian chancellor Hans Georg Herwart von Hohenburg characterized this chapter in one sentence: "His disputations back and forth show that he does not know himself what to accept in this case." Kepler did not even try to decide; he suddenly said that those readers who want to know the future should buy one of the books of prophecy which can be had anywhere. Moreover, he was not employed by the emperor as a public prognosticator.

This discussion has led us to a point which has been almost as bitterly discussed as the nationality of Copernicus—the question of whether or not Kepler was an astrologer. On the one hand we have horoscopes which he cast; on the other we have his statement that he regarded "astrology as the silly daughter of the noble lady astronomy, but with the salaries of mathematicians being what they are, the mother could not live if the daughter did not earn money." He had arguments with Tycho Brahe about astrological rules, but he could not escape the belief that the phenomena of the sky were not accidental, but God's will, hence meaningful. One can conclude from all this that Kepler—who after all was a child of his time—generally believed in the idea of astrology, disbelieved its rules, but cast horoscopes according to these rules because he was paid for them.

Kepler's most important work had been building up from the time he had joined Tycho Brahe; in fact Tycho had provided the first push. For decades Tycho had observed the planet Mars with the greatest of care and had asked Longomontanus (real name Christian Severin) to use these observations to calculate the orbit of Mars. After a while Longomontanus had given up, because he found the problem too difficult. Then Tycho asked Kepler to do it, but Kepler found that the available material consisted of dates and positions only, with all the mathematical work still to be done; hence no worthwhile progress had been made when Tycho Brahe died.

Horoscopium geſtellet durch Ioannem Kepplerum
1 6 0 8 .

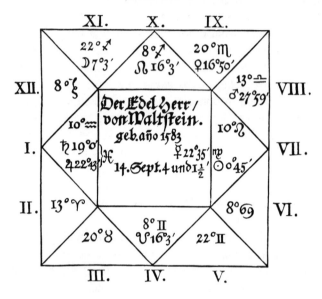

Horoscope for General von Wallenstein, by Kepler

The performance of Mars in the sky is as follows: as Mars and the earth draw together in the same sector of their orbits, as seen from the sun, Mars, as seen from earth, moves more and more slowly and then seems to stand still (the "stationary point"); then it moves in the opposite direction (becomes "retrograde") but resumes its normal movement some time after opposition. This apparent loop is purely an optical effect, the faster-moving earth overtaking the slower-moving Mars, as Copernicus had correctly explained. The problem was that the time interval between two oppositions was always changing. Astronomers from Ptolemy to Copernicus had tried to account for this in order to compute the time and place of the next opposition, but Kepler also wanted to understand what happened. Tycho's observations yielded the times and places of ten oppositions, from 1580 to 1600. From observations by David Fabricius at Emden, augmented by Kepler's own, the two oppositions of 1602 and 1604 were added, giving Kepler a dozen oppositions from which to derive a theory.

But in addition he had an idea. It has been explained earlier that the astronomers who assumed the earth to be the center of the universe had to make an additional assumption, namely that the center of the orbits was *not* in the center of the universe, that is, the center of the earth. The center of the orbits was near the earth. Copernicus had to make a similar adjustment—the center of the orbits was near the sun. But Kepler, as he stated first in his *Prodromus,* thought that the sun somewhat moved the planets; hence it was logical that the outer planets moved more slowly than the inner planets, as the sun had to move a longer "lever." Then, of course, the center of the motion had to be in the sun itself, for Kepler could not use an empty point in space.

The work was incredibly tedious, since Kepler had no computing aids of any kind, neither the slide rule nor the logarithm table having been invented. He had to try various assumptions, arriving at successive approximations. "If this cumbersome mode of working displeases you," he wrote, addressing the reader, "you may rightly pity *me* who had to apply it at least seventy times with great loss of time; so you will not wonder that the fifth year since I began with Mars is already passing. . . ." As he went on, he had to conclude that the orbit of Mars could not be a circle, nor a combination of circular motions. David Fabricius, a most careful observer, wrote to Kepler that his attempts did not properly represent the observations. The orbit showed a compression; the maximum deviation from the circle was 0.00429 times the radius. Suddenly Kepler realized what that figure indicated: it was half the square of the eccentricity

$$(0.0926^2 = 0.00857),$$

which meant that the orbit must be an ellipse.

This discovery is now in the textbooks as Kepler's First Law: *The planets move in elliptical orbits, with the sun in one of the focal points of the ellipse.*[10] Kepler now needed some new terms. First he had to coin terms for the point of the greatest distance from the sun and for that of the least distance from the sun. The least distance, using the Greek name for the sun (*helios*) and the Greek word *peri* ("around"), became perihelion; the longest distance, using the Greek preposition *apo* ("away from"), became aphelion. Then one more term was needed. If the orbit were a circle, the line connecting the sun and the planet could be called the radius. Since it is not, a new term had to be found, which would indicate that something like a radius was meant. Kepler chose *radius vector.* When he checked on the velocity of Mars in its orbit (slower at aphelion, since Kepler's assumed solar force had to act over

[10] Arzachel of Toledo had suggested elliptical motions as far back as 1080, but nobody had paid any attention.

a longer distance), the second law emerged, which is now phrased: *The radius vector sweeps over equal areas in equal times.*

Kepler's friend David Fabricius was aghast; he had to admit that it worked out that way, but he never accepted it: the planetary motions just had to be circular.

In 1605 Kepler presented his book to the emperor, to whom it was dedicated. It appeared in 1609, the delay being caused by lack of cash in the imperial purse. Its title was *Astronomia nova / aitiologetos / seu / Physica coelestis / tradita commentariis / de motibus stellae / Martis / ex observationibus C. V. / Tychonis Brahe* (The New Astronomy causally explained, or Celestial Physics, with commentaries on the motions of the star Mars, after the observations of Tycho Brahe).

It was a remarkable coincidence in time that, just during the years when Kepler was putting the finishing touches on the manuscript of his *Astronomia nova,* the foundation of another kind of "new astronomy" occurred in The Netherlands: the telescope was invented.

One would think that the history of such an important invention would be well known, but rival claims confused the story at the very beginning. The first book about the problem of just who should be considered the inventor of the telescope was published in The Hague in 1655 under the title *De vero telescopii inventore.* Its author was the French physician Pierre Borel, who decided that the credit should go to a lens-grinder in Middelburg named Jan Lippershey. But a number of points remained unclear, causing a Dutch historian, Van Swinden, to go through all available archives. The results were utilized by Professor Gerard Moll of Utrecht for a comprehensive work *Geschiedkundig Onderzoek naar de eerste Uitfinders der Vernkijkers* (Historical Investigation about the First Inventors of the Telescope), which was published in Amsterdam in 1831. But Van Swinden and Moll did not succeed in clearing up all the uncertainties. What we do know is this:

The grinding of lenses for eyeglasses (called *occhiali*) began in Italy near the end of the thirteenth century, though a few isolated examples of magnifying glasses are reasonably well attested from earlier dates. The first *occhiali* were lenses set in a piece of stiff leather which was somehow attached to a cap. The year of this invention must have been between 1280 and 1290. Rudolf Wolf, in his *Handbuch der Astronomie* (vol. I, Zürich, 1890) quoted an Italian manuscript of 1299, which said that "*occhiali* [were] recently invented for the benefit of old people whose eyesight has grown dull." Giordano di Rivalto is known to have preached a sermon at Pisa about 1305, in which he said that the invention was made "less than a score of years ago." An inscription on the tombstone of the Florentine citizen Salvino degli Armati in the Church of Mary Magdalen in Florence states that he was *inventore degli occhiali.* The tombstone bears the date of 1317.

Naturally the invention spread rapidly, from Italy to France and from there to the Netherlands. But an eyeglass lens is not yet a telescope, which needs a minimum of two lenses. The outer lens must be a convex lens, as were all the early *occhiali* that enabled elderly people who had grown far-sighted to read. The lens near the eye can also be a convex lens, or it can be concave. In the first case you get a higher magnification but an upside-down image; in the latter case the image remains upright but the magnification is less. There are two versions of the invention of the telescope. The spectacle-maker Zacharias Janssen in Middelburg—by that time spectacles began to look like ours, glasses in a frame which rested on the nose—is said in one version to have examined a small telescope belonging to an unnamed Italian traveler and copied it. The date given is 1604. In the other version children (Rudolf Wolf asked the parenthetical question: "little or big children?"), playing with lenses observed the weathervane rooster on a nearby church steeple much enlarged but *"hed onderste boven gekeerd"* ("the bottom turned up"). No date is attached to this story; the implication is that this inversion of the image caused Janssen not to follow up on this accidental discovery.

As regards Jan Lippershey, also of Middelburg, the dates are later but the story is well documented. On October 2, 1608, he offered a telescope to Prince Maurits and the States of Holland. It was to be for use in war and did not invert the image. Lippershey called his device *a kijker* (looker) or *kijkglas* and requested either a patent for 30 years or an annual pension as his remuneration. The authorities replied on October 6, praising the invention but requesting the inventor to improve his *kijker* so that both eyes could be used. Lippershey did not have much trouble producing the first binoculars, and the authorities recommended his invention on December 13 and ordered three sets of such binoculars for which they paid the unusually large sum of 900 guilders. The large amount probably was intended to compensate for the fact that no patent or license was granted "because too many people have knowledge of this invention." (Jaakob Metius of Alkmaar, who requested a patent on October 17, 1608, was refused for the same reason.)

The telescope spread even faster than eyeglasses had. One of Lippershey's instruments was given as a present to Henri IV (Henri de Navarre) late in 1608, and at the same time the Spanish Ambassador (Spinola) at The Hague bought himself one and a Belgian offered some for sale in Frankfurt. In April 1609 small telescopes could be bought in a shop in Paris, and in May Archduke Albrecht paid the goldsmith Robertus Staes 90 guilders for two "viewing tubes"; one wonders how much a viewing tube that had not been ornamented by a goldsmith would have cost. All these tubes were for watching distant ships, or troops (or ladies), but a brochure dated November 22, 1608, written in French, pointed out that one could use them for "seeing stars which ordinarily are not in view because of their smallness."

Jan Lippershey's *kijker* renewed astronomy, not because of this brochure but because of a letter written to Galileo Galilei by Jacques Bovedere in Paris, mentioning a tube holding lenses through which distant things can be seen near. Galileo later reported that he built his first telescope "in the course of one night," which is quite credible since all he really had to do was find out at what distance from each other to place his available lenses. He began observing at once, but, with the new instrument, the very word "observing" acquired a new meaning.

6

FROM GALILEO GALILEI TO
SIR ISAAC NEWTON

THERE can be little doubt that young Tyge Brahe, Otto's son, never intended to be anything but what his heritage decreed—a Danish nobleman. And Johannes Kepler felt sad when circumstances compelled him to give up his youthful dream of standing one day in black robes in the pulpit of a Lutheran church as the pastor of the congregation. And the third of the great and fiery triangle of astronomical innovators of the period, Galileo Galilei, also did not dream that posterity would acclaim him in that capacity. If somebody had asked the seventeen-year-old Galileo, when he enrolled at the University of Pisa in 1581 as a student of medicine, what he intended to be after completion of his studies several different answers might have been forthcoming. He might have replied dutifully, "It is my father's wish that I become a great doctor"; or, following his temporary inclinations, he might have answered, "A musician and a composer like my father Vincenzio; or, in a dreamy moment, even, "A painter."

For all their differences in nationality, physical appearance, and temperament, these three men were remarkably alike in many respects. For one thing, all three came from impoverished noble families, though there were differences in degree. Tycho Brahe's family still had some possessions, while Kepler's family, three generations before Johannes, had even dropped the title of nobility. Galileo Galilei's family was somewhere between the two others in worldly resources. Another thing the three great men had in common was great versatility. All three could have followed other careers with a high probability that they would now be remembered no matter what career they had chosen. (In another world we might speak of the composer Galileo, the military engineer Tycho Brahe, and the religious philosopher Kepler.) And all three entered their actual careers through the same gateway: intellectual curiosity.

In the case of Galileo we believe we know the turning point. One day in 1581 while the *studiosus medicinae* Galileo was attending mass in the cathedral of Pisa he watched the swinging of a lamp suspended from the ceiling on a long cord. Nobody knows what accident of vibration set the lamp swinging, but Galileo saw something that anybody could have seen at almost any period in history before him: it did not matter whether the extent of the swing—amplitude, we would call it—was short or long, the time required was the same. Did the time depend on the length of the rope only? This was easy to test experimentally, and Galileo (this is where he differed from most of his contemporaries) did test it.

Galileo Galilei had made his first discovery, but he could not yet follow it up any further, for his father, though an able mathematician himself, had, like Tyge Brahe's uncle Jørgen, forbidden mathematical studies. He did not want his son to be distracted from the study of medicine by anything, but he had not reckoned on the habit of European students—then and now—of sitting in on lectures not in their own course if they had time between classes.

Galileo sat in on a geometry lesson and it fascinated him so much that he, after much effort, obtained his father's reluctant permission to continue mathematical studies. But in 1585 his father had to withdraw him from the university for financial reasons, and young Galileo was more or less on his own. He had not yet earned his medical degree, or any other, but he had made an invention in the meantime, a hydrostatic balance. The description of this invention made the Marchese Guidubaldo del Monte request a treatise on the center of gravity in solid bodies and this treatise again opened the door of the University of Pisa to him, this time as lecturer on mathematics.

By then, Galileo Galilei had a goal.

The work of Archimedes had recently become known in Latin translation, but Archimedes had worked on what is now called "statics" only; he had not dealt with moving bodies. Galileo decided that he would continue where Archimedes had left off. He was interested in moving bodies, especially in falling bodies. And he was at Pisa, and the famous tower of Pisa was already leaning.

There are two events in Galileo Galilei's life which have been written about endlessly. One is, of course, the famous process where he was finally forced to recant his teachings about the moving earth. The other is his experimentation at Pisa. The story is told in virtually every text. The version given by Francis J. Rowbotham in his *Story-Lives of Great Scientists* (London, 1918) may be quoted in part, as a representative example:

It was an accepted axiom of Aristotle that the speed of falling bodies was regulated by their respective weights: thus a stone weiging two pounds would fall twice as quick as one weighing only a single pound, and so on. No one seems to have questioned the correctness of this rule, until Galileo gave it his denial. . . . He invited the whole university to witness the experiment which he was about to perform from the leaning tower. On the morning of the day fixed, Galileo, in the presence of the assembled university and townsfolk, mounted to the top of the tower, carrying with him two balls, one weighing one hundred pounds and the other weighing one pound. Balancing the balls carefully on the edge of the parapet, he rolled them over together; they were seen to fall evenly, and the next instant, with a loud clang, they struck the ground together. The old tradition was false, and modern science, in the person of the young discoverer, had vindicated her position.

For two centuries Italians and tourists alike, when they saw the well-known Campanile (as Pisans call the leaning tower), tried to visualize the scene: the young Galileo with his two weights, traditionally a cannon ball and a musket ball, on top of the tower, the aged professors and the young students around on the ground, with superstitious and therefore frightened townspeople in the background. But then came the German professor Emil Wohlwill [1] and declared that the beautiful story was *"völlig unverbürgt und unwahrscheinlich"* ("wholly uncorroborated and improbable"). In America, at a much later date, Lane Cooper, a professor of English at Cornell University, followed Wohlwill's "debunking" with a small volume of his own, an example of careful literary research. Published by the Cornell University Press in 1935, it bore the title *Aristotle, Galileo, and the Tower of Pisa.*

Wohlwill had based his rejection of the story mainly on the fact that Galileo himself never referred to the experiment in any of his voluminous later writings. Lane Cooper agreed with Wohlwill and performed the very useful service of collecting numerous quotes from ancient and less ancient works to illuminate the general confusion surrounding the case. It must be admitted that Galileo Galilei himself contributed to the confusion, presumably by having quoted from memory at one point.

In his *Discorsi* [2] Galileo wrote: "Aristotle says: 'An iron ball of one

[1] In his *Galilei und sein Kampf für die Copernicanische Lehre* (Galilei and His Fight for the Copernican Doctrine), Leipzig, 1909.

[2] The full title of this book begins with the words *Discorsi e dimostrazioni matematiche intorno a due nuove scienze.* . . . Originally printed in Leyden in 1638, it was translated into English by Thomas Salusbury with the title *Mathematical Discourses and Demonstrations, Touching Two New Sciences.* The translation appeared in London in 1665. Unfortunately a later translation by Henry Crew and Alfonso de Salvio (New York, 1914) has the title *Dialogues Concerning Two New Sciences,* which makes it sound like Galilei's main work, the *Dialogue Concerning the Two Chief World Systems,* which appeared in Florence in

hundred pounds, falling from a height of one hundred cubits, reaches the ground before a one-pound ball has fallen a single cubit.' " But Aristotle never said this; his own statement on falling bodies was not nearly as clear as Galileo's version. There are two statements by Aristotle which Galileo could have had in mind. One, in his book *On the Heavens,* reads: "For any two portions of fire, small or great, will exhibit the same ratio of solid to void; but the upward movement of the greater is quicker than that of the less, just as the downward movement of a mass of gold, or lead, or of any other body endowed with weight, is quicker in proportion to its size." The other statement occurs in Aristotle's *Physics*: "We see that bodies which have greater *rhopé,*[3] either of weight or of lightness, if they are alike in other respects, move faster over an equal space, and in the ratio which their magnitudes bear to each other."

Though Aristotle spoke of motion in general and not of the speed of falling bodies—Lane Cooper's checking of all Aristotle's extant writings revealed the surprising fact that Aristotle used the Greek word for speed (*ptosis*) only in such metaphorical and derived meanings as "falling into disrepair," and *never* with reference to actual speed—it was always assumed that this meaning was included. One Ioannos Philoponos, writing a commentary on Aristotle's *Physics* in 533 A.D., stated: "If you take two masses greatly differing in weight and release them from the same elevation you will see that the ratio of the times in their movements does not follow the ratio of the weights." The way Philoponos words his discussion, saying that "the phenomenon can better be tested by observation than by logic," suggests that he did carry out the experiment, anticipating Galileo by more than a thousand years.

But the question still is whether Galileo dropped weights from the Campanile while he was at Pisa, from the latter part of 1589 to the early part of 1591. The story that he did was told for the first time by his pupil Vincenzio Viviani, who completed his biography of Galileo in 1654, twelve years after Galileo's death, though the book was not printed until 1717. In Viviani's book the "big scene," told with so much dramatic detail by later writers, is virtually told *en passant*. Galileo, Viviani wrote, disproved many of Aristotle's conclusions, among them the statement that falling bodies move with velocities proportional to

---

1632 under the title *Dialogo . . . sopra i due massimi sistemi del mondo: Tolemaico e Copernicano*. To avoid misunderstandings I shall refer to the books by the first word of their Italian titles: *Discorsi* and *Dialogo*.

[3] The Aristotelian *"rhopé"* appears in the Latin translation as *velocitas* or *celeritas,* which is to say "speed," but it can also mean "momentum," "trend," "tendency," or "impulse."

their weight—"demonstrating this with repeated experiments from the height of the Campanile of Pisa in the presence of the other teachers and philosophers, and the whole assembly of students. . . ."

Viviani spent much time with the aged and blind Galileo, who probably devoted many hours to reminiscing about his early years. There is not the faintest reason to assume that Viviani invented the story; the very fact that he treats it so casually speaks against that assumption. Then why did Galileo himself never describe the experiment? Mainly, I think, because it was not really new. Hieronymus Cardanus published his *Opus Novum de Proportionibus* in Basel in 1570, and one of his chapters begins with the categorical statement: "Two spheres made of the same material, falling in air will arrive at a plane at the same instant." [4] The word "plane" is used here in its geometric sense; the illustration given by Cardanus looks as if he had a table top in mind.

Cardanus's book could be bought in the bookstalls when Galileo was not quite seven years old. Nor was he the only one to describe such experiments. The Dutchman Simon Stevin in his *Liber Primus Staticae* . . . , printed in Leyden in 1605, said: "But the experiment against Aristotle is like this: take two balls of lead (as the eminent Jan Grotius . . . and I formerly did), one ball ten times the other in weight; and let them go together from a height of 30 feet down to a plank below . . . the sound of the two in striking will seem to come back as a single report."

When Galileo used the Campanile for a demonstration—and remember that Viviani said that he did so "repeatedly"—he was just conducting an experiment which he probably knew had been performed before. He didn't treat it as "his" discovery and therefore had no reason, at a later date, to write about it at length. And the Aristotelian philosophers in the audience could say in complete honesty that this experiment had nothing to do with the writings of their master since Aristotle had not spoken of "fall" but of "motion."

The ones at fault are the later "popularizers" who transformed a routine demonstration into a one-time dramatic performance with the conclusion that "on this day the Aristotelian philosophy was shaken." Wohlwill was perfectly correct in denying that "the event" described by the popularizers ever took place. But that does not mean that Galileo did not drop things from the Campanile. If he later told Viviani that he had done so, he probably did.

In general he was not happy at Pisa. Many members of the faculty

[4] The original wording is: *Si duae sphaerae ex eadem materia descendant in aëre eodem temporis momento at planem ueniunt.*

were openly antagonistic; professional jealousy probably played a role, but some of their antagonism may have been an attempt to teach the young man proper behavior. Galilei looked for a vacancy elsewhere, and in 1592 he found one at the University of Padua, where the chair of mathematics was available. The post involved the teaching of geometry, astronomy, military engineering, and the science of building fortifications. It paid 180 florins annually, but Galileo succeeded, in time, in having his salary raised to 520 florins. He stayed at Padua until 1610, the decisive events of his life having taken place the year before.

These decisive events were personal as well as scientific. On the scientific side, he had received the description of the telescope and had built several of his own. Also he had started observing. The personal event was that his former pupil Cosimo became grand duke of Tuscany, and Galileo asked him for employment at court. In March of 1610 he published his telescopic discoveries in his *Sidereus Nuncius* (Messenger from the Stars); in June he resigned from the University of Padua; in September he arrived in Florence as Chief Mathematician and Philosopher to the grand duke, Cosimo II de' Medici.

The *Sidereus Nuncius* began with a dedication to the grand duke. In this dedication Galileo first stated publicly his belief in the Copernican system—Kepler in his letters had urged him for years to turn Copernican—by saying that Jupiter performed "mighty revolutions every dozen years about the center of the universe, that is, the sun." Following the dedication, Galilei first recounted how he built his telescope, then told how the glass had revealed mountains and valleys on the moon,[5] and then described the view of the starry sky. "In addition to the stars of the sixth magnitude, a host of other stars are perceived through the instrument which escape the naked eye; these are so numerous as almost to surpass belief. One may, in fact, see more of them than all the stars included among the first six magnitudes." To provide an example for his sovereign, Galileo at first attempted to draw the constellation of Orion as it looked through his instrument, "but I was overwhelmed by the vast quantity of stars and by limitations of time, so I have deferred this to another occasion. There are more than 500 new stars distributed among the old ones within limits of one or two degrees of arc. Hence, to the three stars in the Belt of Orion and the six in the Sword which were previously known, I have added eighty adjacent stars. . . . In the second example I have depicted the six stars of Taurus known as the Pleiades (I say six inasmuch as the seventh is hardly ever visible) which

[5] Quoted in Chapter 11. Galileo's report on his discovery of the four major moons of Jupiter is quoted under "The Moons of Jupiter," in Chapter 14.

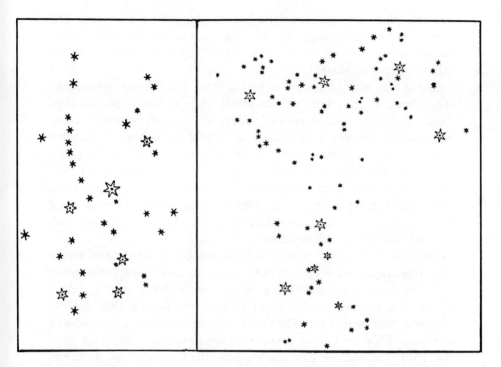

Two star charts by Galileo Galilei from his *Sidereus nuncius:* (*left*) the Pleiades; (*right*) the belt and sword of Orion. The stars drawn in outline are the naked-eye stars

lie within very narrow limits in the sky. Near them are more than forty others . . . I have shown thirty-six of these in the diagram. . . ." Galileo continued to say that the *Via lactea* is "nothing but a congeries of innumerable stars grouped together in clusters. Upon whatever part of it the instrument is directed, a vast crowd of stars is immediately presented to view. Many of them are rather large and quite bright, while the number of smaller ones is quite beyond calculation."

The final portion of the *Sidereus Nuncius* was devoted to a recounting of the discovery of the four "Medicaean planets"—the moons of Jupiter.

As usual after new discoveries, some new words were needed. Galileo, though clearly realizing that the four bodies near Jupiter revolved around Jupiter, still called them "planets." Up to that moment only the earth's moon had been known: there had been no need for a general term for moons. Kepler, who had been wondering for many years why only the earth, and none of the other planets, had a moon, was not only pleased by the discovery, he also supplied the new word. The moons of planets, he suggested in a letter to Galileo, should be collectively known as satellites, a word derived from the Greek *satellos,* which means "attendant."

But it was also necessary to find a name for the new instrument. The Dutch *kijkglas* was not acceptable, though it is a fine word in Dutch. But to Germans it sounded strange and somewhat funny; Frenchmen and Italians could not pronounce it, and it could not be handled grammatically in Latin. Galileo, in the *Sidereus Nuncius,* had used no less than three different terms: *organum, instrumentum, and perspicillum.* None of them was sufficiently distinctive, the last of the three being the term for a lens. When writing Italian, Galileo used the word *occhiale* (the singular of the plural term meaning eyeglasses), which was not distinctive enough either.

The term "telescope" is derived from two Greek words, *tele,* meaning "far away," and *skopéo,* which means "to look" (somewhat in the sense of looking intently; hence *skopós,* a "look-out man"). For a change, this term was devised by a Greek, namely Ioannes Demisiani [6]), who was mathematician to Cardinal Gonzaga. The term was introduced by Prince Federico Cesi at a banquet given in Galileo's honor on April 14, 1611, and because Cesi was the host, the coining of the word was ascribed to him for a long time. Cesi was then president of the *Accademia dei Lincei,* the Academy of the Lynxes, a very exclusive learned society which had elected Galileo as a member.

Johannes Kepler had received a copy of the *Nuncius* on April 8, 1610, via the diplomatic mail pouch of the Tuscan ambassador in Prague, Giulio de' Medici. The courier was to return to Italy on April 19; during the intervening days Kepler wrote a letter to Galileo, which was immediately printed under the title *Dissertatio cum Nuncio Sidereo* (Discussion with the Sidereal Messenger). Kepler had been somewhat vexed with Galileo who had never written him about the *Astronomia nova,* but whatever annoyance there had been in his mind was dissipated when he read of the clear report of Galileo's discoveries. Mountains and valleys on the moon—yes, that was to be expected. Many stars too small to see with the naked eye—that too had been suspected by some. And Jupiter accompanied by four moons: in that case the other planets should have moons, too, Mars probably two because the earth had one, and then Saturn should have either six or eight. And what could be the use of the four moons of Jupiter if their motions

---

[6] See *The Naming of the Telescope* by Edward Rosen (New York: Henry Schuman, 1947).

were not watched by inhabitants of the planet? Kepler went further: "Produce ships and sails which can be used in the air of the sky. Then you'll also find men to man them, men not afraid of the vast emptiness of space."

Strangely enough everyone read into Kepler's *Dissertatio* what he wanted to read. Galileo was pleased because Kepler did not doubt his discoveries, though some of his compatriots did. The imperial ambassador in Venice, Georg Fugger, made the curious remark that Galileo would soon see that Kepler had pulled the mask off his face, and Mästlin wrote to Kepler that he had been most pleased to see how his former pupil had "pulled the feathers out of Galileo" (meaning: "had taken him down a few pegs"), because Kepler had pointed out that Galileo had seen what others (including Kepler) had predicted.

As for Kepler himself, he was immersed in a different problem: just what happened in a telescope so that it enabled an observer to see distant things enlarged? And, of course, he wanted a good telescope himself. One could buy telescopes in Prague now—probably copies of Lippershey's *kijkers*—but these were not good enough to show the satellites of Jupiter. Giulio de' Medici wrote to Galileo asking for a telescope for Kepler, but received no response. Galileo was too busy giving telescopes as presents to crowned heads. Oddly enough this led indirectly to Kepler's obtaining one, as the Duke of Bavaria gave Kepler the telescope Galileo had presented to him.

During August 1610 Kepler saw Jupiter's moons for himself, and during the same month he wrote his *Dioptrice,* a book devoted to the principles of the telescope. The book contains 141 statements, labeled "definitions," "problems," and "propositions." "Definitions" are statements which are axiomatic and don't require proof; "problems" are statements which can be proved experimentally; while "propositions" are statements which are the logical outcome of "definitions" and "problems". Everything now found in a book on "elementary optics" (including most of the diagrams) appeared in Kepler's book, usually for the first time. The most important section is probably Problem 86, concerning the construction of an astronomical telescope, with the use of two convex lenses for a bigger and more sharply defined picture; that the image is inverted is unimportant for astronomical work.

Meanwhile Galileo had continued to observe. Saturn seemed to have two rather large moons and Venus showed phases like our moon, just as the Copernican theory demanded. Since the printing of the *Dioptrice* had been delayed, Kepler could add a preface telling of these new discoveries.

Of course Kepler sent a copy of this book to Galileo but Galileo had decided not to write to Kepler any more. Even earlier he had kept Kepler informed only indirectly, by writing to the Tuscan ambassador in Prague and asking him to relay information to Kepler. Nobody seems to know just why Galileo behaved that way. Maybe he gradually became convinced that Kepler's *Dissertatio* had diminished his fame as a discoverer. Maybe he was angry because Kepler maintained his friendship with Simon Marius whom Galileo considered a detractor and a plagiarist (see Chapter 14). It has even been suggested that he was annoyed because Kepler had been made a member of the *Accademia dei Lincei* six years before his own election to membership. At any event there was no more direct correspondence, with the exception of a single short letter, written a number of years later, to introduce a younger scientist to Kepler.

After the death of Rudolf II, January 20, 1612, the new emperor, Mathias, had confirmed Kepler's appointment as Imperial Mathematician (salary 300 guilders annually, plus 60 guilders "for rent and firewood"), but unlike Rudolf, did not insist that he live in Prague. Kepler moved to Linz on the Danube. At just about that time a new astronomical battle flared up, this time on the problem of whether the sun could be permitted to have spots. The idea that the sun should not have spots came from philosophical and clerical circles, but the main noise of the battle was produced by the debate on who had discovered these spots.

The names of the three men chiefly involved, in alphabetical order, were Johannes Fabricius, the son of Kepler's friend David Fabricius, Galileo Galilei, and Christoph Scheiner, S. J.

One certain fact in the dispute is that Johannes Fabricius was the first to publish his observations. The short book, comprising only 44 quarto pages, was printed in Wittenberg in 1611 with the title *De maculis in sole observatis* (On spots observed in the sun) and has the deplorable drawback that Fabricius tells what and how he observed, but not when. No dates are given, but references to "the beginning of the year" permit the conclusion that Fabricius began observing in December 1610.

When he aimed his newly acquired telescope at the sun—fortunately for his eyesight the first telescopes were quite weak, else permanent blindness would have resulted—he saw that the sun "seemed to have roughness, also around the rim." When he saw a dark spot, his first guess was that a cloud had drifted into the line of sight. But repeated sighting convinced him that a cloud could not be responsible. Then he called his father and, after the father had seen the spot, both waited for the next day. They found the spot at once, but it seemed to have shifted position, which at first, did not seem reasonable.

"To protect our eyes we let the picture of the sun enter a dark room through a hole. . . . Then it was cloudy for three days. When the sky turned fair again the spot had moved slantwise toward the West. We saw another smaller one near the edge of the sun which followed the larger one and reached the center of the sun after a few days. One more appeared and we saw three. The large one slowly disappeared from view at the other edge of the sun and that the following spots intended to do the same could be deduced from their motion. I hoped for a reappearance. Ten days later the large spot began to reappear at the eastern edge, as it proceeded toward the center of the sun's disk, the others followed, becoming poorly visible at the rim. This suggested to me a turning about of the spots, but I did not want to judge from one revolution only, but from several in succession. . . ."

Father Christoph Scheiner, who was then in Ingolstadt, saw sunspots for the first time in March 1611, in the presence of his pupil C. B. Cysat. Since the book by Fabricius was not yet available Scheiner naturally thought that he had made a new discovery. But publication of his work suffered an unexpected delay. When he reported his discovery to his ecclesiastical superior Busaeus he received neither praise nor encouragement. Busaeus looked at him gravely and said: "I have read all the writings of Aristotle several times from beginning to end and I assure you that I have not found anything in them which could be what you are telling me. Go, my son, and calm yourself. I assure you that what you took to be spots on the sun are only flaws in your glasses or in your eyes."

After this rebuff, which may have been more strongly worded than was reported later, Scheiner did not dare to follow up on his own observations until October of the same year, presumably after he had learned that others had also seen spots on the sun. His first recorded observation—of the second set—was made on October 21, 1611. In order to have his name on record somewhere, Scheiner wrote three letters about sunspots to Markus Welser in Augsburg, a member of the famous family of merchants who was known to be very much interested in things scientific. The letters were written under the cumbersome pen name *Apelles latens post tabulam*,[7] meaning "the Author awaiting com-

---

[7] The classical allusion is to Apelles, the court painter of Alexander the Great, who is reported to have hidden behind one of his own paintings to hear the remarks of the spectators.

ment before revealing himself"; obviously Scheiner had not yet forgotten what Busaeus had said to him about sunspots.

Markus Welser had the three letters printed as a brochure under the
title *Epistolae tres ad M. Velserum de maculis solaribus* (Three letters
to M. Welser on sunspots, 1612) and sent copies to many scientists,
requesting their opinions. One of the recipients was Galileo, whose
answer also consisted of three letters, the first one dated May 4, 1612.
After apologizing for the delay in replying (Welser's pamphlet was
dated January 6, 1612) because of "a series of long indispositions,"
Galileo said: "First of all, I have no doubt whatever that they are real
objects and not mere appearances or illusions of the eye or of the lenses
of the telescope, as Your Excellency's friend well establishes in his first
letter. I have observed them for about eighteen months. . . ." It is
not certain how Galileo counted these "eighteen months." If, as I consider likely, he had the date of his own letter in mind he would have
made his first observations in November 1610; eighteen months before
the letters of "Apelles" would have been in the summer of 1610. The
first known mention of sunspots by Galileo was in a letter to the painter
Lodovico Cigoli in Rome, dated October 1, 1611.

Scheiner, of course, had some problems. He did not want to consider
the sunspots as part of the sun itself, for the sun is a "most lucid body."
Galileo remarked that since the sun "shows itself to us as partly impure
and spotty, why should we not call it 'spotted and not pure'? For names
and attributes must be accommodated to the essence of things, and not
the essence to the names, since things come first and names afterwards."
He brushed aside Scheiner's statement that the spots on the sun were
"much darker than any of the dark spots observed on the moon" with
the statement that sunspots are dark only by contrast to the brilliance
of the sun's disk, so that they can best be understood by considering
them analogous to clouds in our own atmosphere.

Scheiner preferred to consider the spots as dark bodies outside the
sun, but here he ran into another difficulty. Though the Church had
not yet rejected the Copernican hypothesis, he himself did not believe
in a moving earth. This, however, did not prevent him from assuming
that other bodies moved around the sun, causing the spots. Galileo, in
his second letter to Welser, cited additional observations that contradict
this explanation:

I therefore repeat and more positively confirm to Your Excellency that
the dark spots seen in the solar disk by means of the telescope are not at
all distant from its surface, but are either contiguous to it or separated by
an interval so small as to be quite imperceptible. Nor are they stars or other

permanent bodies, but some are always produced and others dissolved. They vary in duration from one or two days to thirty or forty. For the most part they are of most irregular shape, and their shapes continually change, some quickly and violently, others more slowly and moderately. They also vary in darkness, appearing sometimes to condense and sometimes to spread out and rarefy. In addition to changing shape some of them divide into three or four, and often several unite into one . . .

This description could be printed in a modern textbook.

In his second letter Galileo also described his own method of observation: "In order to fulfill my promise to 'Apelles,' I shall now describe the method of drawing the spots with complete accuracy. This was discovered . . . by a pupil of mine, a monk of Cassino named Benedetto Castelli. . . . Direct the telescope upon the sun as if you were going to observe that body. Having focussed and steadied it, expose a flat white sheet of paper about a foot from the concave lens; upon this will fall a circular image of the sun's disk, with all the spots that are on it arranged and disposed with exactly the same symmetry as in the sun." Galileo explained that he would first draw a circle on the stiff sheet of paper, then darken the room and place the paper at such a distance from the telescope that the sun's image would fit the drawn circle. Then he would mark the spots with a pen as they appear on the paper. But, he continued, if one merely wishes to see the spots, a telescope is not needed. "From any little hole through which sunlight passes, there emerges an image of the sun with its spots and at a distance this becomes stamped upon any surface opposite the hole. It is true that these spots are not nearly as sharp as those seen through the telescope. . . . I might add that nature has been so kind that for our instruction she has sometimes marked the sun with a spot so large and dark as to be seen merely by the naked eye. . . . Such a spot, no doubt, was that which is mentioned in the *Annals of French History* by Pithoeus, printed at Paris in 1588 . . . where one reads that for eight days together the people of France saw a black spot in the solar disk. . . ."

Galileo went on to explain that this spot was thought to be the planet Mercury, which he declared was "a gross error," because Mercury's motion is so fast that "it cannot remain conjoined with the sun for even seven hours." He added that if "this discovery," namely that of the sunspots, had been made a few years earlier "it would have saved Kepler the trouble of interpreting the passage by altering the text." Kepler had known, of course, that Mercury could not be visible as a spot on the sun for as long as eight days and had supposed that *octo dies* (eight days) was a miswriting of *octies* (eight times).

It is amusing in retrospect that in May 1607, Kepler himself had mistaken a sunspot for Mercury. Since the weather was generally cloudy during that month, he could not observe the spot for several consecutive days or he would have realized that, whatever it was, the spot could not be Mercury. David Fabricius wrote at once to Kepler that he could not possibly have seen Mercury against the disk of the sun (this was just before the invention of the telescope) because the planet is too small to be visible under these conditions. Kepler was annoyed with himself but, of course knew only that he *had* seen a dark spot on the sun. As soon as the discovery of the sunspots was announced, he admitted, and explained his mistake. Kepler, as well as the Parisians, had merely repeated the same error which had been made in the twelfth century by Averroës. He, in turn, had been influenced by other Arabic astronomers who in 807 A.D. observed a spot for eight days and thought it to be Mercury, and in 840 A.D. reported another spot for ninety days and thought it to be Venus.

Before Markus Welser received Kepler's second letter, Scheiner had written him another long letter which Welser had printed and passed on, in this form, to Galileo on September 28, 1612, proudly putting an "L" after his signature, because he too had been elected to the *Accademia dei Lincei*. Galileo's third letter to Welser on sunspots, dated December 1, 1612, begins to show signs of annoyance with "Apelles" who continued to defend his own ideas, though vacillating between the view that Venus and Mercury may move around the sun and insistence on Ptolemy's system. Of course Scheiner was fighting facts of Nature, and Galileo was right all along the line, but the first signs of opposition to Galileo were becoming evident. Galileo stood for too many innovations, and the learned men of the period were still fettered by wrong habits of thought. To begin with, they still thought that logical reasoning should be considered of at least equal value with fact-finding. They might, when pressed, admit that one had to know the facts before one could reason, but to their minds the ancients had established the facts. And there they slipped into their second mistake, that of confusing the age of the ancients with individual age. Their belief in the infinite wisdom of "the ancients" no doubt sprang from the mental image of experienced aged scholars.

Unless the process of learning is artificially arrested at a certain point, an individual scholar is likely to gain experience at about the same rate at which he grows older; hence at the age of sixty he will know many more facts than he did at the age of thirty. But this does not apply to successive generations of scholars. The thirty-year-old scholars of the fourth generation will know as much as, or more than, the sixty-year-old scholars of the first generation.

The opposition to Galileo Galilei gathered slowly. It was by no means organized at first; one might say that it was united only in the beliefs that there was no need for new facts, that the facts were already established, and that they could be found in Scripture.

However, at the higher levels of the Church, Galileo was definitely in favor. Cardinal Maffeo Barberini (later Pope Urban VIII) had sided with Galileo repeatedly ever since the publication of the *Nuncius*. Father Christopher Clavius included the discoveries announced in the *Nuncius* in his last work and even said that the picture of the universe might have to be rearranged to some extent to accommodate these and other possible new discoveries. The successor of Clavius, the Jesuit Father Christopher Grienberger decided that Galileo's conclusions about the sunspots were correct and those of Christoph Scheiner were wrong. (In Italy copies of Galileo's letters to Markus Welser had been published by Cesi.)

Opposition to Galileo arose in Pisa, where he had made enemies before, and from there spread to Florence. The rector of the University of Pisa made new professors promise that they would under no circumstances teach the motion of the earth or even discuss it in private. Cosimo Boscaglia, professor of philosophy at the University of Pisa, while admitting the reality of Galileo's discoveries, insisted that the motion of the earth must be contrary to Scripture. Self-styled leader of the "anti-Galileists"—he even coined the term—was Lodovico delle Colombe. Inevitably the friends and defenders of Galileo called themselves the "Galileists" and named Colombe's group the *colombi* (pigeons). Four books against Galileo were published within half a year. Cesi suggested to Galileo that he not waste time answering them, or, if he insisted on answering, let the answers be written by someone else. Galileo made a typical compromise: he wrote most of the reply himself, addicted to polemical writing as he was, but then had his pupil Benedetto Castelli publish it under his name.

The first all-out attack came in Florence on December 21, 1614. Father Thomas Caccini, a Dominican, preached a sermon based on *Acts,* 1:11, "Ye men of Galilee, why stand ye gazing up into heaven?" In the sermon Caccini attacked Galileo, Copernicus, mathematics, and mathematicians, and declared that all were antireligious, hence both dangerous to the church and enemies of the state. This caused the Preacher-general of the Dominicans, Father Luigi Maraffi, to write a note of apology to Galileo, in which he called Caccini's statements "stupidities." Federico Cesi, as head of the *Accademia dei Lincci,* felt that the counterattack should emphasize the value of mathematics, rather than the more philosophical aspects of the Copernican system. But things took a turn for the worse as a result of a letter Galileo had written to Benedetto Castelli in Pisa. It concerned the relationship between science, especially astronomy, and religion, presumably because Galileo wanted to provide Castelli with arguments to meet the steadily increasing number of attacks. Castelli had used these arguments in discussions at the court of Grand Duke Cosimo II in the presence of other members of the Medici family, and especially of Grand Duchess Christina of Lorraine, Cosimo's mother.

Castelli had also shown the original letter around, and quite a number of copies had been made, if not by Castelli then by others. Another Dominican, Father Niccolò Lorini, who at first had held friendly, or at least conciliatory views, grew incensed when he read one. He first showed it to Caccini (in the probably mistaken belief that this was Galileo's answer to Caccini's sermon) and then passed it on to the Inquisition. He did not yet denounce Galileo personally, but only Galileists in general. The Inquisition then wrote to the Archbishop of Pisa, asking him to secure the original letter. But meanwhile Galileo had learned of this development, and at his request, Castelli returned the original, which Galileo then sent to his friend Piero Dini in Rome. He asked Dini to show the letter to Father Grienberger with the explanation that it had been composed in great haste and that he was working on an amended and expanded version in which he was expressing his beliefs.

The expanded version, completed in midsummer 1615, was addressed to Christina of Lorraine, under the title "Concerning the Use of Biblical Quotations in Matters of Science." It began with a quotation from St. Augustine advising moderation in belief about dubious points: "lest in favor to our error we conceive a prejudice against something that truth hereafter may reveal to be *not* contrary in any way to the sacred books of either the Old or New Testament. To make it quite clear that the attacked doctrine had been conceived by a good Catholic, Galileo pointed out that Copernicus had been a canon, that Pope Leo X had asked him to assist in reforming the calendar, and that his work *De Revolutionibus* had been dedicated to Pope Paul III. He stressed that Copernicus never used "arguments depending in any way upon the authority of sacred writings which he might have interpreted erroneously."

He then stated that very little astronomy can be found in the Bible, "none of the planets except Venus is so much as mentioned," which paucity must be due to the fact that the sacred authors did not wish to confuse the common people. He cited St. Augustine in support of this assertion and also quoted an epigram by a contemporary clergyman, Cardinal Baronius (who died in 1607): "The intention of the Holy Ghost is to teach us how one goes to heaven, not how heaven goes." [8] After many excerpts from St. Augustine advising caution in interpreting the meaning of passages in the Bible, Galileo finally dealt with the passage which Martin Luther had quoted against Copernicus, Joshua 10:12-13. "Then spake Joshua to the Lord . . . and he said in the sight of Israel, Sun, stand thou still upon Gideon; and thou, Moon, in the valley of Ajalon. And the sun stood still, and the moon stayed, until the people had avenged themselves upon their enemies. Is not this written in the book of Jasher? So the sun stood still in the midst of heaven, and hasted not to go down about a whole day."

Galileo first quoted church authorities who had said that it was not just the sun that stood still, but that the miracle stopped all celestial motions, by stopping the *primum mobile,* the source of all motion, thought to be somewhere outside the sphere of the fixed stars. Galileo stated that the sun of the Copernican system, as he had shown in his *Letters on Sunspots,* rotates on its axis in about one month; so if the sun stopped rotating, it would also produce the effect of stopping all motion because the sun "infuses by its own rotation not only light but also motion into the other bodies which surround it."

This sentence echoes Kepler's opinion that the force which moves the planets originates in the sun. Since there is no evidence that Galileo ever read either the *Prodromus* or the *Astronomia nova,* even though he had access to both of these books, there are three possibilities, all equally probable. Either he had read portions of Kepler's works without ever saying so, or Kepler had expressed this idea in one of his letters to Galileo, or Galileo arrived at the same conclusion by "fusing" the concepts of the *Primum mobile* and the sun's dominance.

With this hypothesis Galileo was preparing for the main blow.

The Bible says explicitly that "the sun stood still in the midst of the heavens." But did this mean high up, near the meridian? "If the sun had been at the meridian, it seems improbable that it was necessary to pray for a lengthened day in order to pursue victory in battle, the miracle having occurred around the summer solstice when the days are longest, and the space of seven hours remaining before nightfall being sufficient.

---

[8] That the authors of the Old Testament did not have even a rudimentary knowledge of either astronomy or mathematics (or zoology, for that matter) may have entered Galileo's head, but he prudently did not say so.

Thus grave divines have held that the sun was near setting and the words seem to say so. . . ." But this interpretation produces the problem of what "in the midst of heaven" is supposed to mean. The dilemma can be resolved, Galileo wrote to the Grand Duchess, by accepting Copernicus and placing the sun "in the midst" of the celestial orbs. "Then take any hour of the day, either noon, or any hour as close to evening as you please, and the day would be lengthened and all the celestial revolutions stopped by the sun standing still in the midst of the heavens where it resides."

This passage is very near the end of the letter, making it obvious that Galileo had been building up to using the words quoted against Copernicus in favor of Copernicus. Once he had done that, nothing much remained to be said.

Kepler, in the meantime, had suffered defeat in a different cause. In 1613 he had made an official trip to Regensburg to take part in a discussion about calendar reform. The astronomical phenomena, as well as the calculations involving religious holidays, argued in favor of accepting the Gregorian calendar, with some modifications if desired, and Kepler said so. But the spirit of the times was not inclined to sweet reason. The Protestants were not going to accept the Pope's calendar, and Kepler was suspect anyway, what with his service to a Habsburg monarch and his correspondence with Jesuit fathers. The new calendar was not adopted.

During the year 1615, while Galileo was polishing his letter to Christina of Lorraine, Kepler engaged in a project surprisingly far afield; he tried to evolve a mathematical theory for calculating the cubic content of wine barrels. He wrote his treatise twice, once in Latin to enable other mathematicians to follow his reasoning for the calculation of the cubic content of solids with curved surfaces, and once in German in a much abbreviated form that could be used by coopers, wine merchants, and tax agents. The reception of this work by the guilds of Linz, where he then lived, was most interesting. There was apparently no reaction to the *Stereometria Doliorum Vinariorum,* the Latin work, which was supposed to stimulate other mathematicians to further research. Kepler received a present of 150 guilders for the German book, but was told at the same time that he should continue to do what he was paid for, namely complete the *Rudolphine Tables,* something he could not do because he did not have funds to hire assistants for the routine calculations.

In the conflict between Galileo and the Church, the Church behaved as if it wished that Father Caccini had not preached a foolish sermon and that Father Lorini had not written to the Inquisition. The Inquisition's officer who had been assigned to scrutinize Galileo's letter to Castelli just criticized it mildly, three witnesses at the hearing said nothing damaging, and Father Caccini, who had volunteered to be a witness was not even called. Galileo had traveled to Rome, hoping for an interview with Roberto Cardinal Bellarmino and meanwhile holding endless discussions in favor of the Copernican system.

Just at that moment, in February 1616, Pope Paul V (Borghese) decided to intervene. He did not like intellectual discussions and wanted to put an end to what he regarded as needless talk. Consulting Cardinal Bellarmino about the Copernican doctrine he learned that the cardinal thought it to be probably contrary to the Bible—the cardinal preferred the traditional explanations but did not take an irrevocable stand—and the Congregation of the Index held the same opinion. Consequently, on instructions from the Pope, *De Revolutionibus* (and at the same time a commentary on Job by Didacus à Stunica, or Diego de Zuñiga) was banned, "pending corrections to be made." Galileo was called to Cardinal Bellarmino's house on Friday, February 26, and admonished to abandon the teachings that the earth moves around the sun. Galileo acquiesced, thus making unnecessary the second step in the inquisitorial proceedings, namely injunction. (The third step would have been imprisonment.)

For the moment the Church considered the matter closed.

Let us turn from the battle about the structure of the solar system for a moment to see what was happening to the fixed stars during the first half of the seventeenth century.

By the year 1600 even the southernmost stars had become well known. Astronomers in the north were especially grateful to two Dutch sea captains, Pieter Dirckszoon Keyser (who called himself Petrus Theodorus) and Frederick de Houtman. Both were associated with the Dutch East India Company, which had many colorful and learned employees who went to what is now called Indonesia for trade and stayed to explore, intrigued by the multitudes of new plants and animals on the ground and of new stars in the sky. Petrus Theodorus, who died in 1596, spent the last two years of his life in Java where he determined the positions of 121 of the stars around the southern celestial pole. A list of an even greater number of southern stars was made available by Houtman, who included them in a dictionary of the Malay language, which he published in 1600.

The makers of star charts soon observed a need for innovations in this field too. Ptolemy had had to label the stars somehow and had done it in a manner which looks exceedingly clumsy to us but which probably was already traditional in his day. "The star in the southern eye of Taurus," which was one of his labels, meant Aldebaran. And Rigel was described as "the brilliant star in the left foot of Orion." It seems incredible to us that Ptolemy, or Aristarchos before him, did not merely number the stars in each constellation. But the first man to use this simple method of identification was Alessandro Piccolomini in an often-reprinted book called *Della sfera del mondo,* which appeared first in Venice in 1539. What interests us is the appendix to this work, the *Libro delle stelle fisse,* the "Book of the Fixed Stars."

This appendix contained simplified charts of the constellations, ignoring the fainter stars, and omitting the traditional pictorial representations and labeling the brighter stars in each constellation *A, B, C,* and so on; having given Ptolemy's description of a particular star once, Piccolomini then referred to it as, say, "*C* in Aquarius." The German Johannes Bayer—during daylight hours he was a lawyer in Augsburg— was the first to follow Piccolomini in principle but he improved upon the system and thereby established the method still in use today. In his book *Uranometria* (first published in 1603) he calls the brightest star of each constellation *alpha,* the next brightest *beta,* and so on, through the Greek alphabet, using Latin letters if the number of Greek letters proved insufficient for one constellation. That he occasionally made a mistake, such as considering the fifth brightest star in a constellation to be the fourth brightest, is understandable (he used Tycho Brahe's catalogue for positions, but determined the brightness by personal observation). Such minor errors did not reduce the value of his star atlas, which became the favorite all through the seventeenth century and was often reprinted.

But the same Johannes Bayer got himself involved in another venture which, in retrospect, sounds like a carefully constructed scene for comic relief. Another Augsburg lawyer named Julius Schiller saw an urgent need for another reform. Why retain all the "heathen names" in the sky of a Christian world? Why not make a "Christian sky"? He talked Bayer into joining forces with him and, with the aid of a skillful and talented engraver, they began to design new pictures. The Big Dipper became *Navis Petri* (Peter's ship), and the constellation *Argo navis,* having a nautical flavor to begin with, was turned into Noah's Ark. The constellation *Apus* (Bird of Paradise) became Eve, the Centaur became Abraham, *Canis majoris* became David, Pegasus became Gabriel, Cassiopeia was Mary Magdalen, Orion was Joseph, and the constellation

Hercules was taken apart to make the Three Kings. Bayer died in 1625 and Schiller in 1627, but their nearly finished manuscript was made ready for the printer by Kepler's son-in-law Jakob Bartsch and published in Augsburg in 1627 under the title *Coelum stellatum christianum.* In spite of its pretty pictures, it was fortunately considered a curiosity from the outset. The fact that Schiller insisted in renaming the planets too (Saturn was to be called Adam, Jupiter, Moses and so forth) probably encouraged rejection.

Still, the idea lingered in a few minds. One disciple named Hieronymus Drexel published a *Zodiacus christianus* in 1634, and in 1688 Erhard Weigel, a professor of mathematics and astronomy in Jena and teacher of Wilhelm Leibniz, suggested a "heraldic sky" in which the constellations formed the coat of arms of the ruling families of Europe. A silver globe of the sky, showing Weigel's heraldic pictures, was still preserved in the museum in Kassel in 1920. Simple justice compels me, however, to add that Weigel is better known for a useful deed: just before his death (in 1699) he persuaded the Protestant rulers of Germany and of The Netherlands to accept the Gregorian calendar. He overcame all opposition on three grounds, two of them tricks. The first ground was practicality: the Julian calendar no longer agreed with reality. The two tricks were to call the new calendar *Reichskalender* (Calendar of the Realm) to avoid Pope Gregory's name, and to base the calculations, not on the "Catholic" tables used by Clavius, but on the *Rudolphine Tables* constructed by the two Protestants Tycho Brahe and Johannes Kepler.

Galileo Galilei, officially silenced in 1616, could not keep quiet for very long. By 1618 he had started writing again. Of course he could not defend the Copernican system, since *De Revolutionibus* was still on the *Index,* probably to his surprise. Galileo said he had been told—perhaps by Cardinal Bellarmino—that the corrections to be made in the book were to consist of the deletion of about ten lines and "a word here and there, e. g., where Copernicus had called the earth a 'star' "—minor revisions that should not take years to accomplish. But until this had been done, no matter how long it took the authorities, Galileo could discuss only other things: for example, Aristotle's physics. He could also discuss philosophy in general. He could, and did, say that a philosopher of his time should study the writings of older philosophers, just as an artist might begin to practice his art by copying paintings of older masters. But at some time the artist has to start drawing from nature, or else he is not an artist. "In the same way a man will never become a philosopher by worrying forever about the writings of other men, without ever raising his eyes to nature's works."

In the years from 1618 to 1623 three events, only one of them astronomical, affected Galileo's life. In 1618 three comets appeared in the sky, one of them exceptionally large. Everybody was frightened, and Father Horatio Grassi, S. J., delivered a discourse on comets at the Collegio Romano for both churchmen and public. Galileo read it, making marginal notes displaying both lack of respect and a boiling temper.[9] He wrote a reply; as he could not publish it under his own name, that of his friend Mario Guiducci appeared on the title page. But everybody knew who the real author was. It was published in June 1619. We can say now that Galileo was quite wrong in his interpretation of the comets, but many people in Rome, including Cardinal Barberini were pleased that Galileo could still make contributions to science by restricting himself to acceptable topics. Of course Grassi answered, with many slighting remarks. Galileo was planning an open letter in reply in which, since Grassi had used a pseudonym, he could attack "this unknown" in any way he pleased. But in 1620 Galileo's patron, Cosimo II, died. Galileo had to await developments. The third event occurred in August 1623. Maffeo, Cardinal Barberini, became pope, taking the name of Urban VIII. The new pope took it for granted that Galileo would come to Rome. And Galileo came, bringing with him a manuscript called *Il Saggiatore* (the Assayer), written in the Italian vernacular. It not only demolished "Sarsi" (Grassi's pseudonym), but also exposed the folly of argument from tradition as opposed to experience, without saying a single thing Galileo had been forbidden to say.

Pope Urban VIII congratulated Galileo effusively, but it soon became clear that he now was no longer Maffeo Barberini, fellow member of the *Accademia dei Lincei,* but the pope. However the intellectual climate had undoubtedly changed and Galileo began to work on his great *Dialogo,* which he finished on Christmas Eve 1629. It was his last battle for the Copernican system.

North of the Alps, Kepler had formulated the third of his three laws of planetary motions ten years earlier (see Appendix) and in 1626 had moved to Ulm. There the *Rudolphine Tables* were finally published. The printing had been started earlier, when Kepler was still in Linz, but a fire had destroyed the city's only printshop, as well as the type for the tables and those parts already printed. But by a stroke of good

---

[9] Giorgio de Santillana, in *The Crime of Galileo* (Chicago: University of Chicago Press, 1955), gives a selection; some of those not requiring translation were *ingratissimo villano, ridiculoso, elefantissimo, villan poltrone.*

fortune Kepler had his complete manuscript at his home. In Ulm the printing made good progress, to be finally completed early in September 1627. The first edition consisted of 1,000 copies.

While at Ulm Kepler was asked to produce a standard for weights and measures. The City Fathers had been annoyed by the quibbling of merchants about such questions as the length of a "shoe" (as a measurement) and how much milk or grain a "bucket" should contain. Kepler was intrigued by the problem and constructed what became known as the Kettle of Ulm, which was cast in metal.[10] Its weight was a standard for weight, its diameter a standard for length, its cubic content another standard, and so forth.

Kepler still had literary plans. For years he had planned a great work, which would be called the "Hipparchos"; it was to be the *"Almagest* of his time," and would contain a grand summary of astronomy. Another plan was to complete a much smaller work entitled *Somnium* (Sleep), which was a description of the moon, written as if produced by a traveler on the moon. In July 1628 he moved from Ulm to the small town of Sagan, hoping to find there the leisure to complete both works. But his health was poor, and a trip to Regensburg to attend a political event, the "Prince's Diet" (Kurfürstentag), proved too great a strain. He fell sick and on November 15, 1630, he died.

He had finished the *Somnium* and it was incorporated by his son-in-law Bartsch in Kepler's *Opera omnia*. But the "Hipparchos" existed only in outline form.

The year of Kepler's death was a bad one for Galileo. The *Dialogo* was finished and in the hands of the papal censors. They apparently enjoyed the style but, not knowing what to censor, passed the work on to others who might know more astronomy. And while the *Dialogo* was held up, Father Christoph Scheiner's *Rosa ursina* appeared. It was a heavy volume which owed its strange title to the fact that it was dedi-

---

[10] On the outside of the kettle, in addition to the information that it was made by Hans Braun in 1627, there are instructions by Kepler, reading:

Zween Schuch mein Tiefe	Two shoes my depth
Ein Eln mein Quer	One ell across
Ein gerechter Aymer macht mich leer,	An honest bucket will empty me,
Dan sein mir Vierthalb Centner blieben.	Then I'll weigh four half-centners.
Voll Thonawwasser wäg ich Siben	Full of Danube water I'll weigh seven [centners]
Doch lieber mich mit Kernen eich	But if you fill me with grain
Und 64 mahl abstreich	and do this well 64 times,
So bistu Neunzig Imi reich.	Your fortune will be 90 imi [An "imi" was a grain measure.]

cated to Paolo Giordano Orsini, a member of the powerful Orsini
family. The volume contained all the observations of sunspots made by
Scheiner and others (because of this it became a valuable source book
for astronomers) and all Scheiner's speculations. It also contained the
most vociferous attack on Galileo ever written. Paolo Orsini was quite
unhappy about this, especially since his brother, Alessandro Cardinal
Orsini, had urged the pope in 1616 to rule in favor of Galileo. Scheiner
had correctly assumed that Galileo would not treat him in a very
friendly fashion in the *Dialogo* and had succeeded in having his counterattack published first. That Scheiner did not even present his own opinions honestly was not known either to Galileo or to Orsini. This fact
was revealed years later by the famous Father Athanasius Kircher, who
said Scheiner had told him that Fathers Malapertius and Clavius "did
not really disapprove of the opinions of Copernicus. . . . They had been
pressed and ordered to write in favor of the common doctrine of Aristotle and that Father Scheiner followed only by order and through
obedience."

Because of confusion in the censorship, because Galileo had left Rome
(where there was an epidemic of malaria), and for a few other reasons,
the *Dialogo* was printed in Florence and not in Rome, as originally intended. It was written as a discussion among three characters, Salviati,
Sagredo, and Simplicio. Salviati, named after Galileo's pupil Filippo
Salviati, is Galileo's voice in the book. Sagredo is also named after a
real person, Giovanfrancesco Sagredo, who actually was a Venetian
nobleman just as portrayed in the book. Simplicio ("simple-minded"),
a composite of everybody who ever contradicted Galileo, naturally is an
Aristotelian philosopher.

The book was an immediate success with many people. Friar Ful-
gencio Micanzio of Venice probably summed up the feeling by saying:
"And who, before now, had guessed what the Copernican issue was all
about?"

The best recent summary is probably that of Giorgio de Santillana
(in *The Crime of Galileo*): "The argument starts with a frontal attack
on the science of the professors but soon is deep in the physical realities
shown to us by the surface of the moon. It follows thus the very sequence
of the discussions of the early years. It moves on in a leisurely manner
from one question to another, taking pot shots at casual objectives until
we are far off the track, picks up with a 'Where were we?' and comes
back for a while to playing cat-and-mouse with Simplicio as a butt, but
soon is off again in another direction, in full cry after some luckless lay
figure who has brought up the needed asininity. Meanwhile the web of

proof is being woven unobtrusively, until after a while the reader asks himself what kind of people could be blind to the evidence; what other opinion could be held except the Copernican?"

While the literary public was delighted, quite a number of Church Fathers were aghast. How had this book acquired an *imprimatur?* To make the situation worse, it was in Italian so that anybody could read it; if it had been in Latin the audience would have been more restricted. The pope's own reaction was one of fury, though his reasons were apparently so complicated that no historian has succeeded in unraveling them. Various causes have been suggested, among them the fact that Simplicio, in an especially idiotic manner, uses an argument that Pope Urban VIII, while he was still Cardinal Barberini, had once used in discussion with Galileo. This was tactless, but may not have been deliberate; Galileo had been arguing with countless people for decades and might not have remembered who had used that particular argument. In accordance with the pope's own instructions, Simplicio, the Aristotelian, is the last speaker on every point; the pope, of course, intended that the last word be given to established doctrine. Galileo, by using this device to make Simplicio most ridiculous, managed to obey the letter of the instructions and nullify the meaning. It has also been suggested that Urban VIII was disturbed because ecclesiastical power had been diminishing during the Thirty Years' War, but could not fairly be blamed on Galileo or any other scientist. Another theory is that the pope, in threatening Galileo with the Inquisition, was really threatening the grand duke of Tuscany. But none of these causes, or even the combination, seems sufficient to explain the papal anger. The only honest conclusion is that we don't know why Urban VIII turned against Galileo.

If the motives were confused, the proceedings were not less so.

On October 1, 1632, the Inquisitor of Florence served Galileo with a formal summons to present himself in Rome within thirty days. His departure was delayed by a perfectly genuine sickness—the doctors attested: "pulse intermits every three or four beats . . . attacks of giddiness, hypochondrial melancholia, weakness of the stomach, insomnia, and flying pains about the body . . . serious hernia." The pope, when informed, said that the journey could be made in easy stages, with every possible comfort, but that Galileo had to come. Galileo could have fled to Venice where he would have been safe, and he had offers from Venice, but after his health had improved somewhat he decided to go to Rome. He arrived on February 23, 1633, but the first hearing did not take place until April 12.

This additional delay occurred not only because the Inquisition permitted Galileo a few weeks of rest to recover from the three weeks' journey, but also because the Inquisition did not have a sound case. Galileo had been careful to follow the old admonition and to obey instructions. But every admonition permits a certain leeway, and instructions can be misunderstood; it was difficult to base a case on borderline transgressions of interpretation and possible misunderstandings. Besides, the book by Copernicus, around which everything revolved, had only been banned "pending corrections"; it had not been declared heretical.

But things had come to the point where a show of strength, however unimportant the specific reasons, was needed. And once the machinery of the Inquisition had been set into motion it would run its course from inertia, despite the fact that too harsh a judgment would certainly have unpleasant consequences for a church no longer supremely powerful. The pope himself had asked for a "limited example."

There is no doubt that Galileo was frightened, but there is also no doubt that his judges were worried. The problem was, as the Inquisitor himself expressed it, to settle the case in such a way that "the court will maintain its reputation; it will be possible to deal leniently with the culprit [so that] he will recognize the favor shown him." The judges conferred with the accused and on April 30 Galileo confessed to "vainglorious ambition and [transgression because of] pure ignorance and inadvertence."

Protestant historians have said that this was a case of "ten judges asking for a perjury and obtaining it," but this describes the legal aspect only. It neglects the point that Galileo was a Catholic and had to submit to authority in some manner. Nobody was interested in having Galileo actually change his mind; it was a question of showing who was in authority. On June 22, 1633, sentence was pronounced [11] and Galileo pronounced the formula of abjuration. Two days later he was released into the custody of the Tuscan ambassador and brought to the Villa Medici.

It is, in my opinion, no accident that the best summation of the trial was written by a historian who was born in Rome, namely Giorgio de Santillana. After pointing out that the pope could have simply declared that the Copernican doctrine was heretical (and thus settled the issue as far as Catholics were concerned), de Santillana said:

11 ". . . We ordain that the book of the 'Dialogue of Galileo Galilei' be prohibited by public edict. We condemn you to the formal prison of this Holy Office during our pleasure, and by way of salutary penance we enjoin that for three years to come you repeat once a week the seven penitential Psalms. Reserving to ourselves liberty to moderate, commute, or take off, in whole or in part, the aforesaid penalties and penance." Three of the ten cardinals who were the judges— Francesco Barberini, Caspar Borgia, and Laudivio Zacchia—did not sign the document.

He did not, and that leaves the Galileo trial as a curious inconclusive oddment in history. Such thundering theological persecution combined with dogmatic timidity, this dragging and kicking a man for suggesting his scientific conviction while they dared not formally assert the contrary, left the authorities twice stultified in the end. They could not very conveniently broadcast the real motives, which were that Galileo had taken to writing in Italian and that he had made them look foolish, or that the political meaning of it was that the Jesuits had evened up a score with the Dominicans by way of the new game of cosmological football. They never revoked the sentence of formal prison . . . on the other hand, they never revoked the small pension that the prisoner had been granted in happier days. The whole performance is in tune with the magniloquent papal arches of the period, leading into a dump that was once a road, or with those imposing Baroque gateways of the Campagna Romana, unexpectedly opening out from a drowsy walled-in road onto a field of thistles. It, too, has that persuasive Roman air of having a purpose, where none is visible.

(The Crime of Galileo, p. 320)

Now did Galileo, as popular legend has it, murmur *Eppur si muove*— "And yet, it moves," meaning the earth?

The story first appeared in Giuseppe Baretti's *The Italian Library,* published in London in 1757. Baretti stated that Galileo uttered this sentence after his release, thoughtfully stamping the ground with his foot after looking at the sky. Later the story was reconstructed for better dramatic effect: Galileo was supposed to have said it right after rising from the kneeling position he had assumed when speaking the formula of abjuration. As de Santillana remarks, if he did, the Commissary-General "would have done his best not to hear."

Most historians considered this story pure legend, but the three words appear in a painting by Murillo (1617–1682), which was discovered in 1911. The painting is dated "circa 1650," not quite a decade after Galileo's death. At least the story was extant at that time.

After a rest at the Villa Medici in Rome Galileo returned to Florence and spent the last eight years of his life in his villa at Arcetri. Formally he was under arrest, but he could have all the visitors he wanted to see. Officially he was forbidden to publish, but he could write—or rather dictate, since his eyesight had begun to fail, and he became blind by 1637. His amanuensis was Evangelista Torricelli, the inventor of the barometer; his other steady companion was Vincentio Viviani, who became his first biographer. Under these circumstances Galileo not only carried on a voluminous correspondence, but also wrote his last book, the *Discorsi,* recapitulating his early experiments in the field of mechanics, including the laws of falling bodies and the motion of a

Galileo Galilei

pendulum. Since he was forbidden to publish, he sent the manuscript to Holland; it appeared in Leyden in 1638.

On January 8, 1642, he died.

The Grand Duke wanted to erect a monument over his tomb, but Urban VIII informed him that he personally would consider a monument for Galileo as an insult to papal authority.

What Copernicus had started in Poland with his heliocentric world, what Kepler had revealed to be the correct shape of planetary orbits by his calculations in Austria, what Galileo had strengthened by his observations in Italy—all this still needed a synthesis, which was made in England. The man who made it, Sir Isaac Newton, was born in the year of Galileo's death—on December 25, 1642, at Woolsthorpe near Grantham.

Newton was a premature baby and his mother sometimes said later that he had been so small at birth that she could have hidden him in a one-quart mug. He was not expected to live for more than a few hours; actually he lived for eighty-four years and three months. At the age of fourteen he disappointed his mother by thinking about mathematics instead of doing his farm chores. Newton's uncle, William Ayscough, who was a member of Trinity College, solved the family problem when Isaac was eighteen by sending him back to school to prepare for college. He received his Bachelor of Arts degree at Cambridge in 1665 and was elected a Fellow of the Trinity College two years later, at the age of twenty-five.

At about that time it occurred to him that the number of mathematical operations was insufficient for many purposes. Kepler, incredible as it may seem in retrospect, had done most of his work using only such elementary operations as addition and multiplication. Only late in life had he begun to profit from the introduction of logarithms. Henry Briggs, who "invented" the system of logarithms based on the figure 10 and who calculated the first table of such logarithms, had died at Oxford in 1630, the same year Kepler died at Regensburg. But while the logarithms saved enormous amounts of work and time in calculations, they did not enable the mathematicians to accomplish anything that could not have been done before.

In 1665 Newton conceived "fluxions," which we call calculus. It was his second mathematical discovery, as he had already developed the "binomial theorem." And in 1666, Newton said, he began to "think of gravity extending to the orb of the moon." At the same time he began thinking about optics and the problem of colors. For half a dozen years he devoted most of his efforts to a study of optics which resulted in a very important invention. Because that invention was a new type of telescope it seems logical to assume that Newton's optical studies were prompted by the defects of the telescopes of his time: they all produced rainbow fringes. When Newton bought a glass prism at a fair in Stourbridge in 1666, he saw how a ray of sunlight was spread out by the prism into a ribbon of rainbow colors. After some study of this phenomenon he arrived at the conclusion that light consists of rays which are "differently refrangible."

When Newton was interested in a natural phenomenon his preoccupation must have been complete. His friend Dr. Edmond Halley once asked him how he had made his discoveries. Newton's reply was: "By thinking about the problem unceasingly." His thoughts about colors led to a paper entitled "New Theory about Lights and Colours," which he read to the Royal Society on February 8, 1672. As regards the rainbow fringes in a telescope he concluded that there was no cure. A converging lens (the ordinary magnifying lens) produced an image with a rainbow fringe; a diverging lens placed in contact with the converging lens would make the color fringe disappear but would also nullify the magnifying effect. In short, you could produce magnification *and* a color fringe, or you could suppress the color, suppressing magnification at the same time.

This mistaken reasoning was not experimentally disproved until after Newton's death, when it was found that combinations of converging and diverging lenses of different types of glass would suppress the color but still permit the formation of an image. An "achromatic telescope" was possible, but not in Newton's time, as the art of glassmaking had not then progressed far enough. Since Newton was convinced that a perfect telescope using lenses only could not be built, he invented the reflecting telescope in which the light is gathered by a mirror. The different colors of light would separate on going through a lens, but not when reflected by a mirror. The first man to suggest that a concave mirror might be used instead of a lens was the professor of mathematics at the Collegium Romanum, Father Niccolò Zucchi, S. J., who, in about 1650, even made a few preliminary experiments. But in 1668 Newton built the first practical telescope using a concave mirror with a small plane mirror which reflected the image through a hole in the wall of the tube where it could be inspected with a magnifying glass. Three years later he built a somewhat larger instrument of the same type and sent it to the Royal Society. Soon afterward the Society elected him a Fellow.

By inventing a usable reflecting telescope, Newton had provided astronomers with a new tool which, with various minor adaptations as to the positioning of the elements, became the dominant astronomical tool for centuries to come.

But Newton's chief contribution to astronomy (written at Halley's insistence), was still to come.

7

DR. EDMOND HALLEY AND
THE "YEAR OF THE COMET"

B E F O R E proceeding with Newton's chief work, and the events of the following century, I want to make a digression, which I hope is chronologically justified.

Comets, because they are unusual and spectacular phenomena—especially impressive in times when artificial illumination was confined to the rosin-wood torch, or even to the oil lamp—and because they seemed to appear without warning, have been seen and feared for so many centuries that they cannot be assigned any specific place in the history of astronomy. Since the whole story must be included somewhere, it might as well be told as an adjunct to the period of Newton and Halley, for Dr. Edmond Halley was responsible for its turning point. Before Halley, comets were "omens and portents in the sky" to almost everybody; after Halley they became predictable astronomical phenomena.

The beginning of the comet story is not only remote but also confused (partly because we have to rely on a secondary source). The first two important names are those of Apollonius of Myndus (c. 270 B.C., also called Apollonius the Astronomer or Apollonius epsilon) and Epigenes, both of whom claimed to have studied astronomy among the Chaldeans and therefore to know the opinions held by the Chaldeans about comets. Apollonius is reported to have stated that the Chaldeans considered the comets to be like planets, but moving far from the earth most of the time and therefore invisible. Epigenes is reported to have said that the Chaldeans thought them to be "fires produced by a kind of eddy of violently rotating air." If these two statements of what the Chaldeans did (or did not) think had come to us via two different classical sources it might be possible to select the more likely one, on the basis of the generally greater reliability of one of the two authors.

But both these mutually exclusive statements come from the same source, namely Lucius Annaeus Seneca, contemporary of Pliny the

Elder. That Seneca, in many respects the most clear-headed of the Roman authors, should have misquoted either Apollonius or Epigenes is highly unlikely, and, therefore, the probable answer is that there were at least two schools of thought among the Chaldeans, one reported by Apollonius and the other by Epigenes.

Aristotle, who died in 322 B.C., accepted the belief that comets were atmospheric phenomena. Of course he gave reasons; some may have been what was said among the Chaldeans; others are evidently his own.

Some Greek philosophers, for example, Anaxagoras and Demokritos, he said, had taken comets to be astronomical phenomena like the planets. But that could not be true. In the first place no planet had ever been observed except the known five (meaning Mercury, Venus, Mars, Jupiter, and Saturn) and they all had often been seen above the horizon at the same time. But comets had been visible in addition to them. Moreover, comets had been seen outside the zodiac, which is impossible for planets. Also, they had "vanished without setting, gradually fading away above the horizon . . . without leaving a star." But if they were like planets, one should see comets without tails. In short, they did not fit into the astronomical picture anywhere and hence could not be astronomical phenomena.

And then he drew his conclusion: "We may say, then, that a comet is formed when the upper motion introduces into a gathering of this kind a fiery principle not of such excessive strength as to burn up much of the material quickly, nor so weak as soon to be extinguished, but stronger and capable of burning up much material, and when exhalation of the right consistency rises from below and meets it." In short, comets were merely fires in the air, vapors that rise from the ground and are burned, provided they burn slowly, for if they burn up fast they form "shooting stars." Logically then, since comets are burning vapors from the ground, "when there are many comets . . . the years are clearly dry and windy." There are examples, too. "At the time of the great comet [of 371 B.C.] the winter was dry and north winds prevailed;" there also happened to be an earthquake and a tidal wave in that year and Aristotle thought that the tidal wave had been caused by the strong winds. "Again," he continued, "in the archonship of Nicomachus [341-340 B.C.] a comet appeared . . . and simultaneously with it there happened the storm at Corinth."

Aristotle, without the faintest intention of doing so, started two thousand years of comet fear, by considering them to be "weather signs" that indicated strong and dry winds. His own reasoning was essentially that such winds produced comets as a by-product, but this was later reversed and comets were thought to cause the winds together with the things that strong winds produce, such as floods and fires.

Pliny the Elder, in the second book of his *Natural History* accepted Aristotle's interpretation of comets as atmospheric phenomena, and as was his habit, he enumerated the various names given to comets based on appearance only as one would expect: "the kind named *Cerastias* has the appearance of a horn . . . *Lampadias* is like a burning torch, *Hippias* is like a horse's mane. . . . There was one where the appearance of a mane was changed into that of a spear; it happened during the 109th olympiad, in the 398th year of the City.[1] The shortest time during which any one of them has been observed to be visible is 7 days, the longest 180 days."

As for their motion in the sky, Pliny said that "some of them move about in the manner of planets, others remain stationary." The words which Bostock and Riley translated, "in the manner of planets" are, in the original, *errantium modo*. The meaning is that they change their position with respect to the fixed stars, as the planets do; no orbiting in our sense is implied.

Though Pliny accepted the comets as "omens" without any question, he believed that there were also good omens:

Rome is the only place in the whole world where there is a temple dedicated to a comet; it was thought by the late Emperor Augustus to be auspicious to him, from its appearance during the games which he was celebrating in honor of Venus Genetrix, not long after the death of his father Caesar. . . . He expressed his joy in these terms: "During the very time of these games of mine, a hairy star was seen after during seven days, in the part of the heavens which is under the Great Bear. It rose at about the eleventh hour of the day, was very bright and was conspicuous in all parts of the earth. The common people supposed the star to indicate that the soul of Caesar was admitted among the immortal gods; under which designation it was that the star was placed on the bust which was lately consecrated in the forum." This is what he proclaimed in public, but in secret, he rejoiced at this auspicious omen, interpreting it as produced for himself; and to confess the truth, it really proved a salutary omen for the world at large.

As time went on, comets came to be considered bad omens exclusively. Aristotle and Pliny were still read, but Seneca was forgotten. Seneca had no doubt that the comets were celestial bodies, pointing out that they, unlike cloud formations, follow the diurnal rotation of the fixed stars, with only a gradual change of position among them.

[1] These two figures do not correspond; historians place the 109th olympiad in the 211th year of the City. A later commentator said that one could despair over such chronology—"*desperandum est de Pliniana chronologia.*"

He considered it very likely (*Quaestiones Naturales,* VII) that their motions, like those of the planets, might be determined and predicted and added: "The time will come when those things which are now hidden shall be brought to light by time and persevering diligence. Our posterity will wonder that we should be ignorant of what is so obvious."

But Aristotle's ideas were easier to assimilate, even disregarding his authoritative name, and the fact that accepting Aristotle's statement permitted predictions was no doubt a very important, if unmentioned, factor. Whether the prediction concerned weather only, or all kinds of other calamities, people simply liked to predict things, from the learned professor of philosophy down to the illiterate shepherd. The comet fear seems to have reached its peak at around the time when printing was invented. This coincidence is quite useful to us, because every comet appearance caused a rash of pamphlets, very often in the form of the so-called *Einblattdruck,* which means a one-sheet pamphlet, normally with a woodcut at the head of the page and a title such as "News of the Terrible and Fearsome Comet which has been seen in the Sky over the City of . . ."

The peak of comet fear also coincided, not surprisingly, with a never-repeated abundance of large naked-eye comets. The list for the fifteenth and sixteenth centuries reads as follows: one in 1402, one in 1403, one in 1449, one in 1456 (that was Halley's), two in 1457, and one in 1472. The next century brought one bright comet each in 1500, 1506, 1531 (Halley's again); two in 1532; and one each in 1533, 1538, 1539, 1556, 1558, 1569, 1577, 1580, and 1582.

Considered of especially evil omen was the appearance of Halley's comet in 1456, just three years after the Turks had conquered Constantinople. The legend arose later that the pope, Calixtus III, issued a bull excommunicating the comet. This, of course, is nonsense; not even the pope can excommunicate somebody who is not a member of the church to begin with. What really happened is that the pope ordered supplications and the ringing of all church bells to call the faithful "to aid by their prayers those engaged in battle with the Turk."

A few clear-headed men tried to show that the appearance of a comet and terrestrial calamities were just coincidence. The first known treatise against comet fear was written by Heinrich von Hessen (1325-1397) after the appearance of the comet of 1368; one wonders how many readers it found, not counting the author's own students in his classes on theology and mathematics. The very fact that more than one and a half centuries went by until the next such tract was written argues against the thought that Heinrich von Hessen wielded any influence in that respect. That next tract was written by Philippus Aureolus Bombastus Theophrastus ab Hohenheim, better known as Paracelsus. Paracelsus spent most of his life raging against the many superstitions in medicine, and he did not feel any more kindly toward other superstitions. His book, published in Zürich in 1531, *Usslegung des Cometen erschynen im hochbirg zu mitten Augsten Anno 1531* (Explanation of the Comet which appeared in the high mountains [the Alps] in Mid-August 1531), was the second book on comets to appear in German; the first had been written by one Peter Creutzer four years earlier. Though most writers of other nationalities continued to use Latin for another century or so, after 1532 the writers of the German-speaking nations, Germany, Austria, and Switzerland, wrote most of their comet treatises in German, no doubt because of the great popularity of the subject matter.

Soon after, an Italian living in Paris raised his voice. His name was Giovanni Ferrerior and he did not mince words. His title read *Da vera cometae significatione, contra astrologorum omnium vanitatem*—On the true meaning of comets, against all astrological vanities.

Both the books by Paracelsus and the one by Ferrerior were strong expressions of personal opinions; though meritorious in intent they cannot be called scientific. And though they were probably read they made, at best, a very negligible dent in the pervading atmosphere of gloomy enjoyment of predicting forthcoming catastrophes.

The great number of bright comets during the fifteenth and sixteenth centuries naturally resulted in the making of lists. We do not know how many frightened burghers and curious clergymen made comet lists for their private use; the first one printed had been compiled by the Paris physician Antonius Mizaldus (Antoine Mizauld) and appeared in Paris in 1544 under the title *Cometographia*. It is by no means a complete record of appearances of comets, but after each listing of a comet it also lists the disaster supposedly caused by it.

A few samples of the comet listings then customary (not from Mizauld's book, but similar in style and mood) are:

Anno 942 a comet appeared and soon after followed a great dying of livestock and other animals.

Anno 1477 there was a comet and then the proud Charles of Burgundy was slain at Nantes.

Anno 1531, 1532, and 1533 comets were seen and at that time Satan hatched heretics.

The second book of comet listings was compiled by the Swiss Ludwig Lavater. The original was in Latin (*Cometarum ominum fere catalogus*) and was printed in Zürich in 1556; over a century later, in 1681, it was translated into German and brought up to date.

The mood of the time is probably best expressed in a German hymn which no doubt was sung in church with proper solemnity. It is known from an *Einblattdruck* for the comet of 1661 but seems to be older. The author is not known, nor the melody to which it was sung:

Cometen waren jeder Zeiten	The comets were at any time
Zornbotten Gottes und bedeuten	Signs of God's ire and signify
Wind, Theurung, Pest und Wassers Noht	Storm, famine, plague and heavy floods;
Erdbidem, Endrung, Fürstentodt	Earthquakes and changes, Death of lords
Sollt aber drum der Fromm verzagen?	But should the pious then despair?
Nein, sonder mit Vertrauen sagen	No, but in good faith declare
Wann Erd und Himmel brächen eyn	If earth and sky should fall asunder
Wird Gott mein Port und Anker seyn.	God is my port, also my anchor.

The climax was reached with the very large and bright comet of 1680, which, in addition to the usual rash of pamphlets of all sizes, all degrees of superstition, and in all Western European languages (remarkably little is known about comet fear in Russia at the time, which may have any reason, from stocism to lack of printing presses), produced two innovations. A medal was struck to commemorate the event, and from Rome came the news that, while the comet was in the sky, a "virginal hen" had laid an egg with the picture of a comet on its shell! That "comet egg" was even pictured and seriously discussed in the French *Journal des Savans* (issue dated January 20, 1681).

But before the comet of 1680 arrived to cause the production of miraculous eggs, common sense had asserted itself. A Polish nobleman, Stanislas Lubienitzky, who spent the latter part of his life in Hamburg and in Amsterdam and seems to have been engaged in trade, having some connections with the then flourishing Dutch East India Company, published two folio volumes entitled *Theatrum cometicum*. The work appeared in Amsterdam in 1677. Like the books by Mizauld and Lavater, it was a listing of all naked-eye comets with concurrent events, but Lubienitzky also included good news, and his listings show about the same number of good and bad happenings. This being the case, there is no reason to be frightened by a comet, Lubienitzky said, and his general attitude is more or less that since the balance is neither "good" nor "bad," the comets have nothing at all to do with the events.

Only five years later the French professor of philosophy Pierre Bayle, who taught in Rotterdam, wrote a *Lettre, où il est prouvé que les Comètes ne sont point le présage d'aucun malheur*. This "letter" which "proved that the comets do not announce calamities" was not precisely a "letter" as we would use the word—it filled two volumes, though not folio volumes like Lubienitzky's. The first edition appeared in Cologne in 1682 (in one volume), the third edition (in two volumes) in Rotterdam in 1699. The German scholar Johann Christoph Gottsched, who as a critic exercised a great influence on German literature in his time, thought Bayle's "lettre" important enough to translate into German. His translation was published in Hamburg in 1741.

Now let us backtrack a bit.

The same abundance of bright comets which led to these manifestations—in retrospect fairly amusing—of both superstition and of commercialism exploiting the superstitions, also paved the way for a scientific attack on the comet problem.

A careful observation came first. Johann Müller, who called himself Regiomontanus, in 1472 observed a bright comet. With the aid of his pupil Bernhard Walther, he measured its positions in the sky. These measurements were good enough so that Halley could use them to calculate its orbit; it was one of the appearances of "his" comet.

The first important astronomical discovery concerning comets was made by two men, almost simultaneously and certainly independently. On was Girolamo Fracastoro who, as a young man, may have met the young Copernicus in Padua during the years 1501–1506. He announced, in a book published in Venice in 1538, that the tails of comets are always turned away from the sun. The other was Peter Apian, professor of mathematics at Ingolstadt and astronomer to the two emperors Charles V and Ferdinand I, who came to the same conclusion and published it in 1540.

Though Fracastoro's book appeared two years earlier than Apian's *Astronomicum Caesareum,* Apian received most of the credit, possibly because he was the first to publish a diagram showing the position of the comet's tail with reference to the sun, possibly because his book made a great impression on Wilhelm, landgrave of Hessen-Cassel. Wilhelm devoted a great deal of his time to astronomical observations; he is credited with the discovery of the comet of 1558, which he observed carefully, as he did the comet of 1577.

In an earlier tract on comets, written in German and published in

1531, Apian had apologized for being unable to say anything about the distance of the comet from the earth. The wording of his apology makes it clear that his concept of the parallax was correct.

The determination of the distance of a comet—even if only an approximate one—was carried through for the comet of 1577, which was large and impressive and came at just the right time to stimulate astronomical thought about comets.[2] The roster of observers of the comet of 1577 is a roster of astronomers then living. Tycho Brahe observed it from his island of Hveen; Thaddaeus Hagecius (Tadéaž Hájek) observed it from Prague; the landgrave of Hessen-Cassel observed it from Cassel (and sent his reports to Hveen.) Michael Mästlin and Helisaeus Roeslin observed it from southwestern Germany, passing on their observations and opinions to Hagecius, who passed them on to Tycho Brahe. With all this correspondence underway in several directions, Tycho waited with his own work on the comet until most of the others had published theirs so that he could include as much as possible. He wrote two different treatises, one in German and one in Latin. The Latin treatise was published immediately upon completion; the German treatise (which had been written first) was not published during his lifetime—in fact, it did not see print until 1922.

Doris Hellman's book on the comet of 1577 contains a summary of Tycho's German treatise, which is in ten sections. The first section deals with the opinions of the classical philosophers, the second with the appearance and duration of the comet. It was first seen shortly after sundown on November 11, 1577 (and by him on November 13), and had a head that resembled the appearance of Saturn and a very long tail. But, he said, "seafarers on the 'Northwendic' Sea" (the Baltic) had reported seeing it in the evening of the 9th of November. It decreased in size as time went on—he saw it for the last time on January 26, 1578. Section III contains the positions among the fixed stars which he determined; section IV concerns the comet's tail. At first the tail was 22 degrees long; by the end of Januuary, it had all but disappeared; but for as long as it was visible it pointed away from the sun. As for the nature of the tail, Tycho considered it mainly an optical effect, somewhat like a sunbeam shining through thin mist.

The fifth section is, in many respects, the most important, for it contains a determination of the distance from the earth to the comet.

[2] See *The Comet of 1577: Its Place in the History of Astronomy*, by C. Doris Hellman, Ph. D. (New York: Columbia University Press, 1944).

His observations indicated that the head of the comet was more than four times as far from the earth as the moon and since the distance to the moon is not quite 50,000 German miles [3] that meant a distance of 200,000 German miles for the comet. Section VI dealt with the size of the comet itself. The diameter of the comet's head, calculated from apparent size and just-calculated distance came out to 465 German miles and its circumference to 1460 German miles; the length of the tail to 70,000 German miles and the greatest width of the tail to 5000 miles

Section VII was devoted to the "meaning" of the comet. Here Tycho at first dodged any definite statement. The comets are new and supernatural creations of God and since we don't even understand the meaning of His natural works we can understand the meaning of a supernatural creation even less. The truth is hidden from all men, but something about what such a phenomenon *could* signify might be discovered from old astrological writings without recourse to superstition. Section VIII continued the discussion of the meaning, getting deeply into superstition in the process. Comets had always caused dryness in the air and strong winds and floods; they had always been followed by pestilence and war and bloodshed. This comet resembled Saturn and passed Saturn, and it had a red tail showing the influence of Mars, hence it signified many deaths, both by disease and war. In addition, having its origin in the Tropic of Capricorn, it would cause great changes in religious matters. Section IX continued the astrological trend of thought in trying to predict which nations would suffer most. Since it had first been seen at sunset, it would be the West, specifically Spain, because the Spaniards are ruled by Sagittarius and the comet had been in this sign. The people living in lands ruled by Spain, like the Dutch, would suffer greatly from evil caused by the Spaniards, but the Spaniards themselves would suffer more; they would lose many cattle and many of their best men. The Jews would suffer because they are under the influence of Saturn and all "pseudo-prophets" would suffer greatly because the comet had let itself be seen as a "pseudo-planet."

Section X, finally, deals with the time when these prophecies will come true and how long the events will last. They would begin in the year when the comet was last seen (1578), increase in effect in

---

[3] Like everything else in those days, the length of the German mile was not standardized. The one Tycho Brahe must have had in mind was 4.5 English miles, with 7240 meters to the German mile.

1579 and 1580 and disappear in 1583 when new constellations would become stronger.

At this point, it may be wise to emphasize that Tycho Brahe, despite his astrological beliefs was the greatest astronomical observer since Hipparchus. Also, a book on a comet was expected to have chapters about the "meanings," whether pro or con. What is important is that Tycho Brahe declared the comet to have been much farther from the earth than the moon is, and to have been of considerable size itself. (In the published Latin treatise he gave details of his observations and calculations; evidently the Latin treatise was meant to be the "scientific," the German treatise the "popular" work. Nobody knows why the latter was not published.

Although Tycho Brahe and Michael Mästlin had made it clear that the comet of 1577—and, by inference, all other comets—had been "supra-lunar," farther away than the moon, it was still doubtful that comets were "full-fledged" celestial bodies, like the moon and the planets. Their appearance argued against solidity, and this posed a problem for Kepler. Kepler had observed the comet of 1607—still with the naked eye—at a time when he was already convinced that the orbits of the planets were elliptical. But if comets were not solid, did they have to follow such orbits? One can understand Kepler's uncertainty; he had been able to deduce the *shape* of the planetary orbits, but did not know the *reason* for that shape. However, the lack of periodicity was another argument that the comets were, somehow, fundamentally different. Hence Kepler, in his "Comprehensive Report on the Hairy Star which appeared in 1607," concluded that the motion of a comet was along a straight line,[4] that it came from infinity and disappeared into infinity.

The first man to observe a comet through a telescope also agreed with this conclusion. He was Johann Baptist Cysat, son of the City Clerk of Lucerne, and the comet was the comet of 1618.

But the suspicion that Kepler might have been wrong on this occasion arose in several minds when new bright comets made their appearance. In a letter [5] (later printed) dated February 10, 1665, addressed to Father Stefano de Angeli, Giovanni Alfonso Borelli reported that he had observed the comet of 1664 and, being professor of mathematics

---

[4] His own wording was *"dass der Cometen Bewegung eine gerade Linie sey . . . und nicht circularisch wie die der Planeten"*—"that the comet's movement is along a straight line . . . and not circular like those of the planets." The term "circular" is used here to mean "closed curve."

[5] Discovered by Rudolf Wolf, who reported proudly that "even Pingré missed it"; the reference is to the French astronomer Alexandre-Gui Pingré, whose very careful catalogue of comets was published in 1783.

in Padua at the time, had tried to calculate its orbit. But there he ran into a difficulty: the calculations made sense only if the earth moved, something he was officially forbidden to believe. But one can make assumptions for a calculation, so Borelli assumed the Copernican system to be correct, only for purposes of calculation, of course. And just to be on the safe side he gave the Copernican system a classical name—the *Ipotesi Pitagorica*. Furthermore he himself wrote under an assumed name.[6] After all these precautions he concluded that the comet probably traveled in an elliptical orbit, "or another curved line." In a letter to Duke Leopold of Tuscany, dated May 4, 1665, Borelli said that the curve might be one resembling a parabola.

The same comet which made Borelli toy with Keplerian ellipses caused Louis XIV of France to request a resumé on comets from P. Petit; Petit obliged with a *Dissertation sur la nature des Comètes* which was printed in French in Paris in 1665, in Latin in Altdorff in 1677 and, in German in Dresden in 1681. All astrological ideas received short shrift from Petit; as for the astronomical facts he decided that comets were probably periodical and considered it possible that the comet of 1664 was the same as the comet of 1618 and that it might return in 1710. While the two comets of 1618 and 1664 happened *not* to be identical, it is interesting to see that Petit, who obviously could not have known about Borelli's letter, came to the same conclusions. And like Borelli he had to make a quick bow in the direction of the Ptolemaic system which he did by saying that comets traveled in elliptical orbits either around the sun or around the earth.

The same comet caused Johannes Hewelcke (Hevelius) in Danzig to correct Kepler: the comets(he repeatedly uses the term *pseudoplanetae*) do not travel in really straight lines but along a very slightly curved line which is concave in the direction toward the sun. Many later writers, especially Germans, have seized upon this statement to declare Hevelius a "forerunner of Newton." But since he did not state what kind of curved line he had in mind, one can only say that he had made a step in the right direction, but a very short one.

The man who actually was a "forerunner of Newton," by six years, was the Magister Georg Samuel Dörffel,[7] Newton's almost unknown contemporary.

Pastor Dörffel wrote a total of nine books and papers on astronomical themes; three of them are in Latin, two dealing with a lunar eclipse and

[6] It was Pier Maria Mutoli.
[7] He was born in Plauen in 1643 and died in Weida in 1688. His biography, written in 1882, is virtually inaccessible, since it was a Ph. D. thesis by a high-school teacher, Curt Reinhardt, who lived in Plauen.

the third with a method of making astronomical calculations. The others are in German; one deals with the moon, and five with comets—those of 1672, 1677, 1684, and the two of 1680. Of the comet pamphlets the most important is the one devoted to the brighter of the two comets of 1680, entitled *Astronomische Betrachtung des Grossen Cometen . . .* (Astronomical Examination of the Great Comet . . .). This book contains a final paragraph in which Dörffel says that he had a new "and still unripe" idea which might improve the hypothesis of Hevelius— namely, "whether the path of the motion of this comet (and the others) is not a parabola the focus of which should be in the center of the sun."

At the time the comet of 1680 appeared, Dr. Edmond Halley was twenty-four years old. In England, there was a difference of opinion about this comet. As it approached perihelion, it could no longer be seen from earth, because of the sun's glare. After having passed perihelion it became visible again. The question was whether this was the same comet or another one. John Flamsteed, the first Astronomer Royal, said it was the same; Sir Isaac Newton thought it was another one. Before agreement could be reached, another comet appeared—first seen by Dörffel—the comet of 1682. Through Newton, Halley had a piece of information which Tycho Brahe and even Kepler had lacked: namely that the law of gravity makes no fine distinctions as to whether something is solid, liquid, or gaseous. The physical nature of the comets did not matter—they were subject to the same laws as the earth and the moon. Hence Halley could try to calculate the orbits of comets. It was tedious work, which he did partly to relieve Newton of the burden of detail, starting in 1695.

The first job was, as usual, to collect the data, which meant, in this case, that he had to search through descriptions of the appearances of comets to see whether their apparent path in the sky had been described well enough to attempt a calculation. The earliest one that could be used was that of the comet of 1337, from the observations of the Greek monk, Nicephoras Gregoras. The next available description was of the comet of 1472, observed by Regiomontanus. The third usable one was Apian's comet of 1531. As Halley worried his way through not quite accurate and often verbose descriptions he began to see that a few orbits were the same. "I am more and more confirmed," he wrote to Newton, "that we have seen that comet [the one of 1682] now three times since ye year of 1531."

In 1705 he presented to the Royal Society his *Astronomiae Cometicae Synopsis,* containing a table of twenty-four comet orbits (see Appendix) and his statement that the comet of 1682 was the same as the comets of 1607 and 1531 and probably also that of 1456. He was not certain of the last—the observations had not been good enough. But he felt sure about the three, "whence I would venture to predict with confidence a return of the same *anno scil* in 1758."

For the first time a comet prediction concerned not the alleged dire consequences of an appearance, but the appearance itself. Halley himself did not live to see his prediction fulfilled; he died in 1742. But "his" comet did return in 1758.[8] It was first seen on Christmas Day by Johann

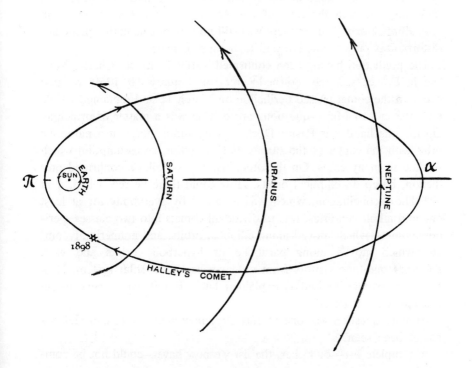

The orbit of Halley's comet

Georg Palitzsch, and its discovery was not accidental. Palitzsch knew about Halley's prediction and had been watching for the comet, although he was not a mathematician or a scientist—Sir John Herschel called him "a peasant by station, an astronomer by nature." His farm was

[8] Of all the comets in the sky
   There's none like Comet Halley.
We see it with the naked eye
   And periodi-cally.

The first to see it was not he
   But yet we call it Halley.
The notion that it would return
   Was his origi-nally.

(Quoted after Sir Harold Spencer Jones)

near Dresden and he worked it himself during the daytime; in the evenings he read books on astronomy, trigonometry, and botany, and had taught himself a reading knowledge of foreign languages. Palitzsch was prepared for a long watch, if necessary, since Halley had pointed out that the time intervals between perihelion passages were not strictly equal, differing by as much as fifteen months. The cause of these unequal intervals, Halley had surmised, was the gravitational fields of the major planets. Ten years before he presented his *Synopsis* to the Royal Society, he had asked Newton "to consider how far a comet's motion may be disturbed by the centers of Saturn and Jupiter . . . and what difference they may cause in the time of the Revolution of a Comett in its so very elliptick orb." But as there was still no way of calculating planetary disturbances, any prediction had to be approximate.

The prediction having been confirmed—after Palitzsch, Charles Messier in France saw the returned comet on January 21, 1759; on that occasion the comet passed perihelion on March 12 and remained visible until the end of May—questions arose. One was a matter of principle. On the one hand was Pastor Dörffel's magnificent guess at a parabolic orbit with the center of the sun as its focal point, an assumption which worked in many cases. On the other hand was Halley's confirmed prediction, based on elliptical orbits. How could these be reconciled, *if* at all? The reconciliation, which was accepted by everybody for at least one and a half centuries, was to divide all comets into two classes, periodic comets, which moved along elliptical orbits, and nonperiodic comets, which moved along parabolic or hyperbolic orbits and were therefore one-time visitors from outer space to our solar system. How this concept was revised is explained later. But it was a very useful concept while it lasted.

Another question was one of curiosity: how many times had Halley's comet been seen?

A complete list—or rather, the list we now have—could not be compiled until an entirely new supply of early comet observations became available. Fortunately such a supply existed in Chinese chronicles and annals. What the Chinese of the period of the Roman Empire in the West thought of comets is not clear, but since they noted their appearances so carefully they probably considered them celestial bodies. An Englishman, John Williams, undertook the task of compiling Chinese observations and published in 1871 a quarto volume with the title *Observations of Comets from B.C. 611 to A.D. 1640*. The list comprises 372 comet appearances.

With the aid of the Chinese sources the earliest known perihelion passage of Halley's comet could be established for the year 240 B.C. There is an earlier Chinese record for the year 467 B.C., which would fit the period of Halley's comet, but as the observations are not clear enough to establish the orbit even approximately, that date is quoted with a question mark. The next appearance after 240 B.C. should have been 163 B.C. But no bright comet was seen in that year, although there were bright comets in 166 and 165. The comet of 11 B.C. was Halley's; this could be proved. And from then on the record is without gaps. In 66 A.D. it was visible for seven weeks, in 141 for

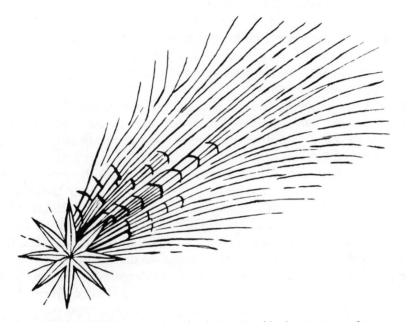

Halley's comet, from the Nuremberg chronicle of A.D. 684, oldest-known picture of a comet

four weeks, in 218 for six weeks, in 295 for seven weeks. The next appearance was in 373, and the next one after that in 451, when it was visible for thirteen weeks. That was the year of the Battle of Chalons, when Attila and his Huns were decisively beaten—hardly a bad thing for the Western world. As for the reappearance of 607–608 we aren't quite sure; there were two comets in the sky then, one of which must have been Halley's.

In 684 it was visible for five weeks, in 760 for eight weeks. In 837 it had much competition—the Chinese list four different comets for that year, the first of them being Halley's. There were reappearances in 912 and in 989. The next reappearance, that of 1066, has a special fame attached to it. That was the year of the Norman conquest of England, and the Bayeux Tapestries (more properly embroideries) which record the conquest, show the comet too. There is not much reference to it otherwise, and the Tapestry merely shows the comet in the sky and a number of men looking at it, with the inscription *Isti mirant stalla(m)* ("These marvel at the star").

In 1145 the comet made a poor showing, was somewhat brighter in 1223, and brilliant for six weeks in 1301; poor again in 1378 and quite conspicuous in 1456. The next reappearance was 1531, then 1607, 1682, and finally 1758–59. After that Halley's comet was due again in 1835. At that time there was a new wave of comet fear, one for which astronomy itself was responsible in an oblique way. The old fear that comets *meant* calamities had slowly faded away. There had been comets without noticeable calamities and there had been very noticeable calamities without comets.

But now astronomers had established that comets were "real" bodies and not just light, and they had proved that comets moved through space among the planets. Hence comets might *be* calamities by colliding with the earth.

If the Reverend William Whiston did not cause this new type of comet fear, he at least contributed heavily to it. When Halley constructed his comet table he naturally attempted to see whether other comets than the one he suspected might have periodicities. He found that there had been comets in 43 B.C., 531 A.D., 1106, and 1680. The older ones had been poorly observed, but the time intervals were about 574 years; one might assume that they had all moved in the same orbit as the one of 1680, the only one that could be calculated.[9] Halley himself did not consider the case established, but his contemporary Whiston did. Whiston, who was both a minister and a professor of mathematics, came to the conclusion that the comet of 1680 had a period of 574 years, but went even further, calculating earlier dates from this assumed period. He ended by publishing a book called *The Cause of the Deluge Demonstrated* (London, 1711). The comet supposedly had approached the earth very closely and caused the Great Flood. Nobody knew then that all the dates involved were fictitious and that the Biblical flood was a local event. What mattered was that a clergyman had stated that the greatest catastrophe ever known had been literally and physically caused by a comet.

---

[9] Johann Franz Encke in 1818 wrote a paper (in German, published in the *Zeitschrift für Astronomie* for that year), entitled "An Attempt to Determine the Most Probable Orbit of the Comet of 1680," which proved that the period of this comet must be more than 2000 years long.

Since impressive nonsense spreads fast—as did, in our day, Velikovsky's ridiculous *Worlds in Collision*—a whole new set of rumors consolidated, helped along by a confusion in a timetable. The great Joseph Jérôme de Lalande, determined to put an end to the nonsense of colliding comets, announced in the early spring of 1773 that he was going to deliver a lecture on the subject. It was unfortunate, first, that the title of the lecture was noncommittal, reading *Réflexions sur les Comètes qui peuvent approcher de la terre* (Reflections on comets which can approach the earth), and, second, that, because the Academy had overcrowded its schedule, Lalande's lecture was dropped. The result was a rumor, believed by a great many Parisians, that Lalande's lecture had contained an announcement of the end of the world on May 12 of the year because of a collision with a comet. The lecture had been dropped, according to the rumor, at the request of the police who wanted to prevent a panic, implying that the police were convinced that the threat was real.

Lalande had his lecture printed at once, and a German edition appeared in Zurich almost simultaneously; other astronomers tried to stem the rumor but nothing helped, until the world proved to be still in existence and reasonably peaceful on May 13. No comet even appeared in that year.

On the next such occasion, about sixty years later, there was at least a comet in nearby space. This time the end of the world was to be caused by Biela's comet. This comet had been named after Wilhelm von Biela, a captain in the Austrian army, who, one can read in many books, discovered it on February 27, 1826. In reality the story was far more complicated. In 1772 two French astronomers, Montaigne and Messier, independently reported the discovery of a faint comet. Thirty-four years later there was another faint comet, which received the designation 1806 I. Friedrich Wilhelm Bessel calculated the orbit and announced that these two comets were identical; a later recalculation caused him to retract his statement and to say that he had been wrong. A few years later an Austrian civil servant named Joseph Morstadt, who had a private observatory in Prague, decided that Bessel's retraction had been wrong and that comet 1806 I had been the fifth return of the comet of 1772. Morstadt then asked Wilhelm von Biela to keep a lookout for the comet early in 1826. Captain von Biela not only looked himself, he instructed the guards of his garrison to watch for a small comet. When he finally found it he kept track of it for twelve weeks and then had enough data to calculate its orbit. It had the surprisingly short period of 6 years and about 9 months, and von Biela proved that Morstadt's suspicion had been correct: Bessel had been right the first time.

Biela's comet was due again in 1832, and Olbers in Bremen announced that this time, on October 29, the head of the comet would go through the earth's orbit. To Olbers this was a most interesting astronomical event; to the newspapers it spelled catastrophe. They were not yet used to the word "orbit" and did not realize that the earth on that day would be some 50 million miles away at another part of its orbit. The director of the Vienna observatory, Joseph Johann von Littrow, in great haste issued a pamphlet in which he explained what was really going to happen. It is amazing that the pamphlet accomplished its purpose—the public accepted the fact that a misunderstanding of terminology had caused a false alarm. Of course nothing happened when Biela's comet crossed the earth's orbit in 1832, and nothing happened when Halley's comet reappeared in 1835.[10]

The victims of the comet panic of 1832 who had expected the comet to destroy the earth found out, if they lived long enough and continued to read about comets, that the comet itself was eventually destroyed, though not by the earth. The return of Biela's comet in 1839 could not be observed because it stayed in the twilight sky.

At the next return, early in 1846, it was accompanied by a nebulous spot which then developed into a second comet. Evidently Biela's comet had split in two. In 1852, the twin comet was observed again, the two parts separated by a much longer distance than six years earlier. The return after that, 1859, was not favorable for observation, but the next one, in 1866, was—or rather, should have been. But, although all observatories which did not happen to be under cloudy skies strained all their instruments, nobody found it—Biela's comet had simply disappeared.

In that same year an interesting announcement came from Italy. Giovanni Virginio Schiaparelli, later famous for his maps of Mars, reported that he had found the orbit of a periodic shower of shooting stars. Because they seemed to originate in the constellation of Perseus, they had been called Perseids. But their orbit was the same as that of another short-period comet, called Tuttle's comet. Two other astronomers, H. I. d'Arrest and E. Weiss, took the cue and announced (simultaneously and independently) that a shower apparently originating in Andromeda moved in the orbit of the now-missing Biela's comet.

[10] Some remnants of comet fear persisted even in 1910-11 and unscrupulous peddlers enriched themselves by selling amulets, antidotes against "comet poison," and similar things to those strata of the public which by then had become literate, though not educated.

Weiss then calculated that the earth would pass through the old comet orbit again, late in November 1872. And the comet, or fragments of it, appeared as a shower of shooting stars such as has rarely been seen. At Moncalieri, Italy, four observers counted 33,400 in six and a half hours; at Göttingen, Germany, 7651 were seen in less than three hours. (In America it was daylight when the earth passed through the stream.) There could no longer be any doubt that the so-called Andromedes were actually fragments of Biela's comet and they were renamed Bielids.

Other such associations were then established: the Lyrids (from the constellation of Lyra) turned out to be associated with comet 1861 I. The Leonids (from the constellation of Leo) were associated with comet 1866 I. Halley's comet even accounted for two showers, the Eta Aquarids in May and the Orionids in October. And quite recently Fred L. Whipple identified the Taurid meteors with Encke's comet, the comet with the shortest period known, only 3.3 years.

Biela's comet was not the only one to be disrupted in full view of the astronomical world. Taylor's comet divided in 1916 and was never seen again. Comet 1926 III (Ensor's comet) suddenly became very diffuse when it neared its perihelion, of only one-third of an astronomical unit (see Appendix), faded and disappeared. Comet Westphal, although its perihelion is outside the earth's orbit (at 1.25 A.U.) had done the same in 1913. These comets were torn to pieces by the sun's gravitational field, but Biela's comet had apparently been disrupted by Jupiter when the comet passed the planet in 1842.[11]

Doctor Halley's prediction of the return of a comet, which then quite naturally was given his name, had created another if relatively minor problem: that of nomenclature. The older comets had always been labeled by the year they became visible. The comet of 1577 and the comet of 1680 have no other names. But then came Halley's comet and later Biela's comet. Sometimes the name of the discoverer was used, sometimes as with Biela's, the name of the man who had done most of the work on this particular comet. It seemed not only advisable but even necessary near the end of the nineteenth century to devise a system which was clear and which everybody would follow.

The international system which was adopted runs as follows: the first comet to be observed in 1963 would be labeled 1963a, the second

[11] The oldest example of such a disruption is the comet of 371 B.C. described by the historian Ephorus of Cyme. This fact has been preserved for us by Seneca, who chided Ephorus as an unscrupulous chronicler who did not hesitate to invent falsehoods to improve his stories.

one 1963b, and so forth. As the year goes on, a different label, which then becomes the permanent one, is introduced. Let us say that the last comet of 1962, 1962k, is the first to pass its perihelion in 1963. It then becomes 1963 I; the second comet to pass perihelion becomes 1963 II. If this is a known comet its name is attached, e.g., if Biela's comet still existed the designation may read 1963 IV (Biela). If 1963 III is a "new" comet, it will receive the name of its discoverer—let's say, 1963 III (Hirsch). But an astronomer who hunts comets usually discovers more than one; Fred L. Whipple once said (at a dinner party at the American Museum of Natural History) that it is pretty certain that a new comet can be found if you examine "the area of one city block of astronomical photographs." Hence the name of the discoverer will usually be followed by a Latin numeral, e.g., (Whipple III), meaning that this is the third comet he has discovered.

While the system of labeling comets was firmly established by the end of the nineteenth century and many comet orbits had been well-calculated, astronomers were by no means happy about their accomplishments. Dr. M. Wilhelm Meyer, who was then director of the Urania observatory in Berlin, wrote in 1879: "The comets have remained mysteries as they were thousands of years ago. When we, today, repeat Seneca's words: 'we must be satisfied with what we have learned and leave it to posterity to find the truth,' it is with some feeling of shame. We must admit that while important progress has been made, we have not yet reached the goal." The goal, of course, was to know the nature of the comets.

What was then known was this: as a comet approaches the sun it is, when still sufficiently distant, undistinguishable from a small star and is as a rule not even discovered. When somewhat nearer, say, after crossing the orbit of Jupiter, it begins to look misty, with no sharply defined outline; astronomers say it develops a *coma* (Latin for "head of hair") and appears to be a large cloud a few dozen miles in diameter. When still nearer, at about the time of crossing the orbit of Mars, the tail begins to form, which grows longer the closer it comes to the sun. The position of the tail, first noticed by Apian, is due to the radiation pressure of the sun, the fine particles composing the tail being swept outward by what is now sometimes called the "solar wind." Occasionally the tail is lost when the comet is at or near perihelion; the comet then grows another and usually shorter tail. Of course a comet may have more than one tail: Donati's comet of 1858 with one wide curved tail and two narrow straight ones, must have been a beautiful sight. The most fantastic of all must have been Cheseaux's comet of 1744, which displayed six divergent major tails and several minor ones. And to make the sight even more fantastic the position of Cheseaux's comet was such that for a while its head was hidden, and only the bundle of tails was visible above the horizon.

To return to the theme: after perihelion passage the tail, now pointing ahead like the headlights of a car, gradually fades and, after the orbit of Mars has been passed going outward, the coma also subsides, and the comet disappears from view. It is observable, as a rule, only when it is inside the orbit of Mars, and not all the time it is inside that orbit, as the comet naturally disappears in the glare of the sun not only during perihelion passage but for some time before and afterward.

At the time Dr. Meyer wrote the sentences previously quoted, most astronomers still felt that comets might be interstellar visitors; the distinction between "periodic" and "nonperiodic" comets was still being made. Nonperiodicity was considered the norm, and only a few dozen comets, while paying a courtesy call on our sun, were thought to have been "captured" (for the sun) by the major planets and to have acquired orbits around the sun which made them periodic. One of the reasons why nonperiodicity was considered normal was that comet orbits, even the periodic orbits, can have any inclination to the ecliptic. The orbits of the planets are more or less in the same plane, but comet orbits can be vertical to that plane; in addition some comets were retrograde, moving around the sun in a clockwise direction instead of counter-clockwise as the planets do.

This reasoning should have been checked by statistics. If, for example, for every three comets in definitely elliptical orbits, there were a dozen or more with definitely established parabolic orbits and a few with hyperbolic orbits, there would have been a basis for the theory. Statistics did not run that way, however. Computers had checked comet orbits only for orbital periods. If an orbital period could be found, a careful calculation was performed. But if no periodicity could be detected, the computer usually assumed that the comet had a parabolic orbit and no additional work was wasted on it. Of course, it was somewhat annoying that a man like Carl Friedrich Gauss had expressed doubt as to whether such a parabola really was one. And Dr. Olbers had gone even further by saying: "Even though the comets never describe parabolas around the sun it is well known that the small piece of their elliptic orbit which is near the sun and in which they are visible, can be assumed without hesitation to be a parabola." [12]

[12] That is, for purposes of calculation.

What Gauss suspected and Olbers assumed was proved by Professor A. O. Leuschner of the University of California, who devoted several years to a statistical study of comet orbits. His report appeared in the *Publications* of the Astronomical Society of the Pacific (April 10, 1907). Professor Leuschner began with observations of the year 1755 and divided the time between that year and the year 1905 into fifty-year periods. For each of these fifty-year periods improvements in both instrumentation and mathematical treatment could be assumed, so that all reports within one of these periods could be considered of roughly equal value. In addition to this subdivision by age, Professor Leuschner paid special attention to the length of time during which a comet was observed. It is obvious that the orbit of a comet which was observed for 60 days will be more reliable than the orbit of one observed for only two weeks.

The result of this study was summed up by Leuschner with the words: "The longer a comet is under observation the more probable it becomes that its orbit cannot be satisfied by a parabola." He then drew up a table, showing the relationship he had just expressed in words:

DURATION OF VISIBILITY	PARABOLIC ORBIT
1 – 99 days	68 per cent
100 –239 days	55 per cent
240 –511 days	13 per cent

"It is," he concluded, "extremely doubtful whether a parabola is definitely established for any comet having remained visible for 240 days or more. . . . The theory that, in general, comets are permanent members of our solar system, seems to have been greatly strengthened by the foregoing preliminary statistics."

As time went on the attack on the once generally assumed open orbits, parabola and hyperbola, was extended. The German mathematician Thraen showed that the hyperbolic orbit of comet 1886 II became an ellipse if the calculation was careful enough. Professor Elis Strömgren, director of the Royal Observatory of Copenhagen, attacked the hyperbolic orbits of comet 1890 II and comet 1898 VII, showing that there is at least grave doubt that these orbits were not just very long ellipses. Strömgren's calculations concerning comet 1898 VII were important because the French astronomer Fayet, who had carried on a similar investigation, stated in his *Recherches concernant les Excentricités des Comètes* (1906) that he had found only five comets— 1844 III, 1863 VI, 1890 II, 1898 VII, and 1899 I—to have had hyperbolic orbits. Elis Strömgren made it look likely that all comets which did not have their orbits perturbed would show elliptical orbits.

But if this was the case the idea that comets were interstellar visitors had to be dropped; they must be permanent, if strangely behaving, members of our solar system.

Quite a good deal of this strange behavior is due to perturbations of the comet's orbits by the major planets. The most customary of these perturbations is the so-called capture process. The comet, traveling sunward along a very elongated ellipse, happens to pass close to one of the big planets, Saturn or Jupiter. The gravitational field of the heavy planet can do two things: it can either accelerate the comet, or slow it down, depending on the relative motions of comet and planet prior to the encounter. If the comet's velocity is increased by the gravitational field of the planet, the orbit of the comet may actually become a hyperbola. If this happens, the comet, after perihelion passage, will leave the solar system forever. But if the orbital velocity of the comet is reduced by the planet's gravitational field the comet's orbit becomes a relatively small ellipse, much smaller, in any event, than it was before the "capture." Again depending on the relative motions before the encounter, the new orbit may be "direct" or "retrograde," but in either case the aphelion of the new orbit will be somewhat farther from the sun than the orbit of the planet which produced the capture.

Whenever a comet orbit is found with an aphelion distance somewhat greater than a planetary orbit it is quite certain that the planet captured the comet for the inner solar system. A comet orbit with an aphelion of, say, 1.2 A.U. would indicate capture by the earth; an aphelion of 6 A.U., capture by Jupiter; an aphelion of 10 to 11 A.U., capture by Saturn. Comets which have been captured by a given planet are called a "comet family." Since Jupiter is the most massive planet in our solar system Jupiter's comet family is of course the largest, numbering more than fifty members.

As time goes on a member of a comet family may again approach "its" planet very closely and then absolutely anything is possible. In a number of cases the planet may accelerate the comet to such an extent that its orbit becomes hyperbolic and it disappears in deep space. But this is only one possibility, as observers and computers were to find out. In 1884 Max Wolf of Heidelberg discovered a comet which was subsequently named Wolf I. Its orbit had its perihelion at 1.59 A.U., its aphelion at about 5.6 A.U., and a period of 6.8 years: clearly a member of Jupiter's comet family. Almost 40 years after its discovery, in 1922, comet Wolf I passed close to Jupiter, within 0.12 A.U. Jupiter threw it into a new orbit with a period of 8.2 years, with the perihelion at 2.36 A.U. and the aphelion at about 5.8 A.U. After this change, Professor Kamienski of Warsaw decided to calculate the orbit of Wolf I prior to its discovery. He found that a very similar thing had happened to the comet in 1875; the orbit found by Wolf had already been the result of a change and the orbit prior to the change in 1875 had been very nearly what it again became in 1922.

Such repeated changes could be found in the case of several other comets, e. g., Lexell and Brooks II, while single changes of orbit are known of several more. Even after capture, a comet orbit is not permanent.

Since the orbital change of a short-period comet may result in a hyperbolic orbit with subsequent loss of the comet, the number of comets in our solar system cannot be constant. Some comets will leave our solar system forever. Theoretically they might become interstellar visitors to another solar system, but in reality this would be exceptionally rare; a comet thrown out of our system in a random direction is not likely to move toward another star, as the stars are too far apart.

But at any event this process is a source of attrition to our comets. A second source of attrition is the disruption of comets, as happened with Biela's comet. Each perihelion passage must reduce the mass of a comet, because the mass constituting the tail (not very much, admittedly) is lost each time, even if we don't see it tear off as a whole. Presumably a comet becomes gradually smaller in the course of time, until it is finally small enough to be torn apart. When Kepler, over three centuries ago, wrote: "I believe that the bodies of comets become washed out, are changed, pulled apart and finally destroyed, and that, just as silk worms by the spinning of their thread, so comets by the discharge of their tails, are used up and eventually fall prey to death," he was biologically wrong, but on the whole astronomically correct.

Since there is this steady attrition from two sources, it is a bit surprising that there are still so many comets in space. True, there has not been a really impressive naked-eye comet since the last appearance of Halley's, but telescopic comets are no rarity at all and many of them are new. Hence, the Estonian astronomer Ernest Öpik reasoned that there must be a reservoir of comets somewhere in space. This reservoir had to be in the gravitational field of our sun but far outside the solar system; Öpik said that it might be as much as one light-year away. A number of years later Jan H. Oort of Leyden elaborated on this thought. Because of their great distance from the sun the comets of the reservoir would have a very low temperature, just a fraction of a degree above absolute zero. Naturally they would be completely inactive, orbiting the sun at a most leisurely pace. Their number was estimated by Oort as being very large, on the order of about 100,000 million. As long as this comet cloud remains undisturbed, no comet from it will appear in the inner solar system. But a disturbance of some kind—say, a passing star—would cause a number of them to lose some of their orbital velocity and then start toward the sun along a very long and narrow ellipse which can be mistaken for a parabola.

Is this what happened two thousand years ago, causing the rash of bright new comets during the fifteenth and sixteenth centuries?

The concept of the comet reservoir at a great distance is closely connected with current thoughts about the nature of comets.

After the spectroscope had been invented observers naturally waited eagerly for the next bright comet. The new instrument seemed to promise that the mystery of the nature of the comets could be solved with a set of good observations. The next available comet was the one of 1864; William Huggins in London, Father Angelo Secchi in Rome, and Giambattista Donati in Florence all tried to obtain spectrograms. The results were partly disappointing—the spectrogram of the comet's head was the same as that of the sun, indicating reflected sunlight—but lines of carbon-hydrogen compounds seemed to show in the tail.

Between 1865, when these results were first published, and 1890, there was considerable discussion about how much of the visible light of a comet is reflected sunlight and how much of it is light emitted by the comet itself. There was general agreement that the light of the comet's head was reflected sunlight, but as for the tail opinions differed. The German Friedrich Zöllner published, in 1872, a book *Ueber die Natur der Kometen* (On the Nature of Comets) in which he ascribed most of the processes of tail formation to electrical activity, while his compatriot Hermann Karl Vogel, ten years later (*Astronomische Nachrichten,* No. 2466, 1882), wrote that the light phenomena of a comet seemed to be completely analogous to the fluorescent light observed in a Geissler tube. And the Russian Fyodor Bredichin, in numerous articles in German and Russian journals, developed a whole theory of the formation of cometary tails.

Reading these books and articles now, one can see that brilliant minds applied themselves to problems which they could not completely solve because much necessary knowledge in the fields of chemistry and radiology (and with it in the interpretation of spectrograms) was not yet available.

In any event everyone agreed on an interpretation which Fred L. Whipple later nicknamed "the flying gravel bed." According to this interpretation, a comet consisted of a large ball of meteoric material which formed the head and which contained enough gases of various kinds to form coma and tail when excited by the sun's heat. This interpretation was not wrong as to the ingredients, but it was far from correct for the distribution of the materials. A loose ball of meteoric matter just could not hold as much gas as was needed for the subsequent phenomena. Whipple, by about 1940, decided to try turning the prescription around, to see what the results would be if a comet were considered to be mainly gases with a little meteoric material imbedded in them. The first publication of his "model" of a comet appeared in the *Astrophysical Journal* (vol. 111, no. 2, March 1950).

If a comet consisted in the main of frozen gases, not only would it be stable indefinitely in Oort's comet cloud, it could and probably would originate there. At that distance from the sun both hydrogen and helium would be present but not as solids, and therefore they play no role in the process of comet formation. Solid particles which might be encountered would be ammonia (NH_3), water (H_2O), methane (CH_4), and the hydrates of methane, all in the form of microscopic crystals. Particle aggregations might consist of about 80 per cent frozen crystals and about 20 per cent matter which is solid even at the temperature of boiling water. In appearance a comet in the reservoir would resemble a gigantic ball of dirty snow.

If the comet approached the sun because of a perturbation of its original orbit, the surface of this giant snowball would be heated and the various substances would evaporate. If it were a matter of evaporation only, we should detect CH_4, NH_3, and H_2O spectroscopically. In reality the spectroscope shows CH, CH_2, CN, OH, NH, and NH_2, substances which chemists call the "radicals" of methane, ammonia, and water, i. e., molecules which have been torn apart by the action of the ultraviolet in the sun's radiation. The CN probably was hydrocyanic acid (HCN) before ultraviolet radiation destroyed it. Along with these radicals, ordinary carbon (C_2) and free metals, such as iron, sodium, chromium, and nickel, have been detected, molecules which were only imbedded in the frozen gases without necessarily having formed compounds.

Assuming a comet to have such a constitution answers, among other things, the problems which Zöllner and Vogel could not solve. The solid particles and the crystals, while still crystals, simply reflect sunlight; the evaporated crystals (before they are broken up) absorb ultraviolet and re-emit light of visible wavelengths. The free radicals, as a rule, do not, which is the reason why a comet does not necessarily grow brighter the closer it is to the sun.

Whipple's comet model also answered another question, namely why comets are often not on time. Halley's comet has been days late; Encke's comet, on the other hand, always has been a few hours early. In the past these deviations from the strict schedule were explained on the grounds of imperfect calculations; not all the planetary influences had been taken into consideration, as it would have made the calculation too difficult. But even when they were all taken into consideration (as was done with Halley's comet) there still remained a difference between observation and calculation which simply could not be explained at all.[13] The delay of Halley's comet, in 1910, amounted to 3 days.

The delays, as well as the ahead-of-schedule appearances, could be explained by the rocket action of the jets of gas which are caused by the sun's heat. Of course the heating of the comet's head will take place on the sunward side, but it would be most surprising if comets did not rotate. And the heating takes some time, so that not many gas jets would break out in the direction of the comet's motion, thereby retarding it, though in the case of Halley's comet this evidently did happen. (It must also have happened with Biela's comet, which was late for every appearance.)

But the rotation may carry a potential jet of gas halfway around the body before it breaks out. Moreover the gas jets are not all issued perfectly vertically, in which case they would affect the rotation of the body itself. Since many gas outbreaks probably cancel one another the over-all effect on the comet's orbital motion is not large, but it is measurable.

The concept of comets as accumulations of frozen simple chemical compounds also permitted the estimation of the actual size of a comet. The only measurement that could have been made earlier was the length of the tail, which in some cases turned out to be enormous, 30 million, 40 million, and even 60 million miles in length. But the dimensions of a comet's head could only be guessed because to make a good estimate one must know both the distance and the reflecting power of the surface. The distance could be measured, and under the assumption of frozen methane, ammonia, and water the density of the comet's head was close to unity, namely that of water and so the reflecting power could be estimated.

It had been known for a long time that the mass of a comet must be

---

[13] A "resisting medium" in space, inside the orbit of Mercury, was assumed by some computers as a means of explaining the deviations. This worked fine in a special case, but since other comets seemed to be uninfluenced by this resisting medium it obviously did not exist.

negligible as compared to the mass of a planet, for the planet which distorts the comet's orbit most thoroughly does not suffer any observable orbital change. But this knowledge permitted only the statement that the mass of the comet had to be less than one-millionth of the mass of the planet.

In 1947 Dr. N. T. Bobrovnikoff tried to estimate the mass of comet Wolf I, which had suffered so much from the gravitational grip of Jupiter. Dr. Bobrovnikoff began by calculating what the mass would have to be to prevent the comet from being disrupted by the gravitational pull of the sun. This minimum mass, if the comet's density were the same as that of the earth, would produce a sphere with a diameter of about 400 feet. Obviously the comets must be less dense than the earth, which would make the diameter larger, but not much larger. A diameter of a hundred miles, for example, seemed impossible, because an asteroid that size looks brighter than comet Wolf I even when seen from a considerably greater distance. Considering the observed brightness and the probable reflecting power (technically known as the albedo), Bobrovnikoff derived 5.5 miles as the probable diameter of Wolf I.[14]

The density which can be derived from Bobrovnikoff's figures, however, is higher than unity; hence Wolf I is probably somewhat larger. Whipple (*Astrophysical Journal,* May 1951) published his own list of maximum diameters. The largest comet in that list is comet Pons-Winneke, with a probable maximum diameter of 102.4 miles—larger than Bobrovnikoff had thought possible. The maximum diameter of Biela's comet, just before bifurcation, was given as 2.1 miles, but Whipple himself remarked that the true value was probably smaller. Wolf I, in Whipple's table, acquires a maximum diameter of 23.7 miles, Encke's comet a shade less than 10 miles and d'Arrests' comet 1.75 miles. These, to repeat, are maximum diameters, the true ones are somewhat smaller.

Nothing could show the ridiculousness of the second wave of comet fear—the fear of the consequences of a direct collision—more clearly than this table does. The impact of a small short-period comet, such as Encke's or Biela's, would cause only a local catastrophe, and if the area of impact were in the middle of Greenland, Antarctica, Central Australia, or the Matto Grosso, the inhabitants of North America or western Europe would learn about it only from astronomical observations, radar space tracking, and, possibly, a shock wave in the atmosphere, which would disturb instruments but not ruffle anybody's hair.

[14] *Popular Astronomy,* March 1948.

8

THE CELESTIAL CENTURY

A F T E R our digression into the realm of the comets we return to Sir Isaac Newton, whose main work has not yet been mentioned by name. It was *Philosophia Naturalis Principia Mathematica*,[1] published in 1687, and the final outcome of the speculations he began to make in 1666 when he first wondered whether the earth's gravitational pull might not "extend to the orb of the Moon."

On December 10, 1684, Dr. Edmond Halley had informed the members of the Royal Society that Newton had showed him a treatise entitled *De Motu* (On Motion) which he had requested Newton to send to the Society to be registered. Newton did so; the treatise was registered in February 1685.

At that time Newton had a new idea: gravitational force seemed to behave as if it were concentrated in the center of the attracting body and, therefore, for purposes of calculation a celestial body could therefore be treated as a point. But was this really correct? Or was it only due to the fact that the bodies in the solar system are so far from one another that they appear as points? Newton decided to work on this problem by assuming a small particle near a very large body (the sun) and calculating in detail what would happen. He had no preconceived opinion as to the probable outcome, but when he had finished his calculations he saw that the sum of the attraction of the particles composing the sun acted as if all the mass of the sun were concentrated in the sun's center. Hence any celestial body, provided only that it was spherical (and no exception was known in Newton's time), could be treated in calculations as a point.

In March 1686 he began writing the book in the form in which it was published. The whole work consists of three books. The first is entitled *De Motu Corporum,* which was finished on April 28, 1686, and shown to the Royal Society that same day. The short time required for the

[1] The first English translation was by Andrew Motte and appeared in 1729; translations into other languages appeared at about the same time. Motte's translation is the basis for the modern edition by Professor Florian Cajori, published by the University of California Press in 1946 as *Sir Isaac Newton's Mathematical Principles of Natural Philosophy and His System of the World.*

writing proves that all the ideas presented had been ready in Newton's mind for a long time. The second book, which also deals with the motion of bodies, but motion in a resisting medium, was finished on June 20, 1687. In the letter to Halley announcing this fact Newton added: "The third I now design to suppress. Philosophy is such an impertinently litigious lady that a man had as good be engaged in lawsuits as have to do with her." Halley may have conceded that there was some truth to the argument but he would not accept the conclusion. He won, and on September 6, 1687, the third book, *De Systemate Mundi*, was presented to the Society, and the whole work was published immediately.

Sir Isaac Newton's *Principia* marked the beginning of what should be known as the "Celestial Century," for in the following five-score years astronomers were more active and achieved better results than ever before. During this century Dr. Edmond Halley predicted the periodicity of his comet (1705) and noted that three bright "fixed" stars—Aldebaran, Arcturus, and Sirius—had shifted position since the time of Hipparchos (1718). During this century Giovanni Domenico Cassini began publishing the first nautical almanac, the *Connaissance des temps* (1679); Immanuel Kant wrote his *General Natural History of the Heavens* (1755), evolving the first of the modern cosmological theories; Charles Messier compiled his famous catalogue of "nebulosities" (1771); and two "transits" of Venus, those of 1761 and 1769, provided measurements on which reasonably good calculations of the size of the solar system could be based. The Celestial Century culminated in 1781 with the first discovery of a major planet since pre-Babylonian times—the discovery of Uranus by William Herschel. This was the century during which astronomical discoveries crowded one another in a way that will probably happen again between 1970 and, say, 2020.

But the Celestial Century began with Newton's *Principia*.

Early in that work, Newton states the three laws of motion:

(I) Every body continues in its state of rest, or of uniform motion, in a right [straight] line, unless it is compelled to change that state by forces impressed upon it.

(II) The change of motion is proportional to the motive force impressed; and is made in the direction of the right line in which that force is impressed.

(III) To every action there is always opposed an equal reaction: or, the mutual actions of two bodies upon each other are always equal, and directed to contrary parts.

These three laws, which are so simple and look almost obvious, at long last provided a firm foundation for astronomical computation. The most important, in many respects, is the first one, which states the concept known as inertia. A body will remain at rest *or* in motion, provided that no external force acts upon it. All at once, the *primum mobile,* that ultimate moving force which had been assumed to be necessary, and which had been both mysterious and annoying, was no longer needed. All the observed motions could be explained by an interplay of inertia and gravitational attraction. A satellite moves in an orbit around a planet because it had once received an impetus setting it in motion; if no other force were acting on the satellite, it would have kept on moving in a straight line. But there is another force—the gravitational attraction of the nearby planet—and this gravitational pull bends the straight line into a closed curve.

The same reasoning, of course, held for the orbit of a planet around the sun, and since gravitational attraction weakens with distance the difference in orbital velocity at aphelion and at perihelion could be explained.

Nobody who reads this now can help wondering why the world had to wait for Sir Isaac Newton to advance the concept of inertia. Why had not one of the famous scholars of antiquity—say Archimedes— thought of it? The answer is probably that everyday observation and experience seems to contradict the idea. A cart, given a strong push, will roll along the road for a short distance and then come to a standstill. It seemed self-evident that the cart stopped moving because the "motive force" was lacking. But the "simple case" of the cart which received a push is not at all simple. The cart is being acted on by a number of hidden forces. There is the friction of the wheels against the road; there is—far more important in this case—the friction of the axles or bearings; there is—though negligible in this case—air resistance. Because friction is ever present on earth, nobody ever tried to conceive of frictionless motion, though innumerable examples were moving overhead.

It is a bit more surprising that the astronomical thinkers a century before Newton, such as Kepler and Galileo, did not arrive at that conclusion, especially since they came so close to it. Galileo Galilei, in his second letter to Markus Welser on sunspots, wrote: "Therefore, all external impediments removed, a heavy body on a spherical surface concentric with the earth will be indifferent to rest and to movements toward any part of the horizon. And it will maintain itself in that state of rest, it will conserve that; and if placed in movement toward the west (for example) it will maintain itself in that movement." [2] This sounds as if Galileo were building up toward a generalization, but instead he restricted his remarks to rotating bodies, the rotation of the sun and the motion of the sunspots being under discussion at the moment.

As for Kepler, he should have derived the inverse-square law of gravitational attraction from his own third law of planetary motion, but he did not go far enough either, though it is anybody's guess what he might have written in his "Hipparchos" had he lived to write it.

Some of Newton's contemporaries had at least thought of the inverse-square law, and Robert Hooke, professor of geometry and general scientist, said so loudly. As time went on Hooke's claims grew larger; at first he had only claimed to have told Newton his idea about the inverse-square law; later, Hooke, according to Hooke, had supplied Newton with all his ideas. Newton, though understandably annoyed, tried to avoid argument by inserting a note in his *Principia,* Book I, Proposition iv. His "sixth corollary" reads: "If the periodic times are as the $\frac{3}{2}$th powers of the radii, and therefore the velocities inversely as the square roots of the radii, the centripetal forces will be inversely as the squares of the radii; and conversely." To this he added a note—he called it a *scholium*—saying: "The case of the sixth Corollary obtains in the celestial bodies (as Sir Christopher Wren, Dr. Hooke, and Dr. Halley have severally observed)". . . . Hooke was not satisfied with this acknowledgment, but fortunately the recriminations did not stop the spread of Newton's ideas. In fact, the normal time-lapse between the publication of an idea and its general acceptance was in this case surprisingly short. Other correct scientific ideas have had to battle much longer for recognition than those in Newton's *Principia*.

Nor did Newton himself have to wait long for rewards, though he fell seriously ill for two years in the interim period. He recovered from his illness, a nervous ailment coupled with insomnia, in 1694. During the following year he was elected a "foreign associate" of the French Academy of Science, a rare honor which he shared with only seven other men. In 1695 he was appointed Warden of the Mint; the elevation to Master of the Mint followed in 1699. Newton then moved to London and in 1701 resigned his professorship and his fellowship at Trinity College. In 1703 he was elected president of the Royal Society and was re-elected every year until his death in 1727. He was Sir Isaac for the

---

[2] Newton was probably unacquainted with this statement. The list of the books he owned does not include any work by Galileo except one called *Galilaeus de Systematae Mundi* (1699), evidently a late reprint of the Latin edition of the *Dialogo*. None of Newton's detractors, to my knowledge, has accused him of having taken the concept from Galileo.

last twenty-two years of his life, having been knighted in 1705.[3] Two
more editions of the *Principia* appeared during his lifetime, one in 1713
and one in 1726.

Books on Newton tend to deal with his work, not with the man; the
one that tries to fill the gap is a small volume appropriately entitled
Newton: The Man, by Lieutenant Colonel R. de Villamil, a retired
officer of the Royal Engineers. The book was published in London,
unfortunately without a date, though from internal evidence it must have
been after 1928 and before 1933. Colonel de Villamil's reason for writing this book was that he had found a missing document. Since Newton
had died intestate, a careful inventory had been taken of his property,
but nobody knew whether the inventory still existed and, if so, where
it could be found. Colonel de Villamil had old court archives searched,
and one day the "True and Perfect Inventory of all and Singular the
Goods Chattels of Sir Isaac Newton" turned up. Though the "Inventory"
was extremely dirty, it could be cleaned up and proved to be legible.
Colonel de Villamil said that it was so complete that with its help Newton's house, were it still standing, could have been refurnished as it had
looked at the time of Newton's death.

The listing of Newton's belongings makes one thing quite clear: for
a man of his official position and accompanying income, Newton led an
extremely simple life. This was not from premeditated austerity, and the
charge of the Abbé Alari (the instructor of Louis XV) that Newton
was stingy is no doubt exaggerated. The abbé reported that when he
was invited for dinner, "the repast was detestable" and he was served
Palma and Madeira wines which Newton had received as presents. This
report is borne out by the fact that the "Inventory" valued the cider in
bottles and "a parcel of wine" in Newton's cellar at only £14/16s/6d.
Add to this that the inventory (incidentally commaless) lists "wearing
apparel woolen and linen one silver hilted sword and two canes" valued
at £8/3s, and it becomes clear that Newton did not "dress well" and
that he had no taste for wine (his normal drink was probably cider) or
fine food. He was very generous with other people; he simply did not
care about luxuries himself. His furniture was simple and what was up-
holstered was in crimson, a color he seems to have liked. The curtains
were all crimson too.

He did not care for poetry or music or art. He made fun of people

[3] The standard biography of Sir Isaac Newton is Sir David Brewster's *Memoirs
of the Life, Writings and Discoveries of Sir Isaac Newton* (2 vols.) first published in Edinburgh in 1855. Another interesting work on Newton is the one by
Augustus de Morgan: *Essays on the Life and Work of Newton,* published in
1914. Of course there are countless derivative biographies.

who collected things—a box containing 151 ounces of foreign coins, 39 silver medals, 6 gold rings and two bars of gold, medals, etc., valued at £106/14s/6d—obviously was not a collection but was kept in connection with his position as Master of the Mint. And he seems never to have kept a pet—a frequently repeated story about a dog named Diamond is almost certainly a myth.

The over-all picture that emerges, then, is that of a man who lived for his thoughts and kept away from anything—the arts, collecting, pets, any kind of luxury—which might have distracted him. As a person he was generally friendly; as Master of the Mint he did his duty efficiently; as a mathematician and a physicist he was a genius. And he did like books; the inventory takers counted 362 books in folio, 477 in quarto, 1057 in sizes smaller than quarto, and "above one hundred weight of pamphlets." Reading over the list of books owned by Newton one is struck by the extraordinarily large number of works in Greek and Latin —not only comparatively recent scientific and philosophical works written in the classical languages, but the classics themselves. If anybody were to check the classical works then available in print against the catalogue of Newton's library he would probably find that Newton owned most of them. Interesting also is the large number of printed sermons; Newton was a serious man all his adult life. (He once rebuked Halley for making a joke about some scientific matter.) The absence of some categories is also interesting: no books dealing with plants, botany, or gardening; no books on art; no poetry. The only language well represented in addition to English, Greek, and Latin is French, with many books on travel, history and commerce and, of course, science. Dutch, Italian, German, and Spanish are not represented; presumably Newton could not read them.

By the time Sir Isaac Newton died many of the astronomers who had been alive when the *Principia* started the Celestial Century had died too, among them Robert Hooke, John Flamsteed, Ole Römer, as well as Giovanni Domenico Cassini, to whom we turn next.

The first Cassini, as he is often called, was born in 1625 at Perinaldo near Nice and baptized Giovanni Domenico. He resided first in Genoa, where he quickly became well known, so well known, in fact, that at the age of twenty-five he was called to the University of Bologna to succeed Father Bonaventura Cavalieri as professor of astronomy.

Being professor of astronomy at a university in Italy in 1650 was not an easy job. The curriculum stated that one had to teach the geometry of Euclid and the astronomy of Ptolemy, but Father Cavalieri had also taught the Copernican theory—as a hypothesis, of course—and had lectured on the discoveries of Galileo. Cassini followed suit but he also had a few side jobs to take care of—a mathematician would have no trouble solving a few problems of hydraulics for the civil authorities or a few problems of fortifications and road building for the military. Cassini stayed in Bologna for nineteen years. Near the end of that period Louis XIV of France appointed him an Academician and invited him to Paris.

The king was building an observatory at the time, with plans drawn up by the great Claude Perrault who had recently won the contest for a new façade on the Louvre. Cassini arrived in Paris on April 4, 1669, and, according to his great-grandson:

. . . as soon as he presented himself to Louis XIV the king ordered that the plans and drawings of the observatory, which was then completed up to the second floor, be shown to him so that Cassini could give his opinion. Cassini quite rightly demonstrated that the project had no common sense [it was to be used for other purposes in addition to astronomical observations]. Then ensued a meeting with Monsieur Perrault to discuss the matter before the king and Monsieur Colbert. Perrault eloquently defended his plan and architectural style with beautiful sentences. My great-grandfather spoke French very poorly and in defending the cause of astronomy he shocked the ears of the king, Colbert, and Perrault to such a point that Perrault in the zeal of his defense said to the king: *Sire, ce baragouineur là ne sçait ce qu'il dit* [Sire, this windbag doesn't know what he is saying]. My great-grandfather kept silent and did well. The king agreed with Perrault and did badly. The result is that the observatory has no common sense.

Although he lost his first argument in Paris Cassini not only stayed on but was appointed director of the observatory. And even though his French offended the king's ears, the king never had to regret bringing him to Paris: he produced an almost uninterrupted stream of astronomical discoveries, among them the division of the rings of Saturn, several satellites of Saturn, etc. (See Chapter 15.) But one great discovery made in Paris at that time was based on work which Cassini had done in Bologna; he had observed Jupiter's main moons long and carefully enough to publish an ephemeris for them.

The discovery was made by Ole Römer, who had been brought to Paris by Christiaan Huygens after Huygens made a trip to Denmark to view what was left of Tycho Brahe's Uraniborg. Römer, who also invented the transit instrument, once the main tool for keeping track of time, read Cassini's ephemeris for the moons of Jupiter with the greatest of care. It showed an interesting discrepancy. The intervals between successive eclipses of the same satellite were not always the same. When earth and Jupiter drew farther apart because the faster earth raced

ahead, these intervals became longer. But when the earth, after completing half an orbit around the sun, "caught up" with the slower Jupiter
and the distance between the two planets grew smaller, the intervals
between eclipses of a satellite became shorter. Nobody could think of
a reason, but there was no doubt about the fact. Römer tried to visualize
what happened. Jupiter's satellites, like Jupiter, received their light from
the sun. Hence the light he saw in the telescope had originated in the
sun, gone to Jupiter's moon, and from there to the earth, specifically to
Paris where he was. Could it be that light needed *time* to travel? Nobody
had ever even thought about that question, but if one assumed that light
did need time to get from one body to another, this discrepancy could be
explained, since the differences were so nicely proportional to the distance between Jupiter and earth. And assuming this to be the case, the
speed of light could be calculated.

Cassini, on whose work this deduction was based, refused to believe it.
But Cassini established another yardstick, the astronomical unit (A.U.),
which is the mean distance of the earth from the sun. Earlier, he had
sent a young astronomer, G. Richer, to the French colony of Cayenne
to study the refraction of light in the atmosphere in the tropics. He
later dispatched additional instructions; Richer was to measure the
angular distance of the planet Mars from bright stars which happened
to show near it. This was to be done at a time when Cassini himself was
making the same measurements in Paris. The combination amounted to
a triangulation of Mars, with a baseline of nearly 6,000 miles. The small
differences in the angular distance between Mars and bright fixed stars
enabled Cassini to calculate the distance between Mars and earth. Once
one distance was known with high precision, the other distances, among
them the astronomical unit, followed as a matter of course.

Cassini became blind in 1710 (he died two years later) and was succeeded as director of the observatory by his son Jacques; two more
generations of Cassinis were to be directors of the Paris Observatory.[4]

During the administration of the third Cassini, Cassini de Thury, an
astronomical event took place which astronomers had sworn to utilize
to the fullest extent. Actually it was an event repeating itself, namely
a "transit" of Venus. Since both Mercury and Venus go around the
sun in orbits smaller than that of the earth, it happens from time to time

---

[4] Jacques Cassini lived from 1677 to 1756. He was succeeded by his son
César-François Cassini (1714-1784), who, to distinguish him from the others, is
usually referred to as Cassini de Thury. He, in turn, was succeeded by his son
Jacques Dominique Cassini, also called Cassini IV. Jacques Dominique lived
from 1748 to 1845, but resigned his directorship in 1793 to write the family's
history, which was published in Paris in 1810.

that one of them passes the line of sight from the earth to the sun, and can then be seen as a black dot slowly moving across the disk of the sun. But a telescope is needed to see it, or at least a camera obscura, such as was used to observe sunspots.

Transits of Mercury occur reasonably often and do not last very long. But a transit of Venus is a rarity. The position of the orbits of the earth and Venus in space is such that two transits will occur eight years apart; then more than a century has to go by until the next pair of transits occurs. The transits of the seventeenth century were not well observed (see Chapter 10) and Dr. Edmond Halley in 1691 especially, exhorted the coming generation of astronomers to pay the closest possible attention to the two transits in the eighteenth century. This, he said, was one way of determining the length of the astronomical unit with high accuracy. He pointed out that a transit of Venus would last up to about seven hours and because of its long duration any minor mistakes would introduce only very small errors in the final determination.

The next generation of astronomers heeded Halley's advice. They got ready to travel. The dates of the two transits were to be June 6, 1761, and June 3, 1769; unfortunately the phenomena would be seen best from inconvenient places. In western Europe only the end of the first transit would be visible, but the whole transit could be seen from either Asia or the Arctic region. Of the second transit the beginning only would be visible from western Europe; the whole transit could be seen from the American west coast, the Pacific Ocean, and the Arctic Region. Since at that time virtually all astronomers were Europeans the project required a great deal of travel. The Swedes and the Russians were best off, comparatively speaking; they had to travel only inside their own countries. But the English and the French intended to establish far-distant, temporary astronomical outposts; the fact that they were at war with each other complicated matters greatly.

One British expedition was scheduled, for example, to go to Bencoolen in the East Indies, and at first the services of the East India Company were requested for transportation. But because of the military situation a warship was supplied, and the leader of the expedition, Mr. Charles Mason, and his assistant, Mr. Jeremiah Dixon—mainly remembered as the surveyors of the "line" named after them—boarded the *H.M.S. Sea Horse*. But *H.M.S. Sea Horse* had sailed only a few score miles when she was engaged by the French frigate *le Grand* and had to turn back to Plymouth with eleven dead and thirty-seven wounded. The two astronomers escaped injury of the body, but their spirits were badly shaken, and Mason wrote a letter to the Council of the Royal Society (dated January 25, 1761) saying, "We will not proceed thither, let the Consequence be what it will." Two days later he wrote another letter, countersigned by Dixon, declaring that he considered it to be impossible to reach any port by way of the Cape of Good Hope.

The Council replied with a thunderous blast: " . . . their refusal to proceed upon this Voyage, after their having so publickly and notoriously ingaged in it . . . would be a reproach to the Nation in general, to the Royal Society in particular, and more Especially and fatally to themselves. . . ." Court proceedings were threatened. On February 3, 1761, Mason and Dixon, signing their letter as "dutiful servants," informed the Council that they were ready to embark for Sumatra. Still, the opportunity of having the last word was handed to them by fate. It was only logical that the travelers themselves should have some discretionary power, considering that a war was going on and that the weather in distant ports could not be predicted. Mason's next letter showed that this discretionary power had been invoked. Writing from the Cape of Good Hope he reported that they had arrived at the Cape on April 27, 1761, and would observe the transit from there. Mason saved his most telling argument for a postscript: in the meantime Bencoolen had been taken by the French!

Because of the war, the preparations for the observation of the transit were divided into an English phase and a French phase.[5] Another English expedition was made by the Reverend Nevil Maskelyne and Robert Waddington to St. Helena, and a "colonial" expedition by Professor John Winthrop of Harvard, sponsored jointly by the provinces of Massachusetts and Newfoundland, to St. Johns in Newfoundland. Professor Winthrop took two of his pupils and the college carpenter along.

As for the French, most of the preliminary work can be ascribed to one man, Joseph-Nicolas Delisle (1688–1768), who was greatly interested in the idea of determining the distance from the sun by means of transit observations. He went to England in 1724 and had discussions with both Halley and Newton, but unfortunately no transit was due for a long time. After returning to France from England Delisle received an imperial invitation from St. Petersburg, asking him to come to Russia to assist in establishing an astronomical institute in St. Petersburg. Delisle decided to go, stating that he would be gone for not more than four years. As it turned out, he stayed for twenty-two years, traveling

---

[5] Fortunately there is a recent work dealing with all these preparations and the personalities involved. It is Harry Woolf's *The Transits of Venus: A Study of Eighteenth-Century Science,* published by the Princeton University Press in 1959. Richard Anthony Proctor's *Transits of Venus,* published in New York in 1875, is worth consulting only for information on astronomical methods and reasoning; as a history it is poor.

a great deal but also training the first generation of Russian astronomers. After his return to France, in 1747, his sovereign appointed him *Astronome de la Marine,* with annuities not only for himself but for his secretary and for his assistant, Charles Messier. Delisle still thought, as he had stated in 1720, that a transit of Mercury could also be used to determine the sun's distance, and he had great hopes for the transit of 1753. His emphasis on Mercury transits might have stemmed from the thought that he might not live long enough to see a Venus transit, and, indeed, he did not live to see the second of the pair.

But when the Mercury transit of 1753 proved disappointing—as British astronomers had expected all along—Delisle enthusiastically went to work preparing for the Venus transit. He worked out a method of using it, in addition to the one suggested by Halley; he checked and corrected Halley's tables; and he began to consider where French astronomers should go for the best utilization of the transit. There were two astronomical points to consider. It would be best, of course, to have observers in an area where the whole transit could be checked by one man. But observers also should be far apart: the path of the planet across the solar disk would look different to an observer at the North Pole and one in Sumatra. The North Pole was, of course, inaccessible and Delisle gave much thought to the best places for observation; weighing with regard to accessibility, living conditions, and probable weather conditions at the critical time.

Then he began to suggest names, presumably after having discussed with the men in question their willingness to make long and at that time dangerous trips. He suggested that Jean Chappe d'Auteroche should go to Siberia with Russian astronomers, most of whom had been Delisle's pupils. Another French astronomer, Alexander-Gui Pingré, should sail to Rodrigues, one of the Mascarene islands in the western end of the Indian Ocean, while the man usually referred to as Le Gentil [6] was to go to India, preferably Pondichery. Both Rodrigues and Pondichery were then French colonies. Delisle also got in touch with his friend the Dutch astronomer Dirk Klinkenberg in hope of persuading the Dutch East India Company to transport Charles Messier to Batavia. For unknown reasons the Dutch did not respond and Messier stayed home. The other expeditions set out as planned. It is an interesting fact that a letter was dispatched to England explaining Pingré's mission and requesting a British safe-conduct letter for him. And the British responded. The office of the First Lord of the Admiralty sent a letter, in which all

[6] His full name was Guillaume Joseph Hyacinthe Jean Baptiste le Gentil de la Galaisière.

captains and commanders of His Majesty's ships and vessels were instructed that, since it was "necessary that the said Monsieur Pingrè [sic]
should not meet with any Interruption either in his passage to or from
that Island, you are hereby most strictly required and directed *not to
molest his person* or Effects upon any Account, but to suffer him to
proceed without delay or Interruption. . . ."

The Abbé Chappe d'Auteroche and Pingré reached their destinations,
in Chappe's case Tobolsk. Le Gentil had bad luck. Just as Bencoolen had
been taken by the French while Mason and Dixon were en route, the
French plantation of Karikal, below Pondichery on the Coromandel
Coast, had been taken by the British, and Pondichery was under siege.
By the time Le Gentil's vessel, *la Sylphide,* carrying reinforcements for
besieged Pondichery arrived in the area, Pondichery had fallen. The
captain of *la Sylphide* decided to turn around and go to "Isle de France"
(Mauritius) from whence he had come. At the time of the transit they
were at sea. Le Gentil saw it, in brilliant weather, from the bridge of
the ship. But this naturally could not be an observation in the proper
sense. Le Gentil then decided to stay in the tropics for the next transit,
eight years later.

Incidentally, Cassini de Thury, the director of the Paris Observatory,
also made a trip, a short and reasonably safe one. He went to the
observatory at Vienna, run by the Jesuit Order and directed by Father
Maximilian Hell, S. J. There he saw the beginning of the transit, in company with Father Hell and Archduke Joseph of Austria.

Unfortunately the results obtained from the transit were not in keeping with the effort expended.

The weather was—as it still is—the main enemy of astronomical
progress.

At Rodrigues, Pingré's station, it rained in the morning of June 6,
1761, but then the weather cleared up somewhat so that the first contact between the planet and the sun could be observed. The end of the
transit was hidden by clouds, but in between Pingré and his assistant
obtained enough measurements to feel that they had been successful.
Maskelyne and Waddington on St. Helena had even worse weather; only
occasionally could they see the black spot of the planet against the
background of the solar disk; though they attempted to make measurements at those times they could not obtain any useful results. John
Winthrop at St. John's on Newfoundland was handicapped in another
way. Part of the transit took place before the sun had risen. But the part
that was accessible to Winthrop was well observed.

Two of the expeditions did well. Mason and Dixon had good weather at the Cape of Good Hope and observed the whole transit. The Abbé Chappe d'Auteroche was so excited about the forthcoming event that he slept the night before the transit in his astronomical station on a mountain near Tobolsk, worrying about every distant cloud or smoke curl from a fire. But the day turned out to be a brilliant Siberian summer day and he made out very well. In addition to his observation and the Mason-Dixon report—the only one from the southern hemisphere—there were some others. The Russians had established two stations of their own in Siberia, and a number of European stations had seen at least part of the transit; because of their locations they could not observe the whole. Though the transit furnished the discovery that Venus must have an extensive atmosphere, the over-all result was meager.

This was partly because a Venus transit had never before been systematically observed. Not only was it a novel experience to the observers, they could not even prepare themselves by reading about the experiences of other observers. The only man who had ever seen one, Jeremiah Horrox in 1639, had used a different technique and apparently had missed the first contact.

This first contact presented the chief problem, a problem which was named the "black drop." This is what happens: Venus, before the transit begins, is of course invisible. Since it is between the earth and the sun, though not yet in a straight line, we see—or rather we don't see—the unilluminated night side of the planet. Then, when Venus touches the sun's rim, it is surrounded by a luminous ring, sunlight shining through the atmosphere of the planet. This phenomenon is most pronounced when the disk of the planet is about halfway across the solar disk. The decisive moment, or one of them, would be when the planet is just inside the solar disk; according to expectations, there should be just a thread of sunlight between the black dot, which is the planet, and the blackness of space around the sun. But this fine thread of light does not appear; between the round dot and the rim of the sun there is a black bridge—the black drop. Eventually the apparent connection seems to snap. But which moment is to be considered the right one? When the black drop first forms? When it finally breaks? Or the middle of the time interval during which it exists?

The black-drop phenomenon is the reason that a transit of Venus is not quite as accurate and as valuable as Halley had thought.

But the astronomers of the eighteenth century were of good cheer. This transit had served to provide practice; there would be another one eight years later and then one would see.

The second Venus transit caused even more travel than the first; more scientists embarked on long voyages and most of the voyages were also longer. This time the areas from which the whole transit could be observed were the Pacific Ocean and the Arctic region.

This had been established by the aging Delisle and by his younger compatriot Lalande, who in 1757 had written a *Mémoire sur les passages de Vénus . . . en 1761 et 1769.* Both had prepared charts of the earth showing how much of the transits could be observed from which places. In the interim between the two transits, Pingré, who had observed the first one from Rodrigues, had written a special treatise about the best places for observation, which, after being carefully examined by both Lalande and Chappe d'Auteroche, was published in Paris. As the title [7] shows, Pingré was especially interested in observations from the South Seas. He had several reasons for stressing this area. One was the simple logical conclusion—which also occurred to the British, as we'll see—that if one has to make a long voyage for one purpose, one should try to make as many other discoveries as possible. Another was based on astronomical reasoning. For the first Venus transit observers had gone to widely separated places because the path of the planet across the sun's disk would look different from points which were far apart. For one observer the planet would cross the sun closer to the sun's center than for another observer, which implied, naturally, that the duration of the transit would be of different lengths for different observers. And Pingré, after a re-examination of the various possible ways of calculating, had come to the conclusion that the method based on the differences in the duration of the transit was the best. This led him to investigate which places would yield the greatest differences. He found that a place far in the north of Scandinavia would yield a duration of 5 hours, 55 minutes, and 10 seconds, while an observer at 242 degrees east and 28.5 degrees south in the Pacific Ocean would find a duration of 5 hours, 26 minutes, and 36 seconds. The difference was a very comfortable 28 minutes and 34 seconds. Of course Pingré's figures were theoretical; the real ones were to be found by observation, but it was the difference that mattered. But here another consideration entered. At that time there was a firm belief in the existence of a very large *Terra australis incognita,* the Great Unknown Southland. If this new continent could be found, large and lucrative colonies could be established (the English thought so, too), and a voyage to observe the Venus transit might also be utilized in looking for it.

---

[7] *Mémoire sur le choix et l'état des lieux où le passage de Vénus du 3 Juin 1769 pourra être observé avec le plus d'avantage; et principalement sur la position géographique des isles de la mer du sud*; Paris, 1767.

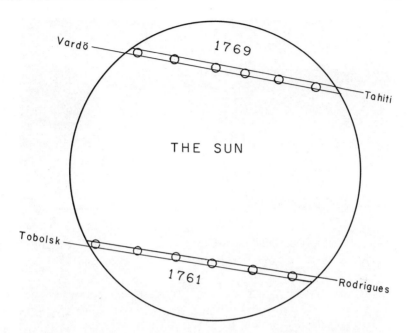

Vardö

1769

Tahiti

THE SUN

Tobolsk

1761

Rodrigues

Transits of Venus. The black lines indicate the center point of the planet as seen from the places indicated. Position of the planet on the sun's disk is given in one-hour intervals

Pingré, who had read everything available on the South Seas and the Indian Ocean, had found a book by Juan Fernandez de Quiros, who had actually discovered a coast of this southern continent, or so he said. The Spanish navigator was just then besieging his king with petitions for men, money, and ships for another expedition to *Terra australis,* and what he said made Pingré believe that his preferred spot for a short-duration transit would be either at the shore of *Terra australis* or not too far inland.

In reality Señor Juan Fernandez de Quiros was the worst navigator and probably the biggest liar Spain has ever produced, but Pingré did not know that.

Actually there *is* an island quite close to the spot he had calculated. It is Pitcairn Island, but as it had not yet been discovered, Pingré could not know that either.

But his call for a station in the far north was heeded. The British sent Jeremiah Dixon and William Bayley to the North Cape. And Christian VII, king of Denmark and Norway, invited Father Maximilian Hell to go to the island of Vardö (originally named Wardhus and located at 70° 22′ N. and 30° 7′ E.). Father Hell (who looked like a cheerful

Father Maximilian Hell

and friendly gnome) did go and afterward deposited with the Vienna Observatory a diary, written in fine Church Latin, which was translated into German in 1835 by Carl Ludwig von Littrow, a later director of the observatory.

Abbé Chappe d'Auteroche had picked the west coast of Mexico as a promising place, but the French ambassador ran into an entirely unexpected hostile attitude at the Spanish court. The Spaniards did not want foreigners in their American colonies. And most especially they objected to foreigners arriving in foreign ships. Finally they agreed to a compromise; the abbé would have to travel in a Spanish ship and would then be guided overland to the west coast and permitted to observe from a "mutually agreeable" but actually Spanish-dictated place. The place was the southern tip of Baja California, a Spanish mission now called San José del Cabo.

While the king of Denmark and Norway invited Father Hell, and the court of Spain gave in to the French requests, there was a different climate in eastern Europe. In the spring of 1767 Katherina Alekseyevna, empress of all the Russias, wrote a letter to Count Vladimir Orlov declaring her imperial wish that the forthcoming transit be observed as widely as possible from Russian soil and suggesting that, since there were not enough Russian astronomers, the Academy should search among the officers of the Imperial fleet for men who could be trained for this work by the professors in the time remaining. Since the empress wished to know where observation posts should be erected (". . . if there is a necessity for erecting some buildings, proper measures may be taken to send workmen there. . . .") and who would be appointed, Count Orlov and the Academy put a broad interpretation on the request. Surely the empress would not object to seeing some foreign savants on the list of appointments; if they contained some famous names Her Majesty might even be pleased. The result of this interpretation was a blanket invitation to European scientists to come to Russia at the expense of the empress.

A number of Frenchmen, Germans, and Swiss responded, the most famous being Father Christian Mayer, S. J., who was professor of mathematics at Heidelberg. The Swede Anders Lexell went to Russia, mainly to study with Leonhard Euler at the Academy; in fact Lexell (1740-1784) stayed in St. Petersburg until he died. The Swiss Jacques-André Mallet (not to be confused with his contemporary the Swede Friedrich Mallet) also went to Russia, as did Mallet's very young compatriot Marc-Auguste Pictet.

As a result of this influx of foreign scientists only two of the Russian stations were wholly staffed by Russians: the Yakutsk station at 130 degrees eastern longitude under Captain Islenieff and the Kola station near Murmansk under Stepan Rumovsky. All other Russian stations— the second Kola station at Ponoi at the very tip of the peninsula, the two stations in the Ural Mountains at Orsk and at Orenburg, and the Caspian Sea station at Guriev at the mouth of the Ural River—were staffed by international teams. This in turn had the result that only

Islenieff's report was printed in Russian; everything else coming out of Russia was in German or French.[8]

Even though the French had Le Gentil "already on location" (as Harry Woolf puts it), the Duc de Praslin, who controlled the official purse, wanted another expedition, which was given the additional job of testing newly constructed timepieces for purposes of finding the longitude at sea. This expedition was to go to Santo Domingo. The Duke wanted Lalande, but Lalande begged off, saying that he got seasick on a vessel anchored in port, and Pingré went in his stead.

The Royal Society decided on several ventures: a team of observers to be sent to northern Scandinavia, an observation post at Fort Churchill on the western side of Hudson's Bay (to be arranged with the Hudson's Bay Company), and an expedition to the South Seas (to be carried out by the Admiralty).

In the course of the preliminary discussions John Bevis of the Royal Society suggested the idea—which to us sounds very "modern"—of constructing a "simulator," a mechanical device for training the observers. Whether this idea was actually carried out is not known. It *is* known that a portable octagonal observatory with a slotted roof was built for the Hudson's Bay expedition, officials of the Hudson's Bay Company having had the foresight to point out that there wasn't much wood for construction purposes in the area.

The South Sea expedition was planned as a multipurpose expedition. The transit was to be observed from Tahiti, but afterward the vessel was to go on, explore the South Seas (and maybe find the *Terra australis*), and produce good nautical charts of the whole region. The Admiralty had purchased a sturdy vessel for the purpose and was spending large sums to make it fit for a very extended cruise. There was an interesting hassle about that expedition. Alexander Dalrymple, the astronomer who had indicated that he was most eager to go to the South Seas, had made the condition that he was to be in charge of the vessel. He did not wish to go as a "Passanger," because the scientific needs had to be regarded as superior to any other considerations. The lords of the Admiralty remembered that, about a century earlier, Dr. Edmond Halley had gone to St. Helena to observe the southern sky (he saw the transit of Mer-

---

[8] The Russian Academy of Science's publication of the work of the Orenburg station was written by Wolfgang Ludwig Krafft, with the title *Auszug aus den Beobachtungen welche zu Orenburg bey Gelegenheit des Durchgangs der Venus vorbey der Sonnenscheibe angestellt worden sind,* St. Petersburg, 1769. (Extract of the Observations which were made at Orenburg on the occasion of the transit of Venus past the disk of the sun.) The report of the Guriev station, by Georg Moritz Lowitz, published in 1770, has precisely the same title except for the different place name.

cury in 1677, which had started his personal interest in transits), and he had been in charge. It was hardly possible to conceive of a better navigator, but Halley had been unable to handle the crew! In the meantime a regulation had been drawn up to the effect that the commanding officer of any of the King's Bottoms had to be an officer of the King's Navy. Since Dalrymple was not, the Admiralty appointed a commander for the vessel. He was Captain James Cook, and the vessel was the *Endeavour*.

An interesting footnote to the British preparations is that King George III had an observatory especially built at Kew so that he might personally observe the transit. The Royal Observatory at Greenwich (commissioned not quite a century earlier by Charles II with a letter to "Our well-beloved Sir Christopher Wren") was in existence, of course, but the king knew that his presence there would interfere with the work.

To return to the French, the man "on location," Le Gentil, had decided that Manila would be the best place for him and wrote to the Academy in Paris asking them to make the necessary arrangements with the Spanish Court. While his letters were still on the way, a Spanish warship bound for the Philippines stopped at Mauritius. He persuaded the captain to take him along and arrived in Manila on August 10, 1766. His original desire to go to the Marianas from Manila was effectively squelched by the fact that ships touched at the Marianas only every third year. He had already made the necessary observations to establish the geographical position of Manila—to find their own position was always the first job of every expedition, maps being as inaccurate as they were—when he was again ordered by the Academy to go to Pondichery. Le Gentil obeyed and this time he was greatly aided by his former enemies, the English. But no amount of international cooperation and good will could prevent the fact that on the day of the transit the sun was obscured by clouds. Le Gentil learned later that the sky over Manila had been brilliant. He had spent more than ten years in the tropics for the two transits without accomplishing the primary purpose of his voyage. But he did get home alive, unlike the Abbé Chappe d'Auteroche, who died in Baja California, a victim of a widespread epidemic about two months after the transit.

The over-all result of the work of 151 observers at 77 different stations can easily be minimized by saying that the main purpose, that of establishing the precise length of the astronomical unit, was only incompletely accomplished.

But had the transit observations not taken place, we would not have the pile of books written by the participants. That pile consists of a number of English reports, usually quite terse and to the point; a number of reports and evaluations in German; and a somewhat larger number of books in French, most of them two-volume works. There is also an enormous compilation in Latin on the work done in Russia, put together by Father Christian Mayer and printed in St. Petersburg in 1769. To show that minimizing of the results of the expedition is a quite mistaken evaluation, one only needs to point out that Captain Cook's *Journal* is one of the English books.

The necessity of finding the precise geographical position of the places of observation produced one direct contribution to knowledge. The location of Cape Town, for example, was far better known after the transits than the location of some cities in France and in Germany. Another by-product resulted from the fact that educated men, many of them all-around scientists, were in remote places with nothing much to do but wait. Naturally they observed their surroundings and wrote about them. If it were not for Pingré, knowledge of the fauna of Rodrigues at the time would be virtually nonexistent. Even if Le Gentil did miss the transits themselves, he supplied us with a wealth of information. Some fundamental discoveries were made during these waiting periods, as for example the discovery that a massive mountain will exert a minor deflection on a plumb line used at its foot. This discovery later led to determinations of the mass and average density of the earth. All in all it was a fruitful effort. And the second transit was also the first example of international cooperation in scientific matters, a forerunner of the international efforts of the Arctic Year a hundred years later, the Antarctic Year fifty years after that, and the International Geophysical Year of the middle of the twentieth century.

A postscript to the work on the second transit relates to Carl Ludwig von Littrow's translation of Father Hell's journal into German. Strangely enough, von Littrow used this opportunity to attack Hell's integrity; he stated that the journal was full of erasures and corrections, often in ink of another color, indicating that Hell had afterwards corrected his figures to conform with the best values found. Father Hell had died in 1792; the attack came in 1835 and it was unrefuted until 1883. The man who refuted it was an American, Professor Simon Newcomb, who went to Vienna, partly because he was preparing a study of his own on the eighteenth-century transits. Looking at the originals of Hell's documents he became convinced (and said so in the *Monthly Notices* of the Royal Astronomical Society, May 1883) that the erasures and corrections had been made at the time of writing and that "ink of a different color" was merely ink over an erasure. Newcomb could make a case of peculiar nature: von Littrow had been deceived by the fact that he was color-blind!

You may remember that old Delisle did not succeed in having the Dutch bring his pupil Charles Messier to Batavia for the first transit. Nobody can tell whether the trip would have made Messier famous, but he established his own fame later, in a different sector of astronomical knowledge. The reappearance of Halley's comet during the Celestial Century had naturally made comets very interesting to astronomers. Messier decided to specialize in the observation of comets. But before a comet develops its tail and so becomes recognizable as a comet, it develops its coma, which looks somewhat like an indistinct star. And that appearance presented a problem, because there were objects in the sky which looked like indistinct stars all the time.

The first of these objects had been noticed long after dark on December 15, 1612, by Simon Marius (Mayr)[9] who wrote that he had found a star in the constellation of Andromeda which bore no resemblance to any other star. His comparison has become famous—the star, he said, looked "like a candle flame seen through the horn window of a lanthorn." It was, of course, the spiral nebula in Andromeda. Only four years later, in 1618, Father Johann Baptist Cysat, S. J., observing in Ingolstadt, found what we now call the Great Nebula in Orion. Christiaan Huygens also found it, in 1656, without knowing of Cysat's observation. These nebulous objects, as they came to be called, were sufficiently interesting for Halley to publish a list of them. It appeared in the *Philosophical Transactions* of the Royal Society (vol. IV, 1721) and begins with the words: "Wonderful are certain luminous Spots or Patches, which discover themselves only by the Telescope, and appear to the naked Eye like small Fixt Stars; but in reality are nothing else but light coming from an extraordinary great Space in the Aether; through which a lucid *Medium* is diffused, that shines with its own proper Lustre. . . . These are Six in Number. . . ."

The six listed by Halley are: (1) the Great Nebula in Orion, its discovery being ascribed to Hugenius (Huygens); (2) the spiral nebula in Andromeda, its discovery wrongly ascribed to Bullialdus; (3) a globular cluster in Sagittarius, M-22, its discovery ascribed to Abraham Ihle; (4) a globular cluster in Centaurus, discovered by Halley himself in 1677; (5) a galactic cluster (M-11 in Scutum), discovered by G. Kirch

---

[9] For his controversy with Galileo see "The moons of Jupiter," in Chapter 14.

in 1681; (6) a globular cluster in Hercules (M-13), discovered by Halley in 1714. After listing them Halley wrote: "There are undoubtedly more of these which have not yet come to our Knowledge, and some perhaps bigger."

More were shown in the next independent list, that of the Abbé Nicolas de Lacaille, who had spent several years in South Africa mapping the southern sky and catalogued about 10,000 stars. From this catalogue he abstracted a list of forty-two nebulous objects in the southern sky alone. It was published in 1755 under the title *Sur les étoiles nébuleuses du ciel austral* (On the nebulous stars of the southern sky); the list is contained in the *Histoire de l'Académie royale des Sciences* but was reprinted several times in the *Connaissance des Temps*. At that time a similar list of twenty nebulous objects in the northern sky existed, but Lacaille could not have known about that. It was in the form of a letter by the Swiss astronomer Jean-Philippe Loys de Cheseaux to his grandfather René-Antoine Ferchault de Réaumur. The letter had been written in 1746, but Réaumur did his grandson the disservice of not publishing it, thereby robbing him of the credit for about a dozen discoveries. One and a half centuries later the letter was found and finally saw print in 1891.

All these were the preliminaries for the work Charles Messier began in about 1760. Earlier, he and his master Delisle had tried to be the first to see the return of Halley's comet; Delisle was so disappointed at not being the first that he refused to credit the report that some "peasant in Saxony," with the incredible—to a Frenchman—name of Palitzsch, had made the discovery. But Messier, who had done all the actual observing, drew a conclusion. A tail-less comet looked very much like these nebulosities which Le Gentil had begun picturing in the *Mémoires* of the Academy. An observer looking for comets might waste his time checking on these similar-looking nebulosities, unless he knew exactly where they were located. In fact, Messier himself had made that mistake in late August 1758, when, in following a comet that he had discovered early in the month, he had seen the Crab Nebula in Taurus and had first thought it to be another comet. The answer was obvious: make a list.

By 1764 Messier had listed forty objects, thirty-nine of which he had verified himself. A subdivision of his list included a few additional nebulous objects reported by others (mainly by Hevelius) which he had not been able to find. In January 1765, he found another one, near Sirius, which he added to his list as M-41. He then extended his list to a total of forty-five objects and this list was published in the *Histoire de l'Académie* for 1771, actually published in 1774. Then he started hunting comets in earnest; he observed forty-six and claimed discovery of twenty-one of them. Nowadays, with stricter standards, he would probably be allowed fifteen of the twenty-one. Messier, naturally, became famous; he was elected to membership in all the learned societies of his day and his king, Louis XV, referred to him as the "ferret of comets." He had a rival in ferreting out comets, his fourteen-years-younger compatriot Pierre Francois André Méchain, but the two rivals seem to have been on good terms, since Messier repeatedly noted that Méchain had informed him of a new comet on the day after its discovery.

Of the two Messier became and remained the more famous, not because he discovered more comets than Méchain, but because of the catalogue which he originally made in order to avoid mistakes. [10]

The man who was to bring the discoveries of the Celestial Century to a climax was born in Hannover on November 15, 1738, and was christened Friedrich Wilhelm Herschel. Since his father was an oboist in the Guards regiment the son was naturally expected to follow a similar career. At the age of fourteen he became a musician in his father's regiment, but as he did not take an oath of military service, he could not have become a deserter, as some later writers asserted.

He left the band of the Guards' regiment in 1757 and went to England as a musician. His first job in England consisted of copying musical scores, excerpting instrumental scores from partituras, and so forth, but in 1760 he was appointed instructor of a military band. He began to compose symphonies and conduct concerts, and in 1766 he was appointed organist at the Octagon Chapel at Bath. "He was soon the centre of musical activity in this fashionable watering place and had a busy life, composing, conducting concerts and taking pupils." [11]

Apparently Mr. William Herschel, as he was known by then, had some spare time, for during that period he learned Italian (possibly in connection with his musical activities) and classical Greek. He also studied mathematics and became interested in optics. And he read every book on astronomy he could lay his hands on. A thought that occurred to him often was one that had also occupied Father Clavius and other earlier astronomers: supposing that all the stars are of the same size, wouldn't their apparent brightness be a clue to their distance?

The problem of the distances inside the solar system had been more

[10] In 1777 Johann Elert Bode, in the *Astronomisches Jahrbuch für 1779,* published a new list of seventy-five nebulosities, a compilation of the earlier lists augmented by some discoveries of his own. Messier followed in 1780 in the *Connaissance des Temps* for 1783, with an augmented list of sixty-eight. The almanac for the following years contains the full list, which is now called Messier's Catalogue.

[11] Sir Frank Dyson, in *Nature,* vol. 142, 1938, on the occasion of the bicentenary of Herschel's birth.

or less settled by the first Cassini and the later work on the Venus transits. Stellar distances were the next problem. Herschel rented a small telescope in 1773, soon making the discovery that countless other people have made, namely that a small telescope merely whets the appetite for a bigger one. But telescopes, especially the still fairly new achromatic telescopes, were expensive. However, Sir Isaac Newton had shown that there was an alternative—the reflecting telescope. Herschel decided that the most expensive part of such a telescope—the mirror—was something one could make at home. The formula for the best alloy for this purpose, called Speculum Metal (*speculum* is Latin for mirror), could be found in astronomical books and it did not seem expensive: just melt 9 pounds of copper and 5 pounds of tin and be sure you get a uniform mixture. Herschel, having read all the instructions, decided to begin with a small mirror; he cast the metal disk and began the tedious work of grinding and polishing it. Of course things went wrong a few times, but a skill is acquired only by practice. Finally he ground himself a mirror which was good. It had a diameter of 6½ inches with a focal length of 7 feet.

The idea that the apparent brightness of a star should be a clue to its distance was still uppermost in his mind, but he did not know how to go about proving it; possibly an additional clue could be found by observing very faint stars which were close to very bright ones.

On March 13, 1781, he saw something in the constellation Taurus which was not a fixed star. It might be one of the nebulosities that Messier was busy cataloguing, or else it might be a comet. The next few nights were cloudy; when Herschel checked on March 17 he saw that the object had moved and he wrote a letter to Maskelyne, then Astronomer Royal. Maskelyne had better instruments at his disposal and he wrote back on April 23 that he had not seen either a tail or a coma and that Herschel's object was likely to be a planet.

It was. It was Uranus, and the size of the solar system had been doubled. George III, when informed, created the new position of King's Astronomer with an annuity of £200 for Herschel, and in Herschel's life vocation and avocation changed places. He still played music, but for his own amusement. Mainly he cast and ground larger Speculum Metal disks for larger telescopes.

The former Hannoverian musician was destined to contribute about as much to astronomy as the first Cassini had. His own main interest was the world of the distant stars. But his discovery of Uranus caused most of his contemporaries to be chiefly interested in our own solar system.

PART II

OUR SOLAR SYSTEM

SAGREDO: *E quando si ha a por termine alle nuove osservazioni, e scoprimenti di questo ammirabile strumento?*

SAGREDO: Oh, when will there be an end to the new observations and discoveries of this admirable instrument?

— GALILEO GALILEI, *Dialogo de due massimi sistemi del mondo*, First Day.

9

MERCURY AND "VULCAN"

O f the five so-called classical planets, Mercury has the reputation of being the most difficult to observe. A large part of this reputation can probably be traced to Copernicus himself, who mentioned that he, to his intense regret, had never in his life succeeded in seeing Mercury. [1]

The great man must have been the victim of the climate of his homeland, because simply seeing Mercury is not difficult. I have seen Mercury myself on quite a number of occasions: twice from New York City, once from the Santa Monica mountains in California, twice from Phoenix, Arizona, and repeatedly from several places in Texas. All these places are admittedly much farther south than any place Copernicus ever reached, but the question is not so much one of latitude as of having a clear horizon. Because Mercury is so close to the sun, it can be seen only for about one hour right after sunset or for the same length of time prior to sunrise. [2] As far as brightness goes, Mercury is actually at times as bright as the brightest fixed star, but Sirius can be seen flaming against the deep black of the midnight sky, while Mercury is always in a sky illuminated by the sun. However, the major problem is not a matter of contrast, but that Mercury cannot be very high in the sky before sunrise or after sunset, hence a cloudy horizon will conceal it.

Although Mercury is not really hard to see, provided you know where to look, observing it is another matter. The first observations after the invention of the telescope were mainly for the purpose of establishing whether it actually showed phases like the moon, as Copernicus had predicted. Since the quality of the earliest telescopes was rather doubtful, according to Dr. Rudolf Wolf (in his *Handbuch der Astronomie*, vol. II, 1892). "Galilei, Marius, Hortensius, and others suspected the

---

[1] In *lib. 5, cap. 30* of the original Latin edition of *De Revolutionibus Orbium Coelesticum*.

[2] Most of the ancient names for Mercury refer to its swift movement, such as the Greek Hermes (or Hermeias), the messenger of the gods. The Roman Mercurius has the same meaning, plus the additional connotation (from *merx, mercis,* wares) of being the god of merchants. later extended to being the god of merchants and that of thieves, both activities involving movement. The Germanic name was Wotan ("the wanderer") while the Near Eastern names are usually the word for "arrow."

presence of the phases of Mercury rather than actually seeing them, but they were seen clearly by the Jesuit priest Ioannes Baptista Zupo on May 23, 1639, and by Johannes Hevelius on November 22, 1644."

The first really extensive series of observations of Mercury was conducted in the early 1800's by Johann Hieronymus Schroeter from his private observatory at Lilienthal, near Bremen. Schroeter, in checking the phases of Mercury, felt sure that the terminator, the border between the light and the dark hemispheres, showed a few sawtoothlike indentations, suggesting the existence of high mountains. Schroeter tried to determine the inclination of the planet's equator to the plane of its orbit and tentatively accepted a value of about 20 degrees—the currently accepted value is "about zero." The period of rotation seemed to be a little longer than an earth day; Schroeter put it down as 24 hours, 5 minutes. The book he wrote remained for sixty-five years not only the best but the only source book on Mercury. [3]

In 1874 Johann Karl Friedrich Zöllner published another study of Mercury, [4] in which he pointed out that Schroeter had exaggerated the albedo of the innermost planet, which did not reflect as much light as he assumed. Zöllner put the albedo at 0.114, which means that only 11.4 per cent of the light received from the sun is reflected back into space. Since Zöllner estimated the albedo of our moon at 0.119, he could justifiably say: "Mercury is a body the surface condition of which must be nearly the same as that of our moon, and which, like our moon, probably does not hold a noticeable atmosphere."

In modern tables Mercury and the moon still have the same albedo, but both have been downgraded to 0.07. While Zöllner's work may be called a refinement of the diligent labors of Schroeter, the next major series of observations produced a minor revolution. The most quoted of all astronomical journals, the *Astronomischen Nachrichten,* in the volume for 1889 contained an article *"Sulla rotazione di Mercurio"* by the Italian astronomer Giovanni Virginio Schiaparelli. The gist of it was that Schroeter's value of 24 hours and 5 minutes for the rotation of Mercury was wrong. The value of 16 hours advanced in the meantime by another astronomer named Vidal was wrong too. Mercury, Schiaparelli said, rotates just once on its axis while completing one orbit around the sun, behaving with respect to the sun as the moon behaves with respect

---

[3] Its title was *Hermographische Fragmente zur genaueren Kenntnis des Planeten Merkur* (Hermographic Fragments to the Better Knowledge of the Planet Mercury) and it appeared in two parts in Göttingen in 1815-16. It was not only the first book about Mercury, but also the first devoted to a specific planet.

[4] Entitled *Photometrische Untersuchungen über die physische Beschaffenheit des Planeten Merkur* (Photometric Researches on the Physical Condition of the Planet Mercury), a section in Poggendorf's *Jubelband* of 1874.

to the earth. Since then Mercury has repeatedly been called "the moon of the sun," which is a nice way of putting it but tends to lead nonastronomers astray in their thinking.

Just what had happened was told by Schiaparelli to an audience which included the King and Queen of Italy at a meeting on December 8, 1889, of the Royal Academy of the Lynxes.

"Observations which are made in the period of twilight," Schiaparelli

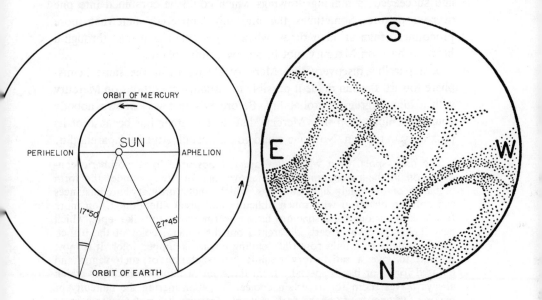

(*Left*) the orbit of Mercury; (*right*) Schiaparelli's drawing of Mercury

explained, "before the rising or after the setting of the sun, are rarely successful, because under such circumstances the planet is always near to the horizon, and so subject to disturbances and unequal refractions in the lowest atmospheric strata as to present for the most part in the telescope that uncertain and flaming aspect which strikes the naked eye as a brilliant scintillation. For that very reason the ancients called it *Stilbon*, which means the scintillating one. Observations by night being impossible, and twilight observations being rarely successful, no other way remains but to make the attempt in full daylight. . . ."

It is strange that nobody prior to Schiaparelli thought of trying for daylight observations. After all, if the sun is in the sky, Mercury must be too, and since its position can be easily calculated, it can be found with a telescope.

"Certain trials made in 1881 persuaded me," Schiaparelli continued, "that it would be possible not only to see the markings on Mercury in full daylight, but also to obtain a series of sufficiently connected and continuous observations of these spots. In the beginning of 1882 I decided to make a regular study of the planet; and in the eight following years I have had the telescope directed upon Mercury several hundreds of times, usually to little purpose and with the loss of much time. . . ."

But he did see the markings on Mercury one hundred and fifty times and succeeded in making drawings which could be combined into one over-all picture. Sometimes the markings appeared somewhat more pronounced than at other times, when they seemed as if seen through a haze—a haze on Mercury, not in our own atmosphere.

Schiaparelli's discovery that Mercury always turns the same hemisphere toward the sun made it possible to visualize conditions on Mercury with a high degree of probability. Before this fact was known nobody could say more than that Mercury had to be rather hot because of its proximity to the sun. Now one could go into detail. And Schiaparelli did:

The dark spots, even when they are not obscured by atmospheric condensation in the manner mentioned above, appear always under the form of bands of extremely light shadings, which under ordinary circumstances can only be observed with much difficulty and great attention. Upon more favorable occasions these shadings have a warm brown tint like sepia, which nevertheless is never greatly different from the general color of the planet. This is usually of a light rose tint, tending toward a copper color. It is most difficult to give a satisfactory graphic representation of such vague and diffused forms or bands specially from the want of fixity of the edges which always leaves room for a certain choice. . . . Considering the difficulty of making a proper study of the dark spots of Mercury, it is not easy to express a well-founded opinion on their nature. They might simply depend upon the diverse material and structure of the superficial strata, as we know to be the case with the moon. But if anyone, taking into account the fact that there exists an atmosphere upon Mercury capable of condensation and perhaps also of precipitation, should hold the opinion that there was something in those dark spots analogous to our seas, I do not think that a conclusive argument to the contrary could be advanced. And as these spots are not grouped in great masses, but are dispersed about in areas and zones of no great width, much ramified and alternated with clear spaces with some uniformity, it might be concluded that no vast oceans and great continents exist upon Mercury. . . .

Schiaparelli, although he established the facts upon which more recent reasoning is based, was loath to part with the idea that life might be possible on Mercury. He did not assume the presence of water himself but, so to speak, permitted others to do so. He stressed the fact that one perpetually heated hemisphere adjacent to a perpetually frozen one should cause strong circulation of the atmosphere from one hemisphere to the other. This, he pointed out, might cause a surprisingly even temperature over the whole planet.

Soon after Schiaparelli, the American astronomer Percival Lowell expressed his belief in the other extreme by calling Mercury, "the bleached bones of a world."

It is now time to give a few statistics. Mercury's diameter is 3100 miles. It has no satellites. Its orbit is quite eccentric for that of a planet, with perihelion at 28.5 million miles and aphelion at 43.35 million miles. To go from perihelion to perihelion takes 88 days. The plane of the orbit is inclined to the plane of the earth's orbit, the ecliptic, by 7° 0' 12". This is a greater inclination than is shown by the orbit of any other planet, except that of Pluto (see Chapter 18), which is in every respect a special case.

Schiaparelli, in stating that a strong circulation of the atmosphere might lead to an even temperature over the planet, or at least to fairly even temperatures for a given area made one mistake, and he was handicapped by lack of measurements. The mistake was to assume a fairly dense atmosphere. His handicap was that in his day it was impossible to measure the surface temperature of another planet. Of course, if Schiaparelli had been able to measure surface temperatures, he might not have made the mistake of assuming a dense atmosphere.

The measurements, carried out subsequently by Dr. Edison Pettit and Dr. Seth B. Nicholson (both of Mount Wilson and Palomar Observatories) gave the following result: A point near the center of the sunward hemisphere of Mercury will assume a temperature of 774° Fahrenheit when the planet is at perihelion. When the planet is at aphelion the temperature has dropped to 530° F., but it will never go lower than that. Now while a spot near the center of the sunward side is more than twice as hot as boiling water at aphelion, and hot enough to liquefy tin and lead at perihelion, a spot near the center of the dark side would have a temperature of −400° F., which is just about cold enough to liquefy nitrogen.

Under these circumstances it becomes clear how right Zöllner was to say that the planet "probably does not hold a noticeable atmosphere." Let us try to visualize what would happen if Mercury, at this moment, were supplied with an atmosphere like that of earth, consisting of nitrogen and oxygen, laden with water vapor and with some carbon dioxide and a trace of argon and the other noble gases. At the sunward side the gases would rise; the oxygen would quickly disappear chemically, by forming compounds with whatever unoxidized metals or oxidizable minerals happen to be exposed. The atmosphere would then flow over the illuminated rim to the dark side, entering an area of many thousands of square miles where the temperature is far below most of the freezing points one could mention. All the water vapor would freeze out almost instantly, falling to the ground as snow. The carbon dioxide would turn into "dry ice." Some of the nitrogen would turn liquid and fall to the ground as a rain of liquid gas. The only gases which would remain unaffected would be the three noble gases—argon, helium, and neon—which have very low freezing points. Naturally not all of the nitrogen would be precipitated on the first trip to the dark side, since a substance needs time to lose heat just as it needs time to acquire heat. But it is evident that after a comparatively short time, everything that will not remain a gas under the temperature prevailing on the dark side will stay on that side. The process may be slowed down by a factor soon to be discussed, the "twilight belt," but even with the ameliorating factor of the twilight belt the process would certainly be completed in just two centuries, if not sooner.

Hence there cannot be much of an atmosphere on Mercury; all its constituents, with the exception of hydrogen (which under the conditions of the bright side is likely to escape into space), helium, argon, neon, and possibly some nitrogen, must lie frozen on the ground around the center of the dark side.

This reasoning is reinforced by transit observations. When, at the beginning of a transit, the disk of Venus has partially entered the disk of the sun, the planet, which of course looks black under these circumstances, is suddenly surrounded by a luminous ring. This ring is an effect of the atmosphere of Venus; in fact, this is how the atmosphere of Venus was originally discovered. A transit of Mercury, however, does not produce this effect.

Instead, the planet seems, when well inside the sun's disk, to be surrounded by a circle of extra brightness, clearer than the sun's surface. A French astronomer, as reported by E. M. Antoniadi,[5] changed oculars during the observation and found that the clear circle remained the same size, thus confirming the general belief that it is merely an effect of contrast. Another phenomenon exhibited by Mercury during a transit is what Antoniadi called a *"tache lumineuse excentrique sur la planète"* ("a luminous spot off-center on the planet"). It has been seen, sometimes brightly, sometimes weakly, and even sometimes double, by many astronomers during many transits. One man who never saw it, how-

---

[5] In his book *La Planète Mercure et la Rotation des Satellites* (Paris, Gauthier-Villars, 1934), the second book written about Mercury and probably the last for a long time to come.

ever, was Schiaparelli. Laboratory experiments by the French astronomer A. Couder (also reported by Antoniadi) indicate that this spot, if visible, is an effect of diffraction in our own atmosphere.

Before we go on, we must explain the origin of the twilight belt and the phenomenon of libration, of which the twilight belt is merely a specific example. If a planet like Mercury turns on its axis at the same rate that it orbits the sun, one should expect, at first glance, that one half is always illuminated by the sun while the other half can never be struck by the sun. This would be the case if the orbit were circular— which in turn means if the planet were moving at a constant orbital velocity. But while the rotation on the axis goes on at a constant rate, the rate of motion in the orbit is constantly changing. In the case of Mercury, the orbital velocity at perihelion is 35.42 miles per second, while the rate at aphelion is only 24.23 miles per second.

The result of these two different rates of motion is as follows. Let us assume that a man is standing precisely at the terminator when the planet is at perihelion. The sun is at the horizon for this observer. At this point the planet is moving fast in its orbit, but its rotation is not fast enough to match the orbital velocity. The result is that the sun is slowly rising above the horizon. Twenty days after perihelion it is 24 degrees above the horizon, which means of course that the sun is *at* the horizon for a man 24 degrees farther into the dark side, if we consider the terminator at perihelion as the norm. A fairly wide strip of the dark side is actually illuminated, though by rather slanting sunlight. During the 24 days which pass between this day and the time aphelion is reached, the sun will slowly sink again and be at the horizon when the planet reaches aphelion; the "normal" terminator is again restored.

To keep it "restored," the planet's rotation should now slow down. But it doesn't; hence the man at the normal terminator is now moving into the dark zone; the sun sinks below the horizon for him, but it rises for areas on the other side of the planet which have been in darkness so far. After another 44 days perihelion is reached again and the terminator is back to the position it holds at perihelion and at aphelion.

But in the meantime, for first one area beyond the "normal" terminator, and then for another area on the opposite side of the planet, also beyond the "normal" terminator, the sun was above the horizon. In that manner a wide belt is exposed to sunlight for some time during each orbit around the sun, the areas just beyond the normal terminator for about forty days, the areas farther into the dark side for a shorter period.

This phenomenon is called "libration," and in Mercury's case it produces the twilight belt.

This twilight belt may possibly provide the answer to the otherwise
unsolved question of the occasional veiling of Mercury's features. E. M.
Antoniadi, who not only confirmed Schiaparelli's discovery of the once-
per-orbit rotation of Mercury but also drew a map which (discounting
variations in individual styles of drawing) is virtually the same as
Schiaparelli's map, also saw the veiling. Schiaparelli could still consider
it water vapor; Antoniadi, knowing that could not be correct, attributed
the veiling to circulating dust particles. Unfortunately even the finest
dust particles cannot be blown around unless there is some air—or,
more generally, some gas—to carry them. But all the evidence is against
an atmosphere—the very large and intensely cold area on the dark side,
as well as the appearance during transit.

The only possibility lies in the twilight belt. Gases which condensed
in the area where the sun shines only for a short time every 88 days,
might each time evaporate again. But whether there would be enough
gas to blow dust around is an unsolved problem.

We now come to the tail end of the story of Mercury, a tail end
suppressed in most books or else "taken care of" with a footnote.

The perihelion of the orbit of Mercury does not stay in the same
place in space. It "advances" slowly, moving to another position in
the orbit. Such shifts can be explained, but Mercury's perihelion advances at a higher rate than theory would permit. If there is a disagreement between facts and theory it is considered self-evident that the
facts are right. In practice it is not always easy, however, to make a
quick decision. And different scientists may attack such a discrepancy
between facts and theory in different ways. One man may prefer to
question the "facts" first. Maybe there was a small inherent flaw in
the instrument. Maybe the method used had such a minor flaw, even
if the instrument was perfect. Or, if one observer consistently gets one
kind of result and another observer another one, using the same equipment and the same over-all method, the fault must lie with one of
the observers.

As regards the orbit of Mercury, all three possibilities had to be
checked—first the measurements taken by the observers, then the
mathematics of the calculation, and finally the possibility of a missing
factor.

The French mathematician and astronomer Urbain Jean Joseph
Leverrier began, around 1855, to attack the problem of the orbit of
Mercury. He concentrated especially on the transits which had been

observed—twenty-one during the period from 1697 to 1848. Even though some of the older observations could be questioned as to the accuracy of timing, the over-all conclusion was that there was an unknown factor—or at least that a known factor had been given a wrong value.

Leverrier, at the time director of the Paris Observatory and famous for his calculation of the orbit of Neptune (see Chapter 17), in a lecture to the Academy in Paris on January 2, 1860, stated that the problem could be solved in one of two ways only. One required the assumption that the planet Venus was more massive than believed, but in order to make the calculations agree with the observations, the mass of Venus would have to be increased by a full 10 per cent. This, said Levverier, would substitute one mystery for another, because a heavier Venus would influence the orbit of the earth in a way which simply did not happen. The second possibility was to assume an unknown mass inside the orbit of Mercury, in "intra-Mercury." Leverrier probably knew that in 1847 the American astronomer Edward Herrick in New Haven, after receiving the news of the discovery of Neptune, had systematically observed the sun every day for a long period in the hope of finding an unknown planet. Herrick had not been successful; Leverrier suggested that the unknown mass inside the orbit of Mercury might be a second asteroid belt rather than a single planet.

Professor Rudolf Wolf in Zürich, after reading Leverrier's account, reasoned that some of these "inner asteroids" might be large enough to appear as tiny black dots if they passed in transit across the surface of the sun. If an astronomer actually saw such a transit and if he kept his eye on this particular spot, he might conceivably become suspicious because of the rate of motion. But his attention would probably be focused on the larger groups of sunspots. Still, it was possible that such a small spot had been entered by an observer. This was before the days of routine photography and there was a considerable element of chance involved; a busily sketching observer might not consider every little black dot worth entering.

But Professor Wolf went through the accounts of sunspots and found fifteen suspicious small round spots. After he had published his list in *Astronomische Nachrichten* (no. 1223 of 1859), another astronomer, C. Haase, came up with a few additional cases, and by 1871 Professor Wolf had a total of two dozen, which seemed to fit the pattern of two bodies, one with an orbital period of 26 days and another with an orbital period of 38 days. Naturally Wolf informed Leverrier, but he in the meantime had had his own experience with the planet inside the orbit of Mercury and seems to have been in no mood to be reminded of it.

On December 22, 1859, Leverrier received a letter from a country doctor in Orgères (near Orléans), named Lescarbault. Lescarbault, who described himself as an amateur astronomer, had seen a black round spot, moving across the upper portion of the solar disk, that looked like a planet in transit. Lescarbault added that he knew what a planet in transit looked like because he had watched the transit of Mercury of May 8, 1845. The black dot he had seen had appeared on the face of the sun on March 26, 1859, had been in sight for an hour and a quarter, and had moved a distance somewhat less than one quarter of the sun's diameter.

Leverrier was rather annoyed when he read the letter; he tended to become annoyed quite easily after he reached middle age. One of his colleagues described him as a *mauvais coucheur* (bad bedfellow), and another said that he might not be the most detestable man in France, but there was no doubt that he was the most detested. Strangely enough, all these harsh judgments came from Frenchmen; Swiss, German, and English scientific colleagues always reported that he had been quite amiable if sometimes somewhat stiff. Apparently Leverrier reserved his bad moods for his compatriots.

This time Leverrier was annoyed because Lescarbault had made an observation in March and waited until December to tell him about it. Leverrier was also intrigued, however, and made a special trip to Orgères to find out for himself. Still annoyed, he requested to see Lescarbault *immédiatement* and did not even state his own name. It has never been learned whether Lescarbault guessed who the visitor might be; later on he found out, of course. The interview has been described by Richard Anthony Proctor (in his book *Rough Ways Made Smooth*, London, 1880), who will have to bear full responsibility for the details:

"So you are the man," said Leverrier, looking fiercely at the doctor, "who pretends to have seen an intra-Mercurial planet. You have committed a grave offense in hiding your observation, supposing you really have made it, for nine months. Tell me at once and without equivocation what you have seen."

Lescarbault described his observation. Leverrier asked for his chronometer, and, hearing that the doctor used only his watch, the companion of his professional journeys, asked how he could pretend to estimate seconds with an old watch. Lescarbault showed a silk pendulum "beating seconds"—though it would have been more correct to say "swinging seconds." Leverrier then examined the doctor's telescope, and presently asked for the record of the observations. Lescarbault produced it, written on a piece of laudanum-stained paper which at the moment was doing service as a marker in the *Connaissance des Temps*.[6]

Leverrier asked Lescarbault what distance he had deduced for the new planet. The doctor replied that he had been unable to deduce any, not being a mathematician: he had made many attempts, however. Hearing this, Leverrier asked for the rough draft of these ineffective calculations.

"My rough draft?" said the doctor. "Paper is rather scarce with us here. I am a joiner as well as an astronomer" (we can imagine the expression of Leverrier's face at this moment); "I calculate in my workshop, and I write upon the boards; and when I wish to use them in new calculations, I remove the old ones by planing." On adjourning to the carpenter's shop, however, they found the board with its lines and its numbers in chalk still unobliterated.

This last piece of evidence, though convincing Leverrier that Lescarbault was no mathematician, and therefore probably in his eyes no astronomer, yet satisfied him as to the good faith of the doctor of Orgères. With a grace and dignity full of kindness, which must have afforded a singular contrast to his previous manner, he congratulated Lescarbault on his important discovery. He made some enquiry also at Orgères concerning the private character of Lescarbault, and learning from the village *curé*, the *juge de paix*, and other functionaries, that he was a skilful physician, he determined to secure some reward for his labours. At Leverrier's request M. Rouland, the Minister of Public Instruction, communicated to Napoleon III the result of Leverrier's visit, and on January 25th the Emperor bestowed on the village doctor the decoration of the Legion of Honour.

Leverrier did not need long to calculate from Lescarbault's data what the orbit of that body must have been, provided it was a planet in transit. An orbital period of 19 days and 17 hours, corresponding to a mean distance from the sun of 13 million miles, with an inclination of 12° 10' to the ecliptic with one node at heliocentric longitude 12° 59' fitted the only observation so far. The diameter, as described by Lescarbault, indicated a body much smaller than Mercury, about one-seventeenth of Mercury's mass. This was by no means enough to account for the misbehavior of Mercury's perihelion, but Leverrier himself had said that a belt of asteroids was a likely cause and such a small planet sounded about the right size for the largest member of that belt. Leverrier gradually fell in love with the idea; he even named the new planet, calling it "Vulcan."

It happened that a total eclipse of the sun took place in 1860. Leverrier mobilized all French and a few other astronomers to find "Vulcan." Nobody did. Leverrier was annoyed once more; people might make jokes about "Vulcan."

Professor Wolf's list of suspicious "sunspots" may have revived his interest somewhat, for Wolf notes that Leverrier mailed him copies of his later calculations almost up to the time of his death in 1877. (Wolf

[6] The French equivalent of the *Nautical Almanac*.

published them in the *Zürcher Vierteljahrsschrift* in 1881). Just about the time of Leverrier's death some more "evidence" found its way into print. On April 4, 1875, a German astronomer, Heinrich Weber, then living in northeastern China, saw a round spot on the sun. This was most interesting to both Leverrier and Wolf. Leverrier's "orbit" of "Vulcan" indicated a possible transit for April 3 of that year. Wolf noted that his body in the 38-day orbit could also have performed a transit at about that time.

Weber's observation would be considered "suspicious" to this day if his "round dot" had not been photographed by Greenwich Observatory and also observed by the Madrid Observatory, with a larger instrument than Weber had in China. Both observatories agreed that it had been an ordinary sunspot, quite small and not quite round.

There was one more flurry after the eclipse of the sun on July 29, 1878.

Two observers of the eclipse claimed to have seen in the vicinity of the sun small illuminated disks which could only be small planets inside the orbit of Mercury. One of them was Canadian-born James Craig Watson, at the time professor of astronomy at the University of Michigan. The eclipsed sun was in the constellation of Cancer. Watson, observing from Rawlins, Wyoming, first picked out a star which he took to be Zeta Cancri and then moved in the direction of the eclipsed sun to find the star Theta Cancri. A little farther to the east (i. e., closer to the eclipsed sun) he saw an object showing a disk. Going over his memories with a star chart afterward he became convinced that the star could not have been Zeta Cancri, and that the actual Zeta Cancri had to have been west of what he had seen. In short, he believed he had found two intra-Mercuries, one near Zeta Cancri and the other near Theta Cancri.

The other observer was Lewis Swift, a New Yorker who at the age of thirty-five had turned to astronomy from being a hardware dealer in Rochester, N. Y., and who later became famous for his work on nebulae. Observing from Pike's Peak in Colorado, Swift saw two stars close together, one of them Theta Cancri, the other "Vulcan." He could not say which was which, but they looked equally bright to him. Watson had said that the "planet" was brighter than Theta Cancri.

Largely because "Vulcan" was never seen again, it was felt necessary to explain this observation away. "It was considered that what Watson thought he mistook for Zeta Cancri was, actually, that star; that his other intra-Mercurial planet was really *theta* Cancri; and that what he thought to be Theta Cancri was a small 6th-magnitude star near it.

By a similar process of substitution it was inferred that what Swift took for Theta Cancri and an adjacent intra-Mercurial planet were really 25 Cancri and a neighboring 7th-magnitude star." [7]

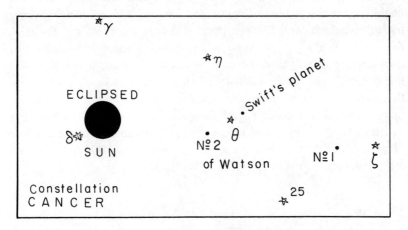

Star chart of the search for the planet inside Mercury's orbit. After Rupert T. Gould

This does seem somewhat strained, though such an accumulation of mistakes could conceivably be accounted for by the hurry of trying to see as much as possible during the short time of an eclipse.

In any event Watson's report, though not flawless, gave new hope to Rudolf Wolf in Zürich, who seems to have felt it his job to finish what Leverrier had started. The mathematician C. H. Peters, after reading all the inconclusive evidence about Vulcan's existence, decided that the flaw in the whole thing had to be at the mathematical end and in 1879 published a criticism of Leverrier's theoretical approach. This, after some delay, drew a counterblast in 1884 from Julius Bauschinger, who went over the work of both Leverrier and Wolf and declared that Leverrier had *not* made a mistake.

What is the situation now, eighty years later?

First, "Vulcan" has never been found. Second, the advance of Mercury's perihelion can be explained by Einstein's theory of relativity; there is therefore no reason for looking for large amounts of matter, planetary, asteroidal, meteoric, or dust, inside the orbit of Mercury.

But there remains a nagging doubt, or rather several. What did Lescarbault see in transit across the face of the sun? He had no reason to tell a fairy tale and even Leverrier accepted his word. Likewise,

[7] From "The Planet Vulcan," in Rupert T. Gould's *Oddities* (New York, Frederick A. Stokes Co., 1928).

would Watson make all the mistakes he was said to have made, with corroboration supplied by other mistakes made by Swift? It is far easier to believe that both of them did see something near *theta Cancri*.

This belief is now permissible because we can state what these men might have seen. A few asteroids (see Chapter 13) have highly eccentric orbits which carry them to points between the earth and the sun— these asteroids have, by convention, male mythological names, and therefore are usually referred to as the male asteroids. It is highly likely that Lescarbault caught one of the male asteroids in transit and that the body near *theta Cancri* was another male asteroid. Its actual distance from the sun could have been quite large but it might have happened to be about in line of sight to the eclipsed sun. Since the existence of such asteroids was then unknown, the observers could only conclude that what they saw was Leverrier's "Vulcan."

10

VENUS

VENUS, as hardly needs to be stated, is at times the most conspicuous object in the sky. The brightness is such that the planet can produce a shadow. It is such that, in 1835, a jittery harbor commandant of a French port ordered a gunboat out to sea to shoot down the probably hostile balloon which tried to shine a searchlight on his harbor installations.

The impressive brightness and serene light of the planet caused it, in all ancient cultures (with the exception of India) to be personified as a beautiful woman. The Babylonian name was Nin-dar-anna, Mistress of the Heavens. To the Chinese it was the Beautiful White One, Tai-pe. In Egypt the planet was called Tioumoutiri when it appeared as the morning star and Ouâti as the evening star, both words being feminine. The Greeks also had two names originally, Hesperos and Phosphoros; the first name derived from the Greek word for "west," the second meaning "light bearer." (The realization that Hesperos and Phosphoros were the same planet is ascribed to Pythagoras of Samos.) The Latin name Venus is that of a goddess, originally the goddess of spring, later the goddess of spring and of love, equated with the Greek Aphrodite. In the north the planet received the name of the chief goddess of northern mythology, beautiful Frigga; who also survives in our word Friday, from the Anglo-Saxon *Friggedaeg*.

Among the Mayas Venus was considered as important a light in the sky as the sun and the moon, and their mythology invented a kind of heavenly triangle. A somewhat different version of the same thing was devised by the Babylonians, in which Ishtar—another of their names for Venus—appears as the moon's sister. Such mythology by itself would be of only passing interest to the history of astronomical science except for one point. Why is Ishtar the sister of the moon? Why not the sister of the sun? Astronomers of the telescopic era of astronomy immediately think of the fact that Venus can show phases like the moon. But could stargazers of pretelescopic times have known this?

Offhand the answer is "no." I have often seen Venus in a fine sickle phase through the telescope and, in spite of knowing that it was in such a phase and even how it looked, have not been able to see it with the naked eye. Of course many people claim that they do, and an astronomer made the interesting experiment of asking some of these people, after they had looked through the telescope, to draw the phase as observed with the naked eye. They readily drew the phase as it appeared in the telescope. The astronomer had refrained from telling them that the telescope inverted the image; if they really had seen it with the naked eye, they would have drawn the horns pointing the other way.

But in relation to the Babylonians the case is not quite so clear cut. A. Pannekoek, in his *History of Astronomy,* writes: "It does not seem impossible that in the clear atmosphere of these lands the horns of the Venus crescent were perceived; modern astronomers, too, have mentioned such instances. An American missionary, D. T. Stoddaert, in a letter to John Herschel from Oroomisha in Persia in 1852, wrote that at twilight Jupiter's satellites and the elongated shape of Saturn could be seen with the naked eye and that through a dark glass the half-moon shape of Venus immediately struck the eye.[1] . . . Thus it can be still better understood that in these ancient times the Babylonian priest-astronomers devoted special attention to Ishtar as a sister-star of the moon."

The invention of the telescope removed all doubt about the phases of Venus. Galileo saw them first and announced his discovery in a letter to Giuliano de Medici, ambassador in Prague, December 11, 1610, in the form: *"Haec immatura a me jam frustra leguntur oy."* This could be taken to be rather poor Latin for "These unripe things are read by me"—unripe for disclosure, that is. But the "oy" clearly indicated that the sentence was an anagram with two letters left over. The true sentence was: *Cynthia figuras aemulatur Mater Amorum* (Cynthia's figures are imitated by the Mother of Love), Cynthia being the moon and the Mother of Love, naturally, Venus.

The next man to see the phases of Venus—at least the next we know about—was Simon Marius in Germany, who was soon to become involved in a violent quarrel with Galileo about the discovery of the satellites of Jupiter (see Chapter 14). As regards the phases of Venus, Galileo did not quarrel with Marius; in the first place his own priority was beyond doubt; in the second place even the poorest telescope showed the crescent. Another German observer interested in the phases of Venus was Matthias Hirzgarter, who described them in detail.

[1] The letter was published in the *American Journal of Science and Arts,* 1855, p. 273. The mention of a dark glass is interesting; possibly Venus is too bright to show the phases to the naked eye.

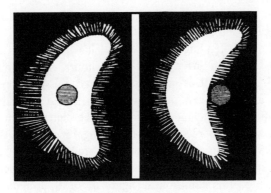

Two drawings of Venus by Francesco Fontana: (left) made in 1645; (right) made in 1646

The title of Hirzgarter's book was in Latin,[2] but the text was mostly in German and partly in German "verse" (these quotation marks are unavoidable). One bit, dealing with both Mercury and Venus, reads:

Der Sonnen sind wir beyd verwandt	We both are related to the sun;
Zunächst um sie her wir den Lauff hand	Next to her around we run,
Wachsend und schweinend wie der Mon	Waxing and waning like the moon,
Wie man durch d'Rohr wol sehen kan.	As through the tubes you can see soon.

By 1640 there was no longer any doubt about the fact that Venus moved around the sun in an orbit smaller than that of the earth. The orbital period, 224.7 days, was not hard to determine but the next problem—the daily rotation—is still unsolved at the time of writing. Whether Simon Marius or Francesco Fontana, both eager observers of the phases of Venus, tried to determine the length of the day is doubtful. If they did, they must have given up.

Giovanni Domenico Cassini did try and believed he was successful. He found an especially bright spot on the monotonously bright surface of Venus and followed it. In his "Lettre à M. Petit touchant la découverte du mouvement de la Planète Vénus autour de son axe" (*Journal des Savants,* 1667), he stated that the diurnal period of Venus was "less than a day, namely 23 hours." The journal made a typographical error in this crucial sentence, printing "less than a day, namely 23 days," which almost foreshadowed the next determination. The papal chamberlain Francesco Bianchini published in 1728—just one year before his death—a book with the title *Hesperi et Phosphori nova phaenomena,*

[2] *Detectio dioptrica corporum planetarum verorum,* Frankfurt, 1643.

in which he stated that Venus rotated quite slowly, needing 24 days and 8 hours for one complete rotation.

Jacques Cassini, reading this, reviewed his father's observations and recalculated them, finding a value of 23 hours and 15 minutes. Now if Bianchini, Jacques Cassini reasoned, had missed opportunities at observation and had seen the planet after it had actually completed several rotations, Bianchini's figure and the figure from his father's observations could be reconciled. If the figure of 24⅓ days actually applied to 25 rotations, a single rotation would take 23 hours and 20 minutes. Jacques Cassini was willing to accept this. Giacomo Filippo Maraldi accepted this compromise figure in 1750. Johann Hieronymus Schroeter felt that the figure was "too even" to be correct and started observations of his own, looking, like the elder Cassini, for especially bright spots. In his *Cythereographische Fragmente* (Erfurt, 1793) he "corrected" Cassini's value to 23 hours, 21 minutes, and 19 seconds.

By coincidence Sir William Herschel's "Observations of the Planet Venus" appeared in the *Philosophical Transactions* during the same year. Herschel was noncommital: the lack of surface features made observation difficult. He had no proof that Cassini was wrong but felt that there was some evidence in favor of Bianchini's much longer period. One may be disappointed that the great Herschel did not take a more definite stand, but Herschel was, first and foremost, the careful observer who reported what he had observed. And in the case of Venus nothing much could be reported.

A mistake which still crops up in popular books is the statement that Herschel's account is the first one to mention the atmosphere of Venus and therefore he should be credited with its discovery. Herschel himself never made that claim; one look through the telescope convinced him that Venus did have an atmosphere. If one can use the term "discovery" at all in this context, the actual discovery was made during the transits of 1761 and 1769. When Venus is in transit across the disk of the sun the observer just sees a dark round spot. But when it is entering or leaving the sun's disk the round dark spot is surrounded by a luminous ring, caused by the refraction of the sun's rays by the planet's atmosphere.

During the transits of 1631 and 1639, no such observations had been made. To be precise, the transit of 1631 had not been observed by anybody, and the only man known to have observed the transit of 1639 was the Reverend Jeremiah Horrox, and while his friend William Crabtree caught an occasional glimpse of the dark spot, Horrox's *camera obscura* method did not lend itself to such a discovery. If the chances to discover the atmosphere of Venus had simply been missed during the two transits of the seventeenth century, they were not missed during the two transits of the eighteenth century. But, incredible as it may seem, both observations were simply "mislaid" for about a century.

The luminous ring was seen during the first eighteenth-century transit by Mikhail Vasilyevitch Lomonósov, who observed it from his home in St. Petersburg, Russia. Lomonósov, who was born in the hamlet of Denisovka, some 45 miles from Arkhangelsk, on November 8, 1711, was then just fifty years old. A peasant boy, he had worked his way up to becoming a member of the then recently founded Akademiya Na-ook (Academy of Science), where he was professor of chemistry. He immediately concluded that this luminous ring indicated the presence of an atmosphere "maybe greater than that of earth" and wrote a paper entitled, in translation, "The Appearance of Venus on the Sun as Observed at the St. Petersburg Academy of Sciences on May 26, 1761." But this paper, like many others by Lomonósov was not printed during his lifetime. Depending on the presumed readers and, one suspects, also on his own whim, Lomonósov wrote sometimes in Russian, sometimes German, and often in Latin. Near the end of the nineteenth century another Russian, M. I. Sukhomlinov, collected all the unpublished material of Lomonósov's that he could find and had it printed, and the paper on the Venus transit appears in the fifth volume of that edition. But Lomonósov's discovery remained unknown outside Russia until 1910, when Professor B. N. Menshutkin published excerpts from Lomonósov's writings in Germany.[3]

The second discovery of the atmosphere of Venus was made during the second eighteenth-century transit by David Rittenhouse from his farm near Philadelphia, which for this purpose bore the temporary designation of "Norriton Station." Why the reports were not printed at once is something nobody seems to know. Rittenhouse's report remained in manuscript form for more than a century, until the *Early Proceedings of the American Philosophical Society* were finally compiled from the old minutes and printed in Philadelphia under that title in 1884.

To return to the theme of the diurnal period of Venus, no new suggestions were made until after the two nineteenth-century transits (in 1874 and 1882), when Schiaparelli attacked the problem. In a paper published in 1890 [4] Schiaparelli reviewed all the earlier work and discarded most of it as being due to optical illusions. His own extensive observations had convinced him that with Venus, as with Mercury, the

[3] In the series *Ostwald's Klassiker der Naturwissenschaften,* No. 178.
[4] *Considerazioni sul moto rotatorio del pianeta Venere.*

periods of rotation around the axis and of revolution around the sun were the same. The French astronomer Henri Perrotin in Nice declared one year later that his own observations had led him to agree with Schiaparelli.

Immediate contradiction came from J. J. A. Bouquet de la Grye, writing in the *Revue scientifique,* June 20, 1891. He said that measurements of the photographs obtained during the two recent transits had convinced him that Venus "had to have several days and nights during one of its years," though he was willing to assume a rather slow period of rotation. Niesten, writing in *Ciel et Terre,* July 16, 1891, insisted that the observations made in Brussels during the period from 1881 to 1890 substantiated the value found by Schroeter. Niesten went further; he compiled from these observations a map of Venus, the second one drawn; the first had been by Bianchini.

By 1891 the discussion was, therefore, back to a choice between a long diurnal period, as Bianchini thought, and one close to that of the earth, as asserted by the Cassinis, father and son, and by Schroeter. Schiaparelli's and Perrotin's assertion that "the Venus day equals the Venus year" was merely a third choice. By now one might say that this third choice is a poor one, for if Venus actually always turned the same hemisphere toward the sun it probably would have a different appearance. It could hardly be the featureless ocean of clouds which makes all observations so uncertain. If Venus moved like Mercury, most, if not all, of its atmosphere, would have condensed on its dark hemisphere. In that case, some definite surface features would be clearly visible time and again. But none are, which in itself proves some kind of rotation. This might be quite slow but the uniformity of what we can see indicates a distribution of the solar heat.

All these statements about rotation, including even Schiaparelli's, presuppose that Venus has an axis. The position of the axis is the next point of disagreement. Just what is the axial tilt? Is it similar to that of earth and of Mars, or is the axis of Venus more nearly vertical to the plane of the orbit, say, like Jupiter's? Bianchini thought he had found an axial tilt of 15 degrees, Schroeter believed in a very strong tilt. His own figure was 72 degrees; the figure of 53 degrees, which is often found in literature under Schroeter's name, is the correction made by F. de Vico (*Astronomische Nachrichten,* no. 404, 1840). Schiaparelli assumed that the axis was nearly vertical.

The faint markings which could be seen, and which by analogy to the polar caps of Mars were also called "caps," are positioned as if the axis of the planet were nearly vertical to the plane of the orbit.

Now, after another seventy years of general frustration, everybody would write, "provided that these markings are real, and provided, furthermore, that they do mark the polar areas of the planet." However, if they are accepted as marking the poles, the axis must be nearly vertical and its "verticality has found defenders to this day. The American astronomer William H. Pickering, in the *Journal of the British Astronomical Association* (vol. 31, 1920), estimated an axial tilt of 5 degrees, while the German Otto Schirdewahn, as recently as 1950, declared that Venus not only had the most nearly circular orbit among the planets, but also was the only planet where the equatorial plane coincided with the orbital plane.

However, most observers do not agree with Schiaparelli, Pickering, and Schirdewahn. E. M. Antoniadi (*Astronomische Nachrichten,* 1934) came out in favor of a tilt between 60 and 80 degrees; William H. Haas, writing in the *Journal of the Royal Astronomical Society of Canada* (vol. 37, 1942) put the tilt at "over 75°," while F. E. Ross, reporting on his photographic work on Venus in 1927, in the *Astrophysical Journal,* July 1928, decided in favor of 90 degrees, making the axis of Venus coincide with the plane of the orbit! But the same journal, in its November 1954 issue, carries a report, also on photographic work, by Gerard P. Kuiper, in which the figure for the probable axial tilt is given as 32 degrees with an uncertainty of 2 degrees.

This varied assortment of axial tilts (the Russian group of Venus observers declared themselves in favor of an axial tilt of 51 degrees), all advocated by competent astronomers after much work, is simply a result of the faintness of the markings observed. Nobody can tell whether such a faint marking is a surface feature, dimly visible through the cloud layers, or an atmospheric phenomenon of some kind.

It has even been argued that most of the markings are simply optical illusions. In 1897 the German astronomer W. Villiger carried out some experiments on which he reported in the 1898 volume of the *New Annals* of the Royal Observatory of Munich. He used rubber balls, painted white, and spheres of plaster of Paris, slightly over 2 inches in diameter. These spheres were suspended on black threads which held them motionless. They were illuminated as a planet is illuminated by the sun and observed with a 5-inch telescope from a distance of 1300 feet. (In order to produce different phases the source of illumination was shifted.) Then the "planet" was drawn by an experienced observer. Comparing these drawings with drawings of Venus made at the same time or a few years earlier cast gloom, instead of light, on the situation. The drawings of these balls, which are known to be featureless, show the lighter rim which is found on all Venus drawings. They show the equally typical faint dark marking along the meridian. They even show the polar "caps," though these are less pronounced on the drawings of the balls than they are on the drawings of the planet.

At the time when Villiger performed his experiments everybody was at least in agreement about the nature of the cloud layer. Of course the clouds on Venus were the same as the clouds on earth, water vapor. And their density showed that Venus must be a very wet planet. Two concepts were disseminated to students and to the public; I remember clearly that a lecturer—whose name I *don't* remember—in the old Urania Observatory in Berlin referred to them as the "romantic" and the "realistic" concept.

The "realistic" concept had the Greek name of *panthalassa*—in English it might be called the "all-ocean concept." Venus was covered by water, from pole to pole and all around its body. There might be a few small islands, or groups of islands, in some places, but only small ones. Any land mass of continental size would exert an influence on the atmosphere above it, since the temperature over a land mass is more changeable than the temperature over an ocean. The existence of a large land mass would break up the cloud layer into moving patterns, enabling us to see portions of the surface on occasion. Since no one ever did, there could be no real land.

In contrast, the "romantic" concept stated that there was no large open ocean. The whole surface of Venus must be land, at least from a sailor's point of view—no "blue water," but plenty of water over the land, enormous swamps, very large and very shallow lakes, the surfaces of which were interrupted by innumerable low islands. At night this swampy landscape was in stygian darkness, since Venus had no moon and starlight could not penetrate the cloud layer. During the day a bright patch in the sky indicated the position of the sun, but the light was generally diffused; just as there was no really firm dry land and no really deep water, there was no pronounced difference between light and shade, no strong shadows.

This picture, however, was not as strange as it seemed on first consideration. While no place on earth today looks this way, in the earth's past there had been a period characterized by enormous swamps, a uniform wet-warm temperature, and probably a low-hanging cloud cover—the Carboniferous Period. Hence the surface of Venus might well be regarded as being covered by an incredibly diversified vegetation, growing out of the shallow water, floating on the water, being carried by the sluggish streams to pile up against the innumerable islands.

There would also have to be abundant amphibian, or rather amphibious, animal life, moving around in the water with great agility, crawling up on the higher spots to sit sluggishly in the moist warm air until some prey appeared in the water. Or perhaps evolution had taken a different turn, and large insects were dominant, big beetles and giant cockroaches feeding on the abundant vegetation, with enormous spiders crouching in ambush.

These two concepts reigned for about four decades, say from 1880 to 1920. And then the picture of a perfectly dry Venus—at least at the surface—was added. The spectroscope had disclosed carbon dioxide in the atmosphere above the cloud layer. Now carbon dioxide (and, in our atmosphere, water vapor) produces something which climatologists call the "greenhouse effect." On earth it works like this: solar radiation of all wavelengths enters our atmosphere. The very short radiation does not reach the ground and is absorbed in the atmosphere. Visible light does reach the ground and is reflected, but it is not reflected precisely as it came in. Part of it is reflected as visible light; another portion is not reflected but is re-emitted as heat. If our atmosphere consisted of nitrogen only, both the reflected light waves and the emitted heat would go out into space. But carbon dioxide and water vapor prevent the radiation of heat; they act like the glass of a greenhouse and preserve the heat for the earth. Since more heat will, as a rule, produce more water vapor, this process is self-perpetuating, and for this reason the surface of the earth is much warmer than it would be if our atmosphere did not produce this effect. In fact, Svante Arrhenius had a theory that the periods of glaciation were periods when our atmosphere had a low carbon-dioxide content, which would, in turn, result from a slackening of volcanic activity, since the volcanoes are the main carbon-dioxide producers on our planet.

If there is a great deal of carbon dioxide in the atmosphere of Venus—whether created by volcanic activity or for other reasons so far unknown—the greenhouse effect should be very pronounced, and the fact that Venus is closer to the sun would also be important. Therefore the surface of Venus ought to be hotter than the boiling point of water, with the result that *all* the water on Venus would exist as a dense and probably deep cloud layer in the atmosphere. Underneath this, the planet would have to be bone dry, probably with high winds producing endless dust storms.

In the 1830s, the Munich astronomer Franz von Paula Gruithuisen had described Venus as a planet with a vegetation "incomparably more luxuriant than even the virgin forests of Brazil" and had gone on to draw conclusions about its inhabitants. These were based on the so-called ashen light, a faint illumination of the portion of Venus which should be invisible because it is dark. This ashen light is not visible all the time; Gruithuisen pointed out that "the principal observations of the ashen light on Venus are those of Mayer in 1759 and of Harding in 1806." The two observations, 47 earth years apart, if referred to the orbital period of Venus, marked an interval of 76 Venus years. Gruithuisen had wondered just what significance there might be in a period of 76 Venus years. "If this period has a religious character we cannot see any justification for that number of years," he admitted. But how about political events? Couldn't the ashen light be well explained as a general festival illumination in honor of the crowning of a new monarch of the planet? "It becomes comprehensible if we assume that some Alexander or Napoleon then attained universal power. If we assume that the ordinary life of an inhabitant of Venus lasts 130 Venus years, which amount to 80 earth years, the reign of an Emperor of Venus might well last 76 Venus years."

Of course the light might merely signify something much more prosaic, like the burning of large stretches of jungle to produce more arable land: "large migrations of people would be prevented and the resulting wars would be avoided by abolishing the reason for them. Thus the race would be kept united."

Gruithuisen's concept of Venus was decidedly more romantic than the "romantic concept" of the lecturer at the Urania Observatory. To pass on from it to modern work, three main items are still to be discussed: the ashen light, the composition of the atmosphere, and current ideas about the surface temperature of the planet.

As for the ashen light, the modern explanation has the advantage of being generally accepted. The ashen light is the equivalent of our aurora, as first suggested by P. de Heen in 1872 in his article *"De la lumière secondaire de Vénus."*

Venus is closer to the sun than we are, and aurorae there may be expected to be both stronger and more consistent. Moreover, there is some evidence that the planet has a considerable magnetic field. In 1955 some interesting results were announced by J. Houtgast of the Sonnenborgh Observatory at Utrecht, Holland (in *Nature,* vol. 175). Houtgast reasoned that if Venus is a powerful magnet, then when Venus lies roughly between the earth and the sun—thus being near inferior conjunction—it should divert the streams of electrically charged particles emitted by the sun; and from studies of magnetic records over a period of 44 years, also taking into account the changes in solar activity, he thought that such effects were measurable. He estimated that the magnetic field of Venus may be about five times stronger than the earth's. Consequently, there is nothing far-fetched about de Heen's idea that the ashen light may be caused by aurorae. It was supported by J. Lamp in 1887 and has gained increasing favor in recent years.[5]

The composition of Venus's atmosphere, until 1935, was not thought to be fundamentally different from that of earth. Some astronomers thought our atmosphere more extensive, others believed Venus's might be deeper. F. E. Ross, in 1927, suggested that the lower layers of the Venus atmosphere might be full of suspended dust, a kind of permanent dust haze, but that did not constitute a fundamental difference. True, the spectroscope did not show either vapor or oxygen, but improved techniques were expected to help. In fact they did, but in between a few very unusual suggestions were made. In 1937 Rupert Wildt published an article in the *Astrophysical Journal* (vol. 86), stating that the clouds might not be normal clouds at all. Under the conditions in the upper layers of the atmosphere, with the sun's ultra-violet radiation as the energy source, carbon, hydrogen, and oxygen might combine into CH_2O, which is formaldehyde. Formaldehyde, colorless when pure, turns into a dense white cloud of small flakes of plastics when water vapor is added to it. But formaldehyde should be detectable with the spectroscope, and a search for it proved fruitless.

In the wake of Wildt's unusual idea, and with the theory of a bone-dry Venus in mind, it was also suggested that the white clouds may be just wind-driven salt crystals, coming from dried-up former ocean beds.

Against these speculations there stood the assertion made by the French astronomer Bernard Lyot that his measurements of reflection and polarization, made in 1929, did not agree with any substance but water droplets. In 1955 Drs. E. Pettit and Seth B. Nicholson of Mount Wilson Observatory succeeded in making temperature measurements of the top of the cloud layer. It turned out to be quite chilly, though this is not really surprising. For the top of the illuminated clouds a temperature of −38° C. (−36.4° F.) was found; for the top of the unilluminated clouds −33° C. (−27.4° F.). Later measurements showed that these temperatures were a bit too high. Basing their reasoning on Lyot's measurements and the temperature measurements of Pettit and Nicholson, Drs. Donald H. Menzel and Fred L. Whipple (both of Harvard), came to the conclusion that the clouds of Venus were what they had been thought to be for more than a century, namely water vapor. Menzel and Whipple had gone back to the view that the

[5] Quoted from *The Planet Venus* by Patrick Moore (3rd ed., New York, Macmillan, 1960). Patrick Moore is the director of the Mercury and Venus Section of the British Astronomical Association. His book is an excellent summary of the history of Venus observations, with a bibliography which appears to be complete.

surface of the planet is a *panthalassa,* completely covered with water.

After things had settled back so nicely to what may be called the original status quo, the news of radio measurements excited the daily press. Radio waves of a wavelength of 3.15 centimeters, emitted by the planet, seemed to indicate a temperature of 300° C. or 572° F. The newspapers immediately jumped to the conclusion that "the surface of Venus is broiling hot." Well, it wasn't that definite yet; *something* on Venus was broiling hot, but it might either be the surface or a layer high in the atmosphere of the planet.

Since observations made from earth never led anywhere, the hopes of all astronomers were pinned on measurements made from a planetary probe passing the planet at close range.

The Venus probe Mariner II was launched on August 27, 1962; a mid-course correction was successfully carried out on September 4; and on December 14 Mariner's instruments scanned the cloud layer of the planet for 35 minutes from distances varying from 22,500 to 25,000 miles. One scan was carried out across the dark hemisphere, one across the terminator, and one across the illuminated hemisphere. The results indicate Venus must be ruled out as a habitable planet.

The summary of the results, as released by the National Aeronautics and Space Agency, began as follows: "Venus is covered by cold dense clouds in the upper atmosphere. It has surface temperature on the order of 800 degrees Fahrenheit, it has a cold spot in the southern hemisphere [20 degrees colder], the temperatures are essentially the same on both the dark and sunlighted sides, it is without the high density electron ionosphere that some scientists had speculated existed there, and the amount of carbon dioxide in the atmosphere above the cloud layer is too small to be detected by the Mariner instruments."

It has been suggested that the "cold spot" may be the result of a high mountain on the surface of Venus, which recalled the fact that Schroeter, one and a half centuries ago, claimed to have seen such a high mountain. However, it is safer to state that we do not know what causes this "cold spot" since there are many arguments against the existence of a really high mountain on Venus. But although the Russians still prefer to believe that Mariner II measured temperatures in the upper layer of the planet's atmosphere, all indications are that the surface is about as hot as was indicated by Mariner's instruments. The temperatures may need to be corrected because the fly-by distance of the planetary probe was about twice as great as had been expected, but the corrections cannot be large.

Such a high surface temperature must be the result of an accumulation of solar heat over a very long period. The clouds, believed to consist of carbohydrates and to be similar to a heavy oily smog, permit very little sunlight to pass. Even with the sun directly overhead the illumination of the surface of the planet is at best as bright as that on a dark and dreary day here on earth. But the small amount of energy trapped below these clouds remains trapped and thus has built up to a temperature hot enough to melt zinc.

The figures derived from Mariner's fly-by are, of course, not the last word but they are thought to be close to the truth. These are the conclusions:

Surface: rough and probably dry, average temperature 800 degrees Fahrenheit, atmospheric pressure at the surface at least 20 times the pressure of our atmosphere at sea level.

Cloud layer: base probably 45 miles above the surface of the planet, base temperature about 200° F., top about 62 miles above the planetary surface, temperature at the top about −65° F.

General: no detectable magnetic field, negligible electron density in the top layers of the atmosphere, amount of water vapor present less than one part per thousand of the water on earth. Mariner II did not detect any rotation of the planet and radar scans from earth carried out at about the same time seem to indicate that Venus may not rotate at all. A planet which does not rotate—this is a very different matter from one rotation per orbital revolution around the sun, as is the case with Mercury—is almost inconceivable. But it would explain why there is no difference in temperature between the light side and the dark side. For a non-rotating planet the sun is overhead around Venus once every Venusian year.

While American radar scans indicated non-rotation, Russian radio measurements, published by Professor A. Martynov, director of the State Astronomical Institute of Kiev, indicated a surface temperature of 212° F. in the unilluminated portion, and between 572° and 752° F. in the illuminated hemisphere. Professor Martynov stated that the conclusion reached by Kotelnikov in 1961, namely a rotational period of about ten days for Venus, is still accepted by Soviet astronomers.

The results obtained by Mariner II have shown that Venus is a far more unusual planet than had been thought in the past. But its mysteries are not yet completely solved by any means.

"THE MOON OF VENUS"

Every book on astronomy printed since the turn of the century lists

Venus as a moonless planet like Mercury. But for two hundred years, from 1690 until 1890, this was not at all certain.

Quite a number of astronomers, all of them reputable and some of them famous, had seen the moon of Venus. One could not simply say that they had all been wrong, even though the majority of astronomers had failed to find a moon of Venus.

The story began in 1672 with no less a man than Giovanni Domenico Cassini. Observing the morning sky he noticed a small object near Venus. Did Venus have a companion? Cassini apparently decided not to announce his observation publicly. But fourteen years later he saw the object again and this time he entered in his journal: [6]

1686, August 18, at 4:15 in the morning. Looking at Venus with a telescope of 34 feet focal length, I saw at a distance of $\frac{3}{5}$ of her diameter, eastward, a luminous appearance, of a shape not well defined, that seemed to have the same phase with Venus, which was then gibbous on the western side. The diameter of this object was nearly one quarter that of Venus. I observed it attentively for 15 minutes, and having left off looking at it for four or five minutes I saw it no more; but daylight was by then well advanced. I had seen a like phenomenon, which resembled the phase of Venus, on 1672 January 25, from 6:52 in the morning, to 7:02, when the brightness of the twilight caused it to disappear. Venus was then horned, and this object, which was of diameter almost one-quarter that of Venus, was of the same shape. It was distant from the southern horn of Venus a diameter of Venus on the western side. In those two observations I was in doubt whether it was or was not a satellite of Venus, of such a consistence as not to be very well fitted to reflect the light of the sun, and which in magnitude bore nearly the same proportion to Venus as the moon does to the earth, being at the same distance from the sun and earth as was Venus, the phase of which it resembled.

Cassini mentioned his observation in his book *L'Astronomie* and astronomers began to wonder whether Francesco Fontana might not have seen the same object some three decades before Cassini. Fontana had drawn the planet Mars with a perfectly round central spot—*"une pillule très noire"*— ("a very black pill") and he had drawn Venus in the same manner. But he had also drawn Venus with a round black spot outside the sickle phase. The black spots in Fontana's drawings had been—and are again—considered to be the result of a flaw in his instrument. But if Cassini had seen an object near Venus, possibly Fontana had seen it too. More observations were necessary.

Astronomers in general had to wait some time, but when the next observation came it certainly sounded convincing. The man who announced it (in *Philosophical Transactions,* vol. 41) was an English instrument-

---

[6] As quoted by Patrick Moore in *The Planet Venus,* op. cit.

maker named James Short. The date was October 23, 1740; the time early morning:

Directing a reflecting telescope of 16.5-in. focus (with an apparatus to follow the diurnal motion) towards Venus, I perceived a small star pretty nigh upon her; upon which I took another telescope of the same focal distance, which magnified about 50 or 60 times, and which was fitted with a micrometer, in order to measure the distance from Venus; and found its distance to be about 10°2'. Fnding Venus very distinct, and consequently the air very clear, I put a magnifying power of 240 times and, to my great surprise, found this star put on the same phase with Venus. Its diameter seemed to be about a third, or somewhat less, of the diameter of Venus, the light was not so bright or vivid, but exceeding sharp and well defined. . . . I saw it for the space of an hour several times that morning; but the light of the sun increasing, I lost it about a quarter of an hour after eight. I have looked for it every clear morning since, but never had the good fortune to see it again.

The next man to see it was Andreas Mayer in Greifswald in Germany; the date was May 20, 1759. He saw it for half an hour. Then followed Joseph-Louis Lagrange in Marseille, with three observations on three consecutive days, February 10, 11, and 12 of 1761. Lagrange felt certain enough of his observations to announce that the plane of the orbit of the satellite of Venus was vertical to the ecliptic. The year 1761 yielded no less than eighteen observations. The three by Lagrange in February were followed by four—March 3, 4, 7, and 11—by Jacques Leibax (called Montaigne); one by an unnamed French observer, June 5; two by Abraham Scheuten in Krefeld, Germany, June 6; and eight— June 28, 29, 30; July 18; August 4, 7, 11, 12—by Roedkioer in Copenhagen. Of these the two made by Abraham Scheuten were especially interesting. Venus was in transit. Scheuten saw the black dot, which was the planet, accompanied by a smaller black dot. The second observation was really part of the same one; Scheuten still saw the smaller black dot after Venus had left the sun's disk. In 1764 there were eight observations, five from Copenhagen by Roedkioer (March 3, 4, 9, 10), some of them corroborated by his associates, and three from Auxerre in France, made by Montbarron (March 15, 28, 29).

One major problem was created by that very convincing transit observation of Abraham Scheuten. Samuel Dunn at Chelsea, England, had also watched the transit. "With the six-foot Newtonian reflector, and its magnifying power of 100 and also of 220 times, I carefully examined the sun's disk, to discover a satellite of Venus, but saw none. . . . After the transit till two o'clock afternoon the same day, I continued observing the disk with this telescope but saw no satellite pass over the sun."

Before Dunn's report became known in France, a memoir was read to the French Academy, stating that the year 1761 would be celebrated in astronomical circles because of the discovery of a satellite of Venus by Monsieur Montaigne of Limoges. It may have weighed quite heavily that Montaigne had repeatedly expressed skepticism toward the existence of a satellite of Venus, until he had to say that he had seen it himself. The voice of a converted skeptic always carries more conviction than that of somebody who has belonged to the fold all along, and there is a certain justification for this attitude.

Now, however, the astronomical world had the word of Scheuten versus that of Samuel Dunn, and the word of about five astronomers who had seen the moon of Venus, against the word of five times that many (or more) who had not seen it, it looked as if it were time to find a good explanation for this riddle.

In 1766 the director of the Vienna Observatory, Father Maximilian Hell, S. J., published a treatise, *"De Satellite Veneris"* (in the Vienna ephemeris), in which he declared that all the observations of the moon of Venus had been optical illusions. The image of Venus, he said, is so bright, that it is reflected by the cornea of the eye back into the telescope, thus giving rise to a secondary smaller image. The fact that nearly everybody who had "seen" the satellite of Venus stated that its phase was the same as the phase of the planet itself was proof enough. If Venus did have a satellite, it might from time to time show the same phase as Venus, but this would be unusual, not the rule. Since it seemed to be the rule with these observations, the probability was that the "object" seen by the observers was merely a secondary image.

Though Father Hell continued to advance his explanation in various places, others went ahead on the assumption that what had been seen was real. The German Johann Heinrich Lambert wrote (in French) an *"Essai d'une théorie du satellite du Vénus"* which was printed in the *Berliner astronomisches Jahrbuch* (Berlin Astronomical Yearbook) of 1777. According to Lambert, the satellite of Venus was at a mean distance of 66.5 Venus radii from the planet, its orbital period was 11 days and 3 hours, and the inclination of its orbit to the ecliptic, 64 degrees. It was hoped that the satellite could be seen during the transit predicted for June 1, 1777.[7]

[7] It is self-evident at first glance that Lambert made a major mistake somewhere. A distance of 66.5 Venus radii is 512,000 miles, or nearly twice the distance of our moon from the earth. Hence the satellite could not possibly have an orbital period much shorter than that of our moon, especially since the mass of Venus is somewhat smaller than that of earth. At a later date Paul Stroobant pointed out that this orbit would imply a mass of Venus roughly ten times the actual one.

Frederick the Great of Prussia read Lambert's essay. A wrong step in the ranks of his grenadiers would have made him wince, a dissanonce in a flute concerto would have caused a scream, but a discrepancy between orbital period and orbital distance escaped his eye. If the good philosopher and mathematician Lambert said it was so, then it was so and the moon of Venus existed. Therefore it should have a name, and Frederick suggested it be named for his good friend Jean Le Rond d'Alembert. Whether d'Alembert was less convinced about the existence of the moon of Venus than his royal friend, or whether he had other reasons, is not known, but he declined the honor with the utmost diplomacy.[8]

In the meantime there had been one more observation (the last), made by Christian Horrebow from Copenhagen on January 3, 1768.

But there were several searches. Sir William Herschel made one, Schroeter in Lilienthal made another one, and Franz von Paula Gruithuisen in Munich made a third. All three stated completely negative findings. Quite late in the game a German, F. Schorr, tried to make a case for the satellite in a small book, entitled *Der Venusmond,* published in Brunswick in 1875. It was a frantic attempt to stick to guns which were either worn out or spiked. The satellite was too faint to be seen normally. But it had one bright hemisphere; only when that one happened to be properly illuminated and pointed in the right direction could an observer on earth hope for a glimpse of it, and so on. Though feeble in itself, the little book contributed by its very existence to the final clean-up of the mystery. It had once again called attention to an unsolved problem; now the problem should be solved.

In 1887 the Belgian Academy of Sciences in Brussels published a long paper by Paul Stroobant called *Étude sur le Satellite Énigmatique de Vénus.* Only the fact that it was written in French saved it from being labeled an example of Teutonic thoroughness. Stroobant, who ended his paper by quoting every report in its original language, began it by assembling a list of observations by date, observer, place of observation, plus special remarks, if required. He numbered the observations from 1 through 33, the first four being Fontana's, the last one Horrebow's. Stroobant's own suspicion was that faint stars in the general line of sight with Venus had fooled the observers. He began to draw for himself

---

[8] He wrote: *"Votre majesté me fait trop d'honneur de vouloir baptiser en mon nom cette nouvelle Planète; je ne suis ni assez grand pour être au ciel le Satellite de Vénus, ni assez bien portant pour l'être sur la terre, et je me trouve trop bien du peu de place que je tiens dans ce bas monde, pour en ambitionner une au firmament."*

charts of the star distribution around Venus for the dates of the observations.

At that point he stopped. Wasn't Venus a very bright object, so bright
that its radiance would drown out faint stars in the vicinity? He waited
until he could himself observe Venus for this purpose and was pleasantly
surprised to find that he could, with a suitable instrument, see rather
faint stars in the immediate vicinity of the planet. He made his observations in March 1887 and recorded that on the 12th he saw an eighth-
magnitude star 30 minutes of arc from Venus, on the 14th another
eighth-magnitude star 50 minutes from Venus, on the 22nd an eighth-
magnitude star 35 minutes from Venus and a ninth-magnitude 40
minutes from the planet. On the 23rd he could even see an eighth-
magnitude star 6 minutes from Venus. It was evident that observers
could have been fooled by stars, too faint to be seen with the naked
eye, which merely happened to be in the line of sight.

Roedkioer's observations "checked out" especially well. He had been
fooled, in succession, by Chi Orionis, M Tauri, 71 Orionis, and Nu
Geminorum. On one occasion Roedkioer had probably seen the planet
Uranus, then still undiscovered.

James Short's observation could be ascribed to a star slightly smaller
than eighth magnitude. All three observations by Lagrange and all four
by Montaigne could be similarly explained. Meanwhile, Stroobant had
demolished Lambert's orbital calculations (see footnote 7). The very
last observation on Stroobant's list, Horrebow's of January 3, 1768,
could be ascribed to Theta Librae.

After Stroobant's essay was published, only one more observation
was reported and it was by a man who had earlier made a search for
the satellite of Venus and satisfied himself that it did not exist—the
American Edward Emerson Barnard. On August 13, 1892, he recorded
a seventh-magnitude object near Venus. There is no star in the position
recorded by Barnard—and Barnard's eyesight was notoriously excellent.
To this day we don't know what he saw. Was it an asteroid which had
not been charted? Or was it, as J. Ashbrook suggested, a short-lived
nova which nobody else happened to see?

Anyway we now know that Venus does not have a satellite large
enough to be visible from the earth. Whether Venus has one or several
really small satellites, a few feet or a few dozen feet in diameter, is a
different question. If reason by analogy is permissible here, even this
can be doubted, for extensive search of the space near the earth has
failed to disclose such small satellites of our own planet.

11

EARTH AND ITS VICINITY

J OHANNES Kepler, you may remember, rejoiced in Galileo's discovery of the moons of Jupiter, partly because he naturally welcomed a new astronomical discovery and partly because it relieved him of the problem of why the earth, and only the earth, had a satellite. Having learned that the earth's moon was not unique he could dismiss the problem as a mistake caused by incomplete information.

Kepler would no doubt be very much surprised if he could be told that we still consider our moon unique, though not in the way it was thought to be prior to the invention of the telescope.

Our moon is unique chiefly because of its size. It is a large moon, with a diameter of 2163 miles. True, some of the other moons in our solar system are larger. Three of the four Jovian satellites surpass it in size: Io (J-I) has a diameter of 2300 miles; Ganymede (J-III) and Callisto (J-IV) measure 3200 miles each. Saturn's largest moon, Titan, has a diameter of 3550 miles, and Neptune's major moon Triton is about 3000 miles in diameter. But it is not the mere size but the size relative to the planet that matters. Saturn's diameter is more than 21 times that of its largest moon, and Jupiter's diameter is 28 times that of Callisto. But Luna accompanies a planet with a diameter only 3.6 times as large as its own.

One might say—and, of course, it has been said—that we are dealing not with a planet and its satellite, but with the double planet Terra and Luna, a system in which the two components happen to be of rather unequal size. The double-planet nature of the Terra-Luna system can also be expressed in another way. The center of gravity of the system formed by Jupiter and any one of its moons is very close to the center of gravity of the planet itself. But the center of gravity of the earth-moon system, though still inside the body of the earth, is only a thousand miles below the earth's surface, nearly three thousand miles from the center of gravity of the planet. As a result, the center of gravity of the earth is in the earth's orbit only twice a month, at the times when a moon is crossing the earth's orbit. The earth, in orbiting the sun, describes a gently wobbling motion, like an artificial satellite slowly rotating off center.

Luna's orbit is sufficiently eccentric so that the disk appears to be noticeably larger when in perigee [1] and smaller when in apogee.

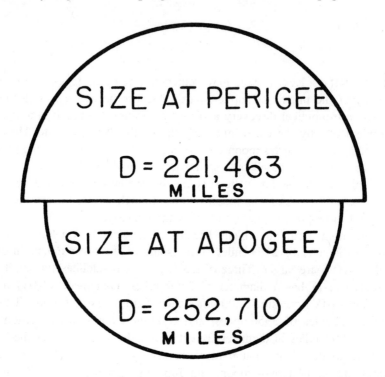

The moon looks noticeably larger when at perigee. This diagram is a tracing of photographs of our moon at perigee and at apogee, taken with the same telescope, same magnification, same location

The center-to-center distance of the two bodies when Luna is at apogee is 252,710 miles and Luna's orbital velocity is then 0.60 miles per second. At perigee the center-to-center distance is 221,463 miles, the surface-to-surface distance is 216,433 miles, and the orbital velocity is 0.69 miles per second. Mean orbital velocity is 0.63 miles per second; mean center-to-center distance 238,857 miles. The plane of the moon's orbit does not coincide with that of the earth's equator, as one should wish for the sake of orderliness and simplicity. In fact, the inclination between the two planes is considerable, being 23 degrees. Pythagoras is credited as being the discoverer of this inclination.

[1] "Perigee" and "apogee" correspond to perhelion and aphelion for a body moving around the earth, the Greek word *gaia* (earth) being substituted for *helios* (sun).

It seems at least very probable that some of the Chaldean compilers of lunar tables noticed this fact before Pythagoras did. But early ideas about the moon are difficult to trace. Many books mention, for example, a Chaldean belief that the moon was a ball light in color on one side and black on the other, as the earliest explanation of the phases of the moon. But none of the books gives a definite source for this "ancient belief." At the time of Pythagoras the true explanation, that the lunar phases are the result of illumination by the sun, was not only known but generally accepted. The moon's continued light in the night sky was the main argument hurled at the Epicurean school against their theory that the sun became extinguished when it set in the ocean.

Plutarch's *The Face in the Moon*, written in about 100 A.D., transmitted two other ancient ideas. "Clearchus says that the face, as we call it, is made up of images of the great ocean mirrored in the moon." The dark spots on the moon, according to this view, were the mirrored image of the earth. But apparently the Greek philosopher cited by Plutarch changed his mind, for only a dozen sentences later, Lamprias, one of the participants in the discussion, said, "Nor will you find Clearchus ready to assume that the moon is a weighty and solid body." Whereupon Lucius, another of the participants, pleaded: "Do give some answer to Clearchus and his assumption that the moon is a mere mixture of air and mild fire, that the air grows dark on its surface, as a ripple courses over a calm sea, and so the appearance of a face is produced." To which Lamprias replied, "It is kind of you, Lucius, to clothe this absurdity in sounding terms. That is not how our comrade dealt with it. He said the truth, that it is a slap in the face to the moon when they fill her with smuts and blacks, addressing her in one breath as Artemis and Athena, and in the very same describing a caked compound of murky air and charcoal fire, with no kindling or light of its own, a nondescript body smoking and charred. . . ." (Quotations are from the translation by A. O. Pickard, London, 1911.)

To us the fact that a heavenly body has darkish spots is not an emotional problem; it merely elicits the question "What are they?" During the Middle Ages it must have been different. Dante devoted most of Canto II of the *Paradise* in his *Divina Comedia* to a diffuse and confusing speech by Beatrice about the spots on the moon, ending with the declaration that the difference in light "comes not from rarity or density" but that the principle of light and dark are as lies in varying goodness. Dante, like Lucius in Plutarch's book, clothed an absurdity in "sounding terms."

The next work to discuss the moon, in chronological order, is Galileo's *Sidereus Nuncius*, and if Dante made you feel as if you were floating in very thin air, being buffeted by swarms of resonant words, Galileo puts your feet firmly on the solid, if somewhat volcanic soil of Tuscany:

> Now those spots which are fairly dark and rather large are plain to everyone and have been seen throughout the ages; these I shall call the "large" or "ancient" spots, distinguishing them from others that are smaller in size but so numerous as to occur all over the lunar surface, and especially the lighter part. The latter spots had never been seen by anyone before me. From observations of these spots repeated many times I have been led to the opinion and conviction that the surface of the moon is not smooth, uniform, and precisely spherical as a great number of philosophers believe it (and the other heavenly bodies) to be, but is uneven, rough, and full of cavities and prominences, being not unlike the face of the earth, relieved by chains of mountains and deep valleys. . . .
>
> Again, not only are the boundaries of shadow and light in the moon seen to be uneven and wavy, but still more astonishingly many bright spots appear within the darkened portion of the moon, completely divided and separated from the illuminated part and at a considerable distance from it. After a time these gradually increase in size and brightness, and an hour or two later they become joined with the rest of the lighted part which has now increased in size. Meanwhile more and more peaks shoot up as if sprouting now here, now there. . . .
>
> (Translation by Stillman Drake.)

Galileo had discovered the "craters" of the moon; he said that "on the moon the variety of elevations and depressions appears to surpass in every way the roughness of the terrestrial surface."

As for the "ancient spots" Galileo stated that: "they are even and uniform, and brighter patches crop up only here and there. Hence, if anyone wished to revive the old Pythagorean opinion that the moon is another earth, its brighter part might very fitly represent the surface of the land and its darker region that of the water. I have never doubted that if our globe were seen from afar when flooded with sunlight, the land regions would appear brighter and the watery regions darker." [2]

Galileo's very reasonable idea that the darkness as well as the smoothness of the "ancient spots" could be explained by water is responsible for their being called *"maria"* (singular *mare,* Latin for "sea"). Though this assumption later turned out to be wrong Galileo interpreted what he saw very well.

He could even go one step further. Luminous spots became visible inside the still dark area some distance away from the terminator. Since Galileo correctly took these luminous spots to be illuminated mountain

---

[2] Stillman Drake's translation at this point contains the following footnote: "Leonardo da Vinci had previously suggested that the dark and light regions of the moon were bodies of land and water, though Galileo probably did not know this. Da Vinci, however, had mistakenly supposed that the water would appear brighter than the land."

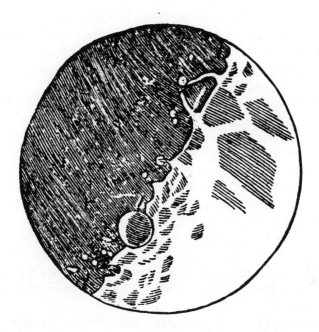

Drawing of the moon by Galileo Galilei. If the light point in the dark area is the crater Tycho (with two of its rays indicated), the round spot must be the *Mare serenitatis.* (To compare this with modern pictures, turn the book upside down. Galeleo's telescope did not invert the image)

peaks he compared their distance from the terminator with the diameter of the moon and from these facts could calculate their height. He found that the height of some of them exceeded 4 miles, a figure well corroborated by later measurements.

Galileo Galilei was satisfied with having made the original discoveries and did not try to draw a chart of the moon. Probably the first lunar map is the one contained in the book *Disputatio physica de phaenomenis in orbe lunae* by Cesare Lagalla, a professor of philosophy in Rome, who published it in Venice in 1612. Although I have not seen it myself, the lunar map probably was of a good size since the book is a quarto volume. The second known map of the moon was made by the Flemish mathematician Michael Florent van Langren who was born in Antwerp in about 1600. He was employed as a mathematician by King Philip IV of Spain and showed his map of the moon to the Infanta Isabella in 1628. The map, which had a diameter of 14 inches and contained 270 topographical features, was printed in 1645 under the name of *Selenographia Langrenia,* but the text to go with it remained unprinted since Langren could not raise the mony to pay the printer. One year later a

map by Francesco Fontana was printed in Naples and in 1649 another
was published by Eustachio Divini. Divini certainly was a versatile man;
a lawyer by profession, he constructed his telescopes himself, made
sketches of his observations, and even engraved the copper plate for
printing the map with his own hands!

That last skill was shared by Johannes Hewelcke (Hevelius), the
astronomer of Danzig who, during daylight hours, was a *Braumeister*
when not occupying his seat on the City Council. Hevelius wrote in 1661
to a personal friend that the copper plates for the astronomical illustrations were not etched, "but I cut all of them by hand which takes more
time and is more difficult too, but you end up with a much cleaner
plate." Unfortunately Hevelius's heirs did not appreciate the work—
though they probably bragged about their ancestor's books—and found
utilitarian uses for the copper plates. The one showing the full moon
was converted into a tea tray, but in that form, it was still preserved in
1900. The copper plate which had this undeserved fate was the main
illustration in Hevelius's *Selenographia,* which had been printed in Danzig in 1647.

The making of lunar maps created a new problem. The topographical
features of the moon obviously had to be named and a system of some
kind had to be established. I do not know what system Lagalla used,
or whether he used place names at all, but van Langren decided that
Biblical names would be most suitable for a mathematician employed
by the King of Spain. Hevelius decided that there was no reason for
Biblical names on the moon. It occurred to him that the lunar formations might be used to honor famous men, specifically philosophers and
scientists. But attaching the names of philosophers and scientists, and
especially *living* philosophers and scientists, to lunar formations might
cause jealousies and controversies. Hence he decided on a safer course,
and used geographical names for these formations. It is because of
Hevelius that we still speak of the Lunar Alps, the Lunar Apennines,
and so forth.

Meanwhile another map of the moon was being drawn in Italy, by
Francesco Maria Grimaldi in Bologna. It was published in Giovanni
Battista Riccioli's *Almagestum novum* in 1651. This book, incidentally,
is the earliest astronomical work to state that there is no water on the
moon. It is also the first in which the names of philosophers and scientists are attached to lunar formations. Nor did Riccioli scatter names
across the lunar landscape in a random fashion, though he indulged in
personal preferences. Since he was an ardent admirer of Tycho, the
largest and most conspicuous crater received this name. A very beautiful

crater some distance away from Tycho was given the name of Copernicus, while Kepler was honored with an equally beautiful but smaller crater near Copernicus. Riccioli gave the name of his student Grimaldi to a small but fine crater. Riccioli must also have thought highly of Plato because this name was given to one of the most conspicuous craters not far from the Lunar Alps. Other craters in this general area all received classical names, such as Pythagoras, Strabo, Aristotle, Timaeus, Eudoxus, Epigenes.

Riccioli's system of names—"due to human vanity," as Rudolf Wolf wrote more than two centuries later—was unanimously accepted and virtually all the names he proposed are still in use. But he had not named by any means all of the features; much room remained for more names and more honors. Naturally enough, most of the names were those of astronomers; Hevelius, who had been reluctant to use the names of people, had a crater named for him. An especially large crater was named after Father Clavius, another after Father Maximilian Hell.[3] Of course Gauss and Newton were honored with lunar craters, as was Maria Mitchell, whilom professor of astronomy at Vassar College. Even a number of people who made no direct contributions to astronomy were so honored, including Mercator, Cavendish, Réamur, Lavoisier, Darwin, Vasco da Gama, Benjamin Franklin, Otto von Guericke, and Kaiser Wilhelm I.

After Riccioli the next attempt to produce a complete chart of the moon was undertaken—as one could easily have predicted—under the direction of the first Cassini. Cassini hired an artist named Patigny who, assisted by the geographer Sébastien Leclerc who was also an experienced artist, made many telescopic drawings of the moon in all its phases. It strikes us as unusual that he was directed to use black and white chalk on blue paper. Cassini then combined all these drawings with his own sketches and measurements into a chart of the moon 12 feet in diameter. It was finished in 1679. An engraver named Mellan was then called in to produce a copper plate of this chart, reduced to a diameter of 20 inches. Cassinin had a dozen or so prints made but for some unknown reason did not publish the chart. The copper plate lay around the Royal printshop in Paris until 1787; then it was finally used and prints were sold to the public.

[3] One night, a few years ago, I was standing on a college campus, looking at the full moon in the company of several Jesuit Fathers. One of them remarked that the full moon was almost the order's honor roll in the sky. I mentioned Clavius; somebody else cited Scheiner; then one of the Fathers grinned at me and said, *"You say it,"* and I said Hell. But Father Hell did not have to worry about this particular connotation; in German his name simply means "bright."

During the years from 1693 to 1698, a gifted German girl named Maria Clara Eimmart, the daughter of an engraver in Nuremberg who had his own private observatory, made more than 350 telescopic drawings of lunar features. She later married Johann Heinrich Müller, a professor of mathematics who willed all the manuscripts of Eimmart père and of Eimmart fille, as well as his own, to a Jesuit college in Russian Poland. The manuscripts comprised 57 folio volumes, all of which unfortunately were destroyed about a century later when the library of the college burned down.

The next forward step was also made in Nuremberg, about half a century after Clara Eimmart's drawings. It was Tobias Mayer's discovery of the libration of the moon. This phenomenon had been noticed before, first by Galileo who observed that formations near the rim— or the "limb," as astronomers say—show more clearly at some times than at others, but had not tried to explain the fact. Tobias Mayer not only noticed the fact but also found the right explanation. His original intention had been to find the lunar equator, and he had picked the crater Manilius for a reference point, measuring its distance from both the eastern and western rim of the lunar disk. Seeing that, if Manilius had moved in one direction, new formations became visible on the opposite limb, he realized that the moon seemed to "wobble" but also recognized this as merely an optical effect, caused by the relative positions of the observer on earth and the moon's rim.

The explanation is the same that applies to the twilight belt of Mercury (see Chapter 9). From earth we can see 59 percent of the lunar surface, or, as it has been put, we see three-sevenths of the lunar surface any time the moon is illuminated by the sun; another three-sevenths— the far side—we never see; and we see one-seventh from time to time.

Tobias Mayer published his discovery in 1750 in a periodical then printed annually for the Cosmographic Society of Nuremberg. Another contribution by Mayer indicates that he was preparing a large chart of the moon; he had strips of a reduced version of this chart engraved on copper. These strips were to be pasted on balls to make globes of the moon; since the strips were to be printed he evidently intended to make a large number of lunar globes, possibly one for every member of the Cosmographic Society. But his early death in 1762, at the age of thirty-nine, prevented him from carrying out his planned work, which was finished by others.

In 1797 the Englishman John Russel published a *Selenographia* in which he stated that he had made the necessary preparations for making a lunar globe. That he produced at least one is proved by an announcement in the Berlin Astronomical Annual for 1811 that "a moon globe by Russel in London, from the estate of Hahn in Remplin" could be bought for the sum of 60 Thalers.

Mayer's map of the moon was finally published in 1881 by Wilhelm Klinkerfues, Gauss's successor at the University of Göttingen, in a memorial volume. The map is 18 inches in diameter and is accompanied by forty detail drawings.

The last extensive work on the moon during the eighteenth century was done by Johann Hieronymus Schroeter in Lilienthal near Bremen. Schroeter devoted the last ten years of that century to very careful drawings of certain portions of the lunar surface. These drawings were published in Göttingen in two volumes in 1802; their title (typical of Schroeter's titles) was *Seleno-topographische Fragmente*. The idea which guided Schroeter was this: If one compared the drawings of a certain lunar feature as made by various observers many years apart, it seemed as if no significant changes had taken place. All the minor changes that could be detected might be explained either by differences in style of drawing, or by different altitudes of the sun over the same formation, or, if the object was near the rim, by differences in libration. But Schroeter could not quite believe that there had been no changes at all; if he had heard the sentence uttered by Simon Newcomb about a century later—"The moon is a world without weather on which nothing ever happens"—he would have been quite incredulous. Under these circumstances the thing to do was to draw with the utmost possible accuracy certain portions which were for some reasons remarkable. Once this had been done and the drawings published, later generations of astronomers, having made their own drawings could then compare them with Schroeter's work and be able to see whether or not changes have taken place.

As we will see, the question of changes on the moon is still one of the topics on which discussion never stops and agreement is never reached, but Schroeter would be pleased to know that his drawings were used by many astronomers for just the purpose he intended.

But the century of detailed studies of the moon was to begin at about the time Schroeter sent his drawings to the printer. The first such study was carried out by Wilhelm Beer and Heinrich von Mädler in Berlin. Six hundred nights of observations, concluded in 1834, produced a chart about 3 feet in diameter, called *Mappa selenographica*. A book to accompany it was issued three years later, in which many details of the chart were carefully explained. Beer and von Mädler prophetically included a short section on the advantages of an observatory on the moon for the investigation of other planets and the fixed stars. They concluded that such an observatory, which to them was of course a wild dream, should be located on the moon's far side so that the astronomers would not be disturbed by the earthlight. Just as Schroeter could not quite convince himself that the moon could be unchanging, Beer and von Mädler could not quite believe that it could be without any atmosphere. But if that were the case the light of the earth, about 60 times as bright as the full moon to us, would cause a sky too bright for astronomical work. Hence the observatory should be in a place over which the earth never rises.

Meanwhile a similar study had been started by the mathematician Wilhelm Gotthelf Lohrmann in Dresden. He published a preliminary report in 1824 (under the title *Topographie der sichtbaren Mondober-fläche,* The Topography of the Visible Portion of the Lunar Surface), but various events prevented him from finishing his work before his death in 1840. His contribution was not forgotten, however, because the astronomer Julius Schmidt, engaged in a similar task, came across his unpublished material. Julius Schmidt finished his own observations in 1874, after thirty-four years, but did not publish them until he had prepared a memorial volume for Lohrmann with all of Lohrmann's drawings. The memorial volume and Schmidt's own work, were both published in 1878, the former in Leipzig and the latter in Berlin.[4]

While Julius Schmidt was getting his work ready for publication in Germany, the English too were busy with works on the moon. Two big and valuable books appeared in London in quick succession. The first, in 1874, was *The Moon: Considered as a Planet, a World, and a Satel-lite* by James Nasmyth, an engineer, and James Carpenter, an astron-omer. The second, in 1876, was *The Moon, and the Condition and Configurations of Its Surface* by Edmund Neison, a Fellow of the Royal Astronomical Society.

Neison's book, 576 pages long, began with a tribute to the work of Beer and Mädler and a statement that he intended it to be an English book of the same type, incorporating the work of the older German book but brought up to date, corrected, and extended. After five chap-ters devoted to the orbit of the moon, the physical conditions of the lunar surface, the lunar formations, lunar history, and variations of the surface, which, together, took up only 130 pages, Neison arrived at his main objective—twenty-two detail maps of the moon, with a careful description of each section.

[4] G. Lohrmann, *Mondcharte in 25 Sectionen,* and Julius Schmidt, *Charte der Gebirge des Mondes.*

Neison's book was a good, competent, and thorough astronomical work, but its immediate predecessor by Nasmyth and Carpenter might almost be characterized as a work of art. It contained twenty-four beautiful large-sized plates, photographs of models of lunar formations, plus many meticulous woodcuts, all of which, as a matter of course, were copied in popular books in diverse languages, usually without stating that the photographs were not telescopic pictures but simply photographs of models. The purpose of Nasmyth and Carpenter was entirely different from that of Neison. As they stated in their preface: "Much valuable labour has been bestowed upon the topography of the moon, and this subject we do not pretend to advance. Enough has also been written for the benefit of those who desire an acquaintance with the intricate movements of the moon in space; and accordingly we pass this subject without notice. But very little has been written respecting the moon's physiography, or the causative phenomena of the features. . . ."

Nasmyth and Carpenter opened up a new phase in selenography, or, better, selenology. Up to their time attention had been directed toward mathematical descriptions of the moon's motions and precise charting of its surface. Nasmyth and Carpenter were the first to try to explain why the lunar surface looks the way it does.

But before I get into explanations, let me bring lunar cartography up to date.

During the nineteenth century a new astronomical tool gradually developed—the photographic plate. Louis Jacques Daguerre himself tried to photograph the moon in 1839, but his plates were not then good enough. If he explained to a visitor that the blur he had obtained was a picture of the moon, the visitor was likely to say, "Oh yes," but without the explanation he would not have known what it was. The first good daguerrotype of the moon was obtained by William Bond in 1850, and seven years later he took the first good photograph of the moon. At the same time a New Yorker, Lewis Rutherford, also started to photograph the moon and not only obtained fine pictures, but also produced stereoscopic pictures of the moon. These pictures, however, exaggerated; if you look at them through a stereoscope you see the moon as a luminous globe floating in black space, an effect that never occurs in reality.

Obtaining good telescopic photographs of the moon presents a number of difficulties because of the moon's relatively fast motion, but these difficulties were overcome many decades ago. The first photographic atlas of the moon was published in 1896 by M. Loewy and P. Puiseux in Paris under the title *Atlas Photographique de la Lune*. It was followed in 1899 by an *Atlas Lunaire* (with 53 plates, published in Brussels) by the same authors. In 1903 Harvard College Observatory published William H. Pickering's *Photographic Atlas of the Moon,* which is superior to more recent works in that it shows each area under five different conditions of illumination.

But it would be a mistake to believe that the photographic plate has replaced the drawn chart completely. W. Goodacre's *Map of the Moon* of 1910 was a drawing, as was H. P. Wilkins's 300-inch map of 1946 and his 100-inch map of 1952. At present (1962) the United States Air Force is preparing a map of the moon which will surpass anything preceding it in size and accuracy. And in 1961 the Pergamon Press published an *Atlas of the Other Side of the Moon,* based on the circum-lunar flight of Russia's Cosmic Rocket No. III. This work is a translation of a Russian book of the same title published by the Academy of Science of the USSR late in 1960. Because the camera in the rocket jammed after only a few exposures, the atlas of the other side of the moon is still quite incomplete, but there will be a complete map not later than 1965, and by 1975 the observatory on the moon that Beer and von Mädler were hopefully writing about in 1837 may be an actuality.

What caused the surface of the moon to look the way it does?

Nasmyth and Carpenter, as is explained in more detail later, credited volcanic activity. But while they were working out their hypothesis with an almost equal mixture of thoroughness and imagination, others were mentioning, occasionally and with some hesitation, that the lunar "craters" seen through a telescope, looked like the impact scars left by cannon balls on armorplate that had refused to shatter or to be breached. Could that mean that the lunar craters were impact craters? If so, what could have impacted? There was only one possible answer: meteorites.

That meteors and meteorites were considered astronomical phenomena at all was due to an odd assortment of scientists. In chronological order they were a collector of fossils, an astronomer, and two physicists; by name, Scheuchzer, Halley, Lichtenberg, and Chladni.

A meteorite, it should be pointed out, is not the same thing as a meteor. The latter term refers to a streak of light (a "shooting star") in the night sky, and the name came about because Aristotle thought meteors were atmospheric, or meteorological, phenomena. The body which caused the streak of light by its passage through the atmosphere, if it reaches the earth, is called a meteorite. The smaller ones usually do not reach the earth, being vaporized in the atmosphere—or, to use a modern term, they are completely ablated.[5]

Of course nobody has ever doubted the existence of meteors. Any one who spent a few hours in the open under a clear sky after nightfall could see them. But until late in the seventeenth century, no one quite knew how to explain meteors. Maybe they were somehow related to lightning, which also was unexplained. More likely, as Aristotle had suggested, they were simply burning vapor high up in the air.

There were also stories about stones that had fallen from the sky, but for many centuries nobody thought of connecting them with meteors. And it cannot be said that the stories of such falling stones were doubted, for people liked to believe in miraculous events. Moreover stones fallen from the sky were mentioned in the Bible. If Joshua 10:11 stated that " . . . as they fled from before Israel and were in the going down to Beth-horon, . . . the Lord cast down great stones from heaven upon them unto Azekah, and they died," then, stones *did* fall from the sky. Learned men could easily add another example: Pliny the Elder had written that in 476 B.C. "a stone the size of a chariot" had been seen to fall in Thrace.

There was also an instance of more recent date which nobody could doubt. On November 16, 1492, just a short time before noon, "a loud crash of thunder and a prolonged noise" was heard in Alsace, and a stone weighing 260 pounds fell into a field near the village of Ensisheim, making a hole 5 feet deep. The stone was taken to the church, but King Maximilian I, who happened to be at Ensisheim, ordered it brought to his castle. He had two pieces broken off, one for Duke Sigismund of Austria and one for himself; then he ordered that the stone should be returned to the church and left undisturbed.

The first man who guessed that there might be a connection between the streaks of light and the falling stones was the Swiss naturalist Johann Jakob Scheuchzer, who is best known as one of the early collectors of fossils. In 1697 Scheuchzer made a public appeal to his contemporaries to pay more attention to natural phenomena and especially to meteors. But nobody showed any interest and the only records from that period of meteors and meteor showers—which can be quite spectacular—can be found in Scheuchzer's own *Natural History of Switzerland.*

Dr. Edmond Halley's contribution to the transfer of meteors from meteorology to astronomy was published in the *Philosophical Transac-*

---

[5] For meteorites still in space, before entering the atmosphere, the term "meteoroid" has been suggested by Fred L. Whipple. Though logical, it has so far failed to find general acceptance.

tions for 1714 under the title "Account of Several Extraordinary Meteors." These meteors had been seen by several observers some distance apart, which enabled Halley to calculate for each of them both the altitude and the velocity. All the figures proved to be so large that Halley had to conclude that the meteors were of cosmic origin. But to his contemporaries Halley's opinion had just as much value as his prediction that a certain comet would return; they could believe it, or else not.

In retrospect the events of the remainder of the eighteenth century look as if Nature herself was building up to a proof. On May 26, 1751, a very bright fireball was seen over southern Germany, moving in an easterly direction. Near Agram in Croatia the fireball exploded and two large pieces of iron, the heavier of which weighed 71 pounds, fell to the ground. There could be no doubt about the facts of the case, but there was still room for interpretation. Andreas Stütz, director of the museum in Vienna, mentioned the case in his book *Bergbaukunde* (Mining Manual, 1790) with strong words: "That the iron had fallen from the sky might have been believed in 1751 even by educated people because of the general lack of knowledge of physics and natural history; but in our time it would be indefensible to consider such fairy tales as faintly probable." But after he had his indignation committed to paper, Stütz made a strange turnabout. He did not wish to call the witnesses liars; they indubitably had described what they thought they had seen and the iron might even have fallen out of the air, but it had not come from heaven; it had formed in the atmosphere, probably as a product of electrical phenomena.

Just at the time when this book became available in the bookshops of Vienna, a hail of stones fell on and around the municipality of Juillac in the Gascogne, France, and the *maire* drew up a *Procès-verbal* about the event. The report was witnessed by three hundred solid and respectable citizens and sent to the Academy in Paris. The members of the Academy did not know what to think, but one of those who found words was the physicist Pierre Bertholon de Saint Lazare. His words, printed in the *Journal des Sciences utiles* (Journal of the Useful Sciences), were: "How sad it is to see a whole municipality trying to verify folk tales by way of a formal protocol. It is pitiful. What could I add to such a protocol? All the necessary remarks will occur to the philosophical reader when he reads this authentic report of an evidently wrong fact, about a phenomenon which is physically impossible."

This was in 1790. In 1792 the French astronomer Joseph Jérôme

Lalande, in an otherwise excellent work of several volumes, devoted a total of six lines to meteors, with the Aristotelian explanation.[6]

But in 1793 Georg Friedrich Lichtenberg, professor of physics at the University of Göttingen, began to wonder. Some twenty years earlier a German physician named Peter Simon Pallas had traveled in Russia and in Siberia for the purpose of learning something about the natural history of those areas. In Siberia, in 1771, he was shown a curiosity that had been found by a wandering Cossack in 1749. It was a large piece of iron which looked pure but was located on top of a mountain that consisted of dark slate. As this was a most unlikely place to find iron in any form or shape, Pallas published a notice about the discovery in a St. Petersburg journal in 1778. Lichtenberg, who saw it and who had heard of the masses of iron at Agram, suggested to a younger associate that he look through the literature for similar events. The younger man, Ernst Friedrich Florens Chladni, started reading his way through a century or two of scientific journals. If he had been merely dutiful at first, he soon became enthusiastic. He had no doubt that stones, and especially iron, did fall from the sky and that they were of cosmic origin.

The quarto volume in which he quoted all the cases he had unearthed and presented his conclusions was printed in Riga in 1794. Its title (misquoted almost invariably) was *Ueber den Ursprung der von Pallas gefundenen und andern ähnlichen Eisenmassen* (On the Origin of the Find of Pallas and Other Similar Iron Masses). Chladni's ideas were wholly "modern." The various kinds of meteorites resemble the composition of our planet and presumably of other planets, too, and are probably fragments of a disintegrated planet. Meteors enter the earth's atmosphere with a high intrinsic velocity which is increased even more by the gravitational pull of the earth. Being subjected to violent friction in our atmosphere they melt on the outside, break apart, and finally fall to the ground.

Chladni's views were translated into other languages, or paraphrased, as in the *Philosophical Magazine* of 1798, but the whole concept was too new. A Frenchman named Patrin wondered whether the whole thing might not be a misunderstanding. Suppose the fireball seen in the sky is just a special form of lightning which looks different from the

[6] *"L'Atmosphère est toujours chargée d'exhalaisons, de vapeurs, de nuages aqueux or de feux électriques; de là naissent une multitude de météores, et surtout ces feux que l'on prend, quelquefois pour des étoiles tombantes, mais que ne sont que des exhalaisons légères, dont la lumière ne dure qu'un instant; quand elles sont près de nous, ce sont des globes de feur qui paraissent étonnants"* (*Astronomie*, 3rd ed., vol. II, p. 555).

more customary form and does not move as fast; but it strikes like lightning and, in striking, melts the ground into the supposed meteorite which, if found soon enough, is still warm. Others wondered whether meteorites might not be the well-known volcanic "bombs" which had been thrown out by distant volcanoes. And while speaking of distant volcanoes, how about the volcanoes on the moon which can be seen through the telescope?

Again Nature stepped in. On April 26, 1803, a hail of stones fell on L'Aigle in the Département de l'Orne. This time the Academy in Paris decided to act; it sent one of its younger members, Jean Baptiste Biot, to L'Aigle to gather firsthand information. Biot's report was thorough and to the point. On that day a fireball had been seen at 1 p.m. at Caën and in L'Aigle and vicinity—"an area 30 hours' journey across," Biot noted. Loud explosions had been heard for five or six minutes, apparently originating from one small cloud in an otherwise clear sky. Immediately afterward, 2000 or 3000 stones, weighing from a quarter-ounce to 18.7 pounds, were seen to fall, the larger ones hot and having a sulfurous smell. The area in which the stones were found was elliptical, its major axis running southeast to northwest and 2½ hours' journey in length, while the minor axis was one hour's journey in length.

Biot's report settled the matter. Stones did fall from the sky.

That they did come from space became clear by elimination. They could not be volcanic "bombs" because they have a different chemical composition, and they could not come from the craters of the moon because nobody had ever seen one of the very numerous lunar craters in eruption.

The first man to turn the argument around, suggesting that the craters on the moon, instead of producing the meteorites that fall on our planet, are themselves caused by meteorites, was Gruithuisen of Munich. He made this suggestion in 1828 but weakened his own case by saying that a number of lunar features might be artificial, old buildings of the "Selenites." Shortly thereafter, the impact theory was advanced by Privy Councillor K. L. Althans, a mining expert, who pointed out the similarity of lunar craters to the "scars" in armorplate produced by the impact of solid shot.[7] In about 1840 Althans began to experiment by throwing musket and grapeshot bullets into semiliquid plaster of Paris. He not only was convinced that most of the formations of the lunar surface were due to meteorite impact, but also believed that meteorite impacts probably had played a considerable role in shaping the earth's surface. His prime example was Bohemia, which seemed to have the right

---

[7] His first publication was in the journal *Gaea,* vol. 27.

shape to be an enormous impact crater. (Amusingly, Galileo, in his *Sidereus Nuncius,* compared a lunar formation to Bohemia.)

From about 1870 to 1890 there was much theorizing on the impact theory, and not only by astronomers, although an astronomer, chronologically speaking, came first. He was Richard Anthony Proctor who, in his book *The Moon* (London, 1873), suggested that at least all the smaller craters of the moon had originated because of meteorite impacts. But Proctor assumed that the moon's surface had to be in a semimolten condition for the process to work. Next after Proctor was the architect A. Meydenbauer, who, reporting on his experiments in the journal *Sirius* (1877 and 1882), said that impact craters would be formed in any loose material like dust or sand, even if the material was cold and hard. Meydenbauer was not consciously contradicting Proctor, because he had not read Proctor's book and had never heard of Althans either.

At the same time a German father-and-son team professionally quite far removed from astronomy—the professor of theology Heinrich W. J. Thiersch and his son, the architect August Thiersch—decided that the volcanic theory advanced by Nasmyth and Carpenter was not satisfactory. The Thiersches worked out an impact theory which embraced not only the smaller craters but *mare* plans, some of which are quite round. Speaking specifically of the *Mare Imbrium,* they wrote: "The impact of a body of considerable dimensions caused a flood wave [of lava] which disrupted the lunar crust over a large area and deposited the rubble around the rim." Because the lunar charts published earlier during the nineteenth century showed many thousands of lunar craters, many thousands of meteorites were needed to make the impact theory work. The Thiersches, *père* and *fils,* had an answer to this possible criticism: "Like Saturn nowadays the earth could have had, possibly to a lesser extent, a ring of tiny satellites. In the course of the eons the largest of these, namely our moon, overcame and swallowed up its smaller companions."

The book, which was first published in 1879 under a pseudonym, but had the full names of both authors in its second edition in 1883, was only a small pamphlet of 42 pages, and it is unlikely that it found any readers outside Germany. But the American geologist G. K. Gilbert ("The Moon's Face," in Bulletin of the Philosophical Society of Washington, 1892) came to remarkably similar conclusions.

Before they are discussed, a quick rundown of the various lunar features to be explained will be helpful. These are, first, Galileo's "ancient spots," the large *mare* plains, uniformly dark in color, very smooth and interrupted only rarely by a single crater or a small mountain. Then there are the mountain chains around the *maria*. Next are the craters, which are circular mountains of all sizes; a diameter of 40 to 60 miles is typical. Very large ones, such as Clavius, are often called "walled plains," mainly to indicate their large size. In about half of all cases the floor inside a crater is smooth; in the other half there is a central mountain in the crater. The proportions of the craters are typical. The inner slope of the ringwall is always much steeper than the outer slope. The floor of the crater is invariably lower than the surface of the moon outside the ringwall. And the central mountain is never higher than the difference between the level of the crater floor and the surrounding surface. Finally, in many cases an astronaut standing in the center of a large crater would not be able to see the ringwall; the ringwall is not very high in proportion to the size of the crater and the horizon is not as far away as on earth because of the smaller size of the lunar globe.

The lower limit of size for craters depends on how good the telescope is: a better instrument invariably shows smaller ones which were not seen before. There are also comparatively tiny markings which appear to be merely round holes; we don't know yet how they would look when seen close by. The same is true for what have been called "domes," small features which almost look like bubbles.

The next lunar feature is one discovered by Schroeter who gave it the German name *Rille,* meaning "groove," with the implication that its walls are perpendicular or nearly so. The English equivalent is "rill." Several hundred rills are known and they are apparently rather deep canyons with nearly vertical walls, usually beginning or ending at a crater. And finally there are the "rays," light streaks which go in perfectly straight lines for enormous distances, crossing craters and rills and sometimes *mare* plains. What rays there are always originate from a crater, radiating out. The crater with the largest system of rays is Tycho. The rays do not seem to have any thickness; even when the sun is very low over the area of a ray, it does not produce a shadow.

These were the features Gilbert set out to explain. The craters he took to be impact craters, their diameters depending on the size of the meteorite that caused them. He explained the central mountain, if there was one, by some kind of reaction of the rock against the impact. The *maria* were caused by very large meteorites which developed enough heat on impact to melt considerable areas. The rills are cracks caused by an impact, while the rays were jets of liquid thrown up by an impact. And again, like the Thiersches, he accounted for the large number of meteorites which have left their traces on the lunar surafce by assuming that the earth originally was surrounded by a ring of matter which condensed to form the moon.

The desire to explain the surface features of the moon had obviously created the necessity of explaining the moon's origin. And that has, to this day, remained the crux of the matter. The visible features of the moon and its origin are tied together. If we could account definitively for one we could explain the other.

The problem of the moon's origin, in turn, is connected with its large size, which makes it the lesser body of a double planet.

At the turn of the century there were three competing theories. One, advanced and defended by the Thiersches and by Gilbert, was that the moon in its present orbit had been formed by the aggregation of matter which had originally formed a ring. The second was that the moon originally had been an independent planet which had described an orbit around the sun and had been "captured" by the earth. The third was that the moon had once been part of the earth.

The originator and chief defender of this last-mentioned theory was Sir George Howard Darwin—Charles Darwin's second son—who, in 1898, published a monumental work with the title *The Tides and Kindred Phenomena in the Solar System*. The theory might be summed up in these words: During the very early period of the earth's existence, when the body of the planet was still red-hot and semiliquid, the earth spun on its axis at a very high rate, about once in four hours. Due to this fast rotation a bulge formed at the earth equator and finally the bulge separated, forming the body we now call the moon. Even the point of separation—or former attachment—can still be seen: it is the enormous basin of the Pacific Ocean. Once the moon was independent, the two bodies acted upon each other by the friction of the enormous tides they caused on each other. The tidal friction had two results: it made the moon slowly drift away from the earth, assuming a larger and larger orbit, and it slowed down the rotation of both bodies. The earth gradually acquired its present 24-hour day, while the smaller moon was "braked" even more, to its current period of about 27 days.

The history of Sir George Darwin's theory can be quickly told. For about a decade it aroused a great deal of interest and even enthusiasm. Then doubts began to stir in the minds not only of astronomers but also of physicists. For another decade the theory received a kind of honorable mention; then it died, as everyone realized that things could not have worked that way.

As regards the theory of capture one can only say that a capture of one planet by another is a most unlikely event. The fundamental difficulty with this theory is that, no matter what assumptions are made, the outcome is always that the two bodies would perturb each other's orbits but would not stay together. Another difficulty is that nobody could say just where the planet Luna, when still independent, moved in space. If we assume that the Bode-Titius rule (see Appendix) reflects a natural law which has not yet been properly formulated, there would simply be no available orbit for such an extra planet. Besides, even if the moon were a captured planet, we would still have the problem of explaining its surface features. And at this point the capture theory is confronted by another major difficulty: did Luna acquire its distinctive surface features before or after capture by the earth?

Which brings us back to the various explanations that have been advanced for the formulation of the moon's surface features. The number of theories is large, but they can be sorted into four categories: the volcanic theory, the tidal theory, the bubble theory, and finally the impact theory.

The book by Nasmyth and Carpenter, which tried to make volcanism and volcanic action responsible for everything we can see on the moon, may be considered the main expression of that school of thought, though they were not the first to say that the "craters" of the moon were volcanic craters. They had many distinguished predecessors, including the astronomers Schroeter and von Mädler. Among nonastronomers who held the same belief, the most distinguished names are those of Alexander von Humboldt, the famous scientist and explorer, and Alexander von Buch, one of the founders of the science of geology. The renowned American geologist James Dwight Dana also had held that opinion, and soon after Nasmyth and Carpenter the great Austrian geologist Eduard Suess came to the same conclusion.

Nasmyth and Carpenter took what was by then the classical position as to the formation of the moon itself: it had originated by the condensation of cosmic dust and gases, just like the planets and other moons. Nothing was said about the problem of whether it had once been in an independent orbit around the sun or whether it had, even in its unformed condition, orbited around the equally unformed earth. But the moon had, at some time, acquired the shape of a ball of molten rock, slowly cooling at the surface. Then volcanic activity had begun. In our terrestrial volcanoes the eruptive material slowly builds up the mountain itself, forming the very typical volcanic cones which everyone has seen, if not in reality, then in pictures of Mount Fuji, Mount Etna, and Vesuvius. Some of the lunar mountains, Nasmyth and Carpenter said, indubitably were such cones of hardened lava and cinders. But the larger (and best-known) craters, such as Copernicus, certainly were not cones. One geologist had suggested that they might be "basal

wrecks" such as we have on earth, A basal wreck is the remnant of
a former volcano which, after a very long period of inactivity, becomes
active again, but which cannot discharge the lava through the thoroughly solidified agglomerate of the former activity. The pressure builds
up to such a point that an enormous explosion blows the whole top off
the mountain, leaving a roughly circular rampart that geologists call
the basal wreck. On earth, the basal wreck usually fills with water to
form a round lake.

Nasmyth and Carpenter could not accept the thought that the lunar
craters were all basal wrecks. They pointed out that we have many
volcanoes on earth, active and otherwise, all of which are cone-shaped,
and that there are only a few basal wrecks. On the moon no unwrecked
large volcanoes are visible, so this evidently was not the explanation.
They assumed a different kind of volcanic action. The lunar volcanoes,
aided by the lesser gravity of the moon, might expel their material in
a fountain-like manner so that the ejected matter would form a ring-
shaped wall. Of course a fair amount of the material would fall straight
back, but it would be blown out again. If such action stopped at one
point, we should see a ringwall around a deep, funnel-shaped hole. As
this is not what we see, an additional process had to be assumed. After
the more violent phase of the eruption which produced the ringwall,
lava might simply well up through the vent hole and produce a smooth
crater floor. Nasmyth and Carpenter thought that this point was proved
by one specific lunar crater named Wargentin, located near the rim of
the visible hemisphere. About 43 miles in diameter, Wargentin would
look like a normal crater if it were not brimful of some material,
making the crater floor higher than the surface outside the wall. Here,
Nasmyth and Carpenter said, we have a case where the lava welled
up in sufficient quantities to fill the crater to the top; there may even
have been an overflow.

In a good many cases, volcanic activity resumed after a lava flow
had smoothed out the floor, but it was a reduced activity which only
built up a cinder cone at or near the center of the crater. Of course
several new vents might form, resulting in several peaks inside the large
crater.

The volcanic action proposed by Nasmyth and Carpenter to build
up a ringwall by a fountain-like action is sheer fantasy. No volcano on
earth has ever done anything like that. The difference in gravity between earth and moon might account for a difference in size of the
same feature but would not produce an entirely different effect. Moreover, the subsequent events, while not unreasonable, would agree with

reality only by sheer accident. It is easy to imagine lava welling up through a vent hole, but why—except in the unique case of Wargentin—would the level of the lava always stop below the level outside the crater wall? It is also easy and reasonable to imagine that resumed volcanic activity would produce a cinder cone. But why did this cinder cone never even grow as high as the crater wall? If the central mountains had formed in that manner one could expect them to be of almost any height—sometimes not reaching the level of the crater wall, sometimes reaching this level, and in a number of cases surpassing it. But none even reaches the height of the wall.

As for the rills and the rays, Nasmyth and Carpenter believed that both are the same type of formation. The rills supposedly originated as cracks in the skin of the moon. In some cases, presumably applying to the older cracks, lava welled up from the interior and overflowed the edges of the crack for considerable distances. The lack of any shadow from a ray was explained by saying that, if the thickness of the shiny lava which looks to us like a ray were less than 20 feet, the shadow would be too small to be visible from earth.

Nasmyth and Carpenter did not try to explain the *mare* plains. The geologist Eduard Suess did,[8] writing: "The temperature of the large mass [meaning the moon as a whole] is by no means completely uniform. In some area it rises, melts down the cover of slag once more, and from there the remelting proceeds in all directions, for hundreds of kilometers. The shape of the molten mass is a section of a sphere, its projection a circle. Finally the process slows down, the temperature of the surface around the rim is lower, the slag is no longer melted down but is pushed outward like a moraine. Then it is all over. What is left is a large plain, circular in shape and surrounded by a wall of slag . . . such as the enormous one which under the name of Apennines, Alps, etc., surrounds the Mare Imbrium."

While the process of melting is understandable it makes no sense that near the end of the process, when the surplus heat has been radiated into space, there should still be enough expansion to pile up unmelted slag into mountainous heaps.

As can easily be seen the volcanic hypotheses make interesting reading but cannot account for the final shapes which we see on the surface of the moon. A German physicist, H. Ebert, therefore concluded that volcanism was not sufficient by itself and an additional force was needed to explain the lunar craters. There was an obvious and powerful force

---

[8] *"Einige Bemerkungen über den Mond"* ("A Few Remarks About the Moon") in the *Sitzungsberichte* (Proceedings) of the Academy of Sciences of Vienna, Vol. 104, 1895.

available: the gravitational pull of the earth, acting as a tide-raising force. His explanation [9] was assisted by an interesting experiment. Ebert's apparatus consisted of an open bowl filled with the alloy known as Wood's Metal, which has a melting point of about 155° F. At the surface of the bowl the metal solidified; at the bottom it was kept molten by an impinging steam jet. The level of the metal could be varied by means of a hand pump which substituted for the earth's tide-raising forces. A small amount of liquid metal was forced through a small hole in the solid metal and then drawn back again. By repeating this process a few dozen times Ebert could produce very nice models of lunar craters.

The question is whether the tide-raising forces would actually work in this manner, since they would act on the lunar surface as a whole and not just on liquid magma which may or may not exist below the solid crust.

The third theory, the bubble theory, can be dismissed without much elaboration. A lunar crater may bear some superficial resemblance to a burst bubble of molten rock, but the size of the ringwalls argues against it. Bubbles several feet in diameter have occasionally been seen in boiling lava. Under the lesser gravity of the moon they might have been several yards in diameter, but there is no material which could form a bubble forty miles across.

Articles about the surface features of the moon, written by competent authors during the period from, say, 1895 to 1905, reflect a curious quandary. The writers usually explained the volcanic hypothesis at great length, but admitted that it required the assumption that lunar volcanism differed in some way from terrestrial volcanism. Near the end of the article, they would then mention that some experts thought that the lunar craters might be impact craters. But here, the author would say, we are faced with another difficulty. If the lunar craters are impact craters, why don't we have impact craters on earth?

Early proponents of the impact theory, such as the Thiersches and Gilbert, had pointed to weather as the answer to that difficulty. On earth rain and snow and vegetation would erase such a formation very quickly, they had said.

By about 1906 an interesting, though disbelieved, piece of news began to circulate, to the effect that we do have an impact crater on earth. It was, unfortunately, located in an inaccessible area, somewhere in Arizona, near something called the Canyon Diablo.

The news referred to Arizona's Meteor Crater, which is now pointed

[9] Published in *Annalen der Physik und Chemie*, N. F. vol. 41, 1890.

out to passengers by the stewardesses on transcontinental flights. Like all interesting landmarks it has a story all its own. When you approach Meteor Crater on the ground it looks just like one more mesa. To see how different it is from the surrounding formations, you have to climb the wall and look down into the mile-wide hole.

Its discoverer is not known. Of course it was familiar to the Indians living in that area; the Hopi tribe went there to gather up finely ground white silica which was used in their religious ceremonies. But the alleged Indian legend of the fire god who came from heaven to find a resting place in the ground sounds spurious. Of the many authors who have told it, not a single one has been able to present anything that might be considered verification; in all probability the story is somebody's invention. By the 1870s the crater had acquired a name (Coon Butte) and during the next twenty years occasional finds of meteoric iron, believed to be silver by optimistic prospectors, were mailed to various assayers who, of course, quickly found that the samples were just iron, though with traces of silver and gold. In 1891 Dr. Grove Karl Gilbert of the U. S. Geological Survey and his party arrived at the crater. Although Gilbert considered the lunar craters impact craters, he stated officially that Coon Butte must be the result of a steam explosion. He recognized the pieces of iron which were found in the vicinity as meteoric iron but considered their presence in the same spot a coincidence.

The presence of sizeable amounts of metallic iron, however, was of interest to industry. One General Williamson, of the now defunct Atlantic and Pacific Railroad Company in Chicago, consulted an expert, Dr. A. E. Foote of Philadelphia. Dr. Foote traveled to Coon Butte, was very much impressed by its appearance, and declared that the iron was meteoritic but that the quantity had been greatly exaggerated. He took samples with him back to Philadelphia and finally wrote a paper entitled "A New Locality for Meteoric Iron with a Preliminary Notice of the Discovery of Diamonds in the Iron." Still no suggestion of the possibility that the whole crater might be due to the impact of the meteorite. But by way of General Williamson and Dr. Foote knowledge of the crater had reached Philadelphia, and Philadelphia was the home of the mining engineer and geologist Daniel Moreau Barringer. He was the man who began the study—one might even say originated the concept—of impact craters on earth.

By 1902 Barringer was convinced of two facts. One was that the crater had been formed by the impact of an enormous meteorite or possibly a cluster of large meteorites. The other was that the main mass of this cluster was buried under the crater floor. Legal preliminaries over, he began test drillings. Between 1903 and 1909 not less than twenty-eight drill holes (plus a few shafts) had been sunk. The scientific results were excellent: the meteorite had smashed through a layer of red sandstone, pulverized the underlying Kaibab limestone and the white Coconino sandstone below. The crater was found to have been partly filled with water at one time. But while the scientific results were good, the commercial results were not; the main mass Barringer was looking for had not been found.

In 1910 he noticed that rifle bullets fired into thick mud always made a round hole, even when fired at an angle. Maybe the meteorite had not come down nearly vertically as had always been assumed. Things he already knew suddenly acquired a new meaning: the east, west, and north rims of the crater looked as if shattered material had been piled up by a force originating in the center of the crater. But the south rim looked as if the rock strata had simply been lifted. This made it probable that the meteorite had struck at an angle, traveling nearly due south. The main mass had to be sought under the south rim, *not* under the crater floor. A drill hole sunk, after a long delay, into the center of the south rim in 1919 found smooth going for the first 1000 feet. Since the vertical distance from the top of the rim, where the hole was started, to the crater floor is 570 feet, this means that there were no obstacles for about 500 feet below the level of the crater floor. Then things became difficult: one day the total progress of the drill, after three hours of continuous operation, was just one foot. Then the drill bit stuck, and since it was impossible to free it the hole had to be abandoned. The depth of the hole, measured from the rim, was 1376 feet.

After Barringer's death in the fall of 1929, several other surveys were made by various institutions, most of them indicating a suspicious concentration of heavy material under the southwest rim, slightly more than 600 feet down, as measured from the crater floor.

The amount of literature published about Barringer's crater is large; a collection would probably fill two books the size of this one. The main point of dispute is the size of the original meteorite. In 1918 Dean William F. Magie of Princeton University estimated its mass as 10 million tons. In 1951 a survey sponsored by Princeton concluded that the buried mass had to be the equivalent of a metal sphere 240 feet in diameter with a weight of 1.7 million tons if buried 600 feet below the crater floor (or bigger if buried at a greater depth). But in 1958 Dr. John S. Rinehart of the Colorado School of Mines, utilizing data from modern high-speed ballistics, calculated that the meteorite was a body approximately 50 feet in diameter, weighing 12,000 tons and striking with an impact velocity of 50,000 feet per second.

Nobody can tell yet which estimate is correct and it would be advisable not to make additional guesses until the buried mass that was touched by Barringer's last drill hole has been more completely investigated.

In 1921 there appeared in Germany a small book by an already famous geologist, Dr. Alfred Wegener, the originator of the theory of continental drift. The title of the book was *Die Entstehung der Mondkrater* (The Origin of the Lunar Craters). Dr. Wegener's conclusion was the same that Gilbert reached—that the moon is the final product of the consolidation of a former ring of particles around the earth. The new thought brought into the debate by Wegener was the following: when dealing with physical events one has to make a strict distinction between molecular forces, such as the tensile strength of a material, and mass forces, such as gravity. If the event is on a small scale, say, the bending of a beam under a load, one deals with molecular forces only, but when a large-scale event, like the impact of a very large meteorite, is under scrutiny, the role of the molecular forces all but disappears and one deals with mass forces only. Hence, in the case of a meteorite impact with an impact velocity of, say, 50,000 feet per second and with a meteoric mass of more than, say, 1000 tons, there would be no noticeable difference whether these 1000 tons were marble, granite, basalt, or iron.

Wegener was trying to find a way of imitating the process of crater formation and since this meant substituting a small-scale event for a large-scale event he concluded that he had to use a material without tensile strength. He decided in favor of cement dust, mainly because the resulting shapes could then be easily fixed by means of spraying them with water. His surface was a layer of cement dust, not quite an inch thick, the "meteorite" a soup spoon full of the same material, dropped from a height of about a yard. His very first experiment was a success. He obtained a crater somewhat intermediate in proportions between Meteor Crater and lunar craters—Meteor Crater, it must be remarked, would be unusually deep for a lunar crater. After repeating the experiment a few times he decided to find an answer to the question "What happens to the meteorite?" In order to answer this he used plaster of Paris for the "meteorite" and saw, to his surprise, that he had a white crater. Careful cross sectioning after the crater hardened explained the puzzle: the meteoritic material covered the floor of the crater very thinly, was piled up around the inside of the ringwall (which was cement dust that had been pushed out radially from the center), while a number of splashes of the plaster of Paris fell down outside the crater wall. Except for the possible buried mass under the south rim of Meteor Crater this experiment agreed nicely with the actual findings at Meteor Crater. Wegener concluded, however, that there could be no "main mass," that the meteorite would be completely shattered.

By 1922 the situation, then, was this: the impact hypothesis could not explain all the surface features of the moon, but it explained the crater formation much better than any other theory did. It could even explain the rays, or, at least, it could make a good try. Impacts in the laboratory did produce rays on occasion; the fact that only a minority of the lunar craters showed rays could be ascribed to the nature of the meteorite. The dust from an impact of a stony meteorite would be invisible to us, while the metal droplets resulting from the impact of an iron meteorite could produce rays. Even Wargentin might be explained by two impacts in the same area, an earlier impact which produced the crater and a later impact which broke through the crater's floor and permitted magma to well up.

And to back up all the reasoning there was an impact crater in Arizona.

In 1923 another impact crater was recognized as one—or rather as two—located near Odessa, Texas. They seemed to be much older than the Arizona crater and without the pioneer work by Barringer in Arizona they never would have been recognized for what they were. During the same year the news came that still another impact crater had been found in Dalgaranga, Australia, and that the impact area of a gigantic meteorite which had been seen to fall in Siberia in 1908 had been located. And in 1927 an Estonian mining expert named Ivan Reinwaldt proved that a round lake on the island of Oesel (in Estonian Saremaa) in the Baltic was also an impact crater. In 1931 a field of thirteen craters of different sizes was discovered near Henbury, Australia, the biggest one having an elliptical shape.[10] One year later two holes in the Arabian desert also were identified as impact craters. Evidently impact craters were not too rare on earth either, in spite of our everchanging weather. But it is true that the majority of those identified have been found in arid areas with little precipitation.

---

[10] Lunar craters located some distance from the center of the visible hemisphere appear to be elliptical as a result of perspective; only a very few actually are elliptical. It is believed that elliptical craters result when two meteorites strike simultaneously a short distance apart.

Once things had progressed to that point, the next question was whether there might be something like a "fossil" impact crater. If our earth had been struck in the recent past by very large meteorites— the one that caused the Arizona crater was actually a small asteroid —it was logical to assume that the same thing had happened in the further geological past. And just as the Arizona crater was known before it was recognized as an impact crater, a "fossil" impact site also proved to have already been investigated.

The place, which was in southern Germany, was known as the Steinhein Basin, a mysterious circular site in Jurassic limestone about 1½ miles across. The investigators were two eminent German geologists and paleontologists, Drs. W. Branca and E. Fraas. The fact that this structure was in Jurassic sediments proved only that it was more recent than the Jurassic Period. But neither Fraas nor Branca could think of any geological event that could have resulted in such a formation. As there was no evidence of volcanism the Steinhein Basin could not be explained that way, and so Branca and Fraas referred to it as *ein kryptovulkanisches Gebilde,* a cryptovolcanic structure. Their report appeared in the 1905 volume of the *Proceedings* of the Academy of Sciences in Berlin, on page 1—a position which may have been a mere accident of date but in retrospect seems very appropriate. Interestingly enough, a very similar cryptovolcanic basin, but 15 miles in diameter, called the Rieskessel, is not far from the Steinheim Basin. Since it is of the same age, one can assume that both were made by the same meteoric mass which split apart when entering the earth's atmosphere. (Other examples of such splitting are mentioned later.)

The relative abundance of impact craters, from fairly recent to very old, on the surface of the earth combines with theoretical reasoning to make it virtually certain that all the typical ring-walled craters of the moon are impact craters. The circular *maria,* especially Mare Crisium and Mare Imbrium, must also have originated by way of collision; Dr. Harold C. Urey has estimated that the Mare Imbrium collision took place about 4500 million years ago. But just why the *maria* look the way they do is a riddle which will not be solved until physical exploration of the moon gets under way. The customary explanation of the *maria* as enormous lava flows, now frozen, works fine in some respects but is highly unlikely in some others. Likewise, the interesting conjecture of Thomas Gold that the *maria* are enormous dust bowls would explain their appearance, but it is hard to see why the dust should have collected in some areas only. The origin of the dust itself is no problem. The steady stream of meteoric impacts of small and tiny size would pulverize the surface rocks sufficiently to account for the dust, especially since this mechanical process is assisted by the more subtle process of the impact of protons from the sun.

To avoid misunderstandings, it should be said that all astronomers are in agreement that there is a considerable amount of dust on the moon; the unsolved problem is merely whether the dust accounts for the appearance of the *maria*.

The numerous cracks may all have the same explanation, namely, the cracking of a solidified surface because of expansion of the moon's interior. If we assume that the moon has its share of long-lived naturally radioactive elements, the heat produced by the decay of the heavy nuclei may have caused an expansion which cracked the surface. And since all radioactive decay leads to the formation of gases (the so-called noble gases, helium, neon, argon, krypton, and xenon), the moon is now generally recognized to have a very thin "atmosphere" consisting of such gases. Lunar gravity is too weak to hold the helium produced; it is also too weak to hold the neon, but if the production rate of neon is great enough some may be present.

In addition to the heavier noble gases the moon is likely to have some carbon-dioxide and sulfur-dioxide molecules in its tenuous atmosphere. H. Percy Wilkins of the Lunar Section of the British Astronomical Association, in his book *Our Moon* (London, Frederick Muller, 1954), points out that on a number of occasions some familiar detail in the interior of a well-known crater could *not* be seen. Since, as Wilkins put it, "craters do not come and go," the lack of visibility must be ascribed to an optical obstruction, a haze of some kind. And that haze has to come from somewhere.

One example of such a temporary obscuration that has been proved (by Dinsmore Alter, in photographs taken October 26, 1956) is the crater Alphonsus, not far from the center of the moon's visible hemisphere And just in the central peak of Alphonsus the Russian astronomer Nikolai A. Kozyrev (of the Crimean Astrophysical Observatory) saw what he called a "volcanic eruption."

Visual inspection carried out afterward did not reveal any change in the formation; on the other hand there is no doubt that Kozyrev obtained a spectrogram of gases containing carbon during the night of November 3–4, 1958. The instrument was aimed at the central peak of Alphonsus, and while the spectrograms were being taken, Kozyrev observed the area through the finder telescope. He noted that the peak looked brighter than usual. He repeated the procedure during the following night but found no deviation from normal.

Because no change could be detected afterward, the "eruption" observed by Kozyrev probably does not quite deserve that name. It seems to have been only a sudden outbreak of gases which carried lunar dust up with them. This dust, illuminated by the sun, could well account for the increase in brightness observed visually.

That the moon is completely dead is a concept which is no longer tenable. But just how much natural activity is left, and of what kind, can probably be learned only by direct investigation. At the moment the fitting conclusion for an account of the moon is the one written by Dr. Harold C. Urey in *Endeavour* (April 1960):

"The Moon has been an object for astronomical study for centuries. We are now entering a period when physical and chemical studies will supplement the astronomical ones. Certainly the petrologists will have a field day if at some time samples of the moon can be secured. However, if the story of the moon as presented here is correct, the usual processes of geology—the mountain uplift, volcanology, erosion, sedimentation, and formation of the fossil record—will have little application to selenology."

We are going to explore a *different* world.

To return to meteorites in relation to the earth, one of the most natural questions is about the largest meteorite known to science. In the order of diminishing reported size, we first have an unverified story from former French West Africa. Not far from a place named Chinguetti in the Adrar Desert, a perfectly enormous meteorite is reported to be buried in the sand. The visible portion is said to be 330 feet in length and the height about 65 feet. A fragment picked up by a traveler was taken to Paris and was found to be meteoritic. But, as Fletcher G. Watson says, the main body "upon inspection . . . will probably prove to be much smaller than the reported dimensions." It is even possible that the fragment was a true meteorite but that the main body is just an unusual rock formation. The reason for all this skepticism is that it is hard to see how a meteorite of such dimensions could have landed without shattering, even if it fell on desert sand.

The largest definitely established meteorite is known as Hoba West. It is still *in situ* in the limestone near Grootfontein, Southwest Africa, where it fell. It is an iron meteorite of approximately rectangular shape and its weight has been estimated as between 60 and 70 tons. The next largest meteorite known, and the largest on exhibit anywhere, is the famous Ahnighito ("the tent"), found at Cape York, Greenland. Together with the two other much smaller ones (called "the woman" and "the dog" by the Eskimos), it was brought to New York in 1897 by the arctic explorer Commander Robert Edwin Peary. A fourth Cape York meteorite, about the same size as "the woman," is in Copenhagen. The four presumably entered the atmosphere as one body and broke apart when aerodynamic heating began. But it is very strange that Ahnighito did not shatter further on impact. The explanation which has been evolved is that Ahnighito fell at a slant that happened to match the gentle slope at Cape York. Moreover, that slope, at the time of the fall, may have been deeply covered with snow.

Apparently there was no means of weighing Ahnighito when it was brought to the United States; hence literature was full of guesses about its weight, guesses ranging from 25 to 59 tons. The guessing stopped on February 14, 1956, when Ahnighito was put on a specially constructed scale and weighed in at 68,085 pounds or slightly over 34 tons. The other two had been weighed earlier; the "woman" was found to weigh 2500 pounds, and the "dog" 1000 pounds.

Another famous large meteorite, like Ahnighito, on exhibit at the Hayden Planetarium in New York, is the Willamette meteorite, discovered in 1902 not far from the Willamette river in Oregon. It weighs 14 tons in spite of very large cavities on one of its surfaces; it is an undecided question whether these cavities existed in the body as it entered the atmosphere or whether they are the result of later erosion.

On large meteorites that have fallen in Mexico, Fletcher G. Watson writes:

"Seven meteorites weighing a ton or more have been found in the uplands of Northern Mexico; at least one of the masses was known to the conquistadores. The largest of these bodies, Bacubirito, having an estimated mass of 24 tons, lies where it was unearthed in the state of Sinaloa. At Chupaderos in Chihuahua two masses of 14 and 6.5 tons lay 100 meters apart. Their surface features dovetail and indicate that they originally formed a single body. The fourth of these giant meteorites is Morito (El Morito), a beautiful conical mass of 20 tons. The Chupaderos masses and Morito are on display in Mexico City." (*Between the Planets*, rev. ed., 1956.)

Another example of such splitting is mentioned in a short notice by M. P. Hiller published in the German journal *Kosmos,* 1908, p. 87. The following is a translation of this note which is the only known source for this particular case: "The District Supervisor of Adjibarang on Java had told me repeatedly about *Pelabuhan Bulan,* i.e., the 'port of the moon,' until I decided to pay a visit to the place. I found a large elliptical hole with vertical walls, about 100 feet long, 65 feet wide and 53 feet deep. On the floor of this hole a large Waringia, one of Java's most beautiful trees, was growing, its crown just topping the rim and filling the full width of the hole. Some 1300-1500 feet eastward of this place I was shown a smaller hole, measuring about 55 by 30 by 30 feet, also with vertical walls. The older inhabitants of the nearest village told me that a very long time ago (none of them had experienced it) the moon had fallen from the sky one evening and not far above the surface had split into two pieces which had caused the holes shown to me. It seems very probable to me that a large meteorite fell in this place, splitting into two shortly before impact. . . . Unfortunately this interesting place has not been investigated by geologists. If my assumption is correct this was perhaps the largest meteorite seen [to fall] in historic times."

Early in this century two most extraordinary events in the field of meteoritics took place. One was a disastrous impact which would have been a major catastrophe if it had not taken place in Central Siberia. And the other was a celestial spectacle which was never forgotten by those who saw it.

The first is known as the Great Siberian Meteor of 1908, or as the Podkamennaya Tunguska fall. The name, of course, is geographical. In central Siberia three rivers, all named Tunguska, come from the east to join the northward-flowing Yenisei which empties into the Arctic Ocean. The northernmost of the three Tunguska rivers is called the Nishnaya, or Lower, Tunguska; the southernmost is the Verkhnaya, or Upper Tunguska; but the one in the middle is called the Podkamennaya, or Stony, Tunguska.

The meteor was seen over an area of thousands of square miles and witnesses hundreds of miles distant from one another agreed that the time was just a few minutes after 7 A.M. on June 30, 1908. A fiery body, "looking like a piece broken off the sun," came up over the southern horizon and moved rapidly northward, almost following a meridian. Then, according to one witness, "the ground suddenly rose and fell again, like a single wave in the sea, but nothing near me was destroyed." Another eye-witness spoke of an enormous pillar of fire, followed by a gigantic black cloud. Next day meteorologists noticed a silvery cloud at a very high altitude, somewhat resembling the clouds which had formed after the explosion of the volcano Rakata on Krakatoa. But the Krakatoa catastrophe had been accompanied by wild oscillations of seismographs the world over; this time the seismographs in western Europe had remained quiet. However, the barographs had recorded a sudden pressure wave in the atmosphere. Putting these facts together a German meteorologist went on record that the silvery high cloud pointed to a cosmic cause "for the recent disturbance in the atmosphere."

Strangely enough the Russian government did nothing. Some seismographs in Russia had quivered for a few minutes. It probably was decided that there had been an earthquake somewhere in central Siberia. But there is nothing one can do about an earthquake; fortunately it had happened in a sparsely settled area.

Scientists did not become involved until after the first World War and the Russian revolution, and then only through a coincidence that no self-respecting novelist would permit himself to use as a story device. Local newspapers in Siberia had printed eye-witness accounts of the event during the first week of July 1908. Nobody paid any attention to their reports except a publisher of calendars. His calendars had detachable leaves and he provided his customers with some entertainment by printing interesting newspaper stories on the backs. He had reprinted an account of the big meteorite and, during the winter of 1920–21, a Russian astronomer found this leaf of the calendar in a book in the library. Probably somebody, years earlier, had used the sheet as a book mark.

Professor L. A. Kulik of the Russian Academy of Science, once alerted, found some more material. The newspapers, at the time, had been unanimous in saying that the event had occurred near Kansk, but A. V. Voznesensky of the Irkutsk Observatory felt certain that the center of the catastrophe had been near the sources—there are two— of the Podkamennaya Tunguska river. Kulik's first expedition of 1921 mainly proved that the area near Kansk had not been the site of the impact. The sources of the Podkamennaya Tunguska could not be reached, as the expedition was not equipped to traverse such virtually roadless territory, and thus far Kulik had only the opinion of one man that this actually was the place to look. But after more verbal reports had been collected by two other Russian scientists Kulik was convinced that the meteorite must have fallen in that area, and in 1927 he set out on a reconnoitering expedition.

Kulik later [11] reported:

The whole region of the river basins Kimchu and Khushmo [these are tributaries of the Podkamennaya Tunguska] is covered with windfallen trees lying fanwise in a circle, their tops pointing outward . . . the trees are uprooted, broken and all of them without top parts. . . . The peat marshes of this region are deformed and the whole place bears evidence of an immense catastrophe. The windfallen trees begin at a certain distance from the center, and between them and the latter there stands a dead forest, its trees devoid of their tops. The whole central region bears traces of a burn. These traces, gradually growing weaker, are evident even farther from the center for a

[11] In *Comptes Rendus (Doklady) de l'Académie des Sciences de l'URSS*, vol. XXII, no. 8, 1939.

distance of 15 or 20 kilometers (ca. 9–12 miles). More marked are the burns on the side of the trees facing the center; the tops of the standing trees or what remains of them are in each case burned, and finally all the trees and bushes show burns at the place where they are broken. The burning of the taiga [scrub vegetation] over an area with a radius of 15 or 20 kilometers explains the fact that the flames were visible in the day time ("a pillar of fire") 400 kilometers away, at Kirensk.

Kulik and other Russian researchers extracted from the Tungus natives the reluctant admission that two of their villages had disappeared. Naturally superstitions had developed and guides were hard to find.

In the area where the impact must have taken place several dozen "hollows" were counted; all of them had filled up with water in the meantime. But since no main crater could be found, Kulik came to the conclusion that it was not a single body which had struck, but a "cloud" of meteorites. However, none of the expeditions found a single meteoritic particle. Kulik's original idea of a cluster of iron meteorites had to be abandoned, and much speculation followed. A writer named Aleksandr Kazantsev advanced the idea that the impact had been made by a nuclear-powered spaceship from another planet which exploded while attempting to land. Serious Russian scientists were quick to ridicule Kazantsev but were at a loss for a while to account for the facts which consisted of all the evidence of a major recent meteorite impact without any traces of meteoric material.

One remote possibility was that this had been a natural nuclear explosion. One had to assume that the meteorite consisted of contraterrene matter, or anti-matter, i.e., matter in which the nucleus of the atoms consists of negatively charged protons (instead of the positively charged protons of normal matter) surrounded by shells of positrons, instead of electrons. A contraterrene meteorite would, of course, begin reacting with our atmosphere, in a mutual particle-for-particle annihilation. The great brilliance of the body while still in flight spoke in favor of this assumption. Contact with the ground would destroy the contraterrene meteorite to the last atom, destroying an equivalent amount of terrestrial matter in the process, and the energy liberated would correspond to that of a large hydrogen bomb. Of course the site would be quite radioactive at first, but nearly two decades had gone by between impact and Kulik's reconnoitering expedition. Besides Kulik was not looking for lingering traces of radioactivity and did not carry the necessary instruments.

The other possibility was that the large meteorite which struck there consisted of material which would completely evaporate, say, frozen ammonia or just ice. The assumption that the entering body consisted of frozen gases would explain the observed physical effects, which are the result of the kinetic energy of the impact body, and also explain the absence of meteoric material. Finally, this assumption would pin a label on the entering body: it would have been a comet. The Russians, in 1961, concluded that it had been a small comet.

This explanation would make the impact of 1908 an entirely different matter from that of 1947, which also struck Siberia.

The impact area this time was several hundred miles north of Vladivostok in the Sikhote Alin mountains. The date was February 12, 1947, the time 10:38 in the morning. The last phase of the penetration of the atmosphere was observed by many eye-witnesses. The fireball was so bright that it produced moving shadows in full daylight, and it left a dusty wake which could be seen for several hours. The sound of the impact was heard over a large area and soon planes were in the air looking for the site. They found it without difficulty; the area was covered with snow but where the meteorites had struck the naked soil showed in circular dark patches.

The craters had been caused by an iron meteorite which had split repeatedly during the passage through the atmosphere. It was later ascertained that the larger of the fragments had shattered again when striking the rocky ground. Numerous trees had meteorite fragments imbedded in their trunks, some slanting downward, where the fragments had hit a tree directly, others slanting upward, showing that these fragments had ricocheted from the ground. In April, after the snow had melted, an expedition, headed by Professor V. G. Fessenkov, went to the impact site, already located by a preliminary survey party. Fessenkov's expedition found 122 "craters," from small holes about 1½ feet across to some with a diameter of 90 feet and a depth of 20 feet. The larger craters lie in the southern part of the elliptical area pelted by the meteorite cluster, while the smaller specimens were recovered in the northern part of this area. About 23 tons of meteoric material [12] were collected, but Fessenkov estimates the total amount at around 70 tons.

A concentrated fall such as that of 1947 is, of course, a great rarity but it brings up the interesting question of how much material the earth gains per year. Fletcher G. Watson, in *Between the Planets*, estimates that the daily infall of meteorites large enough to be found and recognized later is on the order of half a ton daily. In addition to this,

[12] Chemical analysis showed the following composition: 93.5 per cent iron, 5.27 per cent nickel, 0.47 per cent cobalt, 0.20 per cent phosphorus, plus traces of sulfur and other elements.

meteors which are seen account for one ton or more daily while micro-meteorites and interplanetary dust which enter our atmosphere quietly without producing any visible phenomena might account for 1000 tons per day or more. The estimates seem quite large, but these thousand tons do not fall in one place; they sift down over continents and oceans, over deserts and polar ice caps. Averaged out over the earth's surface, the gain of a thousand tons or more per day amounts to a *yearly* addition of between 5 and 10 pounds per square mile of area.

The other remarkable meteoritic event of the early twentieth century was the Great Meteoric Procession of February 9, 1913.[13] It is a pity that both New York and New Jersey had overcast skies; otherwise this spectacle would have been seen by millions of people. Because of the cloudy weather only about 140 observations could be put on record, nearly all from Canada (mainly Ontario); one from Michigan, one from New Jersey, two from Bermuda, and two from ships at sea. The first publication on the "procession" (other than newspaper accounts) came from Professor C.A. Chant of the Royal Astronomical Society of Canada. As seen in western Ontario, the phenomenon looked like this:

At about 9:05 on the evening in question there suddenly appeared in the northwestern sky a fiery red body which quickly grew larger as it came nearer and which was then seen to be followed by a long tail. Some observers state that the body was single, some that it was composed of two distinct parts and others that there were three parts, and each followed by a long tail.

The front portion of the body appears to have been somewhat brighter than the rest, but the general color was a fiery red or golden yellow. To some the tail seemed like the glare from the open door of a furnace; to others it was like the illumination from a searchlight; to others like the stream of sparks blown away from a chimney by strong wind. . . .

Before the astonishment aroused by this first meteor had subsided, other bodies were seen coming from the northwest, emerging from precisely the same place as the first one. Onward they moved, at the same deliberate pace, in twos or threes or fours, with tails streaming behind, though not so long nor so bright as in the first case. They all traversed the same path and were heading for the same point in the southeastern sky. Gradually the bodies became smaller until the last ones were just red sparks, some of which were snuffed out before they reached their destination. Several [witnesses] report that near the middle of the great procession was a fine large star without a tail, and that a similar body brought up the rear.

[13] The literature is unfortunately scattered through many journals, of which the most important are: *Journal of the Royal Astronomical Society of Canada,* vol. 7 (1913) pp. 145-215 (Chant), pp. 404-413 (Denning), pp. 438-447 (Chant); vol. 8 (1914) pp. 112-116 (Monck); vol. 9 (1915) pp. 287-289 (Denning); vol. 10 (1916) pp. 294-296 (Denning); *Popular Astronomy,* vol. 30, (1922) pp. 632-637; vol. 31 (1923) pp. 96-104, 443-449 and 501-505 (all by W. H. Pickering); *Sky and Telescope,* January 1961, pp. 4-8 (O'Keefe); and *Science,* vol. 133 (1961) pp. 562-566 (O'Keefe).

To most observers the outstanding feature of the phenomenon was the slow majestic motion of the bodies; and almost equally remarkable was the perfect formation which they retained. Many compared them to a fleet of airships, with lights on either side and forward and aft; but airmen will have to practice many years before they will be able to preserve such perfect order. . . .

There was disagreement on one point only, namely, the number of bodies. Most witnesses said "fifteen or twenty," but some said "between fifty and one hundred." This discrepancy—aside from the fact that some people have better eyesight than others—was probably due to the method of counting. The first body, evidently consisting of several parts, could have been counted as "one" by some and as "three" by others. The only witness who used an opera glass (Cecil Carley of Trenton, New Jersey, then a high-school student) wrote: "There were about ten groups in all and each group, as seen through the opera glass, consisted of from 20 to 40 meteors."

The reports yielded an over-all picture of a height of 35 miles above Ontario, a velocity of motion about 5 miles per second, distances between the various groups of 50 to 100 miles, and total length of the procession about 100 miles. It is important that, while over Canada, no body dropped out (some observers claim they saw sparks falling, which is probably correct) and the bodies moved in the same position relative to one another.

The reports from Bermuda leave no doubt that the same procession was observed, but some changes had taken place. The height was less— about 30 miles—and the apparent motion therefore faster. The large tail-less body was now in the lead and emitted sparks; W. H. Pickering suggested that this tail-less body was an iron meteorite, while the others were stony meteorites. (It has since been suggested that they were tektites, a comparatively rare kind of meteorite resembling volcanic glass or obsidian.) An iron meteorite would have a greater kinetic energy than stony meteorites and would therefore overtake them when air resistance became noticeable.

The ships that observed the procession at sea were not far beyond Bermuda and to them the picture was the same as reported from the islands. Since there were no observations from Africa, it may be assumed that the bodies fell into the Atlantic Ocean before they reached the African coast. The whole behavior of the meteorites seemed totally strange to people in 1913, but now it can be compared with the behavior of an artificial satellite which has re-entered the atmosphere at a very shallow angle, and is carried halfway around the earth before impact takes place.

A shallow entry of a group of meteorites into the atmosphere is a rare event, but it can happen again and the first question that arose was whether it had happened before. One researcher found an Arabic source indicating that something like the procession had been seen from Cairo in 1029 A.D. But the source stated only that "In the month of *Redjeb* [August] many stars passed, with a great noise and a brilliant light." There is also some meager evidence from the Far East. *Historical Records of Meteor Showers in China, Korea, and Japan,* by Susumu Imoto and Ichiro Hasegawa,[14] in a list of 118 cases, contains two suspicious entries. Case No. 12 from a Chinese source, with the date of April 24, 1022 A.D., states: "Seven stars with trails flew to Crater slowly" (I assume that "Crater" is the name of a Chinese constellation). Case No. 115, from a Korean source, referring to an event in the spring of 316 A.D. (no precise date), says: "Thirty large stars flew west."

THE SEARCH FOR EARTH'S SECOND MOON

The French astronomer Frédéric Petit, director of the observatory of Toulouse, was not one of the famous astronomers of his time. In fact his name is missing from all the standard histories of astronomy written since the turn of the century. But he did leave a mark on the history of his science, even though the impression may be called negative.

In 1846 Petit appeared before the French Academy with a paper (published in the *Comptes Rendus* of October 12, 1846), stating that a second moon of earth had been discovered. He had not seen it himself; it had been seen by two observers, Lebon and Dassier, at Toulouse and by a third one, Larivière, at Artenac, 26 miles from Toulon, during the early evening of March 21, 1846. Upon calculating the orbit of this body, which he first thought to be a bolide (fireball), he found that it was in an elliptical orbit around the earth with an orbital period of 2 hours, 44 minutes, and 59 seconds, an apogee at 2220 miles above the surface of the earth and a perigee just 7.1 miles above sea level! Leverrier, who was in the audience, grumbled that there was need for a revision taking air resistance into account, something which neither Petit nor Leverrier nor anybody else—not even Carl Friedrich Gauss—could have done at the time.

But Petit became obsessed with the idea of a second moon, and a decade or so later announced that he had made a set of calculations about a small moon of earth which caused some then-unexplained peculiarities in the motion of our main moon.

[14] Smithsonian Contributions to Astrophysics, vol. II, no. 6, 1958.

It was an interesting idea, but professional astronomers paid little attention; I doubt that Petit's calculations were published in full anywhere. The whole case would be completely forgotten by now if a young French writer who had a remarkable talent for digging in libraries had not read an abstract.

His name was Jules Verne, and the abstract provided him with an idea which could be used in *Autour de la Lune,* the sequel to his *De la Terre à la Lune* which had first appeared in 1865 (by coincidence the year Petit died). In *De la Terre a là Lune* his heroes had built the moon cannon in Florida—some 60 miles from Cape Canaveral—and had fired it. The problem in the sequel was what to do with the three inhabitants of the aluminum projectile, Barbicane, Nicholl, and Ardan, who are of course assumed to have survived the shock of the firing. Since, in Jules Verne's opinion, they were unable to tell whether they were moving or not, Barbicane looks out of the window to see whether they are in space.

The episode deserves to be quoted (translated from the Paris edition of 1866):

When Barbicane was about to leave the window his attention was attracted by the approach of a brilliant object. It was an enormous disk, the colossal dimensions of which could not be estimated. Its face which was turned in the direction of the earth was very bright. One might have thought it a small moon reflecting the light of the large one. It approached with a high velocity and seemed to travel on an orbit around the earth which would intersect that of the projectile. . . . Instinctively the travelers drew back, but their great fear lasted only for seconds. The object passed several hundred yards from the projectile and disappeared, not so much because it traveled so rapidly but mainly because its dark side merged into the blackness of space. "Bon voyage," said Michael Ardan with a sigh of relief, "certainly there is enough room in infinite space for a miserable little projectile to walk along its path. Now what was this globe that almost struck us?"

"I know!" replied Barbicane.

"Oh, of course! You know everything."

"It is," said Barbicane, "a simple meteorite, but an enormous one, retained as a satellite by the attraction of the earth."

"Is that possible?" exclaimed Michel Ardan, "the earth has two moons like Neptune?" [15]

"Yes, my friend, it has two moons, although it is usually believed to have only one. But this second moon is so small and its velocity so great that the inhabitants of earth cannot see it. It was by noticing disturbances that a French astronomer, Monsieur Petit, could determine the existence of this second moon and calculated its orbit. According to him a complete revolution around earth takes three hours and twenty minutes. . . ."

[15] This was the result of an erroneous report then circulating; actually Neptune's second moon was not discovered until 1949.

"Do all astronomers admit the existence of this satellite?" asked Nicholl.

"No," replied Barbicane, "but if, like us, they had met it they could no longer doubt it. . . . But this gives us a means of determining our position in space . . . its distance is known and we were, therefore, 4650 miles above the surface of the globe when we met it."

The incident is of importance for the further development of the story. In the first volume Jules Verne had made it appear as if the projectile were to crash on the moon, its inhabitants trusting the built-in shock absorbers to save their lives. Now, because of the second moon, the path of the projectile has been somewhat deflected so that it will miss the moon and make a loop around it.

Jules Verne's stories were read by millions of people, among whom there must have been quite a number of astronomers. But not until 1942 did anybody notice that there was a discrepancy in the figures given by Verne, or possibly by Petit. During the years 1942 and 1943 Dr. Laurence J. Lafleur wrote a number of articles for the now defunct monthly *Popular Astronomy* about factual mistakes in early science-fiction novels. In the October 1942 issue he listed the mistakes in *Autour de la Lune,* pointing out that:

(A) A satellite 5000 miles from the earth's surface would have a period of four hours and 48 minutes, not three hours and 20 minutes.
(B) Since it was seen from the window from which the moon was invisible, while both were approaching, it must be in retrograde motion, which would be worth remarking. Verne doesn't mention this fact.
(C) In any case the satellite would be invisible because in eclipse. The projectile does not leave the earth's shadow until much later.

At a later date Dr. Robert S. Richardson (then of Mount Wilson Observatory) also noticed the discrepancy between orbital period and distance. Apparently he was not aware of Dr. Lafleur's publication and his main purpose had been a different one, namely to investigate whether Jules Verne's second moon would have had a sufficiently powerful gravitational field actually to deflect the trajectory of the moon-bound projectile. Of course, the main factor was missing from the story; Jules Verne did not state the size of his second moon. But Dr. Richardson said that one gets the impression that it must be at least one mile in diameter. In that case, its gravitational field would be too weak to change the direction of the flightpath, even if the whole moon were nickel-iron. At that point he also became aware that the orbital period was wrong for the distance. His article was published in the *Bulletin of the Pacific Rocket Society,* October 1952; he later elaborated on the problem in a personal letter:

According to Jules Verne the satellite was at a distance of 4650 miles from the surface and revolved around the earth in 3 hours and 20 minutes. Now if its semi-major axis was 4650 + 3960 = 8610 miles then the period must have been 4 hours 30.7 minutes. On the other hand, if the period was 3 hours 20 minutes then its semi-major axis was 7074 miles. That is, they went together like this:

period:	a/2:
4 h. 30.7 min.	8610 miles
3 h. 20 min.	7074 miles

I was trying to reconcile the two distances somehow.

Jules Verne's second moon was evidently supposed to be in a circular orbit, else Barbicane could not have stated the distance of the projectile from the earth so definitely from just one observation. Therefore the terms "semi-major axis" and "distance from the earth's center" are interchangeable in this case. But Dr. Richardson concluded that the distance mentioned and the insufficient orbital period could be reconciled by assuming that the satellite was on a somewhat elliptical orbit with perigee at 3114 miles (7074 miles from the earth's center) and apogee at 4650 miles. This would be an ellipse with an eccentricity of 0.1784.

This might well be what Monsieur Petit had originally stated; Jules Verne, either to simplify things or because he wasn't too sure of the laws of celestial mechanics, might have chosen two figures that did not go together.

But to return to the history of the idea, Jules Verne made Petit's supposition known all over the world. Inevitably amateur astronomers jumped to the conclusion that here was an opportunity for fame. Obviously anybody, no matter how unknown previously, who discovered the second moon of earth would have his name inscribed in the annals of science. To the best of my knowledge no major observatory ever checked the problem of earth's second moon—or if any did it was kept quiet. But around the turn of the century several German amateurs tried, committing an amusing pun in the process. The second moon of earth was evidently a small moon. The German word for small is *klein,* and Monsieur Petit's name also means "small." Hence they said they were hunting for *"Kleinchen"*—"Little Bit" comes closest in English. Of course they didn't find Little Bit.

It may have been this failure which prompted the American astronomer Professor William H. Pickering to devote his attention to the subject, even if only in theory. If the satellite orbited 200 miles from the earth's surface, he wrote, and had a diameter of 1 foot, with the same reflecting power as the moon, it should be visible in a 3-inch telescope. An assumed satellite with the same albedo and in the same orbit but with a diameter of 10 feet would be a naked-eye object, about magnitude 5. He did not think that either one would be discovered photographically: "The body would move too rapidly to leave a trail on a photographic plate." One might add here that the opposite of Professor Pickering's statement could also have been true. If the body was bright enough to leave a trail on the photographic plate it would have moved so rapidly that the trail would have gone from edge to edge. Any astronomer finding a plate with such an edge-to-edge trail would conclude that he had happened to catch a rather bright meteor and would disregard the trail, concentrating on the objects for which the picture had been taken in the first place.

Though Pickering did not look for the Petit-Verne object, he did carry on a search, both visually and photographically, for another possibility—not a second moon, but a secondary moon: a satellite of our moon. (See "On a Photographic Search for a Satellite of the Moon," in *Popular Astronomy,* 1903.) The result was wholly negative and Pickering had to conclude that if there is a secondary satellite its diameter must be less than, say, 10 feet.

Pickering's article on the possibility of a tiny second moon of earth (he titled it "A Meteoric Satellite") appeared in *Popular Astronomy* in 1922 and caused another short flurry among amateur astronomers, since it contained a virtual request: "A 3-in. to 5-in. telescope with a low-power eyepiece would be the likeliest means of finding it. It is an opportunity for the amateur." But again whatever searches may have been made remained fruitless.

It is, of course, always easy to be wise after the event, but it can be safely said that nobody seems to have taken the trouble to think the problem through in all its aspects. The original idea was that the gravitational field of the second moon should account for the then inexplicable minor deviations of the motion of our big moon. That meant a rather large object, with a diameter of several miles, at least. But if the earth had such a comparatively large second moon it would have been discovered by the Babylonians. Even if it did not show a disk to the naked eye, its comparative nearness would have made it move fast and therefore be conspicuous. Now that *Echo I* (about 100 feet in diameter and about 1000 miles out) has been seen by most people, it is evident that any nearby moonlet large enough to be visible at all would have attracted attention.

On the other hand, nobody was much interested in moonlets too small to be seen. If one had been discovered it would have been interesting, of course, but of no particular importance. It would not have "done" anything; it would not have influenced the movement of any other body in space, and, being small and difficult to observe, it would not even have been of any use in time measurement. Now we know, however, thanks to artificial satellite *Vanguard I*, that such a moonlet, if it could have been observed frequently enough, might have helped to form a better idea of the precise shape of the earth.

The mention of artificial satellites brings us to the next development. When, around 1950, artificial satellites began to be discussed in earnest, everybody expected the first few to be rather small, just the burned-out upper stages of multistage rockets. And at first they were not expected to carry radio transmitters; all tracking was to be by radar, and, with luck, visually. In such circumstances a batch of small natural satellites could have been most annoying, reflecting radar beams meant for the artificial satellites and as a result producing impossible readings. Hence, before any artificial satellite could be put into orbit, it was an absolute necessity to establish the orbits of very small natural satellites, if any.

The method was developed by Professor Clyde Tombaugh, discoverer of the planet Pluto, and a practicing astronomer well acquainted with optical equipment. Supposing you had a natural satellite in orbit around the earth at a distance of 3200 miles from the surface. Its orbital period would be 210 minutes (circular orbit assumed) and its orbital velocity would be 3.58 miles per second. Of course it would rise in the west and set in the east like any other satellite, natural or artificial, that is closer to the earth's surface than 22,300 miles.[16] Assuming the satellite to be in an orbit over the earth's equator, one could calculate just how it would move across the sky.

Searching for an unknown satellite at an assumed distance of 3200 miles would require a telescopic camera to be swept across the sky so that such a satellite would be kept in focus. Since the motion is quite fast, the fixed stars which are caught by the camera would all leave tracks going from one edge of the plate to the other. But the satellite, if any, would produce a dot, if it were precisely at the distance

[16] At the distance of 22,300 miles from the surface a satellite would need 24 hours to complete one orbit around the earth. Since the earth needs 24 hours to turn on its axis, such a satellite would neither rise nor set but just occupy a certain position in the sky. Satellites farther away, like our natural moon, seem to rise in the east and set in the west because their orbital motion is slow and they cannot "keep up" with the diurnal motion of the geographical point above which they happen to be located at a given moment. Satellites closer than the so-called 24-hour orbit, on the other hand, move so fast that the earth's rotation cannot keep up with *their* movement. Hence they rise in the west.

which is being searched. If it were nearer, say at 3000 miles, or farther out, say at 3500 miles, it would produce a short line. From the length of this line one could even calculate how much its actual velocity deviates from the assumed velocity. The result would be a plus/minus value, of course; it could be that much slower or that much faster.

With perfect luck the satellite, as has been said, would make a dot on the plate. But astronomers have learned to be somewhat suspicious about dots. They can be just flaws in the film; even a dust grain could produce such a false indication. For this reason Professor Tombaugh did something further: when the star images were in the approximate center of the plate he caused the telescopic camera to make a tiny move. On the finished plate all the normally unbroken lines which are star images would suddenly shift a fraction of an inch on the plate and then continue. The effect would be very much as if you took a ruled sheet of paper, cut it down the center, and then pasted it carelessly together again so that the ruled lines did not meet in the middle. If there was a genuine dot, made by the suspected satellite, there would be two dots, as far apart from each other as the lines of the same star image. But a flaw in the plate would still make only one dot. Hence any single dot could be disregarded automatically.

This was the principle.

But moving the camera so that it would produce a dot for a satellite at a distance of 3200 miles did not mean that one good exposure for this distance would settle the problem. The satellite could be in that orbit, but outside of the field of vision of the camera. Hence quite a number of exposures would be needed for every given distance. There were other practical problems. For a fast-moving (assumed) satellite near the earth the star trails would go from edge to edge. But for a slow-moving satellite at a distance of, say, 50,000 miles, the star trails would be quite short; the scanning for a still shorter trail would have to be carried out with utmost care.

Professor Tombaugh was willing to undertake the job. The equipment which he proposed was small and light enough to be carried on one truck. And its sensitivity was high, expressed in the much-quoted sentence: "It could discover a white tennis ball in an orbit 1000 miles from the ground and could discover a V-2 rocket in the orbit of the moon."

The proposal was written up in June 1952 and submitted to the Office for Ordnance Research, U. S. Army. Observations began in December 1953 at the Lowell Observatory, Flagstaff, Arizona. The search actually invaded virgin territory; if you disregard the few German amateurs who looked for *Kleinchen,* nobody had ever paid any attention to the space between the moon and the earth! Naturally Professor Tombaugh's methods underwent slight changes while the work was in progress and a little later another camera was added to the original one.

By the fall of 1954 weekly journals and daily newspapers of high reputation carried items stating that the search had brought its first results—one small natural satellite 400 miles out and another one 600 miles out. There was also the subsidiary story that a general in the Pentagon, when he read this report, asked suspiciously, "Is he sure they are natural?" (The first American artificial satellite project, the later-shelved Project Orbiter, was then in the preliminary stages.) The story about the general may be true; the report itself was not. Tombaugh wrote me somewhat plaintively that not only were there no results, these regions had not even been searched at the time. Nobody seems to know how this report originated, or even whether it was a hoax or somebody's garbled version of a purely theoretical discussion.

Natural small satellites can be expected in two regions. One is the plane of the ecliptic, the orbit of the earth around the sun. The other is the plane of the earth's equator. Search for satellites in the plane of the ecliptic for any distance from the earth could be carried out from Flagstaff, Arizona. This also applied to satellites in the equatorial plane, but with the provision that such satellites had to be more than 1600 miles from the surface. An equatorial satellite 400 miles up, say, could not be seen from Flagstaff. Later Tombaugh moved to Quito, Ecuador, to finish the search for nearby equatorial satellites; at Quito they would be vertically overhead.

Before this move took place Tombaugh wrote an interim report, which concluded:

Much of the space about the earth had been searched. Most of this space has been found to be empty of material moving in the most-likely orbits and large enough to be seen by the present equipment. Some "suspects" have been found on the photographic films, but in all save a few instances it has been possible to determine that the record was not that of a satellite. These images, if not due to defects in the photographic plates, could have been tracks of very small asteroids moving past the earth in their journey around the sun. The several suspects not yet eliminated as satellites are ones which cannot be checked until photographic work has started on the equator. From a statistical point of view, it is more likely that they will turn out not to be satellites. The chance of a discovery of astronomical or geodetic value has, from the beginning, been regarded as very small. But a completely negative result, a determination that the space near the earth is free of débris up to a certain size, could have comforting significance to long-range ballisticians and to proponents of space travel.

The over-all outcome of Tombaugh's work, amply reinforced by the tracking of over half a hundred artificial satellites from 1957 to 1961, is that space inside the moon's orbit is actually empty, except for dust.

But this does not mean, strangely enough, that the earth has only one satellite. In the first place the earth can have a very near satellite for a short time. Meteors passing the earth and skimming through the upper atmosphere can lose enough velocity to go into a satellite orbit around the earth. But since they will go through the upper atmosphere each time they pass the perigee of their new orbit, they will not last long, maybe for only one or two, possibly for about a hundred, revolutions (about 150 hours). There are some indications that such "ephemeral satellites" as they are now called, have been seen; it is even possible that Frédéric Petit's observers did see one.

In addition to ephemeral satellites there were two more possibilities as regards the existence of secondary moons of earth. One was that our moon might have a small satellite of its own, but Tombaugh checked this suggestion, without success. The other possibility was that there might be "Trojan satellites"—the term was coined with reference to the planetoids in the orbit of Jupiter (see Chapter 13)—which means secondary satellites in the orbit of the moon. We now know that this is the case.

They were discovered by the Polish astronomer K. Kordylewski of Kraków Observatory. He started his search in 1951, visually but with the aid of a good telescope. He was hoping that there might be reasonably large bodies in the so-called equilateral positions, 60 degrees of arc ahead of the moon and behind it. The trailing position is known technically as the L_5 position, the one ahead of the moon is the L_4 position. A Trojan satellite could, theoretically, be in either of these two positions; in fact both might be occupied.

In spite of many nights spent looking for equilaterals, the search turned out to be negative and Dr. Kordylewski was probably ready to give up. But in 1956, his compatriot and colleague, Professor J. Witkowski, suggested that there might be tiny bodies in these positions that were too small to show up even in a good telescope. However, if there were a whole cloud of dust particles, or particles not much larger than dust, they might be visible, though *not* with a telescope. Such a cloud might be luminous enough to be seen with the naked eye on a dark night. Using a telescope would "magnify it out of existence."

Dr. Kordylewski was willing to try. He went to high mountain stations in Czechoslovakia. Just a dark night with clear air was not enough, however. Other conditions were needed. If the moon itself were near

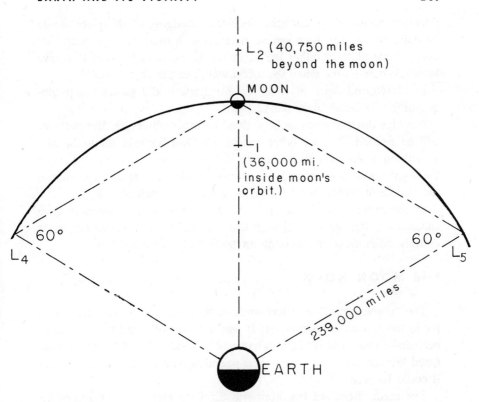

The Lagrangian points in the earth-moon system. Only points L_4 and L_5 can be considered really stable; bodies in points L_1 and L_2 would be easily perturbed. Point L_3 (not shown) would be on the other side of the earth, below the bottom of this diagram

the full phase, which is the time when the so far purely hypothetical dust clouds would be brightest, it would throw so much light into the night sky that they would become invisible. Hence it would do no good to look at positions L_4 and L_5 if the moon also was above the horizon. One of these positions had to be above the horizon; the moon itself had to be below the horizon. Moreover, the position being checked had to be in a part of the sky where the Milky Way would not interfere.

In October 1956 Dr. Kordylewski saw, for the first time, a fairly luminous patch in one of the two positions. It was not small, subtending an angle of about 2 degrees, but it was very faint, only about half as bright as the notoriously difficult *Gegenschein* (counterglow). Dr. Kordylewski decided to try his luck with a camera. But first he checked with the Sonneberg Observatory in East Germany. At Sonneberg they had been taking thousands of pictures every year in the study of variable stars. Maybe they had caught one of the dust clouds and paid no attention to it—likely enough, since the smudging of the plate would be quite minor, and they were concerned with their variable stars. But not a single plate of either the L_4 or the L_5 position happened to have been taken at a time when the moon wasn't in the sky as well!

In March and April of 1961 Dr. Kordylewski did succeed in photographing two clouds near the L_5 point.

Now his discovery has to be verified by other observers. But patience will be needed. The L_4 point (where Dr. Kordylewski thinks he saw something with the naked eye but did not photograph it), will offer the right conditions around the middle of October and again around the middle of November (1961) for a few days each month.

So the century-long search for a second moon of earth seems to have succeeded, after all, even though this "second moon" turned out to be entirely different from anything anybody had ever predicted.

THE MOON HOAX

The "moon hoax," as it has come to be known, is a neglected chapter in the history of astronomy. It was not scientific and may not have been influential, but it shows what was believable in 1835. Many educated laymen accepted it and even scientists wondered at least whether it could be true.

The main "hero" of the affair was Sir John Herschel, the son of Sir William. He had embarked, in November 1833, on the long journey to South Africa for the purpose of getting a good look at the southern sky, which up to that time had been neglected, simply because all the large telescopes, and most of the small ones, were located in the northern hemisphere. Sir John transported a 5-inch refractor and an 18-inch reflector to Capetown.

The carrier of the moon hoax was the daily New York *Sun*, then only two years old, with a circulation of about 8,000. In addition to ordinary news and advertisements the paper was in the habit of running long essays in serial form. One of these had been written by the British-born author and essayist Richard Adams Locke (of the same family as the philosopher John Locke, though not a lineal descendant, as wrongly stated by Edgar Allan Poe). Mr. Locke had been paid $150 for his essay and the proprietors of *The Sun* had asked more. Locke had been reading, in the 1826 volume of the *Edinburgh New Philosophical Journal,* a tediously philosophizing article on the inhabitants of other worlds, especially of the moon. The outcome of this reading, plus the offer of another $150, was what we now call the "moon hoax."

The story began in *The Sun* on August 25, 1835, under the title "Great Astronomical Discoveries Lately Made by Sir John Herschel, LL.D. F.R.S. &c, at the Cape of Good Hope." An editorial stated that the editors of *The Sun* were pleased to bring to American readers "this reprint of a special Supplement of the *Edinburgh Journal of Science*," complete, except for mathematical material of no interest to the average reader.

The article itself began with introductory remarks by the editor of the *"Edinburgh Journal"* to the British public and continued:

To render our enthusiasm intelligible, we will state at once, that by means of a telescope, of vast dimensions and an entirely new principle, the younger Herschel, at his observatory in the Southern Hemisphere, has already made the most extraordinary discoveries in every planet of our solar system; has discovered planets in other solar systems; has obtained a distinct view of objects in the moon, fully equal to that which the unaided eye commands of terrestrial objects at the distance of a hundred yards; has affirmatively settled the question whether this satellite be inhabited, and by what orders of beings; has firmly established a new theory of cometary phenomena; and has solved or corrected nearly every leading problem of mathematical astronomy.

For our early and almost exclusive information concerning these facts, we are indebted to the devoted friendship of Dr. Andrew Grant, the pupil of the elder, and for several years past the inseparable coadjutor of the younger Herschel. The amanuensis of the latter at the Cape of Good Hope, and the indefatigable superintendent of his telescope during the whole period of its construction and operation, Dr. Grant has been enabled to supply us with intelligence equal, in general interest at least, to that which Dr. Herschel himself has transmitted to the Royal Society.

The reader of *The Sun* was given the impression that he was being let in on wonderful discoveries at the earliest possible moment, that the Royal Society was still digesting the material submitted by Dr. Herschel, but that Herschel's friend, working faster, had written it all up for his scientific friends in Edinburgh, and now *The Sun,* by a lucky combination of circumstances (or, preferably, because of the astuteness of its editors) had the first advance copy of the Scottish journal to reach American shores and was sharing all this information with its readers, for only a few pennies.

The first day's installment was somewhat dull, at least by present-day standards. It described the new telescope, with a simply astonishing expenditure of wordage. The technical jargon, all meaningless, was just "thick" enough to convince the reader that he would not be able to follow it if it grew any more detailed and persuade him to accept the supertelescope as described. When Sir John Herschel was satisfied that the telescope was perfect, "he sailed from London on the 4th of September, 1834,[17] in company with Dr. Andrew Grant, Lieut. Drummond, of the Royal Engineers, F.R.A.S., and a large party of the best English mechanics. They arrived, after an expeditious and agreeable passage, and immediately proceeded to transport the lens and the frame of the large observatory to its destined site, which was a piece of table-land of great extent and elevation, about thirty-five miles to the northeast of Capetown. . . . All this, of course, was under strictest government secrecy.

This ended the first day's installment. The sales figures of *The Sun* climbed to about 12,000 copies on that day. The next day's installment got around to the moon.

It was about half-past nine o'clock on the night of the 10th [of January 1835], the moon having then advanced within four days of her mean libration, that the astronomer adjusted his instruments for the inspection of her eastern limb. The whole immense power of his telescope was applied, and its focal image about one-half of the power of his microscope. On removing the screen of the latter, the field of view was covered throughout its entire area with a beautifully distinct, and even vivid representation of *basaltic rock*. Its color was a greenish brown, and the width of the column, as defined by their interstices on the canvas, was invariably twenty-eight inches. No fracture whatever appeared in the mass first presented, but in a few seconds a shelving pile appeared of five or six columns width, which showed their figure to be hexagonal, and their articulations similar to those of the basaltic formation at Staffa. This precipitous shelf was profusely covered with a dark red flower, "precisely similar," says Dr. Grant, "to the *Papaver rhaeas*, or rose-poppy of our sublunary cornfield"; and this was the first organic production of nature, in a foreign world, ever revealed to the eyes of men. . . . At the base of [another rock mass] they were at length delighted to perceive that novelty, a lunar forest. "The trees," says Dr. Grant, "for a period of ten minutes, were of one unvaried kind, and unlike any I have seen, except the largest class of yews in the English church-yards, which they in some respects resemble. These were followed by a level green plain, which, as measured by the painted circle on our canvas of forty-nine feet, must have been more than half a mile in breadth; and then appeared as fine a forest of firs, unequivocal firs, as I have ever seen cherished in the bosom of my native mountains. Wearied with the long continuance of these, we greatly reduced the magnifying power of the microscope, without eclipsing either of the reflectors, and immediately perceived that we had been insensibly descending, as it were, a mountainous district of a highly diversified and romantic character, and that we were on the verge of a lake, or inland sea. . . . The water, wherever we obtained a view of it, was nearly as blue as that of the deep ocean, and broke in large white billows upon the strand. . . .

Having continued this close inspection nearly two hours . . . Dr. Herschel proposed that we should take out all our lenses, give a rapid speed to the panorama, and search for some of the principal valleys known to astron-

[17] Herschel's actual sailing date was November 13, 1833.

omers. . . . The lenses being removed, and the efflugence of our unutterly glorious reflectors left undiminished, we found, in accordance with our calculations, that our field of view comprehended about twenty-five miles of the lunar surface, with the distinctness both of outline and detail which could be procured of a terrestrial object at the distance of two and a half miles. . . . Presently a train of scenery met our eye, of features so entirely novel, that Dr. Herschel signalled for the lowest convenient gradation of movement. It was a lofty chain of obelisk-shaped, or very slender pyramids, standing in irregular groups, each composed of about thirty or forty spires, every one of which was perfectly square, and as accurately truncated as the finest specimens of Cornish crystal. They were of a faint lilac hue, and very resplendent. I now thought that we had assuredly fallen on productions of art; but Dr. Herschel shrewdly remarked that if the Lunarians could build thirty or forty miles of such monuments as these, we should ere now have discovered others of a less equivocal character. He pronounced them quarz formations, of probably the wine-colored amethyst species. . . . On introducing a lens, his conjecture was fully confirmed: they were monstrous amethysts, of a diluted claret color, glowing in the intensest light of the sun! They varied in height from sixty to ninety feet. . . . and here our magnifiers blest our panting hopes with specimens of conscious existence. In the shade of the woods, on the southeastern side, we beheld continuous herds of brown quadrupeds, having all the external characteristics of the bison, but more diminutive than any species of the bos genus in our natural history. . . . It had, however, one widely distinctive feature, which we afterwards found common to nearly every lunar quadruped we have discovered; namely, a remarkable fleshy appendage over the eyes, crossing the whole breadth of the forehead and united to the eyes. We could most distinctly perceive this hairy veil . . . lifted and lowered by means of the ears. It immediately occurred to the acute mind of Dr. Herschel, that this was a providential contrivance to protect the eyes of the animal from the great extremes of light and darkness to which all the inhabitants of our side of the moon are periodically subjected.

The next animal perceived would be classed on earth as a monster. It was of bluish lead-color, about the size of a goat, with a head and beard like him, and a *single horn,* slightly inclined forward from the perpendicular. The female was destitute of the horn and beard, but had a much longer tail. It was gregarious, and chiefly abounded on the acclivitous glades of the woods. In elegance of symmetry it rivalled the antelope, and like him it seemed an agile sprightly creature running with great speed, and springing from the green turf with all the unaccountable antics of a young lamb or kitten. This beautiful creature afforded us the most exquisite amusement.

The lunar unicorn ended the second installment. By that time New Yorkers besieged the offices of *The Sun* and every copy the steam presses could turn out was snatched up. Circulation was at 19,360 copies. *The Sun* had suddenly become the biggest newspaper in the world; even the *Times* of London only printed 17,000 copies.

The following installment consisted of a painstaking, if fanciful, description of a number of lunar formations. Locke pictured a rather watery world, with tidal marks and so forth, although most astronomers were by then agreed that our moon is virtually waterless. Many of his readers must have read somewhere about the lack of water on the moon; presumably the implication that the experts were wrong was welcomed. That the public went along willingly with the story is testified by witnesses.

Edgar Allan Poe, then the editor of the *Southern Literary Messenger* in Richmond, Virginia, wrote later: "Not one person in ten discredited it, and (strangest point of all!) the doubters were chiefly those who doubted without being able to say why—the ignorant—those uninformed in astronomy—people who *would* not believe, because the thing was so novel, so entirely out of the usual way. A grave Professor of Mathematics in a Virginia college told me, seriously, that he had no *doubt* of the truth of the whole affair!"

William N. Griggs, who reprinted the moon hoax with its background, reported that he was present at the door of *The Sun*'s office on one of these hectic days "when a highly respectable-looking elderly gentleman, in a fine broadcloth Quaker suit, completely dispelled the undecided opinions of the listening crowd around him, by asserting, in the calmest, coolest, and most unquestionable manner, that he was fortunately engaged on commercial business at the East India Docks, in London, when the cast lens, of seven tons weight, and the whole gigantic apparatus of the telescope described in the story, was taken on board an East India ship, for erection at the Cape of Good Hope, and that he himself saw it craned on board. He added that the statement in the introductory part of the narrative, that this shipment was made from St. Catherine's Docks, was, therefore, evidently an error on the part of the Edinburgh writer."

There is some reason to believe that Locke expanded his story as he went along; some minor inconsistencies suggest that he interpolated long segments in his original manuscript. The next installment reached the climax: the discovery of "rational beings" of the moon.

. . . we were thrilled with astonishment to perceive four successive flocks of large winged creatures, wholly unlike any kind of birds, descend with a slow even motion from the cliffs on the western side, and alight upon the plain. . . . We counted three parties of these creatures, of twelve, nine, and fifteen each, walking erect towards a small wood near the base of the eastern precipices. Certainly they *were* like human beings, for their wings had now disappeared, and their attitude in walking was both erect and dignified. . . .

Whilst passing across the canvas, and whenever we afterwards saw them, these creatures were evidently engaged in conversation; their gesticulation, more particularly the varied action of their hands and arms, appeared impassioned and emphatic. We hence inferred that they were rational beings, and, although not perhaps of so high an order as others which we discovered the next month on the shores of the Bay of Rainbows, that they were capable of producing works of art and contrivance.

There were several other installments, in one of which the big telescope was nearly destroyed, and finally one in which Sir John Herschel established the nature of Saturn's rings—the details unfortunately "omitted . . . as "being too mathematical for popular comprehension." With a promise of a much fuller account by Sir John himself, the series ended.

Since the presses of *The Sun* were busy printing as many copies of the paper as possible, its proprietors must have employed another printer for the pamphlet edition which they thoughtfully had ready the following day.[18]

The next few days were still hectic. Yale professors, named Olmstead and Loomis, journeyed to New York to ask for the omitted pages of mathematics. Locke told them that the original was at a print shop and supplied the address. Then he raced ahead and instructed the printer to direct the two professors to still another address. They finally gave up, convinced that they had been tricked but still unable to say that the supplement to the *Edinburgh Journal* did not exist.

Another New York newspaper, the *Journal of Commerce,* wanted to reprint the whole story and also asked for the *Edinburgh Journal.* Locke first tried the tack that this was old stuff by now and the *Journal of Commerce* would just be wasting space. Then he apparently told the truth, because the *Journal of Commerce* was the first publication to label the whole story a hoax.

It was later surmised that Locke had a collaborator, a French astronomer named Jean Nicolas Nicollet who had recently arrived in New York, having left France because of financial difficulties. Whether or not he helped Locke for a cash consideration, will probably never be known.

[18] After its original publication in *The Sun,* the moon hoax first appeared in the pamphlet mentioned, with a reported total edition of 60,000 copies in two or three printings. The next reprint, edited by William Gowans, appeared in New York in 1859 as the title *The Moon Hoax*; or, *A Discovery that the moon has a vast population of Human Beings,* by Richard Adams Locke, with a short appendix of editorial opinions from newspapers other than *The Sun.* A small book, entitled *The Celebrated "Moon Story," Its Origins and Incidents,* by William N. Griggs (New York: Bunnell and Price, 1852), gives the background of the story, a biographical sketch of Locke, the story itself, and, in an appendix, an "authentic description of the moon." All the quotations in this chapter are from this book. In 1937 the text of the moon hoax was again reprinted in *The Sky* (New York), in several installments, with an introduction by William H. Barton, Jr. Grigg's book mentions French and German translations, which probably were in contemporary magazines and newspapers; my search for German or French editions in book or pamphlet form was unsuccessful.

There are two more items of interest, the first concerning a friend of Sir John Herschel. Naturally copies of *The Sun* had reached Europe. The director of the Paris Observatory, François Arago, was outraged, not so much because a hoax had been perpetrated upon the public, as because it besmirched the name of Sir John Herschel. Arago read a full translation of the moon hoax to the French scientists assembled at the Academy and asked for a resolution. The resolution declared that while the piece was not to be regarded as a willful malicious attack on Sir John Herschel, its contents had to be declared "utterly incredible."

The second item concerns Sir John Herschel himself, who was actually in South Africa, making astronomical observations.

Telescope of Sir John Herschel erected at the Cape of Good Hope

At intervals, for example, when the weather was bad, he went to Capetown, where he stayed at a hotel to read the papers and relax. Soon after the appearance of the moon hoax a Mr. Caleb Weeks, who lived in Jamaica, New York, and was the proprietor of a menagerie, went to Capetown to buy up some African animals. He took copies both of *The Sun* and of the pamphlet edition with him, hoping to find Sir John Herschel. Capetown probably did not have many good hotels at the time—Weeks stayed at the one that was visited almost daily by Sir John. The astronomer was there when Weeks asked the hotel clerk where he could be found. Weeks had himself announced, saying that he wished to discuss Sir John's new astronomical discoveries with him. Sir John received him with some surprise; he said that he was, of course, flattered by American interest, but did not understand how his discoveries could be known in America, since he had not yet even written a report.

Weeks handed him the pamphlet and a bundle of the New York newspapers and withdrew. Only minutes later Sir John rejoined him in some agitation, asking whether the story was really a reprint from an Edinburgh journal, or a hoax made up in New York. According to Griggs, who knew Weeks personally, Weeks replied that the account was taken to be gospel truth in New York and elsewhere in the United States, and wasn't it a maxim that what everybody says must be true? Sir John Herschel started to laugh and invited Weeks and the other Americans with him into a private room to tell him the full story.

In general he was amused.

Most Europeans however, did not accept the hoax as light-heartedly as did its chief victim. That this "contribution" to astronomy had come from an English journalist was obscured by distance, and for decades to come astronomical news from America was received with great caution in Europe. The skepticism did not die out because American astronomers made more and more genuine and valuable contributions; it ended because the moon hoax itself was gradually forgotten.

ZODIACAL LIGHT AND GEGENSCHEIN

In decades past, when a voyage to the tropics was a rare event and a difficult feat, returning travelers not only told of flying fish, large and brightly colored birds, and slender palm trees silhouetted against the sunset. They also described an astronomical phenomenon which received the name of zodiacal light. No later travelers surpassed, either in accuracy or in sentiment, the description provided by the Baron Alexander von Humboldt:

He who has lived for years in the zone of the palm trees holds an enchanted memory of the zodiacal light which, rising like a slender pyramid, illuminates a part of the always equally long tropical nights. I have seen it with a luminescence sometimes surpassing that of the Milky Way in Sagittarius—not only in the thin and dry atmosphere of the 12,000- and 14,000-foot peaks of the Cordillera de los Andes but also in the limitless grassy plains, the Llanos, of Venezuela and at the seashore under the eternally clear sky of Cumana. The phenomenon was especially beautiful when small and thin clouds were visible against the zodiacal light and acquired their own refulgence against the illuminated background. At one point in my journal which refers to a sailing voyage from Lima to the western coast of Mexico I mentioned this: . . . For 3 or 4 nights (between 10° and 14° of northern latitude) I saw the zodiacal light in a splendor which I have never beheld before. In this part of the southern sea [in German usage, "southern" is applied to all tropical seas, not merely to the seas south of the equator] the atmosphere is wonderfully transparent as proved by the splendor of the stars and the nebulae. From March 14–19 [1803], with absolute regularity, no trace of the zodiacal light was visible for three-quarters of an hour after the disk of the sun had submerged itself into the sea, even though it was completely dark. One hour after sunset it suddenly appeared, in full splendor, between Aldebaran and the Pleiades. On March 18 its tip was 39° 5′ above the horizon. Scattered slender elongated clouds of a lovely blue color appeared near the horizon as if against the background of a yellow carpet. The uppermost of them occasionally display divers colors; one might think to watch a second sunset. In the sector of the sky near the zodiacal light the night sky seems to brighten, almost as if the moon were in its first quarter. At about 10 P.M. the zodiacal light was usually quite faint; at midnight I could discern only a trace. When, on March 16, it was at its brightest, the Gegenschein with its gentle light became visible in the east. . . .

It is hard to understand that such a conspicuous natural phenomenon should not have attracted the attention of physicists and astronomers until as late as the middle of the seventeenth century. . . . The first clear description of the zodiacal light can be found in [Joshua] Childrey's *Britannia Baconica* of the year 1661; the first observation may have been made two or three years earlier; but Dominicus Cassini deserves undeniable credit for having been the first (in the spring of 1683) to have explored the dimensions of this phenomenon. . . . One may suspect, with much probability, that the strange pyramid-shaped light which was seen from the high plateaus of Mexico for forty nights in 1509 in the eastern sky (mentioned in the *Codex Telleriano-Remensis* in the Royal Library of Paris, where I saw it) was the zodiacal light. (*Kosmos*, 1st ed., 1845, vol. I, p. 142ff.).

The zodiacal light also becomes visible before sunrise, and this aspect was especially noticed at an early date by the inhabitants of the Near East because of religious rituals connected with the rising of the sun. According to an article by Redhouse in the *Journal of the Asiatic Society* (1878) the zodiacal light was given a name meaning "false dawn," to distinguish it from the true dawn of religious significance.

Though the zodiacal light—which has that name, of course, because it extends along the zodiac—is rarely seen in Europe, it is sometimes visible in the spring and fall. Tycho Brahe observed it, as did others, but as Humboldt stated, it was Cassini who first paid special attention to it. He suggested an observational program to Niccolò Fatio. Fatio was then working at the Paris Observatory, but he continued his work for two more years after he moved to his own private observatory at Duiller near Geneva. Fatio was the first to establish that the zodiacal light followed the sun during the sun's apparent annual motion and that it could not be seen equally well at all times of the year. It was Fatio who supplied Cassini with the material for his book *Découverte de la lumière céleste qui paroit dans le Zodiaque,* which appeared in

Paris in 1685. Though Cassini mentioned Fatio's name often, later (and presumably hurried) readers often gave all the credit to Cassini.

Cassini himself guessed that the zodiacal light might be caused by an extension of the solar atmosphere. Fatio, as quoted by Cassini, assumed the presence of a very large number of particles in space, reflecting the light of the sun. At a later date (1730, in *Mémoires de l'Académie,* vol. VIII) Cassini fully endorsed this opinion, declaring that the zodiacal light formed a ring around the sun and that if the orbits of Mercury and of Venus were visible they would appear to us as does the zodiacal light. He stated that he considered this ring to consist of a very large number of tiny bodies in planetlike orbits around the sun.[19] He also thought that the appearance of meteors and fireballs might be connected with a passage of the earth through the fringes of the zodiacal light.

Alexander von Humboldt, in a footnote, pointed out that the idea that the sun might be a diffuse star with an enormous atmosphere which accounted for the zodiacal light "was advanced by Mairan in 1731 . . . it was a renewal of Kepler's ideas." [20] Humboldt himself finally agreed with Cassini's later concept:

The phenomenon, first discovered in Europe by Childrey and Cassini, but evidently very very old, is not the luminous atmosphere of the sun. The laws of mechanics require that the sun cannot be flattened more strongly than in the ratio of 2:3, hence its atmosphere could not be more extended than to $\frac{9}{20}$ of the distance to the orbit of Mercury. . . . Because of this limitation of the sun's atmosphere, the cause of zodiacal light must be the existence of a very flat ring of nebulous [21] matter, freely circling in space between the orbits of Venus and Mars. Of its actual dimensions, of the increase due to the exhalations of the tails of myriads of comets, and of the changes in extent, since it sometimes does not seem to extend beyond the earth's orbit . . . nothing can be said right now with certainty. The nebulous particles which form the ring and which orbit the sun in accordance with the laws of planetary motion might be self-luminous or else illuminated by the sun.

Between Alexander von Humboldt and the end of the nineteenth century there was the customary number of wrong guesses. In 1856

[19] See "The Rings of Saturn" in Chapter 15 for Cassini's ideas about the constitution of Saturn's rings.

[20] Actually Kepler had not referred to the zodiacal light, which he probably never saw, but had assumed a very extended solar atmosphere to explain why "there is no real night" during a total eclipse of the sun.

[21] The original has the word *"Dunst,"* which might be translated as "vapor," "mist," or nowadays even "smog." Usage of the word was, and is, such that *Dunst* is distinct from a gas by being visible, implying the presence of tiny particles, as in smoke, a meaning obviously intended by von Humboldt.

G. Jones published his *Observations on the Zodiacal Light* from 1853–1855, in which he reported a series of very fine observations, but ended with the conclusion that the light was caused by a ring of the earth inside the orbit of the moon. And Alessandro Serpieri, in discussing Jones's set of observations in 1876, even concluded that the light, like auroras, was a phenomenon of the upper atmosphere.

This treatise appeared just one year after Jean Charles Houzeau (then director of the Observatory at Brussels) had proved that the zodiacal light had to be far outside the earth's atmosphere, to say the least, because no noticeable parallax could be found. A. Wright (*American Journal of Science,* 1874), emphasizing the fact that the spectrogram of the zodiacal light is the same as that of the sun, re-established Fatio's original idea that the cause must be a "dust lens" around the sun, consisting of small solid bodies. This is still the generally accepted explanation.

But modern astronomy is not fully satisfied with an explanation as to the nature of something, unless it also knows how and why, or why not, as the case may be. If the zodiacal light is caused by solid particles orbiting the sun, information is then desired as to the size of these particles and their origin.

The size of the particles cannot actually be deduced by calculation but a general idea can be gained if an average albedo is assumed. A likely color is that of dark gray rock or lava. Assuming such a color, the observed brightness of the zodiacal light could be accounted for by particles 10 feet in diameter and 1000 miles apart. It could also be accounted for by particles 1 millimeter in diameter and 5 miles apart. Offhand, the tiny particles only a few miles apart sound more reasonable, except for the problem of the so-called Poynting-Robertson effect, which states that a small particle orbiting the sun must gradually approach the sun and finally be consumed by it. The reason for this is that the warming effect of the sun's rays on one side of the particle causes a small shift in the center of gravity of the particle.

For large bodies, such as a planet or a moon, the Poynting-Robertson effect is negligible,[22] but a particle 10 millimeters in diameter, orbiting the sun at the distance of 1 A.U., would enter the sun's corona after 20 million years. Considering the age of the solar system, all the still remaining bodies producing the zodiacal light should be rather large,

---

[22] If a is the radius of the particle expressed in centimeters, D its density in grams per cubic centimeter, and R the initial distance in astronomical units, the time required to reach the sun from the original orbit reads $7\ aDR^2$ million years. Obviously a large and dense body will be virtually unaffected.

with diameters to be measured in yards and weights to be expressed in tons.

But other findings contradict this assumption: the average size of the particles encountered by the earth in its orbit is that of a small grain of sand. The existence of such very small particles can be explained only by assuming a continuous fresh supply. Humboldt's idea—voiced repeatedly after him by modern astronomers—that material stripped off comets might add to the zodiacal light is probably correct but cannot explain the attrition caused by the Poynting-Robertson effect. The answer to that problem lies in the asteroid belt, where glancing collisions must happen quite often. Head-on collisions in the asteroid belt, if they ever occurred, must be a thing of the distant past; by now all bodies with orbits which could produce head-on collision must have been eliminated. But glancing blows are likely any day and possibly any hour of the day. And each such glancing blow will produce new splinters, new clouds of rock dust which then drift slowly inward in the solar system.

The *Gegenschein*, which Humboldt also mentioned in his description of the zodiacal light, is an intriguing problem in itself. One of its peculiarities is that it was discovered independently several times. The first discoverer was a French Jesuit priest and professor of mathematics named Esprit Pézénas, who published a note about it in the *Mémoirs* of the Parisian Academy in 1731. Not much notice was taken of his discovery, but Humboldt must have read this volume of the *Mémoirs*—as he seems to have read everything else—because when he observed this patch of light on March 16, 1803, he did not think that he had made a new discovery. However, it was Humboldt who gave it the name *Gegenschein,* which it bears to this day. The English equivalent is "counterglow." Many books on astronomy state that "counter" refers to the fact that this light is always opposite to the position of the sun in the sky. However, Humboldt's words *"das Thierkreislicht und sein Gegenschein"* ("the zodiacal light and its counterglow") make it perfectly clear that the "counter" refers to opposition to the zodiacal light and only incidentally to the position of the sun.

The man usually called in textbooks the discoverer of the *Gegenschein* was the German Theodor Brorsen, born in 1819 in the township of Norburg on the island of Alsen. He saw the *Gegenschein* in 1853 and published a first account in a German weekly scientific periodical in 1854 under the title *"Über eine neue Erscheinung am Zodiakallicht"* (On a New Phenomenon of the Zodiacal Light). Brorsen followed this first publication with two more, one in the *Monthly Notices* in 1856 and another in the *Astronomischen Nachrichten* in 1859. Having searched astronomical literature before publishing his own observations, he credited Pézénas as having been the first to report on this light. It is rather strange that it was not seen earlier, especially by observers in desert climates.

Just how difficult it is to see the *Gegenschein* is a somewhat moot point. It is admittedly faint and does not show in the sky when the moon is full or nearly so. Nor can it be seen in June and July or in December and January, because during these periods its position in the sky is covered by the Milky Way, which is much brighter. I have never succeeded in seeing the *Gegenschein* myself, but those who have state that it is a roughly elliptical patch of light without a clear outline and with a largest diameter between three and four times the diameter of the full moon.

Like Pézénas's report, Brorsen's reports did not produce additional observations. But twenty-two years later the *Gegenschein* was discovered again, this time by an Englishman, T. W. Backhouse, who lectured to the Royal Society about it. His paper was published in the *Monthly Notices* in 1876 under the title "On the Aspect of the Zodiacal Light Opposite the Sun."

The next discoverer of the *Gegenschein* was an American, Edward Emerson Barnard. He saw it one night in 1882 and thought that it was a very high thin cloud illuminated by starlight. But during the following night the "cloud" was still in the same place. Barnard, who had not been educated as an astronomer but was originally a photographer, did not know at the time about the earlier reports. But he immediately concluded that this was an astronomical phenomenon.

The next step was to look for an explanation. Barnard himself concluded from the appearance of the patch of light that it must be a dust cloud. Since its position opposite to that of the sun placed it on the elongation of the line from the sun to the earth he resorted to an old mathematical analysis of stable positions in space. The *Gegenschein* might easily be in one of the so-called libration points (for a more detailed explanation see Chapter 13). The specific libration point with reference to the earth would be 900,000 miles beyond the earth, on the line connecting the earth with the sun. In that position the earth's gravitational field would drag the dust cloud along, even though it describes a somewhat larger orbit than the earth and would, if the earth did not exist, need more than 365¼ days to complete one orbit.

In the meantime other astronomers had wondered about the *Gegen-*

schein too, and had advanced another hypothesis. Maybe the *Gegen-schein* was actually a part of the zodiacal light; if the latter is caused by a dust lens around the sun, one only had to assume that the dust lens, in an attenuated form, extends beyond the earth's orbit. Each dust particle would naturally behave like a tiny moon. Those particles closer to the sun than the earth is would have their dark sides toward us so that we could not see them. Those at the same distance from the sun as the earth would show a half-moon phase, but since there are not many of them we would not notice them. But those farther away would have "full phase," comparable to the full moon when it is farther from the sun than the earth is. Those are the ones we see, as a very dim patch of light. That the *Gegenschein* is always opposite to the sun is, therefore, easily explained. The laws of optics demand it; we see only those which, to us, are fully illuminated. And they are opposite the position of the sun. Barnard himself improved on this idea by pointing out that the earth's atmosphere should act as a lens and concentrate sunlight in that direction.

The reason anybody bothered to think of additional explanations was that, as time went on, astronomers had less and less use for that much dust in space and found more and more reasons to doubt its existence.

Other researchers, especially Svante Arrhenius in Sweden, had wondered whether the earth might not have a tail like a comet, a very faint one, of course, but a tail just the same. Such a tail would be pointing away from the sun because of the sun's radiation pressure. If the planet Venus also had such a tail, which was likely from the general reasoning employed by Arrhenius, we would not be able to see it because we would always look through the very tenuous tail from the side. But in the case of earth's own tail we would look from its root along its length and then it would be faintly visible under good conditions.

By the time the first World War began, there were, then, three competing theories trying to account for the *Gegenschein*: Barnard's dust cloud in a libration point; the bigger dust cloud of the zodiacal light which looked like a luminous patch because of the laws of optics; and a gaseous tail of our own planet.

Still later—beginning in about 1937—Dr. Edward O. Hulburt, then one of the research directors at the Naval Research Laboratory, evolved another theory which has some similarity to the comet tail postulated by Arrhenius. It is known as the "atmospheric ion theory" and assumes a hairpin-shaped "veil" of ions around the earth, with the two "legs" of the hairpin pointing away from the sun. The light of *Gegenschein*, according to this theory, is the end-on view of the "legs" of the veil, much as Arrhenius thought. The zodiacal light would be caused by the ions of the hairpin's bend, re-emitting solar energy as visible light.

In about 1949 the Russians began to feel that some modern work should be done on both zodiacal light and *Gegenschein* and at the Gorna Astrophysical Observatory at Alma Ata they tried to take spectrograms of both. They succeeded in taking spectrograms, but these turned out to be just somewhat more powerful versions of the lines that the night sky would produce anywhere.

Some additional research was, in a way, a by-product of tracking artificial satellites, specifically the satellites of the *Discoverer* series in their polar orbits. Special cameras, known as Baker-Nunn satellite trackers, were set up in several places, including Hawaii and the Astronomical Observatory near Tokyo. The Tokyo Observatory, in between tracking satellites, decided to check on the *Gegenschein*. The astronomer Hiroyoshi Tanabe was especially interested in this work and from observations made in Tokyo and in Colorado he succeeded in adding a little to our knowledge. The *Gegenschein* changes what intensity it has with the seasons. It is dimmest in about March and September and theoretically brightest in June and November when the Milky Way makes observations impossible. Tanabe feels strongly that the light of the *Gegenschein* cannot be caused by the hydrogen tail postulated by Hulburt and others, and believes it to be sunlight reflected by cosmic dust. Accepting Tanabe's findings and reasoning would bring us back to the two earlier explanations, the isolated dust cloud or the optical effect in the zodiacal-light dust lens. The decision will probably be rendered by an unmanned space probe, if such an investigation can be combined with other research. By itself the *Gegenschein* is not important enough to rate a separate space probe in the near future.

12

MARS

A s one progresses outward through the solar system, Mars is the first of the "naked-eye" planets to have an orbit larger than that of the earth. Since its orbit is farther away from the sun—the mean distance is 1.5237 A.U., or 141.5 million miles—its mean orbital velocity is, naturally, less than that of the earth. It is very nearly 15 miles per second, hence Mars needs 687 earth-days to complete one orbit around the sun. This means that every two years and two months, on the average, the faster-moving earth overtakes the slower-moving Mars and both planets are in the same direction as seen from the sun.

To the early astronomers who believed that the earth was the center of the universe this position indicated that the sun and Mars were on opposite sides of the sky, with the earth in the middle. Hence they called it an "opposition." In reality, Mars and earth are closest to each other at this time, and Mars therefore looks especially bright in the sky. To pretelescopic times, when the true motions of the planets were unknown, the over-all result was that every twenty-six months there was an unusually bright red "star" in the sky, which was at first rather weak, reached maximum brightness, and then faded out again.

Of course nothing but the motion of the planet and this gradual increase and decrease of its brightness could be observed in those days. All the ideas and associations which we have in connection with Mars were still far in the future; to the ancients Mars was just one of the "wanderers," and the only characteristic that made it conspicuous was its reddish color.

Just as the white light of Venus inspired names dealing with female beauty in almost all languages, the reddish color of Mars produced with equal unanimity thoughts of blood, fire, and war. The Chaldeans called it Nergal, the name of the god of the dead and of battles. In Persia Mars was *Pahlavani Siphir,* the Celestial Warrior. To the Greeks the planet became *Ares,* a name derived either from ἄρω, meaning "to kill," or from ἀρά ("disaster" or "vengeance"). The Roman name Mars is, of course, also the name of the god of war, and the origin of such terms as "martial music," "court martial," and so forth. Even the ancient symbol for Mars (♂) is "martial" in origin, since it is believed to be composed of shield and spear.

Once the fact that Mars moves around the sun outside the orbit of earth had been realized, it was clear that Mars could not show a sickle phase as Venus does. But it could have a "gibbous" phase (from Latin *gibbosus,* meaning "humped"), and Galileo Galilei looked for it, as he described in a letter to Castelli, written on December 30, 1510. But as his telescope was not yet good enough for this purpose, he failed to see it. The first to view the gibbous phase was Francesco Fontana, in the evening of August 24, 1638. His drawing exaggerates the gibbous appearance, most likely because of lack of artistic skill. Much discussion had been wasted on the round dark spot in the center of Fontana's drawings of Mars, but since a dark center spot also appears on Fontana's drawing of Venus (see Chapter 10), it must simply have been caused by a flaw in the lens system of his telescope.

The first drawings of Mars which show the surface features we know are the ones made by Christiaan Huygens on November 28, 1659, and on August 13, 1672. The earlier of these two definitely shows Syrtis major, while the other is the first to show the ice cap of the Martian south pole. In his posthumous work *Kosmotheoros* (1798), Huygens speculated a bit about conditions on Mars. As the first English edition of this book phrases it:

Mars . . . has some parts of him darker than other some. By the constant returns of which his nights and days have been found to be of about the same length with ours. But the inhabitants have no perceivable difference between summer and winter, the axis of that planet having very little or no inclination to his orbit [1] as has been discovered by the motion of his spots. Our earth must appear to them almost as Venus does to us, and by the help of a telescope will be found to have its wane, increase, and full like the moon; and never to remove from the sun about 48 degrees, by whose discovery they see it, as well as Mercury and Venus, sometimes pass over the sun's disk. They as seldom see Venus as we do Mercury. I am apt to believe that the land in Mars is of a blacker colour than that of Jupiter or the moon, which is the reason of his appearing of a copper colour, and his reflecting a weaker light than is proportionable to his distance from the sun. His body, as I observed before, though farther from the sun, is less than Venus. Nor has he any moons to wait upon him, and in that, as well as Mercury and Venus, he must be acknowledged inferior to the earth. His light and heat is twice and sometimes three times less than ours, to which I suppose the constitution of his inhabitants is answerable.

[1] Huygens was wrong here; the tilt of the Martian axis is somewhat greater than that of the earth's axis, and the seasonal differences must be pronounced, at least as far as average temperatures are concerned.

Before we can go on, it is necessary to understand why, in the case of Mars, the oppositions are of such importance. Opposition, as has been noted, is the same as "closest approach." For planets orbiting the sun inside the earth's orbit there can be no such thing as an opposition; Venus cannot possibly be in the earth's sky in a position opposite to that of the sun. And while there is, naturally, a "closest approach" between Venus and earth, this is the time when Venus disappears from view because we then face the unilluminated hemisphere of the planet.

But the so-called superior planets, the ones with orbits larger than that of the earth, present their illuminated hemispheres to us when at opposition. Obviously the time for observing all the outer planets is when they are at and near opposition, but an opposition is of greater importance with Mars than with any of the other superior planets. This will become clear if we compare a number of figures, beginning with the extreme case of Neptune. Neptune's mean distance from the sun is 2793 million miles. If the earth is on the straight line connecting the sun and Neptune, the distance is 93 million miles less; if it is on the other side of the sun the distance is 93 million miles greater. Obviously this makes very little difference either way, provided only that the sun is not in the line of sight between the earth and the planet. Extending this simple arithmetical operation to other outer planets, we get the following table:

PLANET	MINIMUM DISTANCE (MILLIONS OF MILES)	MAXIMUM DISTANCE (MILLIONS OF MILES)
Neptune	2700	2886
Uranus	1690	1876
Saturn	793	979
Jupiter	390	567

Evidently an opposition is useful for the observation of Jupiter and helps a little for Saturn, but beyond Saturn becomes unimportant. With Mars, however, the difference is enormous. Using the mean distance only, the minimum distance is 48.5 million miles while the maximum distance is 234.5 million miles. In reality, the figures are even more extreme, because the orbit of Mars is a pronounced ellipse. The aphelion of its orbit is 154.1 million miles from the sun; the perihelion only 128 million miles. Mars passes its aphelion in a place in space which corresponds to that occupied by the earth in the last week of February. The perihelion of Mars corresponds to the position of earth in the last week of August.

If Mars passes through its perihelion when the earth happens to pass through the corresponding section of its orbit we get a "perihelion opposition"—the term, of course, refers to the perihelion of Mars, since the orbit of the earth is very nearly circular, with just 3 million miles difference between perihelion and aphelion—at the shortest possible distance, 34,797,000 miles. If the opposition takes place when Mars passes through its aphelion point, the distance is almost twice as great, namely 61,516,000 miles. The greatest possible distance is 248 million miles. It becomes self-evident why Mars is observed at opposition time only, preferably, of course, when a perihelion opposition is in the offing.

Because of the high eccentricity of the orbit of Mars and the noticeable difference in its orbital velocity (13.64 miles per second at aphelion and 16.45 miles per second at perihelion), there is no set time interval between two oppositions. The figure of 780 days is mentioned in many books, but this figure is based on the mean orbital velocities of both planets,[2] and only by a remarkable coincidence would it ever actually hold true.

However, if a larger number of revolutions is taken into consideration, it is possible to derive a rule.[3]

NUMBER OF REVOLUTIONS OF MARS	CORRESPONDING NUMBER OF TERRESTRIAL YEARS	DISCREPANCY IN POSITION IN EARTH'S SKY (DEGREES)
8	15.046	16.6
17	31.974	9.4
25	47.020	7.2
42	78.994	2.2
151	284.0008	0.3

After 284 years, then, we have virtually a repetition of an opposition which took place at the beginning of this period. The very fine perihelion opposition of 1924 was a repeat of one that took place in 1640. The good opposition of 1950 was a repeat of the one of 1666 which was utilized by the first Cassini. Naturally the poor oppositions also repeat in the same way.

One more fact has to be mentioned before we can return to the history of the planet. The axis of Mars is tilted by 25° 10′ which is not much more than the 23.5° of the earth's axis. But the two axes do not point to the same area of the sky. They are not even roughly parallel in space; their tilts are almost opposite to each other. The result is that

[2] The mean daily motion of the earth is 59′ 48.2″; that of Mars is 31′26.5″—or, in seconds of arc, 3548.2 for the earth and 1886.5 for Mars. The Earth, therefore, gains on Mars by 1661.7″ daily. Dividing the number of seconds of arc of a full circle (1,296,000″) by the daily gain of the earth results in the figure of 779.92 days.

[3] Published by Robert Henseling in his *Mars, sein Rätsel und seine Geschichte* (Stuttgart, 1925).

the northern hemisphere of Mars has winter when the northern hemisphere of earth has summer. Therefore we always see a southern-hemisphere summer and a northern-hemisphere winter at perihelion opposition, while during an aphelion opposition the northern hemisphere of Mars has summer and its southern hemisphere winter.

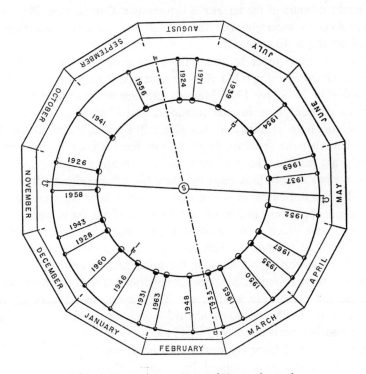

Orbit of Mars and its positions relative to the earth

Beginning with the opposition of 1638, when Fontana succeeded in seeing the gibbous phase, almost every opposition added something to the knowledge of Mars, even though it was often very little. During the opposition of 1659 Huygens observed Mars in order to establish its period of rotation. The picture he could see—Percival Lowell, over three hundred years later, called this the "presentation"—was just about the same every night, and on December 1, 1659, Huygens made a note in his diary that "the rotation of Mars seems to take 24 terrestrial hours like that of earth." A few oppositions later, in 1666, Cassini spent a good deal of time on the same problem, observing from Bologna. His drawings of the appearance of Mars are not very good from our point

of view, but by timing the positions of the spots which he did draw,[4]
he concluded that Mars presented the same appearance 40 minutes later
every night. It may sound surprising, but this fact alone does not justify
the conclusion that the diurnal period of Mars is 24 hours and 40 minutes. If it were 12 hours and 20 minutes the observational result would
be the same, since the first return of the "presentation" would fall into
the daylight hours of the terrestrial astronomer. Cassini took all possible
precautions to ascertain that the period was actually more than 24
hours by about 40 minutes.

The next astronomer to attack the same problem was a nephew of
Cassini, Giacomo Filippo Maraldi. He observed during every opposition,
beginning in 1672. By 1702 Maraldi felt sure of two things. One was
that his uncle's figure for the rotational period of Mars was about 1
minute too long (actually it was about 2½ minutes too long). The
other was that the spots on Mars did not remain unchanged; both the
white areas marking the poles and the darkish areas marking the equatorial regions did not look quite the same from opposition to opposition.
In 1719 Maraldi could announce that he had seen changes taking place
during an opposition but could not be sure which spots were surface
markings and which were clouds, and the observed changes might be
those in cloud formations. However, he could add another discovery
in 1719: the white spots marking the polar areas were round, but the
centers of these round white spots did not coincide with the geographical
poles of the planet. He was correct. The ice (or snow) caps of Mars
are eccentric to the poles, as are the polar caps of the earth, a fact
which had not been discovered in 1719.

The next set of favorable oppositions occurred in 1777, 1779, 1781,
and 1783. These were utilized by William Herschel, who, as usual,
expressed both the purpose and the result of his observations in the
titles of the papers in which he reported them. In this case there were
two papers. The first one was called "Astronomical observations on the
rotation of the planets round their axes"; and the second, "On the
remarkable appearances at the polar regions of the planet Mars, the inclination of its axis, the position of its poles, and its spheroidical figure;
with a few hints relating to its real diameter and atmosphere." They
were published in the *Philosophical Transactions* for 1781 and 1784
respectively. His observations convinced him that the white polar spots,
noncommittally so labeled by Maraldi, were actually accumulations of
snow and ice. (He also noted their eccentricity to the geographical

[4] He published the drawings in *Martis circa proprium axem revolubilis obser-
vationes Bononiae habitae,* 1666.

poles.) He stated unhesitatingly that Mars has an atmosphere, "so its inhabitants probably enjoy conditions analogous to ours in several respects." He was the first to observe color changes on Mars, and he established the beginning of spring on the planet. He found the axis of Mars inclined to the ecliptic by 59°, 42′, and calculated the length of the Martian day as 24 hours, 39 minutes, and 21.67 seconds. Herschel's papers on Mars mark the last important work done prior to the nineteenth century.

The next important observer of Mars was Dr. Johann Hieronymus Schroeter, whose first telescope was a 7-foot instrument made by Herschel. Schroeter was only a part-time astronomer; during the day he was *Amtmann* at Lilienthal near Bremen. There is no English equivalent for this title; its literal translation is "the official," and if this term is taken literally to the utmost it also comes close to the meaning of the word. An *Amtmann* was *the* official of a district; anything that had to do with government, from the registry of a birth to the enforcement of a law, went through the *Amtmann*'s office. This explanation of Schroeter's official standing is necessary because as a result of his position his valuable private observatory was destroyed during the Napoleonic wars. The property belonged not to a mere citizen of another country but to an "official of an enemy principality."

The story of Schroeter's work on Mars has another sad aspect besides the destruction of his observatory—his work remained unknown for many years. Schroeter's observations covered the oppositions from 1785 to 1802; the manuscript and his drawings somehow found their way into the library of the observatory of the University of Leyden. Almost eighty years after they were made, the director of the observatory, Hendricus Gerardus van de Sande Bakhuyzen, decided that they should be published in memory of Schroeter's diligent work. The publication, in 1881, was in Schroeter's original German under the title of *Areographische Beiträge zur genaueren Kenntnis und Beurteilung des Planeten Mars* (Areographic Contributions toward a Better Knowledge and Understanding of the Planet Mars). The term "areographic" was apparently coined by Schroeter by analogy with "geographic," using *"Ares"* instead of *"Gaia"* (earth).

Schroeter's work was published when scientific and popular interest in Mars was at a peak. The turning point in Mars's history, the moment when it ceased to be just one planet among others and came to be acclaimed a "second earth," came in the wake of the very fine opposition of 1877.

But the oppositions between Schroeter's observations and 1877 were not wasted. During those of 1830 and 1832, Wilhelm Beer and J. H. von Mädler, working on a map of the moon in their private observatory in the Tiergarten in Berlin, took time out to draw the first maps of Mars. One of the two men—since they collaborated constantly one can only rarely tell what was done by Beer and what by von Mädler— wrote a sentence which will produce a nod of agreement from everybody who has ever looked at Mars through a telescope. It read: "Usually some time had to elapse before the indefinite vague mass at first seen dissolved itself into clearly distinguishable forms." This is typical for Mars. One has to sit behind (or lie under) the telescope for several minutes before one sees anything at all. I suspect that quite a number of possible observations have been missed because an astronomer, after looking for a while at an orange-red ball of indistinct shadings, decided that the seeing was not good enough for Mars that night.

By comparing the drawings they made in 1832 with those made in 1830 the two observers established the period of rotation of Mars as 24 hours, 37 minutes, and 23.7 seconds.

During the opposition of 1858 Father Angelo Secchi, S. J., in Rome made the first color drawings of Mars, with fine shadings of green in the dark and equally fine shadings of yellow in the light areas of the planet. Two oppositions later, Sir Joseph Norman Lockyer in England produced a number of fine drawings of Mars, while Frederick Kaiser in Leyden made the first attempt to consolidate his own drawings in a globe of Mars. Kaiser also concluded, from a comparison of all available material, that the figure for the diurnal period given by Beer and von Mädler was 1.1 seconds too long and should read 24 hours, 37 minutes, 22.6 seconds. (This is the currently accepted figure, except for 0.1 second; it now ends with 22.7 seconds.) And during the late November opposition of 1864 the Reverend William Rutter Dawes made several drawings of Mars which remain outstanding to this day.

Three years later, in 1867, another English astronomer, Richard Anthony Proctor, drew a new map of Mars, one of his innovations being that he named the Martian features. Following the precedent set by Riccioli in naming the features of the moon, he used the names of astronomers, dead and alive. The largest of the dark areas he named the Dawes Ocean, which had an eastern extension called the Hooke Sea and a western extension called the Herschell II Strait. The two "continents" to the south of the Dawes Ocean were named the Dawes Continent and the Herschel I Continent—Herschel I and Herschel II referring to Sir William and Sir John respectively.

The criticism with which this map was greeted on the European

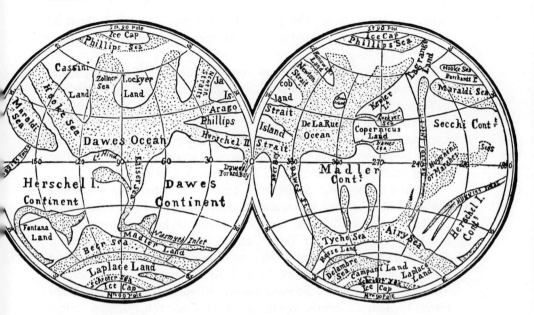

Richard A. Proctor's map of Mars, drawn in 1867, which was strongly criticized for naming four different features after the Rev. William R. Dawes

continent amounted to a howl. Not because Proctor's map was not good. Though it isn't good by present-day standards, it was not bad for its time. The howl was based on the fact that Proctor had given the names of English astronomers to all the biggest markings. Oh yes, there was a Beer Sea and a Maraldi Sea, a Cassini Land and a Laplace Land, but the only large area bearing a non-English name was the Mädler Continent. And to have the name of the Reverend William Dawes, no matter whether he merited it or not, represented four times was just too much! Strangely enough, the third feature, Dawes Forked Bay, is the only one for which Proctor's designation has survived. The reason it did is that he used it to mark the zero meridian, the only thing in the network of latitude and longitude that is chosen arbitrarily. The other main features are determined by geographical or astronomical facts. The poles are obvious and so is the equator; they are derived from the planet's rotation. The zonal borderlines, arctic and antarctic and the tropics, are given by the tilt of the planet's axis. But the zero meridian is something that has to be agreed on. On earth we use the location of the Royal Observatory at Greenwich, England; for Mars, Proctor's decision to use the Forked Bay was accepted.

The fact that Proctor had applied names, necessary as they obviously were, had its dangers. The possibility of a not very subtle kind of chauvinism could be avoided, but not the confusion resulting from differences in languages.

The next two attempts to draw complete maps of Mars were made by a Frenchman and an Italian. The rather beautiful French map was published in 1892 by Camille Flammarion. A number of names were the same as Proctor's. The Dawes Ocean remained Océan Dawes, and Laplace Land Terre de Laplace. Mädler Continent also kept its name, but its neighbor, Dawes Continent, became, logically enough, the Beer Continent. Proctor's Kaiser Sea became *Mer du Sablier*.

The Italian, who was Schiaparelli, drew a still better map which was published in 1878, and which also solved the linguistic and nationalistic problems by discarding the names of people. What on Flammarion's map had been called Mer Terby became Solis Lacus on Schiaparelli's. The Kaiser Sea, or Mer du Sablier, turned into Syrtis Major. The light area around Solis Lacus, called Terre de Kepler by Flammarion, became Thaumasia; the Mer de Fontana became Elysium, and the Mer Oude- mann Trivium Charontis. By the grace of God, Schiaparelli's system won out in all countries, and most of his names are still in use. Being Latin they need no translation and create no rivalries.

But what suddenly made Mars the most popular of all planets, as it still is, was a particular feature of Schiaparelli's map—the lines con- necting the dark areas. Schiaparelli called these lines *canali,* an Italian word which means "grooves" when applied to man-made objects, and "channels" (like the English Channel) when applied to natural features. Schiaparelli used the term with the latter meaning; since the dark areas on Mars were then believed to be seas, he thought the dark lines were connecting channels. It was no fault of his that in all other languages, a "canal" is an artificial waterway. Schiaparelli had not been the first to draw such lines on a map of Mars; Kaiser in Leyden and the Rev- erend Mr. Dawes had done so before him. He was not even the first to use the term—Father Secchi had also used it with the same Italian meaning in mind. But these facts were not recognized for a number of years; for decades the words "Mars" and "Schiaparelli" were virtually synonymous. (I still remember my surprise when in my last year in high school, I learned that Schiaparelli had done work on Mercury and Venus—what he was doing away from "his" planet?)

Schiaparelli's report, which struck the imagination of the civilized world, was anything but sensational in either appearance or style. It was a "memorial" of the Royal Academy of the Lynxes in Rome, and the title was "Astronomical observations concerning the axis of rotation

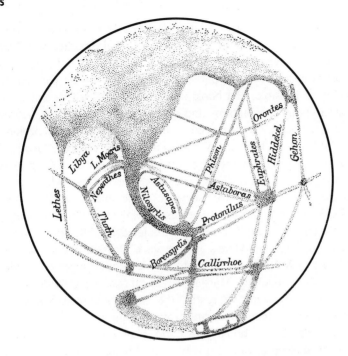

Composite map based on G. V. Schiaparelli's sketches made during the nights of 2, 4, and 6 of June, 1888, showing the gemination of the canals

and the topography of the planet Mars." [5] But behind this sober title lurked the possibility of intelligent beings on another planet; the philosophical speculations of centuries (themselves secret desires in hiding) had found a focal point.

The years from 1880 to 1914 saw a flood of publications on Mars: scientific, popular, speculative, and purely crackpot. The outbreak of World War I in 1914 dammed the flood, partly by creating a host of immediate and urgent problems, partly by causing a severe paper shortage in most European countries.

For a discussion of the literary developments of that period the material may be divided into two classes—scientific astronomy on the one hand and everything else on the other.

The story of the para-scientific literature began just two years after the opposition of 1877, with a well-meant popularization by a scientist. Professor Jakob Heinrich Schmick of Cologne, later to become known in restricted circles as a theorist in the field of paleoclimatology, in

[5] *Osservazioni astronomiche e fisiche sull'asse di rotazione e sulla topografia del pianeta Marte,* published in 1878. A second memorial by Schiaparelli appeared in 1881 and a third in 1886.

1879 published a book with the title *Der Planet Mars, eine zweite Erde* (The Planet Mars, a Second Earth); it is significant that he added the words "after Schiaparelli" to the title page. Presumably he was anxious to make the results of Schiaparelli's work known to the German public as quickly as possible. His book was, in the main, a free translation of Schiaparelli with explanations and emendations by Schmick. About the same can be said for the second popular book of the period, one entitled *Mars, eine Welt im Kampf ums Dasein* (1901). *"Kampf ums Dasein"* is the phrase coined by Darwin's German translator to represent "Struggle for survival"; hence this title means "Mars, a World Engaged in the Struggle for Survival." The author was an Austrian named Otto Dross. Dross had later astronomical material at his disposal than Schmick had had. The report, circulated in 1892, that a new dark area had appeared on Mars's surface gave Dross a chance to describe the struggle of Martian engineers to rescue another piece of arable land from the all-encroaching Martian desert. It was all very dramatic and inspired in every sensitive reader the wish to donate half an ocean to the Martians if there were any way of doing it.

Between Schmick's book and Dross's an episode occurred, which touched on science in that it involved the French Academy of Sciences, and which had legal implications, if only because it involved the sum of 100,000 gold francs, but which made scientists in general, and astronomers in particular, walk around muttering for awhile. A rich French woman named Madame Clara Goguet, early in December 1900, had deposited the sum mentioned with the directorate of the Academy, to establish an award to be known as the Pierre Guzman Prize, in memory of her son by a former marriage. The sum was to be paid: *"à celui qui aura trouvé le moyen de communiquer avec an astre autre que la planèt Mars."* In English, "to him who has found the means of communicating with a star other than the planet Mars." The wording shows why Camille Flammarion labeled it *"une idée bizarre."* Madame Goguet, who presumably had read articles in French periodicals about the struggling Martian engineers, apparently thought that communication with Mars would be too easy to deserve a prize. The only reason the professionals remained polite (in addition to the fact that the Academy was involved) was that Madame Goguet had foreseen that "the prize might not be awarded quickly" and had stipulated that the interest on the money be used for a secondary award every five years for important astronomical discoveries. The first such award was to be made in 1905.

It went to the widow of the French astronomer Henri J. A. Perrotin, Perrotin having died the year before, and was made for Perrotin's work on Mars! Of course the award was killed off later by the French inflation.

While most of the popular and more or less fanciful literature on Mars explored the question of survival with a limited water supply, three different authors—all writing in German—evolved different theories based on a very watery Mars. The first was Ludwig Kann with his "New Theory about the Origin of Coal and Solution of the Mars Problem"; the second was Adrian Baumann with his "Explanation of the Surface of the Planet Mars"; and the third was Philipp Fauth, then very well known as an amateur astronomer, with his "Hörbiger's World Ice Doctrine." [6]

Kann apparently had been reading discussions of the origin of coal in some of the geological literature of his period. Although most geologists by the year 1900 were convinced that the coal deposits we find today are in the same geographical locations as the carboniferous forests which produced them, there were still a few doubters. Some preferred to think that a coal deposit owed its origin to the action of rivers which,

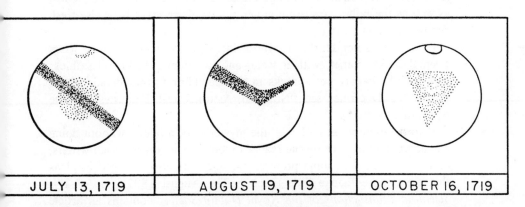

| JULY 13, 1719 | AUGUST 19, 1719 | OCTOBER 16, 1719 |

Three early drawings of Mars by Giacomo Filippo Maraldi. Dates indicate the nights during which the observations were made

for millennium after millennium, washed the fallen trees and brushwork of large forests into the same quiet bay, while others felt that a few coal deposits might have originated with masses of floating seaweed similar to those in the Sargasso Sea of our own time. Kann was fascinated by the Sargasso Sea idea (and had an enormously exaggerated

[6] Ludwig Kann: *Neue Theorie Über den Ursprung der Kohle und die Lösung des Marsrätsels* (Heidelberg, 1901); Adrian Baumann: *Erklärung der Oberfläche des Planeten Mars* (Zurich, 1909); Philipp Fauth: *Hörbiger's Glacial-Kosmogonie* (Minden, 1912).

idea about the density of the Sargasso Sea); he soon concluded that it accounted for most coal deposits and that the accumulation of fallen trees in a quiet bay was only a fairly exceptional case. As for Mars he thought it was actually a *panthalassa* like the planet Venus. Three-quarters of this shoreless ocean was covered by floating seaweed of the same yellowish-brownish color as some terrestrial types. The dark areas were those where for unknown reasons this seaweed did not grow; these areas looked dark because the dark ocean bottom could be seen through fairly clear water. The "canals," finally, were lines where the floating weed had been parting by swift-flowing ocean currents.

Adrian Baumann also made Mars mostly water, but to him it was frozen water. The dark areas, he asserted, were land, with vegetation, and probably with animal life too. The yellow areas were frozen oceans, colored yellow by a layer of dust from active volcanos, and the eruptions of the volcanos caused the yellow clouds which astronomers see from time to time. The canals which run from the volcanic islands to the vegetated land areas are wide cracks in the frozen seas, the logical result of active volcanism in large masses of solid ice. The white clouds, as well as the polar caps, were either clouds of ice crystals or else fresh deposits of hoarfrost.

Fauth, or rather Hörbiger, whose ideas he expounded, made Mars a small rocky planet, with a water-and-ice mantle 1000 miles thick; here too the canals were cracks in the ice. (For further details of the World Ice Doctrine, see "Note on Astronomical Fantasies" in the Appendix.)

If these attempts at "solving" the mysteries of a planet without doing any actual research, cause the reader to feel harshly toward such writers, he must realize that some professional scientists also indulged in ideas that were more than a little fanciful. The August 1897 issue of *The Scientific Transactions of the Royal Dublin Society* contains an article "On the Origin of the Canals of Mars," by J. Joly in which the "canals" are declared to be really ridges, caused by the gravitational attraction of asteroids in nearly horizontal trajectories passing close over the Martian surface prior to impact!

Let us now return to astronomy proper with the opposition of 1879, the one following the history-making opposition of 1877. During the 1879 opposition, C. A. Young, as he reported in the *American Journal of Science* (1880), succeeded in measuring the diameter of Mars with high precision and in establishing the difference between its equatorial and polar diameters. And Schiaparelli drew another map of the planet, on which the *canali,* though in the same places as before, look straighter. On his first map the *canali* were, to quote Percival Lowell,[7] "depicted as narrow winding streaks, hardly even roughly regular . . . indeed, to a modern reader prepared beforehand for geometric construction there will probably appear no 'canals' at all." On the 1879 map "the lines were straighter, narrower and in every way less natural than they had seemed two years before."

Lowell meant to imply that Schiaparelli at first did not believe his own eyes and tried to make artificial structures look natural. But discounting the implications, his statements were perfectly correct; Schiaparelli's first map does look quite different from his later ones, which are the ones usually used as illustrations in books.

Aside from the "evolution" of Schiaparelli's drawing style, the year 1879 brought one more discovery on his part. Not only did he add *canali* to those he had seen two years earlier; he saw with utmost surprise that the Martian canals can play a trick that had been completely unsuspected. One of his *canali,* which he had named Nilus, suddenly appeared double. This was the first example of what Schiaparelli called the "gemination" of the *canali*; during the following opposition, in 1882, he was to see many more examples. Henri Perrotin in Nice and A. Stanley Williams in England corroborated the phenomenon of the gemination with their own observations. Both Schiaparelli and Perrotin pointed out that the gemination could not be an optical illusion; if it were, a canal under observation might turn indistinct and then split and appear as a double canal. What the observer sees is different, however; the canal under observation stays unchanged, but some distance away a parallel canal appears. The distance between the two is on the order of 50 to 80 miles.

Other results of the observations by Schiaparelli, Perrotin, and others were that the dark areas of Mars showed definite seasonal color changes. That the white polar caps disappeared during the summer was known, since William Herschel had stated that only one Martian pole has a white cap at a given time. Schiaparelli added that the dark areas grew darker during the Martian spring and lighter during the Martian winter. He also found that, wherever several *canali* came together, a round spot existed. He called these round spots "lakes." By 1892—the first good opposition since that of December 1881—the American astronomer William H. Pickering added the information that small round spots could be seen wherever two *canali* crossed each other. They were far

[7] *Mars and Its Canals* (New York, 1906).

smaller than Schiaparelli's "lakes," and Pickering suggested "oases" for them.

In 1893 the story of the planet Mars moved into a new phase; another new name, that of Percival Lowell, began to gain prominence. By coincidence Schiaparelli, at the beginning of that year, published a summing up of his own thoughts, which appeared in the magazine *Natura ed Arte* (February 15, 1893) and was translated into English by William H. Pickering. It is still worth quoting because here the existing knowledge of our neighbor in space is condensed, not by a man who had studied the literature (others, especially Camille Flammarion, had done excellently in that respect) but by a man who had studied the planet.

Schiaparelli discussed the Martian features type by type, beginning with the polar caps.

. . . it is manifest that if the white polar spots of Mars represent snow and ice, they should continue to decrease in size with the approach of summer in those places, and increase during the winter. Now this very fact is observed in the most evident manner. In the second half of the year 1892 the southern polar cap was in full view; during that interval, and especially during the months of July and August, its rapid diminution from week to week was very evident . . .

About the Martian atmosphere Schiaparelli continued:

In every climate, and under every zone, its atmosphere is nearly perpetually clear, and sufficiently transparent to permit one to recognize at any moment whatever, the contours of the seas and continents. . . . Here and there we see appear from time to time a few whitish spots changing their position and form, rarely extending over a very wide area. . . . It is possible that they may be layers of cloud, because the upper portions of terrestrial clouds, where they are illuminated by the Sun, appear white. But various observations lead us to think that we are dealing rather with a thin veil of fog, instead of a true nimbus cloud, carrying storms and rain. Indeed it may be merely a temporary condensation of vapor, under the form of dew or hoar frost. Accordingly, as far as we may be permitted to argue from the observed facts, the climate of Mars must resemble that of a clear day upon a high mountain.

After an extensive description of the map which accompanied the article, Schiaparelli progressed to the *canali*:

All the vast extent of the continents is furrowed upon every side by a network of numerous lines or fine stripes of a more or less pronounced dark color whose aspect is very variable. They traverse the planet for long distances in regular lines, that do not at all resemble the winding courses of our streams. Some of the shorter ones do not reach 500 kilometers [300 miles], others extend for many thousands, occupying a quarter or sometimes even a third of a circumference of the planet. Some of these are very easy to see, especially the one . . . designated by the name of Nilosyrtis. Others in turn are extremely difficult, and resemble the finest thread of spider's web drawn across the disk. They are subject also to great variations in their breadth, which may reach 200 or even 300 kilometers [120 to 180 miles] for the Nilosyrtis, whilst some are scarcely 30 kilometers [18 miles] broad. . . . These lines are the famous canals of Mars. . . . Their length and arrangement are constant, or vary only between very narrow limits. Each of them always begins and ends between the same regions. But their appearance and their degree of visibility vary greatly, for all of them, from one opposition to another, and even from one week to another. . . .

As for the gemination, he reported, after stating that this happens very rapidly—in a few days "or even perhaps only a few hours":

The two lines follow very nearly the original canal, and end in the place where it ended. One of these is often superimposed as exactly upon the former line . . . but it also happens that both the lines may occupy opposite sides of the former canal, and be located upon entirely new ground. The distance between the two lines differs in different geminations, and varies from 600 kilometers [370 miles] and more, down to the smallest limit at which two lines may appear separated in large visual telescopes—less than an interval of 50 kilometers [30 miles]. . . .

Returning to the canals in general, Schiaparelli concluded:

. . . The most natural and the most simple interpretation is that to which we have referred, of a great inundation produced by the melting of the snows—it is entirely logical, and is sustained by evident analogy with terrestrial phenomena. We conclude therefore that the canals [here it would have been better to use "channels" in the translation] are such in fact, and not only in name. The network formed by these was probably determined in its origin in the geological state of the planet. . . . It is not necessary to suppose them the work of intelligent beings, and notwithstanding the almost geometric appearance of all of their system, we are now inclined to believe them to be produced by the evolution of the planet, just as on the earth we have the English Channel and the Channel of Mozambique.

As to the explanation of the *canali* and the existence of intelligent Martians, Schiaparelli was careful to straddle the fence to the end of his life. In April 1910 the German scientific monthly *Kosmos* published a long article by Svante Arrhenius, who considered Mars to be far too cold to be inhabited or even inhabitable. Arrhenius's article is discussed later.) A Mr. Franz H. Babinger wanted to make sure that Schiaparelli did not miss Arrhenius's opinion, and was also curious to learn what Schiaparelli would say about it. Knowing that Schiaparelli read German easily (he had studied under Johann Franz Encke, then director of the Berlin observatory) he mailed him a copy of the magazine. Schiaparelli wrote in reply:

For my person I have not yet succeeded in formulating an organic whole of logical and credible thoughts about the phenomena of Mars, which are perhaps somewhat more complicated than Dr. Arrhenius believes. . . . I believe with him that the lines and bands on Mars (the name "canals" should be avoided) can be explained as the results of physical and chemical forces, always excepting certain periodical color changes which are likely to be the result of organic events of large magnitude, like the flowering of the steppes on earth and similar phenomena. I am also of the opinion that the regular and geometric lines (the existence of which is still denied by many persons) do not yet teach us anything about the existence of intelligent beings on this planet. But I think it worthwhile if somebody collected everything . . . that can reasonably be said in favor of their existence.

The letter (printed in *Kosmos,* 1910, p. 303) was dated May 19, 1910, and is probably Schiaparelli's last utterance on Mars, since he died on July 4 of the same year.

While Schiaparelli refrained from taking sides, Percival Lowell became the most outspoken advocate of the existence of the Martians. Lowell came from a patrician family in New England and looked the part so perfectly that in several European books of the period from 1910 to 1914 his portrait is captioned "Sir Percival Lowell," even when the text stated that he was an American.

Lowell, whose mathematical ability had received the highest praise from his teacher, Professor Benjamin Peirce, who prided himself on his eyesight, and who, when he was troubled, read Latin classics in the original, decided in 1893 that an observatory was needed which would devote full time to Mars whenever the planet was observable. Lowell stated that Pickering had taught him that three factors make for a good observation. One is eyesight, though the telescope tends to eliminate minor differences in that; the second is insight; and the third is the atmosphere. The best telescope and the best observer were no use if they were located in an area where the atmosphere was not suitable. Pickering, for that reason, had started an observatory at Arequipa, Peru, and had later gone to Jamaica. Lowell sent somebody to Arizona to find a suitable site, high up, in a dry climate, with a transparent atmosphere.

Lowell Observatory at Flagstaff was the result.

After observing the melting of the Martian ice cap and the darkening around it, followed by the gradual darkening of the normally darker areas through the darkening *canali,* Lowell decided that the network of the *canali* must be artificial and should hence be called "canals." Lowell was mainly responsible for the general theory (later adopted by Dross and others) that Mars is an old planet. In favor of this idea were the thin atmosphere, and the small remnants of water which had to be carefully conserved by its inhabitants—probably now fused into one nation by an environment growing more hostile, or rather more penurious, all the time.

Lowell was probably the first to discover a "canal" in one of the dark areas. This forced him to assume that the dark areas were not bodies of water but vegetated areas, probably lowlands, surrounded by a desert of generally higher elevation. This discovery tightened the picture further; civilization was now restricted to the dark areas only, areas which comprised only one-quarter of the total surface of the planet.

Lowell did not expect that his conclusions would be accepted by everybody, and even in his very first book on the subject (*Mars*, Boston, 1895) he defended himself in advance, so to speak.

Startling as the outcome of these observations may appear at first, in truth there is nothing startling about it whatever. Such possibility had been quite in the cards ever since the existence of Mars itself was recognized by the Chaldean shepherds. . . .

To be shy of anything resembling himself is part and parcel of man's own individuality. Like the savage who fears nothing so much as a strange man, like Crusoe who grows pale at the sight of footprints not his own, the civilized thinker instinctively turns from the thought of mind other than the one he himself knows. To admit into his conception of the cosmos other finite minds as factors has in it something of the weird. Any hypothesis to explain the facts, no matter how improbable or even palpably absurd it be, is better than this. . . . Meteors ploughing tracks across its surface with such mathematical precision that they must have been educated for the performance [J. Joly's hypothesis], and so forth and so on, in hypotheses each more astounding than its predecessor, commend themselves to man, if only by such means he may escape the admission of anything approaching his kind. Surely all this is puerile and should as speedily as possible be outgrown. . . .

Actually Lowell did not need such a spirited defense of his thoughts. The educated public was perfectly willing to be fascinated by the idea and waited eagerly for more news. Many scientists in various fields were also willing to go along and to consider their own specialties under the Martian conditions Lowell described. Sociologists speculated about the probable form of government; an engineer calculated the number of pipelines required to handle the waters from a 5-foot-thick polar cap and the energy required to pump it from the polar areas to the equator;[8] and popular writers wondered where the capital of the planet might be located. Most of them agreed on Solis Lacus, whose location seemed ideal for this purpose.

Though Lowell had an enormous popular following—probably larger

[8] C. E. Housden: *The Riddle of Mars, the Planet* (London, 1914).

than he himself realized—a large number of other people tried to see whether the observed facts could be explained without the assumption of struggling intelligent Martians. The main problem was, of course, the *canali,* with the additional question of whether these were a "fact" of observation. Many astronomers, especially in northern Europe, took the position that the *canali* did not exist. Their reasoning was as straightforward as it was wrong. They said that they were experienced observers. They could prove that they had at their disposal instruments at least as powerful as those used by Schiaparelli and Lowell and others who had gone on record in favor of the existence of *canali.* And they had never succeeded in seeing any *canali.* Therefore *canali* did not exist. This amounted to saying that there is no climatic difference between Hamburg or the Rhine Valley and Arizona or Milan.

On the other hand, Schiaparelli and Lowell could not very well be accused of having invented the *canali*; hence they must have made a mistake of some kind. The Italian astronomer Vincenzo Cerulli, who had a private observatory named Collurania, is the author of the idea that the *canali* are just a special kind of optical illusion. If the surface of Mars is covered with very many uneven surfaces of different color, whether rocky outcroppings or patches of vegetation or just chemicals in the soil, these dark spots, invisible by themselves, may form patterns which to the eye appear as straight lines. Cerulli published bulletins from his observatory containing his theory and also his own drawings of Mars. He weakened his own case by publishing drawings showing *canali*; no matter how convinced he was that his eyes were being fooled by invisible detail, they still were fooled.

An Englishman, E. Walter Maunder, tried to prove Cerulli's hypothesis. In his book *Are the Planets Inhabited* (London, 1913) he reported on an experiment using 200 pupils of the Greenwich Hospital School. The boys were selected on the basis of having keen eyesight, of being accustomed to do what they were told without asking questions, and of knowing nothing about astronomy in general and Mars in particular. Then a large diagram was hung on the wall, showing the features of Mars taken from an actual astronomical drawing but without *canali*. Instead, "a few dots or irregular markings were put in here and there," presumably by Mr. Maunder himself. The boys were then requested to draw what they saw. "Those nearest the diagram were able to detect the little irregular markings and represented them under their true forms. Those at the back of the room could not see anything of them and only represented the broadest features of the diagram, the continents and seas. Those in the middle of the room were too far off to define the minute markings, but were near enough for those markings to produce some impression upon them; and that impression always was that of a network of straight lines. . . ."

Interesting, but hardly definitive. In the first place, the "dots and irregular markings" had been put in by the experimenter; the actual invisible markings on Mars would probably be elsewhere. In the second place, the actual markings must still form approximately straight lines, which in itself calls for an explanation.

To recount all the ideas which were put on paper during the first few decades of the present centuries would make a book in itself, one more addition to the three dozen or so books on Mars which already exist. Only a few of the more seriously discussed hypotheses can be mentioned here. One was quite simple: the *canali* are water courses, but they are not artificial and they are not even straight. They might be quite winding, but since they were the only source of water they produced a strip of vegetation which would be approximately the same width, covering up all the meanderings of the actual water course.

An interesting variation was suggested by Elihu Thompson. He also considered the *canali* strips of vegetation but ascribed them to be migration of animals which seasonally go north or south, carrying seeds from the vegetated areas in their fur or on their hoofs (or whatever they have), or leave undigested seeds in their excrements, which also help to fertilize the migration routes.

William H. Pickering had stated in one of his publications that one might think of the *canali* as more or less continuous natural cracks in the Martian surface. Such cracks were likely to exude both volcanic carbon dioxide and water vapor which would sustain a vegetation in the vicinity and would thereby become visible. Alfred Russel Wallace, the English naturalist who had independently conceived the idea of organic evolution at the same time as Charles Darwin, was asked by some periodical in 1906 to write a review of Percival Lowell's books. Wallace disagreed with Lowell, and the more he wrote the more furious he became. The review grew into a book of 110 pages, which was published in London in 1907 under the title *Is Mars Habitable?* Wallace had read many of Pickering's writings and decided that the *canali* must be cracks. But what would cause cracks covering the whole planet? Wallace could conceive of a reason: if the core of the planet no longer contracted but the outer mantle of the planet still did, cracks would form. Having gone that far, he had to show that these were the prevailing conditions on Mars; in short, he traveled a considerable distance from his own fields, which were the zoogeographical distribution of animals, evolution, and related subjects. The result is slightly embarrassing since Wallace took what had been a cautious statement by Pickering and treated it as a fact.

He made the categorical statement that "all physicists are agreed that, owing to the distance of Mars from the sun, it would have a mean temperature of about *minus* 35° Fahrenheit"; he then stated that there is "independent proof that water-vapour cannot exist on Mars," from which he drew the surprising conclusion that "therefore, the first essential of organic life—water—is non-existent." And he finished by declaring: "Mars, therefore, is not only uninhabited by intelligent beings such as Mr. Lowell postulates, but is absolutely UNINHABITABLE."

Aside from the faulty logic, it must be noted that in 1906 no temperature measurements of the surface of Mars had yet been made, so that any figure which could be quoted would be based on calculation only. Of course a calculation which corresponds to reality can be made, provided all the factors are known. That all the factors were not known was shown by the first actual measurements.

But before we can go on to the measurements, Arrhenius's theory has to be evaluated, since it came earlier, having been published in 1910. Arrhenius was primarily a chemist; he had won the Nobel Prize for chemistry in 1903 and was director of the Nobel Institute for Physical Chemistry. Naturally, he tried to explain the appearance of the planet, including the color changes, by a series of physical and chemical reactions.

Arrhenius also started with a mean temperature of −34° F., calculated, by Christiansen in Copenhagen in 1890. But he pointed out that the same calculation made for our own earth would give values of about 9° C. (16.5° F.) below the actual values; if this correction was also applied to Mars, at noon the actual temperature might rise above freezing point. Such a temperature would cause rapid melting or evaporation, since it is abetted by the low pressure of the Martian atmosphere. The deserts of Mars are old enough to have had time to accumulate considerable quantities of cosmic dust, mostly iron, which oxidized and thereby caused the typical red color of the planet. The so-called lakes were just low areas and the canals earthquake cracks. But they did not become visible because of vegetation; the whole process of color change, the famous "wave of darkness," was a purely chemical phenomenon. He assumed that in low-lying areas there might be occasional true lakes, "like the desert lakes on earth very shallow, with very salty water and often evaporating completely." When such a lake does evaporate, the least soluble salts, the sulfur salts, will appear first at the shores in crystal form. Ordinary salt and magnesium chloride will follow suit. In the center there will still be liquid water, or rather a saturated watery solution of calcium chloride, which does not freeze until the temperature has dropped below −65° F. But finally this solution also freezes, and the ice crystals evaporate because of the general dryness of the atmosphere and are carried to the coldest part of the planet, the pole, which happens to be having winter, where they form a polar cap. When spring comes and the polar cap evaporates, the water is attracted by the unusually highly hygroscopic salts, which then appear dark again. And, concluded Arrhenius, if one makes the assumption that some water vapor, mixed with carbon dioxide, sulfur dioxide, and hydrochloric acid, still comes from the interior in some places, the wave of darkness can be explained by two partly interlinked causes. One is the direct darkening action of moisture, the other a chemical reaction which changes the reddish iron oxides into black sulfides.[9]

It was a most interesting explanation, but one can only echo old Schiaparelli's comment that things on Mars are probably not as simple as Arrhenius presented them.

The oppositions of 1907 and 1909 had been quite good as far as the distance between the two planets was concerned, but they did not bring any unusual results. After 1911 the oppositions grew progressively poorer, including the first opposition after the World War, in 1920. But astronomers knew that the June opposition of 1922 would be fine, while the August opposition of 1924 should be perfect, since it took place when Mars was only a few degrees from its perihelion.

And on that occasion temperature measurements were made. Scientific Paper No. 512 of the Bureau of Standards (April 28, 1925) reported on radiometric measurements made at the Lowell Observatory, during twenty-four nights from July to September 1924. Both the temperatures of the bright yellow areas near the center of the disk and those of dark areas like Syrtis major had been measured, at sunrise, at sunset, and at noon Martian time. The figures were much higher than was expected. At sunrise at opposition the temperature of a given area measured −45° C., or about −49° F. At the sunset side of the planet the temperature was precisely at freezing point; 0° C. or 32° F. (Of course these measurements, being made from the outside through the Martian atmosphere, would not be quite correct. An area that measured freezing point through the Martian atmosphere would actually be somewhat warmer.)

---

[9] This condensed translation of Arrhenius's ideas is repeated from *The Exploration of Mars* by Willy Ley and Werner von Braun (New York: The Viking Press, 1956).

At the center of the disk—high noon for that spot—there was a considerable difference between light desert, presumably high ground, and dark lowland. The desert temperatures at noon ran from $-10°$ C. $(14°$ F.) to $+5°$ C. $(41°$ F.). In the dark areas the noon temperatures ran from $+10°$ to $+20°$ C. (50 to 68° F.). For a human explorer, the noonday temperature in a dark area would be pleasant, but *only* the noon temperature. The average for the whole disk during the day was $-30°$ C. $(-22°$ F.). The nighttime temperatures could not, of course, be measured, but they could be estimated from the early morning temperatures; the average for the whole night side must be $-70°$ C. or $-94°$ F. W. W. Coblentz, who wrote the paper, added:

"The observed high surface temperatures may be accounted for on the assumption that the dark areas contain vegetation having the properties of the tuft-forming grasses of our high prairies and the tussock mosses and lichens of our dry tundras, which have a high absorptivity for solar radiation and a low thermal conductivity. . . . The radiometric observations indicate that during the summer season on Mars temperature conditions at noonday are not unlike the bright cool days on this earth, with temperatures ranging from 5 to 15° centigrade, or 40 to 50° Fahrenheit."

Since Arrhenius there has been no really new theory on Mars except one reported at the meeting of the National Academy of Sciences in April 1960. It resembles Arrhenius's in that it also tries to solve all the Martian problems by chemical trickery. The originators of this theory, Drs. C. C. Kiess, C. H. Corliss, and Harriet K. Kiess, felt that most of the observed phenomena could be explained by the behavior of nitrogen-oxygen compounds. The composition of the Martian atmosphere is now generally assumed to consist of about 98 per cent nitrogen, somewhat over 1 per cent argon, less than 1 per cent of carbon dioxide, with traces of oxygen and occasional traces of water vapor. Dr. Kiess and his collaborators therefore have all the nitrogen they need at their disposal; the absence of oxygen is explained by saying that all of it has combined with nitrogen.

In this theory the polar caps are not ice or snow, but chalky-white deposits of nitrogen tetroxide; their yellowish tint (when it appears) is caused by nitrogen dioxide in equilibrium with the solid nitrogen tetroxide. The low reflecting ability of Mars for green, blue, and violet light is explained by absorption by nitrogen peroxide. The dark belt around the melting polar cap is caused by nitrogen tetroxide with other nitrogen compounds in solution, and the seasonal change in color is the spread of heavy gaseous nitrogen tetroxide. Clouds of crystals of these compounds produce the white clouds; when the air is warmed by the sun in summer the nitrogen tetroxide changes to nitrogen dioxide which produces the yellow clouds. The presentation concluded with the statement that nitrogen oxides are known to be toxic which "argues against the existence of living organisms on Mars."

Mars would be a most interesting planet, if this theory were correct, but I have yet to find anybody who is enthusiastic about it.

Another, far less radical theory about Mars, conceived by Dean B. McLaughlin and published first in the *Astronomical Journal* (vol. 60, 1955), tries to account for the dark areas, or at least some of them, under the assumption that they represent drifts of volcanic ash. If one assumes, for instance, that the two points of Dawes Forked Bay are two volcanoes and that the wind blew in the right direction while they were active, one would get the picture as it appears in the telescope, two gradually widening narrow triangles which also weaken in color the farther they are from their points of origin.

While the possibility that some of the dark areas are the result of such volcanic fallout has to be admitted, this theory also has found few friends among astronomers.

The current beliefs about Mars can be summarized rather quickly. The polar caps are snow or/ice, a few inches in thickness (Robert S. Richardson once said that "all the water on Mars would just about fill Lake Erie"), which partly evaporate and partly melt. Two Russian astronomers, G. A. Tikhov and V. V. Sharonov, after studying numerous pictures of the polar cap obtained during the 1939 opposition, decided that it is ice covered by hoarfrost. This statement agrees well with the assumed melting after partial evaporation: the hoarfrost would evaporate and render the atmosphere above the cap somewhat moist, then the ice would melt. The "dark fringe" around the melting cap is logically explained as the darker color of moistened soil.

The Martian atmosphere probably produces a ground-level pressure between 62 and 70 millimeters of mercury, which corresponds to the pressure 10.3 to 11 miles above ground in our own atmosphere. In spite of its thinness the Martian atmosphere can support clouds, since the gravity is also weaker. There are three types of clouds. The "yellow" clouds are easily explained under desert conditions: they are fine dust, carried by storms. The next type, is called "blue-white" or "white," these probably consist, like our cirrus clouds, of ice crystals. Sometimes these white clouds are very conspicuous; seventy or eighty years ago some people, seeing them brightly illuminated by the sun near the rim of the disk, thought they were "light signals" sent into space by the Martians to attract our attention.

Some researchers list "blue clouds" as a separate type—the word refers to the color of the filter used, not to the color of the clouds. They show up only in blue-light pictures which generally produce featureless pictures of Mars, except for the polar cap and white clouds if there happen to be any. The "blue" clouds may be just white clouds which are too faint to be observed directly.

If we consider the "blue" clouds as very weak white clouds, the third cloud phenomenon on Mars might be called "gray" clouds. These are both rare and especially mysterious.

The Japanese astronomer Tsuneo Saheki reported on several observations of such clouds in *Sky and Telescope* (February 1955). On January 15, 1950, he observed an enormous dark-gray cloud in the area of Eridania and Electris. It was about circular and measured 450 miles in diameter. It differed from the "normal" yellow clouds not only in color but also in the fact that it rose to a great height, estimated by Saheki to be between 60 and 100 miles. American and European observatories could not see it since they had daylight at the time, but the observation was confirmed by other Japanese astronomers.

On March 29, 1950, another Japanese astronomer, S. Ebisawa, saw a similar gray cloud over the southeastern part of the Mare Sirenum. It could still be seen on April 2, but had changed color and looked dull bluish-white. Such a cloud had also been seen over Eridania in February and early March 1952 and another in the same general location on April 16, 1952. This cloud had been first noticed by Ebisawa and was confirmed by Saheki. A single cloud of this nature could easily be explained as the telltale sign of a crash of a very large meteorite or small asteroid, but since all four of them occurred in an area not much more than 500 miles in diameter it is more likely that they were of volcanic origin. In 1909 and 1911, Antoniadi repeatedly saw clouds which he thought to be volcanic in the area of Deucalionis Regio, a long distance from Eridania.

Saheki could also report on another phenomenon which had been seen occasionally in the past. On June 4, 1937, the late Sizuo Mayeda suddenly saw an intensely bright spot which scintillated like a star and was far brighter than the polar cap, but which disappeared after about five minutes. It was in the area of Tithonius Lacus, near the Martian equator at about longitude 95 degrees. The next instance was seen by Saheki himself on December 8, 1951. "I saw a sharp, bright, glaring spot suddenly appear on Tithonius Lacus. It was as brilliant as a sixth-magnitude star—decidedly brighter than the north polar cap—and shone with scintillation for about five minutes. Fading rapidly, it looked like a whitish cloudlet [5 minutes later] as large as Tithonius Lacus. [Another 5 minutes later] it was barely visible as a very faint and large white spot, and [after 40 minutes] this part of the Martian surface had returned to its normal state." Another but less brilliant flare was seen by the same observer on July 1, 1954, at Edom Promontorium.

Frank B. Salisbury, professor of plant physiology at Colorado State University, in an article on "Martian Biology" (*Science,* no. 3510, April 6, 1962), referring to this report, makes the somewhat facetious remark: "Was this volcanic activity, or are the Martians now engaged in debates about long-term effects of nuclear fallout?"

Saheki's own summation was a careful examination of possibilities: "We can rule out the possibility that these flares were sunlight reflected from a hypothetical water surface on Mars—their locations on the planet with respect to sun and earth preclude this. Reflection from an ice-covered mountainside is free from this objection, but cannot explain the formation of a cloud just after the disappearance of the light, as in 1951. A meteorite fall on Mars might produce both light and a cloud, but meets difficulty in accounting for flare durations as long as five minutes. . . ."

One more atmospheric phenomenon that must be mentioned is the "blue mist." "Blue" again refers to the filter used and "mist" is merely a label—we don't know what it is. Remember that a blue-filter picture does not reveal any of the surface markings that are visible to the eye and also show up well in a picture taken with a red filter. What the "blue" picture shows is the scattering of blue light in the Martian atmosphere, but an atmosphere that thin and consisting almost wholly of nitrogen should not scatter blue light. Therefore, to quote E. C. Slipher, a layer "with an astonishing power of diffusion and absorption of short waves" must exist. To make the mystery somewhat more mysterious, astronomers occasionally find what they call a "blue clearing" which may be planet-wide but is more often patchy. Blue-filter pictures taken during a "blue clearing" look the way yellow-filter pictures normally do. The "blue clearing" seems to take place most often when Mars is near opposition, but so little observing is done when Mars is far from opposition that any statistics about the frequency of "blue clearings" near opposition are likely to be misleading.

As for the Martian deserts, almost everybody accepts the literal meaning of the name. They are deserts. Naturally astronomers have tried to find some more specific information about the material composing the deserts. A. Dollfus of the Meudon Observatory, Paris, checked the polarization of light by several hundred different terrestrial minerals, trying to find one for which the light matched that polarized by the bright Martian desert areas. He found just one, pulverized limonite (Fe_2O_3), which could be, as Arrhenius suggested, oxidized cosmic iron.[10]

We now come to the dark areas, which some astronomers call *maria,* by analogy with the *maria* of our moon. These are especially interesting, because if there is life on Mars it is in these areas. Not everybody concurs with the "majority opinion" that they are vegetated areas.

One of the strongest arguments in favor of the traditional position was expressed as late as 1950 by the Estonian astronomer E. J. Öpik, in the *Irish Astronomical Journal.* That dust storms cover up a dark area had been observed quite often, but not long afterward the dark color returns. Öpik simply stated that a dark area which owes its color to darkish minerals would say covered, but living plants would grow through the dust. It is not impossible also that partly covered plants may develop a reflex action which shakes off the dust; we have analogous examples on earth, though the reflex actions we know do not serve this particular purpose. Even if the plants simply turned their leaves in the course of the day to expose their full area to the sun, the result would be the same.

Öpik's argument that only living vegetation would break through a dust layer and become visible again seemed to end all discussion on this point, until Gerard P. Kuiper came up with a counterargument in the *Astrophysical Journal* (Vol. 125, 1957). He suggested that the Martian *maria* might be hardened lava flows, one of the standard explanations for the lunar *maria.* Terrestrial lava flows remain conspicuous from the air, even when they are very old. Windblown sand and dust will fill in cracks and crevasses but does not stay on the vitreous surface. The next storm removes it again.

But the odds still favor the vegetation theory. It has been mentioned that a new dark area was observed during the opposition of 1892. Another new dark area, the size of Texas, was seen by Dr. Earl C. Slipher during the 1954 opposition. On both Schiaparelli's and Lowell's maps this area shows as desert. It appears far more likely that plants would have grown up in these areas than that wind should have removed a dust layer from an ancient lava flow for the first time after eighty years of observation. Professor Salisbury, in the article previously mentioned, also favors the vegetation theory:

The changes in color, size and shape of the markings fit the living organ-

[10] Gerard P. Kuiper of the University of Chicago does not agree with Dollfus's findings; in his work, iron oxides gave poor results and he obtained his closest match with brownish fine-grained igneous rocks.

ism theory most readily. These changes in color and size are relatively extensive and spectacular, and if the markings consist of vegetation of some sort, the cover must be fairly complete. Rocket photographs of our western deserts, for example, show a light brownish expanse, devoid of much detail, but an observer on the ground sees an abundance of living organisms. Only the fairly heavy cover of our forest and grass areas appears really green on such rocket photographs. This, and the changes in color and size, seem to indicate a very flourishing life form on Mars, and not the barely existing lower plant forms so often suggested.

One especially interesting hint as to the nature of Martian vegetation was obtained by William M. Sinton of Lowell Observatory, Flagstaff. He reported in *Science* (1959, p. 1234) that there were three bands in the infrared in spectrograms of the dark areas which were lacking in the desert areas. Two of these bands were duplicated by terrestrial plants; the third was not. In a letter to *Science* (1961, p. 529) N. B. Colthub of the Stamford Research Laboratories pointed out that the third band (at 3.67 *mu*) agrees well with those of organic aldehydes (but not formaldehyde) which have strong bands between 3.65 and 3.7 *mu* and stated that "the most likely aldehyde is acetaldehyde." He then went on to say, "The presence of the terrestrially reactive aldehyde is perhaps a reflection of the near absence of oxygen on Mars and the consequent lack of oxidation. If I may be permitted to speculate a bit, acetaldehyde may be an end product of certain anaerobic metabolic processes. A familiar one is the fermentation of carbohydrates to acetaldehyde and then to alcohol. This process yields much less energy for the organism than conventional oxidation but certain organisms on earth use fermentation as their source of energy when oxygen is not available and perhaps this happens on Mars."

Experiments by the Department of Space Medicine of the U. S. Air Force also indicate that biochemical processes on Mars may go in another direction—they would not be *fundamentally* different from what we have on earth, but what is an exception on Terra may be the rule on Mars. Some six years ago, when I visited Randolph Air Force Base where the Department of Space Medicine was then located, Dr. Hubertus Strughold offered to show me "Mars in jars." [11] The jars were of glass, filled with a nitrogen atmosphere under a pressure of 64 millimeters of mercury. A trace of water had been added. At night the jars were placed in a freezing unit; during the day they were in the air-conditioned office which had a temperature of about 75. Thus atmospheric pressure, atmospheric composition, and the day and night

[11] The report on the experiment bore the more dignified title "The Behavior of Microorganisms under Simulated Martian Environmental Conditions."

temperatures on Mars were all closely simulated; the only thing that could not be done was to reduce the gravity.

Soil bacteria from Texas and Arizona were placed into the dry soil samples of the jars. At first the number of bacteria dropped sharply; all the aerobic bacteria (those requiring oxygen) died off. But among the bacteria there were also anaerobic forms which not only held their numbers but multiplied.

One exception to the evidence in favor of vegetation was the character of the light reflected by the presumably vegetated areas. It does not correspond to that reflected by, say, the forests of France or of New England or the vegetation of Florida. But G. A. Tikhov, as he reported in his *Astrobotanika,* made comparisons with plants of the northern tundra on the high Pamir plateau. The plants growing in such an environment do not reradiate any infrared (heat) rays; they cannot afford to. Neither could Martian plants. And, like the tundra plants, the Martian areas look bluish-green, rather than green.

At a scientific symposium on "The Exploration of Mars," held in Denver in June 1963, Dr. Clyde Tombaugh—in an unscheduled speech —pointed out that there is a decided difference in the color of the vegetated areas: those in the southern hemisphere of Mars show bluish-green shades, while those in the northern hemisphere look decidedly gray.

Quite a number of definite statements about Mars can be made, but the limit of what observation from a distance can accomplish seems to have been reached. The next step in the exploration of the planet is the launching of a planetary probe, preferably one that will land in a dark area and can televise a close-up view.

THE MOONS OF MARS

The moons of Mars are interesting for two reasons. The first is that they were "guessed" repeatedly before they were discovered. The second is that after their discovery it was found that a "natural law," which had been silently accepted by everybody, did not hold true in all cases. That "law" was the statement that the period of revolution of a secondary must always be greater than the period of rotation of its primary; no planet could orbit the sun in a shorter time than the time the sun needed to turn on its axis; likewise, no moon could orbit its planet in a shorter period than the planet's rotation. But the inner moon of Mars has a period of revolution shorter than the Martian day.

The first one to guess that Mars might have two moons was Johannes

Kepler in his *Narratio de Jovis satellitibus* (1610). Kepler thought that Galileo's anagram which really refers to the rings of Saturn (see Chapter 15) might conceal the discovery of the moons of Mars, but trying to solve it was too much even for his patience.

Soon after (in 1643) the Capuchin monk Anton Maria Schyrl claimed to have actually seen the moons of Mars; we now know that this was completely impossible with the optical instruments of the period. Schyrl probably was deceived by small fixed stars in the optical vicinity of Mars and may have taken the motion of the planet itself for the motion of its "moons."

Either Kepler's book or Schyrl's must have been the source for Dean Jonathan Swift's reference to the two moons of Mars in the "Voyage to Laputa," one of the "Travels" of Lemuel Gulliver, written in 1727. The oft-discussed amazing fact was not that Swift talked about two moons of Mars (there was precedent for that) but that his guess came so close to reality. In the third chapter Captain Lemuel Gulliver learns that

the Laputan astronomers spend the greatest part of their lives in observing the celestial bodies, which they do by the assistance of glasses far excelling ours in goodness. For this advantage hath enabled them to extend the discoveries much farther than our astronomers in Europe; for they have made a catalogue of ten thousand fixed stars, whereas the largest of ours do not contain above one-third part of that number. They have likewise discovered two lesser stars, or satellites, which revolve about Mars, whereof the innermost is distant from the centre of the primary planet exactly three of his diameters, and the outermost five; the former revolves in the space of ten hours, and the latter in twenty-one and a half; so that the squares of their periodical times are very near in the same proportion with the cubes of their distance from the centre of Mars,[12] which evidently shews them to be governed by the same law of gravitation that influences the other heavenly bodies.

François Marie Arouet, better known as Voltaire, adopted the two moons of Mars from Swift for his *Micromégas*, the story of a giant from Sirius who pays a visit to our solar system:

On leaving Jupiter our travelers crossed a space of about a hundred million leagues and reached the planet Mars. They saw two moons which wait on this planet, and which have escaped the gaze of astronomers. I know well that l'Abbé Castrel wrote against the existence of these two moons; but I agree with those who reason from analogy. These good philosophers know how difficult it would be for Mars, which is so far from the sun, to get on with less than two moons.

---

[12] Kepler's "third law"; the actual periods of revolution are 7 hours, 39 minutes, for Phobos and 30 hours, 18 minutes, for Deimos.

Voltaire's *Micromégas* appeared in 1750; a few years earlier a German sea captain named Kindermann had claimed to have seen one of the two moons of Mars. The date claimed for the observation was July 10, 1744, but the claim was not published until a book with the title *Collegium astronomicum* (Dresden, 1747) was ready. Captain Kindermann was quite precise; the moon of Mars (just one) had a period of revolution of 59 hours, 50 minutes, and 6 seconds and from the description would be assumed to be quite large. Of course no such Martian moon exists; one wonders what Kindermann saw.

It did not take long to find out that Kindermann's claim was unfounded, but in spite of this setback belief in the moons of Mars persisted. Joseph Johann von Littrow, in *Die Wunder des Himmels* (1834), called on all astronomers "to search the vicinity of Mars at opposition time with strong telescopes carefully and repeatedly" in order to find the moons. During the opposition of 1864 Heinrich Ludwig d'Arrest, who had helped in the discovery of Neptune, did make the search with the 10.5-inch telescope of Copenhagen Observatory but failed to find anything.

The actual discovery came during the opposition of 1877; the discoverer was Asaph Hall, though Mrs. Hall should be given a large share of credit. Hall first searched some distance away from Mars; it was his idea that he would slowly "move in" on the planet. Our own moon is roughly 30 earth-diameters from the earth; Hall began at a somewhat larger proportional distance from Mars. When he was far inside the equivalent of the orbit of our moon he was ready to give up. It was his wife who urged him to go on.

As Hall later told the story of his discovery,[13] his attention had at first been

directed to faint objects at some distance from the planet; but all these proving to be fixed stars, on August 10 I began to examine the region close to the planet, and within the glare of light that surrounded it. This was done by sliding the eye-piece so as to keep the planet just outside the field of view, and then turning the eye-piece in order to pass completely around the planet. On this night I found nothing. The image of the planet was very blazing and unsteady, and the satellites being at that time near the planet, I did not see them. The sweep around the planet was repeated several times on the night of the eleventh, and at half past two o'clock I found a faint object on the following side and a little north of the planet, which afterward proved to be the outer satellite. I had hardly time to secure an observation of its position when fog from the Potomac River stopped the work. Cloudy weather intervened for several days. On the night of August 15, the sky cleared up at eleven o'clock and the search was resumed; but

[13] *Observations and Orbits of the Satellites of Mars,* Washington, D. C., 1878.

the atmosphere was in a very bad condition, and nothing was seen of the object, which we now know was at that time so near the planet as to be invisible. On August 16 the object was found again on the following side of the planet, and the observations of that night showed that it was moving with the planet, and, if a satellite, was near one of its elongations. On August 17, while waiting and watching for the outer satellite, I discovered the inner one. The observations of the 17th and 18th put beyond doubt the character of these objects and the discovery was publicly announced by Admiral Rodgers. Still, for several days the inner moon was a puzzle. It would appear on different sides of the planet in the same night, and at first I thought there were two or three inner moons, since it seemed to me at that time very improbable that a satellite should revolve around its primary in less time than that in which the primary rotates. To decide this point I watched this moon throughout the nights of August 20 and 21 and saw that there was in fact but one inner moon, which made its revolution around the primary in less than one-third the time of the primary's rotation, a case unique in our solar system.

Of the many names suggested for the Martian moons, Hall accepted those from a Mr. Madan of Eton (England); the inner satellite he called Phobos, the outer one Deimos.[14]

In appearance the moons of Mars, as seen from the planet's surface, differ considerably from what one would expect two moons to look like. To begin with, because of their nearness they are not even visible from every point of the planet. Phobos would be just at the horizon for an observer at latitude 69 degrees north or south; in higher latitudes it is not visible. The corresponding figure for Deimos is 82 degrees north or south.

From the equatorial regions Phobos, at its largest, which means straight overhead, would have an apparent diameter of about one-fifth that of our moon. With respect to the center of Mars it completes more than three full revolutions during one Martian day. But since the surface of Mars is moving in the same direction as Phobos because of the diurnal rotation, the satellite seems to complete only a little more than two orbits per day. This still means that it overtakes the motion of the surface and therefore rises in the west and sets in the east. For an observer on the ground, 11 hours and 6 minutes will go by from moon-rise to moonrise, but the time from moonrise to moonset will be only 4 hours and 18 minutes. Phobos's climb from the horizon to the zenith will take just 2 hours and 9 minutes during which time it will noticeably increase in size. Of course it will also change its phases while doing this.

[14] Hall pointed out that these are normally the names of the horses that drew the chariot of Mars, but Mr. Madan was referring to the fifteenth book of the *Iliad*: "He (Ares) spake, and summoned Fear and Flight to yoke his steeds, and put his glorious armor on," where Phobus (Fear) and Deimos (Flight, better Terror or Panic) appear as the attendants of Mars.

Moreover it will frequently enter the shadow of Mars and set, or rise, in eclipse.

Deimos travels around Mars only slightly faster than the rate at which Mars turns. It would appear to hang almost motionless in the sky; for an observer on the surface, more than 60 hours would go by from moonrise to moonset. Because it is farther away than Phobos, Deimos would not look like a moon but like a very bright star—say, Venus at its brightest. Of course it would change its phases, but these would appear as variations in brightness to the naked eye. Though Deimos must also enter the shadow of Mars, it is not eclipsed quite as often as Phobos. The latter can become "full moon" only once for every three revolutions without being eclipsed; Deimos will be eclipsed only twice in nine revolutions. Because of their small size neither of them can "eclipse" the sun; the passage of either one across the sun's disk will have the appearance of a transit.

Very soon after the discovery of Mars's moons some astronomers began to wonder why it had been delayed until 1877. The moons of Mars were tiny, with even the bigger one hardly measuring 10 miles in diameter, but they could be seen. Chiefly because Phobos violates the rule about the relationship between the primary's rotation and the secondary's revolution, it was suggested that they might be captured asteroids. A concomitant idea was that Mars had captured them recently, which explained why they had not been seen before. But the shape and type of their orbits argued against capture. Both move in very nearly the same plane, which is also very nearly the plane of the Martian equator. That one captured asteroid might accidentally move in the plane of its captor's equator is possible, but that two would is too much.

Professor Simon Newcomb, the director of the U. S. Naval Observatory, in 1878, explained in a letter to the British astronomical journal *Observatory* his opinion as to why Phobos and Deimos had not been discovered earlier. During the favorable opposition of 1862 there had been, Newcomb pointed out, only two or possibly three telescopes powerful enough to see them. The 1864 opposition, during which d'Arrest made his search, had not been good enough, and during the opposition preceding that of the discovery, the one of 1875, Mars had been too low on the horizon for observation in the northern hemisphere.[15]

---

[15] I think this also takes care of the suggestion made in 1960 by the Russian astrophysicist Dr. Shklovsky that the Martian moons are artificial, having been put into orbit by the Martians around 1875.

13

THE "GAP" BETWEEN
MARS AND JUPITER

D URING the fall of the year 1800 a small group of astronomers met in the home of Johann Hieronymus Schroeter in Lilienthal near Bremen to discuss the problems of the day, scientific and otherwise. Among those present in addition to Schroeter himself were Wilhelm Matthias Olbers, M. D., who lived in Bremen but had traveled the "strong mile" (as the local idiom called the distance) to Lilienthal, Karl Ludwig Harding, and Franz Xaver, Baron von Zach, the court astronomer of Duke Ernst of Saxe-Gotha. Franz von Zach was also the editor of the *General Geographical Ephemeris* which had appeared in Weimar monthly since 1798.

At the meeting Franz von Zach told the others that he had, in a manner of speaking, suffered a setback, as a result of having undertaken a research project that was too large for him or for any other one individual. It was the project of finding the "hidden planet" in the gap between Mars and Jupiter.

In looking for this "hidden planet" von Zach was carrying on a long tradition. Johannes Kepler, pursuing a line of thought which no longer seems very scientific to us, had to assume a planet between Mars and Jupiter. Later, in 1766, Johannes Daniel Titius, professor of mathematics and physics in Wittenberg, developed his empirical formula for planetary distances (see Appendix), which also required a planet between Mars and Jupiter. On the other hand the planet Uranus, discovered long after Titius' death, did fit into his formula, and this discovery convinced von Zach, who not only predicted that a planet would be found in the gap but even tried to calculate its orbit.[1] In 1787, two years after he wrote down his prediction, he began a "revision of the stars of the zodiac," partly as a piece of research which he considered necessary, but mainly, as he told the meeting in Lilienthal, in the hope of

[1] The prediction, written in 1785, appeared in the *Berliner Jahrbücher* for 1789. It offered the following figures for such a planet: distance from the sun 2.82 A.U.; eccentricity of orbit 0.14; orbital period 4.74 years; inclination to ecliptic 1° 36'; heliocentric longitude of perihelion 192° 6'.

finding the hidden planet in the course of the work. But, especially because of the crowding of the stars in some areas of the zodiac, the job
had proved too much for one man. He therefore proposed the formation
of a society of astronomers with observatories of their own, consisting
of a total of twenty-four members, each to be assigned a specific section
of the zodiac. Each member was to produce a good new star chart of
his sector, and these combined would form the new chart of the
zodiacal stars. In addition, each member was to watch carefully for the
hidden planet which might be found in any of these twenty-four sectors.

The proposal appealed to his colleagues and letters outlining it were
sent to astronomers in other countries, among them Father Giuseppe
Piazzi in Palermo. Piazzi, who naturally was unaware that such a letter
was on its way, happened to be revising a star catalogue that fall.

During the night of New Year's Eve 1800, Piazzi saw in the constellation Taurus a small star which was not in the catalogue. He checked its
position again the following night and found that it had shifted somewhat. Next night it had shifted again. Piazzi began to wonder if he had
discovered a small comet. On the 23rd of January he wrote letters
about his observations to Barnaba Oriani in Milan and on the following day one to Johann Elert Bode in Berlin. The mails were slow and
uncertain, partly because they traveled by coach, partly because wars
were going on. Oriani received his letter on April 5, while the letter to
Berlin, which had to travel much farther, arrived on March 20. In the
meantime Piazzi had had to discontinue his observations; around the
middle of February he had fallen sick, and later the weather had turned
nasty. By the time the weather improved, the constellation Taurus, and
with it the "comet," had moved into the daylight sky.

The date on which Piazzi received the letter asking him to become a
member of the "zodiac committee" has not been recorded. Judging
from the travel times of the other letters, it was probably after von Zach
had heard of his discovery from Bode, and they had decided that no
committee would be needed since Piazzi by himself had done the main
job, that of discovering the "hidden planet." There was not enough observational material to enable either Bode or von Zach to calculate the
orbit, but two things were evident: the orbit was *not* that of a comet,
and it resembled a circle with a radius of 2.8 A.U.

In the summer of 1801 von Zach published an account of Piazzi's
discovery in his monthly astronomical magazine, which numbered among
its readers the young Carl Friedrich Gauss. Gauss thought that there
was enough material for an orbit calculation; of course a new method
was needed, but that was easy for Gauss, who invented the new method

then and there. But the more he thought about the problem, the more interesting it became from the mathematical point of view. His next move was to calculate the ephemeris for what would now be called "Object Piazzi" for the following winter. Then he went on with the mathematical work and, a few years later, produced one of his fundamental treatises, this one fundamental for the history of astronomy as well as for that of applied mathematics.

The treatise was published in Hamburg in 1809 under the title *Theoria motus corporum coelesticum in sectionibus conicis Solem ambientium* (Theory of the Motion of Celestial Bodies in Conic Sections around the Sun). But from a letter Gauss wrote in December 1809 to Christian Heinrich Schumacher, founder of the *Astronomische Nachrichten,* we know that Gauss wrote it in German. His publisher thought that a work of this type would sell better if it were in Latin and had it translated, with an incredible error on the very first page.[2] Half a century later the work was still important but the percentage of scientists who could read Latin as easily as their native tongues had evidently dropped considerably. An English translation (by Davis) appeared in Boston in 1857, a French one (by Dubois) in Paris in 1864, and finally a German edition (translated by Haase) in Hannover in 1865.

Also in the summer of 1801, the professor of philosophy Friedrich Hegel was reading the proof on a dissertation which he was about to publish in Jena. It was called *Dissertatio de orbitis planetarum* and concerned the rule originally found by Titius and later "rediscovered" by Bode (hence usually called the Bode-Titius Rule) and its philosophical implications. The philosophical implications, said Hegel, were that such a rule was impossible. No philosophy could go along with an attempt to express the distances of the planets by a series of figures.

Professor Bode could not explain *why* the rule worked—we still don't really know, though there have been a number of attempts to find out—but anybody who could add and multiply had no doubt that it did work. It had worked for Uranus; it had just worked again for Piazzi's discovery. Duke Ernst of Saxe-Gotha said what he thought. Even though he stated it in Latin, it ameliorated the verdict very little, if at all. Hegel's essay, the Duke declared, was the *"monumentum insaniae saeculum decimi nonae,"* "the monument of insanity of the nineteenth century."

After Hegel's death in 1831, his pupils naturally arranged for the publication of his collected works. Heinrich Schumacher noticed that

---

2 The error was the use of the word *inversa* instead of *composita.*

the *monumentum insaniae* had been included. Taking advantage of the fact that the German translation of the Bible uses the word "shame" as a term for the genitals and the genital area, he wrote to Gauss, "Among Noah's sons there was at least one who covered up his father's shame, but the Hegelians pulled off the cloak which time and forgetfulness had spread over the shame of their master." Gauss replied by return post that the comparison limped badly, for according to the Bible Noah got drunk only once, while Hegel's *"insania"* was pure wisdom compared to what he wrote later.

Returning to Piazzi's discovery, the next step was taken by Olbers. Using the ephemeris calculated by Gauss for the winter 1801–1802 he started searching. He rediscovered the object, during the night of December 31, precisely one year after the original discovery. Piazzi had named the planet Ceres. Olbers continued to check on its motion, for the purpose of providing Gauss with raw material for a definite orbit calculation. On March 28, 1802, he discovered, not too far from Ceres in line of sight, a second planet in the "gap." This one received the name of Pallas.[3] This raised an interesting question. On June 1 Olbers wrote to Bode: "Did Ceres and Pallas always travel in their current orbits in peaceful proximity or are both part of the débris of a former and larger planet which exploded in a major catastrophe?" Interestingly enough Johann Sigismund Huth, professor of physics and mathematics at the University of Dorpat (now Tartu, Esthonia), had also considered the same problem and arrived at the opposite conclusion. In September of the same year he stated that "these tiny planets were as old as all the others, and it seemed more probable to him that the matter which formed the planets had coagulated into many small spheres in the space between Mars and Jupiter. . . . In fact he would not be surprised if Ceres and Pallas had at least ten co-planets" (*Berliner Jahrbücher,* 1807).

---

[3] On April 25, 1812, Gauss published the anagram:
$$111 \qquad 1000 \qquad 10010 \qquad 1001$$
without giving a method for its solution. On May 5 he wrote to Bessel that it referred to the mean orbital motions of Jupiter and of Pallas, which are in the ratio of 7:18. But he died without telling how these four figures were supposed to express the relationship 7:18. The solution was not found until 1937, when Erich Göllnitz (Annual Report of the Society of German Mathematicians) guessed that the solution might lie in the nature of the Greek alphabet. He labeled the mean motion of Jupiter with the Greek letter iota, and that of Pallas with the letter pi, which leads to:
$$7:18 = \iota : \pi \qquad \text{or} \qquad 7\pi = 18\iota.$$
Since pi is the ninth letter of the Greek alphabet, and from iota to pi there are 8 letters, the equation turned into
$$7(8) = 18(9),$$
which, when expressed in the binary system reads
$$111(1000) = 10010(1001).$$

The problem of whether the planetoids [4] are the result of a catastrophe or whether they never formed a larger body is still with us; at that time it was more important that Huth expected more to be found and that Olbers made it sound at least likely, since one would not expect an exploding planet to form just two pieces of débris. Olbers and his younger friend Karl Harding kept searching, keeping an eye especially on the two constellations Pisces and Virgo, in which the planes of the orbits of Ceres and Pallas intersected. If the catastrophe had produced more large pieces, these were likely to pass through the same areas. On September 1, 1804, Harding found one in Pisces; it was named Juno. And Olbers, on March 29, 1807, found the fourth, Vesta, in Virgo.

By about 1816, when the search had failed to produce more discoveries, Olbers decided to stop. If there had been an explosion it might easily have produced additional splinters, but apparently there were only four masses large enough to be seen from earth.

At the time Dr. Olbers gave up his search, a young man of twenty-three had just passed several Civil Service exams and was properly installed in the postoffice of his home town of Driesen. Later he became the postmaster—none of which would be of interest now if his name had not been Karl Ludwig Hencke and his hobby astronomy. In 1830, at the age of thirty-seven, Hencke began to make specialized star charts for his own use and to look for more planetoids. He was as persistent as he was careful, and on December 8, 1845, he discovered number 5, Astraea, following up his own discovery with number 6, Hebe, on July 1, 1847. The director of the Berlin Observatory, Johann Franz Encke, was so pleased with the first discovery of his near-namesake that he devoted a long research paper *(Ueber die Astraea)* to the new member of the solar system. If Encke had delayed the writing of his paper six or seven years he could have added that Encke's discovery of Astraea was actually far more fruitful than Piazzi's original discovery.

When Dr. Olbers decided that there were only four planetoids, he had, figuratively speaking, closed a door. Since Olbers had discovered two out of the four then known (and one of the other two, Juno, had been found under his direction), he obviously knew more about the planetoids than anybody else and his opinion was accepted without much question. The two discoveries by Postmaster Hencke opened the door again more widely than ever before. The next discoverer of a

[4] Since these bodies orbit the sun the designation "planetoid" is the logical one; "asteroid," which is more customary among English-speaking astronomers, literally means "little star" (from Greek *aster*) and therefore is descriptive of the appearance only.

planetoid (No. 7, Iris) was an Englishman, John Russell Hind, the superintendent of the *Nautical Almanac,* who, within the space of seven years, discovered ten. His nearest rival during the same period was A. de Gasparis with eight.[5]

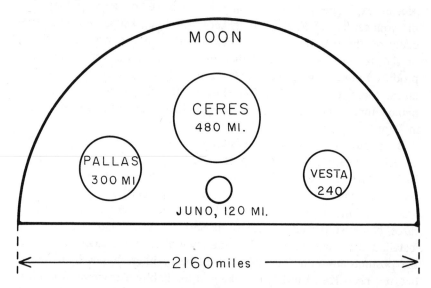

The sizes of the four largest planetoids compared to that of our moon.

By the end of 1850 thirteen planetoids were known, and during 1851 two more (Irene and Eunomia) were discovered. Expecting a further increase in numbers, various European astronomers conferred, in person and by mail, on a few principles to be laid down. Piazzi, Olbers, Harding, and Hencke had started the custom of using classical female names. This custom could be continued without doing harm or causing confusion. But the invention of a symbol for every planetoid, which had originally been done from force of habit since the major planets had long-established symbols, was to be discontinued. The symbols would become quite complicated in the course of time, would be hard to draw, and even harder to remember. Rudolf Wolf in Zurich suggested a way out: numbers. It was quite customary even then to refer to Astraea as "No. 5"—why not refer to all planetoids by number in order of their discovery? Rudolf Wolf suggested putting a circle around the number to signify that it referred to a planetoid and Professor Encke in Berlin accepted this suggestion. Nowadays, for typographical simplicity and because the numbers have grown too large, the circle has been discarded

[5] See table of the first hundred discoveries in the *Appendix.*

and number and name are printed either as "(1240)–Centenaria" or "1224–Fantasia." It was also agreed that these objects should not be called either "asteroids" or "planetoids" but, in German, *"Kleine Planeten,"* and, in English, "Minor Planets." This agreement was almost immediately violated by the participants themselves, and the designation "Minor Planets" appears mainly in official listings, in almanacs, etc.

The year 1852 brought eight new ones; the year 1853 four; and from then on, until about 1870, five new planetoids were discovered every year. After that the number rose sharply; by 1890 three hundred were known. "Their supervision," wrote Rudolf Wolf with some indignation, "requires an unduly prodigious amount of time. In fact even now the value of a new discovery is hardly in proper proportion to the additional work it causes." Another German astronomer resignedly referred to the rash of new discoveries as the *"Kleine Planetenplage"* ("Plague of Minor Planets"), but no reflections of this kind could dim or curb the joy of discovery.

The individual "records" of planetoid-hunting astronomers approached the unbelievable. Hermann Goldschmidt, a German historical painter who settled in Paris and Fontainebleau, discovered thirteen in nine years. The Frenchman J. Chacornac and the German Wilhelm Tempel, who lived in Italy, competed successfully with Goldschmidt but in turn were surpassed by others like C. H. Peters who was apparently prevented only by his death (in 1890) from bringing the number of his discoveries to a full half-hundred. The all-time champion of the prephotographic period was no doubt Johann Palisa in Vienna who had fifty-three discoveries to his credit in 1900 and added several score more before his death in 1925.

But even this was only the beginning.

In 1891 Professor Max Wolf of Heidelberg, following a suggestion made by Dr. Isaac Roberts, began to hunt for planetoids with the astronomical camera, achieving the incredible total of 228 discoveries. The method used by him, and soon after by others as well, was to follow the apparent motion of the fixed stars with the telescope. The fixed stars would then appear on the plate as round dots, some larger and some smaller. The size of the dots has nothing to do with the actual size of the star; it is wholly a result of its brightness. While the fixed stars produced round dots, a body with a perceptible movement would produce a short line.[6] Of course a short line might also indicate a comet;

[6] At a later date the opposite method was introduced: If you wanted to photograph a planetoid with a fairly well-known orbit and therefore a known rate of apparent movement, the telescope was made to follow the planetoid. This method was useful in that a faint planetoid threw its light for a long time on the same

the question of whether it was the one or the other was normally settled by visual observation at the very next opportunity.

While the new method proved to be very effective it was not completely without problems of its own, the most obvious of which was caused by the inferior quality of the clockwork drives then in existence. The clockwork drive was supposed to compensate for the rotation of the earth by following the apparent motion of the fixed stars. But the clockwork often lagged behind, or else it was too fast; it might even be quite reliable for a certain position of the telescope but not trustworthy for another position. For this reason the clockwork drive had to be supervised usually by an assistant or an advanced student. A conveniently located bright star was picked as the "guide star" for the exposure and the cross hairs of the telescope (and with it the center of the photographic plate) were centered on it. The observer then checked at regular and usually rather short intervals as to whether the guide star was still centered, and, if it was not, corrected the situation manually.

It was with an unreliable instrument of this kind that the next big discovery was made concerning the gap between Mars and Jupiter—which meanwhile had acquired the name Planetoid Belt or Asteroid Belt. Like the discovery of Ceres, it was made by chance. The story was told in some detail on the fifteenth anniversary of the event by Felix Linke, who had been in charge of checking the position of the guide star. Linke later became an engineer, but from 1897 to 1899 he assisted Dr. G. Witt, the director of the Urania Observatory in Berlin. Linke wrote in *Kosmos,* December 1948:

In 1896 Witt began to photograph the minor planets. He did not intend to discover additional bodies—his scientific goal was to find known planetoids which had not been observed for some time, so that he could provide material for a better determination of their orbits, a job which was handled with great zeal and diligence by the Berliner Astronomisches Recheninstitut [now the Kopernikus-Institut]. Witt had only a rather primitive instrument for this purpose. The clockwork drive worked middling well only for certain areas of the sky, the areas we used to photograph, but even there it was hardly possible to neglect checking on the guide star for more than a few seconds. Its position had to be constantly corrected. I had volunteered for this job in 1897 and did many of the exposures myself. We exposed our plates for two hours and always developed them at once so that they could be checked the following morning. . . .

---

spot of the plate. On such a plate the planetoid would appear as a dot, or as a very short line if the rate of its apparent movement had been misjudged, while the fixed stars appeared as longer lines. It was an adaptation of this method which Clyde Tombaugh used during his search for secondary satellites of earth (see Chapter 11).

For the purpose of finding Planetoid Eunike (No. 185) which had not been seen for years, we centered the plate on the star *beta* Aquarius during the night from August 13 to August 14, 1898, and I exposed the plate for two hours. Eunike had to be in that area. The temperature was tropical even during the night, the only refreshingly cool place was the dark room. Next morning, after the plates had dried, the plate was checked and it was found that both Eunike and another known planetoid had been registered, so that the goal of this particular observation had been reached. But a third and longer line drew our attention. It was so long (0.4 millimeters) that we first thought it to be a flaw in the emulsion, but it was too clean to be that, hence we suspected an actual object with a high rate of apparent motion, a comet. Since the evening of August 14 was again clear, we could look for the suspicious object with the 12-inch refractor of the Urania Observatory, at that time the largest telescope anywhere in Prussia. A few quick measurements proved that it had such an unusually fast movement as had never been observed for a Minor Planet. Its appearance spoke against the thought that it might be a comet; it was a tiny dot of light without any appendages. . . .

The Observatory at Kiel, at that time the central clearing house for new astronomical discoveries, put the temporary label "1898DQ" on the new planetoid, and all observatories which had telescope time available did their best to record its position and movement. Only thirteen days after the original discovery, an incredibly short time, Dr. Berberich of the Recheninstitut announced a preliminary orbit and to everybody's surprise, including and especially, Dr. Berberich's "1898DQ" did not move between Mars and Jupiter. Its perihelion was far inside the orbit of Mars. Witt and Berberich decided to break with tradition, or rather to establish a new one in case there should be more such discoveries. The new planetoid received a male name. It became (433)–Eros.

Strictly speaking, Eros was not the first planetoid discovered which comes closer to the sun than Mars does. But the three or four previously known could claim this peculiarity only on a technicality. Their orbits are such that the perihelia are closer to the sun than the aphelion of Mars. If you look at the mean distance of Mars from the sun, all the planetoids known were farther away. Eros was the first for which even the mean distance is less than the mean distance of Mars.

The orbit calculated by Dr. Berberich indicated that Eros would be nearest to the earth if it were passing through its perihelion when the earth was at the point of its orbit that it occupies on January 22. This information yielded two results; the first was that Dr. Witt and Linke had succeeded in discovering Eros when it was almost at its aphelion and not when it was particularly near. The second was that Eros must have made an especially close approach 4½ years before its discovery, in late January 1894. Routine plates were searched and Eros was found to have been photographed seventeen times on that occasion by Harvard College Observatory. In 1896, it had been photographed four times by the observatory at Arequipa, Peru. These two observatories could easily have made the discovery, but the plates had been examined for other purposes. However, these plates helped to calculate Eros's orbit more precisely than could have been done from the ten days of observation in 1898. The next close approach of Eros will be in late January 1975, at which time a close approach by a television-equipped planetary probe will certainly be attempted—and possibly even a landing by a manned ship.

A close-up view of Eros is of considerable importance because observations during the oppositions of 1931 and 1938 have indicated that Eros is not spherical. Its shape seems to be that of a brick, probably with rounded ends; one might even say that it probably resembles a big potato about 17 miles long with a thickness of 5 or 6 miles. This conclusion about the shape was drawn from fluctuations in brightness with a period of 5 hours and 16 minutes; if it is correct, a close examination would enable us to draw reliable conclusions about the formation of the Minor Planets.

The story of Eros caused me to abandon historical sequence temporarily; it is now necessary to backtrack for a look at some theoretical work. When about two hundred planetoids were known, it was a rather obvious idea to make a list of their mean distances from the sun. The innermost then known had a mean distance of 2.13 A.U. and the outermost then known (two of them) moved at a distance of 3.94 A.U. Combining these figures with the mean distances of Mars and Jupiter gave the following: Mars 1.52; planetoids 2.13 to 3.94; Jupiter 5.2. There was a fairly clean separation; the "belt," aside from possible stragglers, did not touch the orbit of Mars on the inside and was even farther touched from the orbit of Jupiter on the outside. But arranging the known planetoids themselves by distance revealed the suspicious circumstance that the distribution was by no means even; three definite gaps could be seen, one at 2.5 A.U., the next at 2.95 A.U. and the third at 3.3 A.U. These gaps were soon referred to as "Kirkwood's gaps," because Daniel Kirkwood, professor of mathematics at Indiana University, had found the answer in 1858 and published it in the *Monthly Notices* (vol. 29). Kirkwood calculated the orbital periods for these three gaps, and for a suspected fourth one at 3.65 A.U., and called these orbital periods t. They had to be related to the orbital period of Jupiter, called T, in accordance with Kepler's Third Law [7] and Kirkwood found for t/T the following figures:

0.3334	0.4273	0.5056	0.5881
approx. $\frac{1}{3}$	$\frac{3}{7}$	$\frac{1}{2}$	$\frac{2}{5}$

which means that in the first gap the planetoids would have an orbital period one-third that of Jupiter, in the second three-sevenths that of Jupiter and so forth. The existence of the gaps shows that whatever had been there originally had been thrown out of its orbit by the perturbations caused by Jupiter. (The same reasoning applies to the rings of Saturn too; see Chapter 15.)

The question whether astronomers do not tire of the profusion of planetoids can probably be answered with a "yes." One planetoid was a sensation, a dozen were fine, and fifty were still interesting. More than 1400—the present supply—is too much, and orbiting observatories will probably add another 3000 without trying very hard. The name "vermin of the skies," given to the planetoids by an astronomer who carefully preserved his anonymity, is proof that some astronomers at least were thoroughly tired of them more than twenty years ago. Others, of course, glory in detail and are happiest when disentangling conflicting reports.

A special job is the rediscovery of planetoids that have been "lost." One case in point is that of (175)–Andromache, which was originally discovered by the American planetoid-hunter J. C. Watson. Watson foresaw that, as the number of discoveries grew, identification might become difficult, and left a special fund for the continuous observation of "his" planetoids. In spite of this, Andromache disappeared. In fact, it had started off badly. Three planetoids were discovered at about the same time, and since 175 was the next number in sequence, all three were designated as No. 175. To make things worse, Watson's telegram to Harvard announcing the discovery was lost or misplaced, so that nobody had checked on this planetoid but Watson himself. So Andromache was lost between 1877, the year Watson discovered it, and 1893, when it appeared as a "new" planetoid, labeled provisionally 1893Z. Comparison of the orbits established its identity, but also created new problems. Andromache's orbital period was very nearly half that of Jupiter; hence she moved at the edge of Kirkwood's main gap, which meant that Jupiter could (and probably would) perturb the orbit considerably. The over-all outcome was useful insofar as it led to the development of a new method of dealing with perturbations.

[7] The relationship is:
$$t : T = (a : A)^{3/2}$$
where a is the "gap" and A the distance of Jupiter in A.U.

Another rediscovery which attracted much attention was that of
(515)–Athalia, a result of a collaboration between the Cincinnati Observatory (which, under the direction of Dr. Paul Herget, is now the
computations center for minor planets) and the Goethe Link Observatory of Indiana University, under the direction of Dr. Frank K. Edmond-
son. The latter observatory conducted a special search for lost planetoids
from 1949 to 1954, in the course of which 1972 photographs were taken
in 1786 hours of observing time. With the aid of these plates 560 numbered asteroids were identified, 189, which had either been lost or insuffi-
ciently kept track of, were reobserved, and 886 unidentified minor
planets were found, many of them probably new. Among those rediscovered was (515)–Athalia which had been photographically discovered
on September 20, 1903, by Max Wolf. Though it had been photographed again on September 20, October 13, and October 19, it had
somehow been lost.[8] It was reobserved during the Herget-Edmondson
search on October 14, October 31, and November 5, 1953, with one
additional position being reported by the Simeïs Observatory. The orbit
resulting from these observations was so close to Wolf's orbit for (515)–
Athalia that its identity was accepted.

Although a few astronomers, in the United States as well as in Germany and in Russia, are interested in keeping the ledgers up to date,
most of them won't look up from whatever they are doing when
"another planet" is mentioned, unless it happens to be a "male." One
day they may become sated with "males" too, but so far they are still
interested.

The second planetoid to be given a male name was (588)-Achilles,
discovered February 22, 1906, by Max Wolf and first designated 1908
TG. The first work on the computation at the Recheninstitut seems to
have been to assign a circular orbit to a new discovery. Let us say that
the rate of motion of a new object discovered on January 16 indicated
a distance of 4 A.U. The computer would first assume that the object
moved at that distance in a circular orbit, with a mean orbital velocity
of 9 miles per second. Only a few moments were then needed to say
where the new object *should* be on January 23 and on February 1. A
comparison of this assumed position in the sky with observed positions
on these dates provides the first indication of the true orbit.

---

[8] There is no absolutely firm rule for numbering and naming a planetoid. In
general it is preferred that it be reobserved after it has gone around its orbit once.
But if the first observation can be repeated days, or preferably weeks, apart so
that an orbit can be computed, it will receive a number and a name. The term
"unnumbered" is about equivalent to "not enough observations for computing
an orbit."

Planetoid 588 did seem to be in a nearly circular orbit, and its mean orbital motion was 8 miles per second, or very slightly more. The implications of this information—though meaningless to a layman—were at once clear to Dr. Berberich. A nearly circular orbit with a mean daily motion of 300 seconds of arc (which is the same in this case as 8 miles per second) meant that No. 588 *moved in the orbit of Jupiter*! At first glance this was impossible, but a second glance resolved the problem of how a mere planetoid could hold out against Jupiter's gravitational pull. The second glance followed the observation by Professor C.V.L. Charlier of Lund Observatory that the angle formed by Achilles, the sun, and Jupiter was 55½ degrees, the planetoid preceding the planet.

Professor Charlier immediately remembered a mathematical concept (already mentioned in Chapter 11) which had been evolved more than a century earlier. In 1772 Joseph Louis Lagrange, at the time director of the Berlin Academy of Science by appointment of Frederick the Great, had written an essay on the "three-body problem," the eternal despair of all astronomical computers. Lagrange had pointed out that the case of one body in orbit around another one was not the only stable configuration possible. Three bodies could also form a stable system, provided that the mass of one of them was so small that it could be neglected. In fact there are five points in space which are called the "libration points." Three of these are called the straightline solutions, the other two the "equilaterals."

If we assume that our solar system consists of the sun and Jupiter only, the three straight-line points are located on the line connecting the sun and Jupiter. One of these points, known as L_3 is on one side of the sun with Jupiter on the other side. Point L_1 is also on that line, but closer to the sun than Jupiter. Point L_2 is on that line but beyond Jupiter—remember that Barnard thought the *Gegenschein* to be a dust cloud in the earth's L_2 point—while L_4 and L_5 are in Jupiter's orbit, forming equilateral triangles with the planet and the sun. Point L_4 precedes the planet; point L_5 trails it. Although every astronomer, at some point in his education, had read Lagrange's theory of libration points, or at least read about it, nobody had really thought that Lagrange's mathematics would be actually represented in the sky. Barnard's speculation that earth's L_2 point was occupied was also known too, of course, but was not regarded highly, maybe simply because the *Gegenschein* is so hard to see. Now Jupiter's L_4 point was suddenly occupied by a planetoid!

That Achilles, when discovered, was 55½ degrees ahead instead of the proper 60 degrees did not matter; the theory provided the possibility of oscillations around the libration points.

The year had not yet run its course when it was found that Jupiter's L_5 point too was occupied—by (617)–Patroclus. The name for No. 588 had probably been more or less accidental; Max Wolf had decided on a male name because his new planetoid moved outside the planetoid belt and had picked an especially well-known classical name. But when No. 617 was named Patroclus, a pattern began to take form. Both Achilles and Patroclus were heroes of the Trojan War, hence the term "Trojan planetoids" for the planetoids in Jupiter's orbit was virtually inevitable. Under these circumstances it is sad to report that somebody did not know his *Iliad*. As more "Trojans" were discovered all the planetoids in point L_5 should logically have been Trojan heroes, and all the ones in point L_4 Greeks. But the naming of Patroclus had ruined the logic of the situation; he is among the Trojans, while on the other hand Hector circulates among the Greeks. If Odysseus were lurking among the Trojans there would still be a certain literary logic to the situation, but Odysseus is virtuously in the Greek group, where he belongs.

The early "Trojans" were rather large for planetoids, Achilles being estimated as having a diameter of 150 miles. It seemed probable from the outset that smaller members would be discovered in time. The current line-up is: in the preceding L_4 point, (588)–Achilles, (624)–Hector, (659)–Nestor, (911)–Agamemnon, (1143)–Odysseus, (1404)–Ajax, (1437)–Diomedes, plus two or three unnamed; and in the trailing L_5 point (617)–Patroclus, (884)–Priamus, (1172)–Aeneas, (1173)–Anchises, (1208)–Troilus, 1957 MK–Menelaus, plus two unnamed.

As has been said, these planetoids oscillate considerably around the mathematical libration points, and the possibility exists [9] that Saturn may cause a "Trojan" to leave its group and assume an independent orbit around the sun. If this can happen, there is one planetoid to which it probably did happen; (944)—Hidalgo, discovered by Dr. Walter Baade in 1920. Hidalgo's orbit is typical for that of a comet. Its perihelion is at 2 A.U., but its aphelion is at 9½ A.U., which is close to the orbit of Saturn. Its inclination to the ecliptic is an incredible 42.5 degrees. Hidalgo at some time has clearly been wrenched out of a more "normal" orbit by a powerful planet.

While the planetoids in the orbit of Jupiter have been given male

---

[9] Much work has been expended on their orbits by Professor E. W. Brown in his papers in the *Monthly Notices* (vol. LXXI, 1911) and in the *Transactions of Yale University Observatory* (1925 and 1927). *Planetary Theory* by E. W. Brown and C. A. Shook (Chapter IX) also deals with the "Trojans."

names because they move outside the planetoid belt, the determining characteristic of a true "male" is that it crosses the orbit of a major planet. Eros was the first of these; the second was discovered in 1911. The discoverer was Professor Johann Palisa, who was also famous for a very special brand of humor—he got himself "separated" from the Austrian Naval Service by wearing absolutely inappropriate civilian headgear during an admiral's inspection—and who gave planetoid 719 the name Albert. Its orbit was established by Palisa as having its perihelion near the earth's orbit and its aphelion at 4.2 A.U., near Jupiter's orbit. But the tiny planetoid—estimated diameter: 3 miles—was promptly lost and has never been seen again.

However, more "males" were soon found. Max Wolf's (887)–Alínda turned out to have an orbit almost like Albert's, but, as with Patroclus, it was too late to change the name. Like Albert, Alindus-Alinda is probably 3 miles in diameter. Still another planetoid in a very similar orbit, but with a larger diameter (estimated: 20 miles) was found by Baade in 1924. It is (1036)–Ganymede.

Max Wolf's introduction of the astronomical camera as a means for catching planetoids was so overwhelmingly successful that a system of "provisional designations" became necessary. Each new planetoid received a year-plus-letter symbol, similar to that used for comets, and only after the computers had caught up with the constantly growing backlog did it receive its number and name. The first year in which such provisional designations were used was 1892. The first discovery of 1892 (by Max Wolf) became 1892A, later named (333)–Badenia. For 1892 the letters of the alphabet were sufficient; in fact the alphabet was not completely exhausted—the last one was 1892V. Its discoverer was also Max Wolf, and it later became (351)–Yrsa. The first discovery in 1893 was 1893W and there were enough discoveries to use the alphabet through to Z; the next one then became 1893AA, the next 1893AB and so on through to 1893AP. These designations were continued into the next year, the first to be discovered in 1894 becoming 1894AQ; all the letters to AZ were used up in that year, and the counting began over with 1894BA. The year ended with 1894BO.

By the end of August 1907 the letters had run their course to ZZ, which designated another discovery by Max Wolf, later (643)–Scheherazade. The double alphabet was then started over again. The next discovery, made early in September by Max Wolf's associate A. Kopff, received the provisional designation 1907AA, and later became (644)–Cosima. In August 1916 the alphabet was again exhausted and in September 1916 it was started once more.

Some confusion was created because not all observatories used the same provisional designations. Arequipa (Peru) used numbers preceded by the letter S (for Stewart). And the very busy planetoid hunters at Simeïs (Crimea) tagged every one of their successes with three Greek letters. Fortunately for those trying to establish who saw what and what he called it, a patient German astronomer, Dr. Gustav Stracke, compiled all the information in a book called *Identifizierungsnachweis der Kleinen Planeten* (Material for the Identification of the Minor Planets), which was published in 1926 as one of the reports of the Astronomical Computing Institute in Berlin-Dahlem. Only twelve years later Dr. Stracke had it all to do over; he noted that the number of discoveries between 1926 and 1938 was larger than the number for the whole period from 1801 to 1926.

The *Identifizierungsnachweis* is a book of tables, not to be read for entertainment. No orbital elements are given, just names of planetoids, names of discoverers, dates of discovery, and references to astronomical literature. Half of each page is given over to helpful footnotes of which the following is a sample:

The unnamed Object Palisa of 1877, Dec. 29 (*A.N.* 90, 191) is identical with No. 164 (*A.N.* 92, 31); the unnamed Object Watson of 1877 Aug. 8 (*A.N.* 90, 191) is identical with No. 141 (*A.N.* 90, 381; 91, 57).

Beginning with January 1, 1925, a new system for provisional designations was introduced and used by everybody, including Simeïs. It consisted of dividing the whole year into twenty-four half-month intervals, designated alphabetically. Thus the first planetoid discovered in 1962 would be known as 1962AA, provided that the discovery took place between January 1 and January 15. The next discovery would be labeled 1962AB, the next one 1962 AC, always provided that they were discovered prior to January 15. All discoveries after January 15 but still in January begin with a "B," the first of them being 1962BA, the next 1962BB, and so on. The first planetoid discovered between February 1 and 15 would be 1962CA; a new one discovered on February 16 would be 1962DA. The first in March would be 1962EA, if found before March 15; after March 15 the designation begins with the letter F. And so on. The letter J is omitted; May has I and K. December has X and Y.

The new system has the advantage of making evident at once at what time of the year the discovery was made. Taking a random example: in 1904 Max Wolf discovered a planetoid which received the designation 1904OO. It is (541)–Deborah. The actual date of discovery was August 4, but one has to look at a list to find it. Under the new system a planetoid discovered August 4, 1962, would have the designation 1962PA, while a planetoid labeled 1962OO would have been discovered during the latter part of July—considering the second O, probably quite late in the month.

After 1930 there was a sudden rush of discoveries of very unusual "males." On March 13, 1932, E. Delporte in Uccle near Brussels announced the finding of an unusual "object." The term indicates that Delporte wanted to leave open the possibility of its being a comet, though he himself probably did not think it was. "Object Delporte" was observed for several successive nights and, nine days after its discovery, approached the earth within 10 million miles. It was then named and numbered, becoming (1221)–Amor. Its perihelion is quite close to the earth's orbit (on the outside) and its aphelion about halfway between Mars and Jupiter. Only a month later Karl Reinmuth of Heidelberg, successor to Max Wolf, announced an "Object Reinmuth." Preliminary designation was 1932HA; the name given later was Apollo. On that occasion Apollo approached the earth within 6.5 million miles, but it was not the closest approach possible. If Apollo approaches its perihelion, just inside the earth's orbit, while the earth is passing the same point, it could be as close as 2.5 million miles.

For just four years Apollo was considered to be the body which could come closest to earth, except, of course, our own moon. But early in 1936 (as shown by the preliminary designation 1936CA, another "Object Delporte" was announced from Brussels. This one was Adonis, passing the earth at a distance of 1.3 million miles. During the years preceding the second World War Delporte and Reinmuth might have been thought to be running a race to see who would find the planetoid with the closest possible approach. Reinmuth won with Object Reinmuth, 1937UB.

During the night of October 28-29, 1937, Reinmuth was systematically hunting planetoids with the 15.7-inch telescope in his observatory on a mountain in the Rhine Valley called the Königstuhl. (The name means King's Chair; the observatory belongs to the University of Heidelberg, which is therefore credited with work performed by Max Wolf and Reinmuth.) Each plate was exposed for two hours, and Reinmuth, from past experience, could be fairly certain that the night would bring some result. It was a standard remark among German astronomers at that time that only a cloudy night could prevent Reinmuth from finding a planetoid that could at least be suspected to be new. But even Reinmuth did not expect to find a trace 27 millimeters in length. This indicated a very fast movement relative to the earth, which in turn meant that the body must be quite near. But a very important question still remained to be answered. The trace on the plate showed the path traveled by the object during the two hours of exposure time. *But which way was it going?* Whether the object had traveled from left to right or from right to left, the trace would look the same.

Naturally, just when the next observation was most needed, namely the next night, before the planetoid could run away, the weather turned bad over the upper Rhine Valley. A break in the clouds permitted two simultaneous exposures. Reinmuth photographed the sky to the west of the previous night's trace and his colleague Wempe the area to the east. No result! But had other observatories photographed this area of the sky at that time for other purposes? They had.

Sonneberg Observatory, checking on variable stars, had obtained seven accidental images; Harvard's Oak Ridge Station had one, and the Union Observatory at Johannesburg, South Africa, had two. This was enough for a preliminary orbit, which was calculated by Dr. Friedrich Gondolatsch of the Recheninstitut. The reason 1937UB had not been found again by Reinmuth was that it moved from the night sky into the daylight sky in just two days. (All the other plates had been taken earlier; they were so-called prediscovery plates, showing the object but not examined for this purpose.) On the last day of October it moved so fast that an observer could have seen it move while he watched; it needed only 6 minutes to move a distance equal to the diameter of the full moon.

On December 22, 1937, it was officially announced that: "With the agreement of the discoverer, Reinmuth, 1937UB receives the name Hermes."

Hermes had passed the earth at a distance of 485,000 miles, just about twice as far away as the moon. That was not the closest it could have come; the closest possible distance is 220,000 miles—even closer than our moon.

It is not at all surprising that a rash of scare stories spread through the newspapers of the world after the facts about Hermes had been released. Hermes has an estimated mass of 3000 million tons. Though tiny for a planetoid, it has many times the mass of the object which caused the mile-wide impact crater in Arizona. Astronomers could not give absolute assurance that a body like Hermes might not run into the earth. Of course Hermes could not be a menace in the orbit it followed in 1937 even if the closest possible approach were only 50,000 miles, for its orbit crosses that of the earth the way a bridge crosses a road running next to a river—the two orbits are, one might say, on two different levels. And the same is true for the orbits of Amor, Apollo, and Adonis. Still, astronomers had to admit, when questioned, that such elongated orbits as those of the male planetoids could be perturbed by the larger planets. Albert, after all, was never seen again after its original discovery by Palisa. We simply do not know which orbit it is following now.

A collision with one of these bodies is most improbable, but not completely impossible. Still, even then the probability is that we would escape with just bad atmospheric disturbances, since three quarters of the earth's surface is ocean and at least half the land area uninhabited.

Under no circumstances could such a planetoid become another moon of earth as the result of a close passage. An artificial satellite 1000 miles from the earth's surface moves with an orbital velocity of nearly 4 miles per second. Obviously a planetoid passing at this distance must not be faster than an artificial satellite if it is to become another natural satellite. But the velocity of a male planetoid passing through the earth's orbit is on the order of 17 to 20 miles per second, relative to earth, and it passes much more than 1000 miles away. Even if such a body swept through the upper layers of our atmosphere, which would cause a considerable loss in its orbital velocity, it would still continue in its own orbit, though that orbit would be quite different from the one it had before.

Since this whole book could be devoted to the planetoids without being "complete," there is space to mention only one more interesting male, 1949MA, discovered by Walter Baade. Making a one-hour exposure of the region around Antares on the evening of June 26, 1949, Baade obtained an unusually long planetoid trace. It wasn't quite as spectacular as the one of Hermes taken by Reinmuth, but it was long enough to indicate something interesting. Since this was almost literally on the eve of Baade's vacation, he persuaded Robert S. Richardson and Seth B. Nicholson to follow up on the discovery. They took more pictures quickly (the object was already in the early evening sky) and by July 6 had completed the measurements of their plates. About a week later they told Bruce Rule, the observer at Palomar, what region to photograph. And a day or two after that, they heard from Dr. Leland Cunningham at the University of California at Berkeley that the three positions obtained could unfortunately be made to fit a very large variety of orbits.

Among other things, this meant that the instructions given to Rule might be meaningless. But Rule was successful even though by then the position of the object was unfavorable. Baade, who had meanwhile returned from his vacation, also obtained three more positions with the 100-inch telescope at Mount Wilson. An orbit could be then calculated. The new planetoid did not come particularly close to the earth (about 4 million miles) but it approached the sun more closely than any other body. Apollo, Adonis, and Hermes all have their perihelia just inside the orbit of Venus; that of the new body was only 17 million miles from the sun, far closer than even the perihelion of Mercury. Hence Baade selected, from among the names submitted, that of Icarus, the mythological boy whose wings melted because he flew too close to the sun. Its aphelion is at 180 million miles, beyond the orbit of Mars.

The "Trojans" and the other male planetoids are interesting because of their unusual orbits. But some others are interesting for other reasons. J. Comas Sola of Barcelona repeatedly photographed (182)–Elsa, (224)–Oceana, and (899)–Jocasta with haloes, as if they had atmospheres. And a number of planetoids show light fluctuations, which may very easily be the periods of rotation. Among these are:

	PERIOD
(4)–Vesta	5 hours, 30 minutes
(7)–Iris	7 hours, 7 minutes
(15)–Eunomia	6 hours, 5 minutes
(39)–Laetitia	5 hours, 13 minutes
(511)–Davida	5 hours, 3 minutes

The main question is, of course, why there isn't a planet between Mars and Jupiter, but instead many small bodies, the total now estimated at 30,000 or more. Are they fragments of an exploded planet? If so, Simon Newcomb reasoned, it might be possible to calculate "backward" from the present orbit and arrive at the orbit of the original planet and, at least approximately, at the time of its explosion.

Newcomb could not pursue the idea, because of his other duties. The amount of work involved in such a calculation was enormous. The man who had the courage to undertake it was Kiyotsugu Hirayama, then (and until his death in 1943) director of the Tokyo Observatory. Presumably he delegated part of the detail work to his staff and to graduate students. As to the outcome, at the time there would have been two guesses. The more likely one was that in the course of time the orbits had been altered so much that nothing could be found any more; it would be like trying to identify the footprints of a military band leader after the band and the whole regiment had trampled over his spoor. The less likely was that the attempt might succeed—other difficult problems have been solved by perseverance and patience, qualities which a Japanese scientist would certainly possess.

To Professor Hirayama's and everybody else's surprise the result of

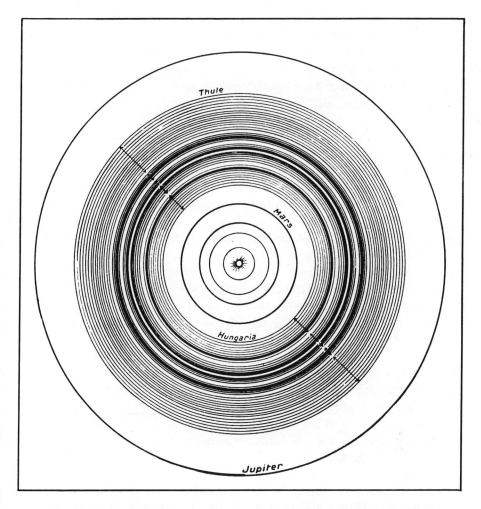

Kirkwood's gaps in the planetoid belt

the work was neither a confession of inability to disentangle the orbits
nor the discovery of the original explosion. Instead, Hirayama found
five explosions, each one resulting in what had already been called a
"family" because of the similar orbits of its members. The families are
named for their brightest member, and Hirayama stated that he could
account for the following:

1. The (8)–Flora family at 2.2 A.U. with 57 members
2. The (170)–Maria family at 2.5 A.U. with 13 members
3. The (159)–Koronis family at 2.9 A.U. with 15 members
4. The (221)–Eos family at 3.0 A.U. with 23 members
5. The (24)–Themis family at 3.1 A.U. with 25 members

At first, this result made the whole idea look worthless. All the planetoids together do not make a planet the size of Mercury and it had seemed strange that the smallest planet in the system should have been the one to explode. Now there were supposedly five still smaller planets, all of which blew up. Subsequent work by Dr. Brouwer added a few more "families," so that eight or nine planet explosions had to be assumed instead of just one.

Professor E. W. Brown, in 1932, declared that all the work expended on the problem had only the negative result of showing that "the original of asteroids circulating between the orbit of Mars and Jupiter cannot be deduced by gravitational methods from their present orbits." As for Hirayama's "families," Brown said they "would appear to be groups of comparatively stable orbits developed by attractive forces"; in other words, a "family" would not be a group with a common origin, but strangers that struck up acquaintance while traveling.

Brouwer's rejoinder was: "Brown's arguments are based upon the assumption of an age of at least two billion years." He meant, of course, that the series of explosions resulting in the present planetoids might have taken place much more recently; say, perhaps only, 100 million years ago.

Of course the break-up of a planet must have a cause. Two possibilities exist: a more or less head-on collision with another body of about the same mass, and an actual explosion as the result of a long building-up of internal heat and pressure due to natural radioactivity. Both processes could conceivably have worked in combination, with an explosion as a result of radioactivity followed by a collision between the biggest fragments.

An alternative to the explosion hypothesis is the theory that the proximity of enormous Jupiter prevented the formation of a large planet, causing disruption of any mass which, by the process of accretion, grew too large.

The problem is unsolved.

Maybe direct examination of a planetoid—Eros is the most likely—will provide a clue.

14

JUPITER

J U P I T E R, the planet beyond the belt of medium-large, small, tiny, and diminutive planet fragments, happens to be the largest planet in the solar system. The strongly flattened spheroid which is Jupiter has an equatorial diameter of 88,700 miles, while its diameter from pole to pole is 82,700 miles. Its mass is 2½ times that of all the other planets combined. And Jupiter is, from time to time, the most conspicuous naked-eye object in the sky, second in brightness only to Venus among the normal sky phenomena.

Consequently there is no history of discovery for Jupiter. It was always known, and since very early times the fact that it is in opposition at thirteen-month intervals must have been known also. At that time Jupiter is above the horizon all night long.

Jupiter never needed to be discovered, any more than Africa or Europe did. They just were. But one can discover facts *about* Europe and Africa and in precisely the same sense facts about Jupiter were discovered, producing a history of the planet in a somewhat different sense. And it might as well be stated at the outset that this history is one of ever-deepening puzzlement. We know far more about Jupiter now than did the astronomers of a hundred years ago. But they, at least, had definite ideas about the planet, ideas which were believable and seemed reasonable. The astronomer of today, with far more knowledge of detail, can hardly make a statement about Jupiter without qualifying it or referring to "an alternate hypothesis."

Jupiter, when seen through a telescope, presents an unmistakable appearance; it could not be confused with any other planet even for one moment. The planet somehow conveys an impression of its large size almost immediately. The flattening at the poles is clearly visible if the magnification is sufficient and the over-all color has reddish overtones. Quite easily visible, too, are the typically Jovian markings of the parallel cloud belts. They are as typical for Jupiter as are the rings for Saturn and the featureless whiteness for Venus. Quite often one can see a round black spot on the planet, the shadow of one of its major moons.

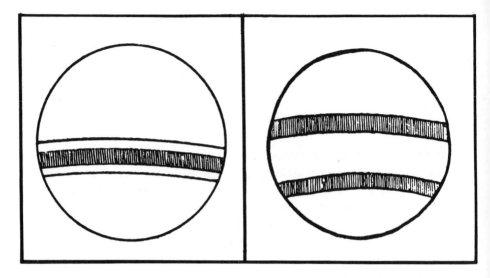

Two early drawings of Jupiter: *(left)* by Bartoli in May 1630; *(right)* by Grimaldi in 1634

Though the cloud belts are typical and quite conspicuous there is considerable doubt about who, among five men, was the first to see them. Of the five, three were Italians, one a Belgian who resided in Rome, and one an Englishman. Galileo Galilei is not one of the three Italians; his instrument was not powerful enough to see the markings. The main contender is an early Italian instrument maker called Campani of Bologna, who mentions them in his *Raggvaglio di nuove osservazioni* (Rome, 1664). The second Italian is Niccolo Zucchi, and the third, Giovanni Domenico Cassini (*Astronomical Letter to Sign. Ott. Falconieri,* etc., published in Rome in 1665). The Englishman is Robert Hooke, who stated that he saw the bands on May 9, 1664 (*Philosophical Transactions,* 1665). The Belgian, Father Gilles-François Gottigniez, got into the story in a somewhat oblique way; he stated that he had called Cassini's attention to the cloud belts as a means of establishing the period of rotation of Jupiter, but that Cassini had brushed his suggestion aside, saying that the dark spots on Jupiter were just the shadows of the satellites.[1] If Cassini actually said that he quickly changed his attitude, because his "astronomical letter" contains a determination of Jupiter's diurnal period. Cassini found it to be 9 hours and 56 minutes, in one case only 9 hours and 50 minutes. This surprisingly short period for the largest of the planets was equally surprisingly predicted

[1] ". . . *et assurait que toutes ces taches n'estaient que l'ombre des satellites de Jupiter.*"

by Kepler, who wrote in his *Dissertatio* of 1610 that the period of rotation of Jupiter would be found to be much shorter than 24 hours. The period naturally was checked by other observers, and Cassini himself continued to check it till the end of his life.

The next careful checking was done by William Herschel, roughly one century later. In his paper "On the Rotation of the Planets Round their Axes" (*Philosophical Transactions,* 1781) he reported on many determinations, finding that they did not vary much from the mean value of 9 hours, 55 minutes, and 40 seconds. But in 1779 he also obtained a value which differed considerably from his mean; it was 9 hours, 50 minutes, 48 seconds, which agreed closely with the value derived by Cassini from one specific observation. The two values (now

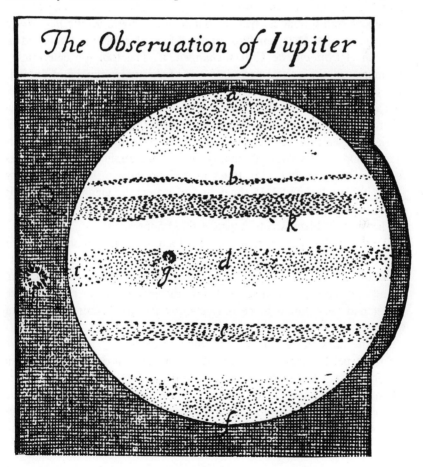

Jupiter as drawn by Robert Hooke, June 26, 1666

referred to as "System I" and "System II" for reasons which are explained later) are 9 hours, 50 minutes, 30.003 seconds; and 9 hours, 55 minutes, 40.632 seconds, respectively.[2]

After Herschel's determination of Jupiter's period of rotation the giant planet was rather neglected by astronomers for a number of decades. Herschel's discovery of Uranus may have contributed to this neglect of a long-known planet, but there must also have been a general feeling that nothing much could be added to the existing knowledge. Once in a while somebody would check on Cassini's value for the flattening of the planet ($\frac{1}{15}$), only to find that his own result hardly differed.

One astronomer who rechecked this value was Friedrich Wilhelm Bessel in Königsberg who was working on a special task. The title of his report states what he had set out to do—*"Bestimmung der Masse des Jupiter"* (A Determination of the Mass of Jupiter), published in 1842 in *Astronomische Untersuchungen,* II. The tool for determining the mass was the orbital period of one of the major moons of Jupiter, but the very complex and incredibly precise formula which Bessel developed required the knowledge of many other factors, including the difference between equatorial and polar diameters. Incidentally, Bessel carried his calculation through four times, one for each of the four major moons. His over-all findings were that Jupiter had 388 times the mass of earth, but 1250 times its volume. Hence the mean density of Jupiter was around 1.35 times that of water; the gigantic planet was surprisingly light.

The next problem was to interpret these figures.

Here was the biggest planet of the solar system. Nobody had ever seen its surface; all one could see were swirling cloud masses of enormous dimensions, straightened out into belts by the speed of rotation. Clouds are gases, of course, and now the mean density of the whole planet had been found to be only about one-third higher than that of water.

All the facts suggested just one thing: heat.

Some specific indications rounded out this reasoning. A German named H. C. Vogel systematically applied the spectroscope to the moon and to all the planets which appeared above the horizon during the period in which he did his work. The result was a book *Researches on the Spectra of the Planets* which appeared in Leipzig in 1874 and which won a prize from one of the royal academies in Germany. In

---

[2] *The Planet Jupiter,* by Bertrand M. Peek (New York: Macmillan, 1958), to date the only book exclusively devoted to Jupiter.

this book Vogel pointed out that Jupiter's spectrum greatly resembled that of the sun, hence the light received from Jupiter was essentially reflected sunlight. But at the red end of the spectrum there was a very dark band, missing in the solar spectrum. This might indicate light which originated on Jupiter. A few years later the American Henry Draper,[3] who had built himself a very modern observatory for its time, seemed to deliver the final proof. The *Monthly Notices* (Vol. 40, 1880) contained a report by Draper with the title "On a photograph of Jupiter's spectrum, showing evidence of intrinsic light from that planet." Jupiter, Draper reasoned, was still hot but would not be luminous all the time. It was only hot enough to emit light in periodic eruptions in its equatorial latitudes.

What had been put forward somewhat tentatively and with proper professional caution in scientific books and journals was summed up for popular consumption by Professor Richard A. Proctor in his *Other Worlds Than Ours* (New York: Appleton, 1896):

It seems to me that these considerations [the rapid changes in the appearance of the cloud formation in spite of the relatively feeble sunlight at the distance of Jupiter] point with tolerable clearness to the conclusion that, within the orb which presents so glorious an aspect upon our skies, processes of disturbance must be at work wholly different from any taking place on our own earth. That enormous atmospheric envelope is loaded with vaporous masses by some influence exerted from beneath its level. Those disturbances which take place so rapidly and so frequently are the evidences of the action of forces enormously exceeding those which the sun can by any possibility exert upon so distant a globe. And if analogy is to be our guide, and we are to judge of the condition of Jupiter according to what we know or guess of the past condition of the earth and the present condition of the sun, we seem led to the conclusion that Jupiter is still a glowing mass, fluid probably throughout, still bubbling and seething with the intensity of the primeval fires, sending up continuously enormous masses of cloud, to be gathered into bands under the influence of the swift rotation of the giant planet. Not otherwise, as it seems to me, can one explain the intense vitality, if one may use the expression, of a planet circumstanced as Jupiter is. Not otherwise can one understand whence this atmosphere is loaded with vapor-masses whose contents must exceed, on a moderate computation, all the oceans on the surface of the earth.

A modern reader may be surprised by the extent to which Proctor elaborates; the explanation is that he was arguing against the English philosopher William Whewell who had "proved" that the purpose of planets was to be inhabited. Naturally a nearly red-hot planet could not be habitable, and since Whewell was apparently still widely read in Proctor's time, he felt it necessary to make clear that the facts of

[3] The Draper Star Catalogue is named in his honor.

observation could lead to conclusions different from philosophical reasoning.

At just the time when the available evidence seemed to point to a planet of very high temperature, another event seemed to reinforce the conclusion of a planet "still in its igneous period." [4]

This was the appearance of the famous (and still mysterious) "Red Spot."

What seemed to be the first report about the Red Spot, written by Wilhelm Tempel who had observed it in August 1878, appeared in the *Astronomische Nachrichten* (No. 2284) in 1879. The spot was oval and was about 20 degrees south of the equator on Jupiter's southern hemisphere. Its length was about 30,000 miles, its width between 7000 and 8000 miles. The color was bright brick-red. Of course such a conspicuous object was seen by very many astronomers and for the following half-dozen years astronomical journals were full of reports and drawings. The first definite fact, aside from determinations of its location and size, was that the Red Spot seemed to be fading. The sudden appearance and gradual fading suggested an explanation—the spot was, no doubt, the reflection on the Jovian clouds of a lava flow on the surface, a lava flow of fantastic size.

Most astronomers were satisfied with this assumption. The surface of Jupiter was probably mostly covered by drifting lava floes, just as the surface of the Arctic Ocean is covered by drifting ice floes. To explain the origin of the Red Spot, it was only necessary to assume that these lava floes were cool enough to be no longer luminous and that they had now either been flooded by much hotter liquid and luminous material from the interior of the planet, or merely melted by such material.

One or two speculated that this opening of the crust of Jupiter might have been caused by the crash of a planetoid. And Dr. M. Wilhelm Meyer in Berlin wondered about the opposite possibility. The Kant-Laplace hypothesis was still fully accepted, and the satellites were believed to have been originally parts of their planets. Maybe, Meyer wrote hopefully, the Red Spot is the first sign of the birth of another large moon of Jupiter.

Meyer's hopes were quickly blighted by the realization that the Red Spot was not as new as had been thought. An observation of 1872 had shown a spot of some kind—though not a *red* spot—in the right loca-

---

[4] I am paraphrasing Houzeau's summation in *Ciel et Terre* (May 15, 1885) ". . . à voir dans Jupiter une planète qui, par suite de son énorme volume, n'est pas encore arrivée à la fin de la période ignée."

tion. Then it was recalled that the Reverend W. R. Dawes, one of the early observers of Mars, had recorded the spot in 1857. When not red the spot is usually referred to as "the hollow," because it looks as if there were a large hollow in the cloud belts. The English astronomer W. F. Denning then decided to trace it by checking all published descriptions of Jupiter and all published drawings. He found a very clear drawing of the hollow, made by S. H. Schwabe on September 5, 1831. A "dark spot on the southern hemisphere of Jupiter" observed by Robert Hooke in 1664 may or may not have been the Red Spot, but a drawing made by G. D. Cassini in 1691 shows the spot, as does an earlier Cassini drawing of 1672.

For some time, there was doubt that these Cassini drawings actually refer to the Red Spot of current terminology. The spot drawn by Cassini looked "too round" to be the Red Spot, although it is at the proper distance from the equator. And nobody saw the Red Spot for more than a century after Cassini. But evidence which has come to light rather recently makes it virtually certain that Cassini did see the Red Spot, though it may not have been red in his time. The picture gallery of the Vatican contains a group of paintings with astronomical themes, which are not signed but are believed by art experts to be the work of Donati Creti of Bologna. Creti, who lived from 1673 to 1749, was a younger contemporary of Cassini, who usually painted religious or allegorical scenes. The eight paintings which concern astronomical observations are not only identical in style but also show virtually the same scene— two or three well-dressed young men, standing near a portable telescope, or sitting on the ground, with bushes and trees around the telescope and mountains in the background. Only the heavenly bodies vary.

The object under observation is painted into the night sky very much out of scale, as it appears in the telescope. The painting depicting the observation of Jupiter shows the disk of the planet and three of the four major moons. The disk shows the cloud bands and, unmistakably, the Red Spot, elongated and in the correct place. It seems evident that Donati Creti painted what he had seen himself; it may be useful to remember that the famous telescope-maker Campani also lived in Bologna.[5]

The Red Spot, then, in spite of its "sudden appearance" in 1879, has to be considered a permanent though not a changeless phenomenon. It changes in various ways, of which the changes in intensity are the most noticeable. For a few years it may be very prominent and cannot pos-

[5] For reproductions of three of the eight paintings see *Kosmos*, June 1961.

sibly be overlooked, then it will fade and be barely visible for decades and longer. Changes of color go with the changes in prominence; it has been described by various observers as brick-red, almost blood-red, intensely pink, pinkish gray, and even deep magenta. The Red Spot also changes its shape to some extent. It is always elliptical (and must be curved to fit the curvature of the planet) and more or less maintains its width. But its length changes within rather large limits; occasionally it has been more than one and a half times as long as at other times.

Most interesting, also most important—and most difficult to explain —is the fact that the Red Spot moves on the planet, having a period of rotation different from that of the planet. The drift, however, is not regular. From December 1894 to June 1901, the spot lagged behind the rotation of the planet by a total of 46 degrees. Then it began to accelerate, but irregularly, and drifted more than twice around the planet between 1901 and 1938. In the following year it reversed its motion—or rather its apparent motion, since the effect is just created by a change in rotational velocity—and by November 1952 had fallen about half a revolution behind. Between 1831 and 1952, it had shifted its position on the planet by either three or nearly ten revolutions, depending on the method of counting. No matter which total is the "true" one, it quickly became clear that the Red Spot could not be a "surface feature" of the planet. At first, when it was believed to be the reflection of red-hot lava, a small amount of drift could be accounted for. If red-hot material from the interior of the planet flooded or melted dark lava floes on the surface, such melting might well be progressive. At one end of the red-hot area the dark lava continued to melt, while at the other end it cooled off and became dark again.

This theory, however, had to to dropped when the total drift had grown to about half a right angle in seven years. The Red Spot could no longer be considered an atmospheric reflection of a surface event; it had to be something in the atmosphere itself.

Early in this century it looked as if the Red Spot was going to have a companion. On February 28, 1901, P. B. Molesworth saw a dark hump at the edge of the so-called South Equatorial Current, which quickly grew in size, spread across that belt, and began to elongate. When it was quite large, a white spot could be seen at each end. This phenomenon was named "the south tropical disturbance." Like the Red Spot it is in Jupiter's southern hemisphere, but somewhat nearer to the equator. The "southern disturbance," as it is usually called, also had its own rate of rotation; it moved faster than the Red Spot. When it passed the spot a decided attraction could be observed between the spot, or its hollow, and the southern disturbance, although they do not seem to have merged, in the proper meaning of that word, at any time. The dark material of the southern disturbance must have passed the Red Spot in some manner, but whether it flowed around it or under it is not known. The rotational velocity of the southern disturbance, like that of the Red Spot, is somewhat variable.

In checking the motions of the Red Spot and the southern disturbance one question interfered persistently, namely the question of the rotation of the planet itself. Astronomers divide the visible top of Jupiter's atmosphere into ten areas. The Great Equatorial Current is flanked on either side by an Equatorial Current, then follow two Temperate Currents, and finally the Polar Currents, North and South, respectively. The average period of rotation of the Great Equatorial Current is 9 hours, 50 minutes, and 30 seconds, while all the other currents have a rate of rotation of 9 hours, 55 minutes, plus a number of seconds which is not the same for any two. Nor is the rate symmetrical, counting from the equator to the pole; in other words the North Temperate Current does not move with the same velocity as its southern counterpart. Even the two polar currents have different velocities. They have only the figure of 9 hours and 55 minutes in common; the additional number of seconds varies from less than 20 to slightly above 50. None reaches the figure of 9 hours and 56 minutes.

It has become customary to call the rotational period of the Great Equatorial Current—10 degrees north and south of the equator—System I, and all the other period System II; with the figures given at the beginning of this chapter.

But all this is movement of Jupiter's upper atmosphere. Somewhere below that atmosphere there must be something that can be labeled "surface," no matter what it is and how far it is below what we can see. Does the diurnal period of this surface correspond to System I or to System II or does it have a value of its own? Most astronomers seem to have accepted the idea that the diurnal period of the surface must be closer to System II.

None of the techniques we have now can penetrate to the surface of the planet. Even if a planetary probe can be put into Jupiter's atmosphere, we could not really be sure that this probe has reached the surface when its radio signals tell us that it has assumed a definite period of rotation. The English astronomer E. J. Reese, however, reasoned that the sudden appearance of spots might be caused by events at the surface and that such spots then could be used as an indicator of surface rotation.

Bertrand M. Peek (in *The Planet Jupiter*) explains Reese's idea by saying that we should imagine the earth's atmosphere to be so opaque that an observer on the moon could not see any of the terrestrial surface features, but that an active volcano intermittently threw volcanic débris to altitudes where it could be seen from the moon. The observer on the moon would then have to watch for the first appearance of this débris, later drift in the atmosphere being irrelevant and misleading. If he could check on a number of eruptions he should be able to derive a rather good value for the diurnal period of that volcano, and with it that of the planet as a whole.

Between December 8, 1919, and October 2, 1952, there were six sudden outbursts, all in the South Equatorial Current. The dates are important: there was one eruption each in 1919, 1928, 1949, and 1952, and two in 1943, on February 7 and February 27, which were labeled 1943A and 1943B. The latitude of all six was the same, and the problem was to find a period of rotation which would put all of them in the same longitude. If a period of 9 hours, 54 minutes, and 52.53 seconds was assumed, five of the six eruptions could be fitted together with a rather small margin which could be explained as due to observational difficulties. But one eruption, namely 1943B, would not fit at all. If a period of 9 hours, 55 minutes, and 42.66 seconds was assumed the eruptions of 1928, 1943A, 1949, and 1952 fitted well, but both 1919 and 1943B were way off. But Reese noticed that both were off by the same amount and concluded that these two eruptions had been from a different source. Assuming that there were two sources for the observed disturbances, both located in about the same latitude but 88 degrees of longitude apart, all observations could be made to fit the period of 9 hours, 55 minutes, and 42.66 seconds which, therefore, was the true period of rotation of the planet's surface, or at least very close to it.[6]

Reese's work has greatly strengthened the general belief that System II is more or less the true period of rotation of the planet. It is not an absolute proof but it is the best that can be accomplished with known techniques and methods.

Before we go on to twentieth-century concepts of the nature and composition of Jupiter, I must mention an interesting older paper on Jupiter, which was written by A. Stanley Williams and published in 1899 in the *Monthly Notices* (vol. LIX). Just as the color values assigned to the Red Spot changed as time went on, the color values assigned to the various currents (which are called "belts") did not stay

[6] E. J. Reese in *Journal of the British Astronomical Association,* vol. 53, 1953.

the same. Williams compiled all the observational material from the year 1836 to the year 1898 with special reference to the belts to the north and the south of the Great Equatorial Current. These two belts are, in the literal sense of the word, the most colorful, but one observer had called, say, the North Tropical Current simply "red," while a number of years later another observer called it "brown," or "gray" or even "bluish." Tabulating all these statements, Williams found that each belt went from red via brown to gray and bluish and back, through the same sequence, to red. Then he saw that, while the northern belt was in the red phase, the southern belt was in the bluish phase. The "period" from red to red for each belt was just about 12 years, very close to the orbital period of Jupiter. Moreover, the period of minimal coloration took place shortly after the autumnal equinox for the hemisphere in question.

Twenty years later Williams announced that the Great Equatorial Current also showed a definite periodicity in coloration; it assumed a dull orange or tawny hue shortly before the planet passed its aphelion.

If Jupiter were warmed by the sun, such seasonal color variations would seem logical, even though it might be impossible to explain just what changes color. But Jupiter receives from the sun less than 4 per cent of the amount of light and heat per square mile that is received by the earth; [7] in fact, this was the main reason for assuming that the planet had considerable heat of its own. And Jupiter's axis is nearly vertical on its orbital plane (the deviation is only $3° 7'$) and its orbit very nearly circular. The very small inclination would make seasonal differences between northern and southern hemisphere quite small, even if heat received from the sun were important. And the difference between perihelion and aphelion, just about ½ A.U., also seems too small to be directly responsible for color changes of the Great Equatorial Current.

Some observers have pointed out that the changes in coloration are not as clear-cut as Williams implied; others have tried to explain them as a result of light dispersion in the earth's atmosphere. The latter explanation does not apply to the two belts next to the equatorial zone, as Peek also mentioned, and the former objection merely states that there are changes in coloration in addition to the periodic ones pointed out by Williams. For the present at least, the reality of periodical color changes has to be accepted; the cause is just one of Jupiter's multiplicity of mysteries.

In 1923 an article by Dr. Harold Jeffreys dealing with the constitution

---

[7] Since Jupiter's mean distance from the sun is 5.2 A.U., the figure is $1/5.2^2$ or $1/27$.

of the four large outer planets appeared in the *Monthly Notices*. At that
time the idea still lingered that these planets were mainly gaseous because they were hot. The turbulent activity in Jupiter's belts, also found,
though to a lesser extent, in Saturn's atmosphere, had first given rise
to this theory. But even more weighty than the observational evidence
were the measurements and calculations. Jupiter's over-all density came
out as 1.33 times that of water, Saturn's density only 0.71 that of water,
and the densities of Uranus and Neptune 1.56 and 2.47, respectively.
Jeffreys thought that these figures could also be explained, and in his
opinion better explained, if the four giant planets were assumed to be
cold and composed of low-density materials, materials much lighter at
any temperature than terrestrial rocks.

He first calculated how much heat Jupiter must have radiated into
space during its existence, assuming it to be the same age as the earth.
Though the figure assumed for the age of the earth now looks quite
small, the time interval was still long enough for the planet to have
solidified. If this held true for Jupiter it held true all the more for
Saturn, Uranus, and Neptune which receive even less light and heat
from the sun and have lesser mass. Even the outer planets must have
acquired solid surfaces which were probably quite cold.

At that stage of the reasoning a side issue entered. A planet like the
earth—that is, one fairly near its sun—has three heat sources, one
external and two internal. The external one is of course the sun, which
is negligible for the outer planets. The internal heat sources are the heat
left over from condensation and the heat produced by natural radioactivity. The heat from condensation, the "original heat," so to speak,
radiates away until the cooling planet acquires a solid crust which is a
very poor conductor of heat. After that a small amount of heat might
seep through from a still-hot interior, but our own planet is a fine example of how little does. Except in areas of active volcanism the surface temperature is not at all changed by the fact that there are molten
rocks below, as they are exceedingly well insulated by rocks which are
no longer molten. But how about natural radioactivity? Jeffreys
turned the question around: how much radioactive material would there
have to be in Jupiters's body to produce as much heat as the earth
receives from the sun? The answer was the fantastic figure of 10,000
times as much as in the earth's crust. This figure could be rejected as
a complete impossibility. Hence the surfaces of the outer planets were
cold.

Had Jeffreys stopped at this point we would have been left with the
picture of a small rocky planet, with an enormous atmosphere to ac-

count for the observed bulk. In the case of Jupiter this would have
meant a rocky sphere about 25,000 miles in diameter surrounded by
an atmosphere with a depth of 32,000 miles from the surface to the
top of the cloud layer we can see in the telescope. This sounded impossible too. Jupiter's atmosphere was indubitably very deep by terrestrial standards but it could not be that deep. There was only one way
out of this dilemma: the material composing the bulk of Jupiter had to
be very light material. It might be ice. But if, with the prevailing low
temperatures, all the water was frozen and was, indeed, a major com-
ponent of the planet's body, the clouds in the atmosphere could not be
water vapor. Jeffreys said that the evidence "suggests that the clouds . . .
are probably composed of some material with much lower melting and
boiling points than water."

During the same year in which Jeffreys calculated the traditional high
temperature of Jupiter out of existence, Dr. Donald H. Menzel of Harvard evaluated a number of direct temperature measurements made by
Coblentz and Lampland. These had been largely concerned with Mars
and Venus, but Jupiter and Saturn had been measured, too, and the
result of Menzel's calculations was $-110°$ C., ($-166°$ F.). We now
know that this is still somewhat too high, but for the first time very low
temperatures for the outer planets had been established by measurement.

Jeffreys then published a second paper, in which he stated that the
outer planets probably consisted of a small rocky core, surrounded by
a thick ice layer, which, in turn, was surrounded by a very deep atmosphere, possibly as deep as one-fifth as the radius of the planet. (He was
referring to the radius from telescopic measurements, not the calculated
radius of the solid body.) The atmosphere probably consisted of hydrogen, helium, nitrogen, oxygen, and perhaps methane, while the clouds
could be crystals of frozen carbon dioxide.

Incidentally, Dr. Jeffreys, lecturing at a meeting of the British Astronomical Association, told his audience of seasoned observers that he
personally had never looked at the planets through anything larger than
a portable telescope with an aperture of 2 inches!

Naturally astronomers needed a little time to get used to the new
ideas—not merely because Dr. Jeffreys had never looked through a
large telescope. But all subsequent investigation showed that Jeffreys
had been correct in principle, even if not in details.

Vogel's work in the 1870's, already described, had showed that
Jupiter's over-all spectrum was the same as that of the sun, indicating
that the light was reflected sunlight. But it also contained a few bands

which could not be identified, one of which had been misinterpreted as indicating that Jupiter radiated some light of its own. Early in this century somebody—I have not been able to find out who—claimed that one of the unidentified bands was "a typical line in the spectrum of chlorophyll," which led to speculations in popular literature about a rich floating "aerial plankton" in the "hot and steam-laden atmospheres" of the outer planets.

In reality Dr. V. M. Slipher in 1905 had found an unidentified line in the red end of the spectrum of Jupiter and that of Saturn (Jupiter's being much stronger) and, four years later, a few more unidentified lines in the infrared. The reason the lines could not be identified was very simple and also a little embarrassing; the laboratory spectra which were needed for comparison did not exist.

In 1932 Dr. Rupert Wildt pointed out that six of Slipher's lines agreed with six lines in the spectrum of ammonia, while the others might be due to methane. Wildt's articles appeared in the publications of the Observatory of the University of Göttingen (1932, Heft 22), and when this publication reached California, Mount Wilson Observatory put the 100-inch reflector to work on this problem. Both ammonia (NH_3) and methane (CH_4) were identified with certainty in the atmospheres of Jupiter and Saturn. That the ammonia bands of Saturn were much the weaker was only logical, as ammonia freezes at *minus* 78° C. (−108.4° F.) and since Saturn was farther from the sun, it was colder, hence less ammonia would be in the atmosphere.

This did not mean that the atmosphere consisted of ammonia and methane, merely that these two gases were present. What constituted the bulk of the atmosphere? Logical reasoning said mainly hydrogen and helium, both of which remain gaseous at very low temperatures. Both were also likely to be "left over" after the planet had cooled off. Helium would be left over because it does not form any chemical compounds at all. Hydrogen, at an earlier period would have combined with oxygen to form water, with nitrogen to form ammonia, and with carbon to form methane. Pure hydrogen would be left over by virtue of its abundance.

But Jupiter's hydrogen-helium atmosphere remained a theoretical, though immensely reasonable, concept for a quarter of a century to come, because neither hydrogen nor helium can be detected spectroscopically under planetary conditions. It was, in a way, a very interesting situation: the bulk of the atmosphere remained undetectable, but the existence of the impurities, methane and ammonia, could be proved. But astronomers knew that late in 1952 Jupiter was going to "occult" a star. From earlier occultations of stars by both Jupiter and Saturn it was known that the star could be seen for a while through the stratosphere of the planet. It did not go out like a light bulb that is turned off; the phenomenon is close to what movie makers call a fade-out. The occultation was to occur November 20, 1952, and W. A. Baum and C. A. Code had decided to take full advantage of it with the spectroscope of the 60-inch telescope at Mount Wilson Observatory.

The decrease in the brightness of the star—it was *sigma Arietis*—as it was seen through more and more of Jupiter's upper atmosphere would be due mainly to refraction by the atmosphere, which would spread the light rays apart. In order to calculate this effect one has to know the following factors: the apparent motion of Jupiter and its surface gravity, the temperature of the gas and its molecular weight. Since all these factors but the last were known, one could first obtain the light curve and then make the calculation for the one unknown factor. The actual method used by Baum and Code was to calculate a number of curves for assumed molecular weights and to compare the actual curve with the theoretical ones. The result was a mean molecular weight of 3.3 for the gases forming the upper stratosphere of Jupiter. The hydrogen molecule (H_2) has a molecular weight of 2; helium (He) has a weight of 4. Jupiter's stratosphere had the intermediate molecular weight of 3.3; proving it to be a mixture of hydrogen and helium, just as had been deduced theoretically.

By that time Dr. Rupert Wildt, who had meanwhile moved to Yale University, had done some more theoretical work on the concept originally advanced by Dr. Harold Jeffreys, who had by then become Sir Harold. Jeffreys' idea of a Jovian atmosphere of negligible density but with a depth of nearly 4,000 miles did not make sense to Wildt. The bottom of a 4,000-mile-deep atmosphere had to be quite dense, regardless of what gases composed it. Nor could the ice layer below that atmosphere be homogeneous throughout. The American physicist Percy W. Bridgman had found that ordinary ice undergoes a minimum of five changes in the structure when subjected to very high pressures. Wildt therefore produced a new model of the structure of Jupiter.

COMPOSITION OF JUPITER

| | Jeffreys, 1924 | | | Wildt, 1938 | |
		KILO-METERS	MILES		KILO-METERS	MILES
Radius of core	(d = 3)	46,000	28,580	(d = 6)	30,200	18,765
Ice mantle, thickness	(d = 1)	18,000	11,184	(d = 1.5)	27,200	16,890
Outer shell		—	—	(d = 0.25)	12,600	7,830
Atmosphere of negligible density		6,000	3,728	a score or so		

Like Jeffreys, he assumed a core of metal and rock, smaller than Jeffreys', but of a higher density. Around that core was an ice mantle of the highly compressed ices found by Bridgman's experiments, and around that an outer shell consisting mainly of solid hydrogen. The atmosphere outside the solid hydrogen shell was negligible in density, but not very deep.

Ten years later, still another model of Jupiter's structure was conceived by Dr. W. H. Ramsey. Just as Wildt's model relied heavily on the structural changes in ice under high pressures, producing ices with densities greater than 1, Ramsey's model relied on a similar phenomenon in hydrogen under very high pressures. When hydrogen is strongly compressed its density naturally increases, but rather slowly. Even under the enormous pressure of nearly 800,000 atmospheres the density is only 0.35. But when the 800,000-atmosphere mark is passed, hydrogen undergoes a sudden change. It assumes what has been called the metallic phase and the density jumps to nearly 0.8. If the pressure is increased still more the density also increases, but again more slowly. The sudden jump is the point at which hydrogen becomes metallic.

With this fact in mind Ramsey undertook to explain the internal constitution of Jupiter. If one assumed Jupiter to be a sphere of pure hydrogen, the resulting mass and density would be very close to the true figures. Ramsey then made a model in which there was 1 atom of helium for every 13 atoms of hydrogen. The radius of a sphere of the same volume as the actual spheroid of 69,900 kilometers (43,434 miles) gave the "surface" of Jupiter, while the sphere representing the "metalic core" (mainly hydrogen in its metalic phase) had a radius of 61,000 kilometers (37,003 miles). The pressure at the center of the planet came out as 31,200,000 atmospheres and the density at the center as 3.66. While this model agreed with the real planet as far as mass and mean density was concerned it failed to give the proper value for its "moment of inertia." This means that a Jupiter-sized planet built of hydrogen and helium in the ratio of 13 to 1 would not rotate as the actual planet does. To correct this difference it was necessary to assume that more mass was concentrated in the center.

To quote Peek's *The Planet Jupiter*:

So, Ramsey, working this time in conjunction with B. Miles, computed the circumstances of a series of models, in which varying percentages of the masses were concentrated at their centres. . . . The new series began with the extreme case of a model consisting of 84 per cent by mass of pure hydrogen and 16 per cent of helium and the heavier elements, all except the hydrogen being concentrated at the centre. Later members of this series were constructed by withdrawing more and more helium from the centre to make various homogeneous mixtures with the hydrogen. The best representation of the planet is provided by a model 95 per cent of which by mass is composed of a homogeneous mixture of 1 atom of helium to 22 of hydrogen, the remaining 5 per cent, which consists (ideally) of the rest of the helium together with a small admixture of heavier elements, being concentrated at the centre. The total hydrogen content of this model is 80 per cent by mass; apart, however, from the fact that on approaching the center the pressures and densities begin to run higher, there is singularly little in the calculated figures to differentiate this model from the homogeneous arrangement of which details were given above. For instance, the radius at which the metallic phase sets in, is now 60,500 kilometers [37,592 miles].

We do not know whether Wildt's model, consisting mainly of ice, or Ramsey's model, consisting mainly of hydrogen, is closer to reality. Either of them presents a much stranger picture than the old concept of the red-hot planet. Though wrong, as we now know it to be, that was somehow easier to visualize than a world which, under turbulent hydrogen-helium atmosphere, consists mainly of what on earth are the lightest gases, frozen and compacted not only into solids but into metals.

The removal of the heat from Jupiter's body has unfortunately also eliminated an easy explanation for the turbulence of its atmosphere. Only one night of observing is needed to see that large-scale atmospheric events are going on all the time; Jupiter's atmosphere seems to be about as agitated as our own and on a much larger scale. Such agitation requires energy, and the source of that energy is an unsolved problem. In the case of earth the energy is supplied by the sun. But for Jupiter? Peek says that astronomers seem to feel "that solar radiation, while admittedly rather feeble at the distance of Jupiter, would be found upon investigation to be adequate. Nevertheless, the author knows of no attempt to place the justification of the last assumption upon a quantitative basis" (Peek, op. cit.)

There is, without detailed mathematical analysis, one argument in favor of the idea that the sun's rays can cause the turbulence in the Jovian atmosphere. The atmosphere of Saturn must have a composition very similar to that of Jupiter. It also shows turbulence, but much less of it. Since Saturn is farther from the sun, it receives just about one-third the light and heat received by Jupiter.[8] The fact that the atmosphere of the more distant planet is quieter does point to the sun as being the cause of the turbulence. But in the case of Jupiter one could think of subsidiary causes, mainly the aerial tides caused by the four large moons. Another

[8] Since Saturn's distance from the sun is 9.5 A.U. the amount of radiation received is $1/9.5^2$, or 1/90 in round figures (compared to the earth), while the figure for Jupiter, as has been mentioned, is 1/27.

possible energy source for sudden and irregular disturbances would be the entry of large meteorites into the Jovian atmosphere.

Judging the whole problem is very difficult (read: impossible at present), because of several factors alien to terrestrial experience. The composition of Jupiter's atmosphere is different, the over-all temperature is far below even the freezing point of ammonia, and the pressure in the lower strata of Jupiter's atmosphere is unknown since the depth is unknown. Moreover, the interaction between the bottom of the atmosphere and the surface cannot even be guessed, since we don't know the nature of the surface (ice or solid hydrogen or a surface layer of frozen ammonia) and have no idea whether it has irregularities, such as mountain ranges, or is essentially smooth.

That energy is available is proved by Jupiter's emission of radio noises. The first indication that Jupiter emits radio waves came in January, February, and March 1955, when Drs. B. F. Burke and F. L. Franklin of the Carnegie Institute, working at Seneca, Maryland, received, at irregular intervals, a rather strong signal. It could soon be traced to Jupiter. When the news reached Australia, Dr. C. A. Shain of the Commonwealth Scientific and Industrial Organization in Sydney, attempted to pick up radio signals from Jupiter himself, and he also had the records searched for signals which had not been identified but had been assumed to be interference from terrestrial sources. He found two series of such records. One running from the middle of October to the end of November 1950 and the other from about the middle of February to the middle of April 1951. These series had been long enough to draw a few conclusions. Whatever caused the emission rotated with System II (period: 9 hours, 55 minutes, and 13 $\pm$ 5 seconds) which indicated that it was probably located in the South Temperature Current.[9] Possibly the radio waves originated from the white areas in that current.

Radio signals from Jupiter have been received ever since; they are random bursts resembling thunderstorm interference, which is why the Australian researchers first recorded them as such. The natural event which causes them must also be the equivalent of a terrestrial thunderstorm. Since we don't understand an atmosphere like Jupiter's—we still have trouble understanding our own—no more detailed explanation is possible.

And now to return to the Red Spot.

After the hypothesis of the lava flood broke down because of the extensive movements of the spot, no new theories were proposed for

[9] Original publication: *Australian Journal of Physics*, vol. IX, 1956, entitled *18.3 Mc/s Radiation from Jupiter* by Dr. C. A. Shain.

a while. The American astronomer George Washington Hough, director of the Dearborn Observatory in Chicago, was the first to suggest that the Red Spot was probably a floating object. Speaking to the American Association for the Advancement of Science in 1903 he stated: "I assume that the visible boundary of Jupiter has a density of about one-half that of water. This medium is in the nature of a liquid; in it are located the Great Red Spot and the egg-shaped white spots. . . ."

In 1939 Rupert Wildt, speaking to the American Philosophical Society, also suggested a floating body, but one floating in the atmosphere. Wildt thought this body to be generally egg-shaped, with the length and width as it appears from earth and about as thick as it was wide. Expanding on this suggestion by Wildt, Bernard Peek thought it to be not egg-shaped but flattish, and perhaps 2000 miles in thickness. As for its composition, Peek, thinking of Bridgman's high-pressure ices, assumed that the bottom of this floating body consisted of a different ice phase than its top. (There is some doubt that this assumption is necessary, but Peek made it.) On the assumption that the altitude of this floating body changes occasionally because of changes in the atmospheric pressures, both the motions and the different degrees of conspicuousness can be explained. To account for the motions, altitude changes not surpassing 6 miles have to be assumed, certainly a small figure. Peek first advanced this hypothesis during his presidential address to the British Astronomical Association in the fall of 1939, and included it in his book in 1958, with the statement that the only excuse he can offer for the theory is that he "honestly does not know of a better or more probable ones."

In restating his own hypothesis Peek admitted that the phase change of the ice composing the Red Spot may not be necessary. On the other hand, he had made careful comparisons between the darkness of the spot and its movements and concluded that he was willing "to throw prudence to the winds and make a definite prediction: that, if and when the Red Spot again becomes outstandingly dark, the phenomenon will be accompanied or slightly preceded by a rapid positive acceleration in longitude."

Although Peek did not try to account for the color of the red spot, the *Monthly Notices* for 1939 (vol. 99) contain an interesting suggestion by Rupert Wildt about the colors on Jupiter in general. If metallic sodium (assumed to be present) is dissolved in solid or liquid ammonia (known to be present) the temperature of $-112°$ C. $(-170°$ F.) is critical: if it is lower the solutions will be gray, if it is higher they will be brown. If the temperature is above −78° C. (−108.4° F.) the solutions will be in liquid ammonia and will be bluish.

It would be rash to say that we cannot go farther with present techniques; the results of the occultation of *sigma Arietis* have showed that present techniques can progress another long step when aided by an unusual event. But many of the currently unsolved problems, and especially that of the Red Spot, will remain unsolved until new methods and techniques can be applied—beginning with observation from outside our atmosphere.

Until then Jupiter—or, to give it its ancient name, *Iovis pater*—will, like Mars, keep its secrets.

THE MOONS OF JUPITER

While Jupiter itself was "always" known, the moons of Jupiter had to be discovered—even though two of them had undoubtedly been seen before the invention of the telescope. It has been reliably established that if the air is perfectly clear some people with exceptional eyesight can see the outer two of the four major moons of Jupiter (the third is the largest) without optical aid. The experiments that proved this were prompted by Jules Verne's *Hector Servadac*—which had a wide circulation—and were conducted in Europe by astronomers who were not sure whether the statement in that book that some people could see Jupiter's moons was true or an invention of Jules Verne's. Obviously people with especially good eyes who inhabited locations better suited to such exploits—say Tibet, the high Andes, or the elevated sections of the African deserts—had also seen the outer moons.

But seeing and discovery are still two different things. Even if somebody, here and there, saw near brilliant Jupiter a tiny star which other members of his tribe could not see, no special attention would have been paid to his statement. He could also see tiny stars elsewhere in the sky which the others could not see.

The discovery of the four large moons of Jupiter, complete with the realization of what they were, belongs, as is well known, to Galileo Galilei. What is less well known, and no longer mentioned in most books on astronomy, is that Galileo's claim was disputed in his lifetime. But let us begin with Galileo, whom one might call the "main" discoverer. In his *Sidereus Nuncius* he has left us a very fine account of the discovery, which reads, in the translation of E. S. Carlos:

I have now finished my brief account of the observations which I have thus far made with regard to the Moon, the Fixed Stars, and the Galaxy. There

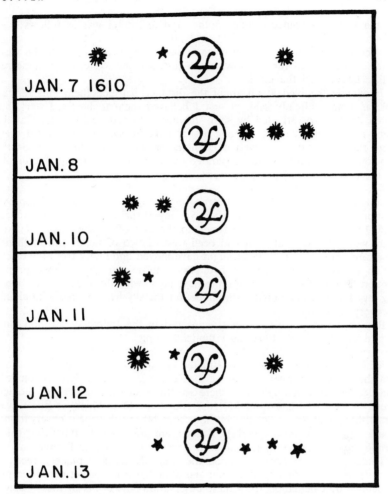

Positions of Jupiter's moons, by Galileo Galilei, from *Sidereus nuncius*

remains the matter, which seems to me to deserve to be considered the most important in this work, namely, that I should disclose and publish to the world the occasion of discovering and observing four Planets, never seen from the very beginning of the world up to our own times . . .

On the 7th day of January in the present year, 1610, in the first hour of the following night, when I was viewing the constellations of the heavens through a telescope, the planet Jupiter presented itself to my view, and as I had prepared for myself a very excellent instrument, I noticed a circumstance which I had never been able to notice before, owing to want of power in my other telescope, namely, that three little stars, small but very bright, were near the planet; and although I believed them to belong to the number of the fixed stars, yet they made me somewhat wonder, because they seemed to be arranged exactly in a straight line, parallel to the ecliptic, and to be brighter than the rest of the stars, equal to them in magnitude. The position of them with reference to one another and to Jupiter was as follows:

Ori.   *   *   , 0   *   Occ.

On the east side there were two stars, and a single one towards the west.
The star which was furthest toward the east, and the western star, appeared
rather larger than the third.

I scarcely troubled at all about the distance between them and Jupiter,
for, as I have already said, at first I believed them to be fixed stars; but
when on January 8th, led by some fatality, I turned again to look at the
same part of the heavens, I found a very different state of things, for there
were three little stars all west of Jupiter, and nearer together than on the
previous night, and they were separated from one another by equal intervals,
as the accompanying figure shows:

Ori.   0   *   *   *   Occ.

At this point, although I had not turned my thoughts at all upon the approximation of the stars to one another, yet my surprise began to be excited,
how Jupiter could one day be found to the east of all the aforesaid fixed
stars when the day before it had been west of two of them; and forthwith
I became afraid lest the planet might have moved differently from the calculation of astronomers, and so had passed those stars by its own proper
motion. I, therefore, waited for the next night with the most intense long-
ing, but I was disappointed of my hope, for the sky was covered with clouds
in every direction.

But on January 10th, the stars appeared in the following position with
regard to Jupiter, the third, as I thought, being

Ori.   *   *   0   Occ.

hidden by the planet. They were situated just as before, exactly in the same
straight line with Jupiter, and along the Zodiac. . . . I, therefore, concluded,
and decided unhesitatingly, that there are three stars in the heavens moving
about Jupiter, as Venus and Mercury round the Sun; which at length was
established as clear as daylight by numerous other subsequent observations.
These observations also established that there are not only three, but four,
erratic sidereal bodies performing their revolutions round Jupiter. . . .

These are my observations upon the four Medicean [10] planets, recently
discovered for the first time by me; and although it is not yet permitted me
to deduce by calculation from these observations the orbits of these bodies,
yet I may be allowed to make some statements, based upon them, well worthy
of attention.

And, in the first place, since they are sometimes behind, sometimes before
Jupiter, at like distances, and withdraw from this planet towards the east
and towards the west only within very narrow limits of divergence, and
since they accompany this planet alike when its motion is retrograde and
direct, it can be a matter of doubt to no one that they perform their revolutions about this planet, while at the same time they all accomplish together
orbits of twelve years' length about the centre of the world. Moreover, they
revolve in unequal circles, which is evidently the conclusion to be drawn
from the fact that I have never been permitted to see two satellites in conjunction when their distance from Jupiter was great, whereas near Jupiter
two, three, and sometimes all four, have been found closely packed together.[11]

[10] See page 362-63, and Chapter 6.
[11] Translation quoted from *A Source Book in Astronomy* by Harlow Shapley
and Helen E. Howarth (New York: McGraw-Hill, 1929).

In the introduction to the *Sidereus Nuncius,* Galileo proposed names for the four satellites. In this introduction, addressed to the "Most Serene Cosmo de'Medici, the second, fourth Grand Duke of Tuscany": Galileo wrote:

"And so, inasmuch as under your patronage, Most Serene Cosmo, I have discovered these stars, which were unknown to all astronomers before me, I have with very good right determined to designate them with the august name of your family, and as I was the first to investigate them who can rightly blame me if I give them a name, and call them the Medicean stars (*Medicea Sidera*), hoping that as much consideration may accrue to these stars from this title as other stars have brought to other [mythological] heroes."

In particular Galileo recommended that the innermost of his four satellites be named Catharina or Franciscus, the next one Maria or Ferdinandus, the third one *Cosmus major* and the fourth one *Cosmus minor.*

The main reason that these names were disregarded was, as a French astronomer pointed out later, that while the name of Medici was glorious in Italy, it meant little or nothing to people in France, England, or Germany.

The designation competing with Galileo's *Medicea Sidera* was *Sidera Brandenburgica,* which was proposed by Simon Marius—(1570–1624; real name Mayr), court mathematician to the margrave at Kulmbach.

In addition to being the margrave's court mathematician, Simon Marius was one of the first to use the telescope for astronomical observations, and it is now generally accepted that he did so somewhat earlier than Galileo. Whether he saw the four large moons of Jupiter before Galileo did, as he claimed, is not so clear; in fact, it is quite possible that he was one more of those who saw them without actually discovering them. As Professor Rudolf Wolf phrased it in his *Handbuch* (vol. II, p. 464): "Perhaps he did see the Jovian satellites in November 1609 but it seems rather certain that he did not realize the nature of these little stars at first, else he would certainly have sent the news to his friend Kepler. . . ."

His behavior, in any event, was such that his contemporaries became suspicious. Over two years after the publication of the *Sidereus Nuncius,* Simon Marius published his *Practica auf 1612,* in which he first told of his own observations. He followed this up a year later with another pamphlet and in 1614 he published a book with the title *Mundus jovialis Anno 1609 detectus* (The World of Jupiter, as Detected in 1609), printed at Nuremberg, in which he gave tables of the motions of the four satellites and figures for their periods of revolutions [somewhat more accurate than Galileo's], but in which also he used much material from the *Sidereus Nuncius* without crediting his source, thus making it appear that he were speaking of his own observations throughout. Galileo, who obviously was both supremely self-confident and somewhat testy, noted this immediately and called attention to it in no uncertain terms in his *Discorsi* [12]). Marius might possibly have had something to say in self-defense, but by that time he was sick and died soon afterward.

Two other people also discovered Jupiter's moons independently of Galileo, but somewhat later and without claiming priority. The first was Joseph Gualterius (real name Gaultier), a French clergyman, who watched the Jovian satellites beginning in October 1610. The second was the English mathematician Thomas Harriot who started in the same year and month, but a week later than Gualterius. The first one to see—or at least to record that he had seen—the shadows of the satellites on Jupiter's disk was Cassini.

While Simon Marius did not convince the astronomical world that he had seen *and* recognized the Jovian satellites before Galileo, he did, in collaboration with Johannes Kepler, invent the names now in use for them. At first Marius had a rather clumsy scheme in mind. Like Galileo he was pleased to find that Jupiter and his satellites demonstrated a solar system *en miniature* and he wanted to express this in the names of the moons. Consequently he proposed to name the innermost moon Mercurius Jovialis, the Mercury of Jupiter, corresponding to Mercurius Solaris, the Mercury of the Sun. The next moon would then be Venus Jovialis, the third moon Jupiter Jovialis, and the outer moon Saturnus Jovialis.

The first question that arises today is, what happened to the earth and to Mars, which should logically follow Mercury and Venus? Marius did not mention the earth, but he did point out that the astrological significance of Mars was in such contrast to that of Jupiter that a "Mars of Jupiter" would not be harmonious.

Probably realizing that few people would be enchanted by his scheme, he continued:

Perhaps there will be some who will . . . demand from astronomers a name for these four satellites of Jupiter that will be appropriate to each and every one of them. I think that these persons can actually be satisfied in this respect; however I want the thing done without superstition and with the sanction of theologians. Jupiter especially is charged by the poets with illicit loves. Especially well known among these are three virgins, whose love Jupiter secretly coveted and obtained, namely: Io, the daughter of the

[12] *Il Saggiatore,* 1623.

river god Inachus, then Callisto, daughter of Lycaon, and finally Europa, the daughter of Agenor. Yet even more ardently did he love the beautiful boy Ganymede, son of the king of Troy, to the extent that, having assumed the form of an eagle, he placed him on his shoulders and carried him to heaven [Olympus]. . . . And so I believe that I have not done badly in naming the first Io, the second Europa, the third, on account of the splendor of its light, Ganymede, and lastly the fourth Callisto. These names are comprised in the following distich:

> Io, Europa, Ganimedes puer, atque Callisto
> Lascivo nimium perplacuere Jovi
> [Io, Europa, the boy Ganymede, and likewise
> Callisto aroused to excess the lust of Jove.] [13]

Marius and Kepler had discussed the proposal in Regensburg in October 1613 and Kepler welcomed the idea of keeping names of actual people out of the sky and using mythological names only. But the attacks on Marius by Galileo and his pupil Favaro mitigated against these names for a long time. To use the names proposed by Marius would look as if one took sides with Marius against Galileo. If the proposal had come from Kepler it would have been another story. Cassini made a compromise suggestion. He wanted to use the classical verse *"Pallas, Juno, Themisque, Ceres tibi Jupiter abstant"* and give the names of these four goddesses to the satellites. When he failed to receive much applause he modified a practice which Galileo had started in 1611. For simplicity's sake Galileo would mark the satellite closest to Jupiter with one dot, the next one with two dots, and so on. Cassini started writing Jupiter-I, Jupiter-II, etc. His system (in the form of J-I, J-II, etc.) is in use to this day. The mythological names advocated by Marius did slowly creep into usage later, mainly because astronomers who discovered the moons of other planets could not resist exercising their privilege of naming them.

One complication threatened when E. E. Barnard, about midnight on September 9, 1892, discovered a fifth moon of Jupiter by blocking out the glare of the planet itself. On the following night he verified his belief that the quickly moving "tiny speck of light" was another satellite. The orbit of the new satellite was inside the orbit of J-I, which at first seemed merely an interesting circumstance, but one that might create confusion if Barnard's satellite were simply called J-V. Barnard himself in an article in the first volume of *Popular Astronomy* (1893), said:

So far this satellite has not received any name, although many names

---

[13] Translation by Dr. W. W. Blancké, quoted from an article by Samuel C. Barton in *Popular Astronomy*, March 1946, which also contains Marius's original Latin text.

have been suggested for it. Most of these are mythological and have some connection with Jupiter. Columbia, on account of the satellite being found in the Columbian Year [1892 was called the Columbian Year since it marked the four-hundredth anniversary of the landfall of Columbus in the Western Hemisphere], and Eureka, because of California [Eureka is the motto of the State of California], the state in which it was discovered, have been suggested. It would seem, however, almost to have found itself a name—"The Fifth Satellite." In astronomical literature there is a strong tendency to call it simply "The Fifth Satellite" as it was called on the announcement of discovery . . . I would say also, in this connection, that the celebrated French astronomer, Camille Flammarion, has written suggesting the name Amalthea, the nurse of Jupiter (the smallness of the satellite would make this name rather inappropriate), and giving various reasons why it should be so called.[14]

Professor Barnard ended his article by saying that "the mythological names of the four older satellites are seldom used. It may be necessary, however, to give it a mythological name to prevent confusion." A year later he appears to have made up his mind. "The numerals," he wrote in the *Astronomical Journal* (1894) "to me at least, stand as names and do not necessarily have any bearing on the relative distances of the satellites. It would be dangerous and absurd to change the present notation to introduce the new satellite as I, and it would be equally absurd to call it 0, as some have suggested, for we cannot tell what development the great telescopes of the future may bring about in the Jovian satellite-system. I think, therefore, that this new moon should continue to be called the 'Fifth Satellite,' or Satellite V, as I have always called it. This will also be correct if we assume the other satellites were numbered in the order of their discovery, which can be done without violating the facts."

Barnard got his way, in that no Jovian satellite after J-V ever received a name. But for J-V, Flammarion's "Amalthea" is used with increasing frequency.[15] Barnard of course could not know that no satellite closer to Jupiter would be discovered later, or that J-V was to be the last satellite, not only of Jupiter, but of any planet, to be discovered visually. All satellites discovered since have been found photographically.

---

[14] Flammarion also suggested the name Triton for Neptune's larger moon.

[15] Samuel G. Barton, in his article "The Names of the Satellites" (*Popular Astronomy*, March 1946), added the following comment: "W. T. Lynn (in *The Observatory*, xv 429) suggested for the satellite the name Fulmen, the Latin name for thunderbolt, or Keraunos, the Greek equivalent, and discussed names in general. Other names of the nature of those used by Marius come to mind, such as Dione, Leda, Leto or Latona, Maia, Metis, Mnemosyne, and Semele, all of which however have been used as names of asteroids, but then so have Io, Europa, Ganymede, and Callisto and I think no confusion has thus been created. Dione is also the name of a satellite of Saturn. Amalthea is likewise the name of an asteroid. What, indeed, isn't?"

Just about the time of Amalthea's discovery, debate about the four large satellites was once more active. Several observers—Barnard himself, J. M. Schaeberle in California, William Lassel and the Reverend T. E. R. Phillips in England, Father Angelo Secchi in Italy, and Edward Singleton Holden, director of the Lick Observatory, to name only a few—had observed the four large moons in an effort to discover surface detail. Even though these moons are large, the distance to Jupiter under the most favorable conditions is so great that not much can be seen. Father Secchi published some drawings of J-III showing irregular dark spots, while Barnard, in addition to darkish spots, saw a white one.

Much attention was paid to transits of the moons across the disk of the planet, partly because Sir William Herschel had stated back in 1797 that the satellites of Jupiter did not seem to be spherical. In 1850 both William Lassell and Father Secchi corroborated Herschel's observation, but the Reverend T. E. R. Phillips showed later that this lack of sphericity was apparent only, being caused by the spots on the satellite. In 1888 E. S. Holden observed that J-I was darker around both poles, with a white zone around its equator, the width of all three areas (from pole to pole along an assumed meridian) being about equal. Barnard tried to check on this during a transit of J-I in 1890. Using the 12-inch refractor at Lick Observatory he saw, to his immense surprise, that the satellite showed up in transit, as *two* satellites, two grayish circles of which the larger one had about 1½ times the diameter of the smaller one. Of course this was merely an optical illusion, as was proved by the 36-inch refractor, but Barnard, who was very proud of his remarkable eyesight, must have been shocked that such a thing could happen.

But aside from the general problem that observers, being human, can make mistakes, the existence of darker and lighter areas on the large Jovian moons suggested differences in terrain; the whitish spot seen by Barnard on J-III could be a polar cap, like those of earth and Mars. The probable existence of a polar cap suggested that the darker and less dark areas might be land and water. That these four bodies were 483 million miles from the sun did not matter. They were close to Jupiter, and Jupiter was at that time considered a "semi-sun."

Again let me quote Proctor's *Other Worlds Than Ours*, simply because it was a popular work that attempted to give a comprehensive picture of the scientific attitudes of its time.

If Jupiter be still in a sense a sun, not indeed resplendent like the great centre of the planetary scheme, but still a source of heat, is there not excel-

lent reason for believing that the system which circles around him consists
of four worlds where life—even such forms of life as we are familiar with—
may still exist? Those four orbs, which our telescopes reveal to us as tiny
points of light, are in reality globes which may be compared with the four
worlds that circle nearest to the sun. . . .

That Jupiter may supply an immense amount of heat to his satellites is
perfectly clear, since the amount of light he emits is no adequate measure
of the amount of obscure heat which radiates from him to the four worlds
around him. When we consider the enormous apparent size of Jupiter as
seen from his satellites, we recognize at once how large a supply of heat
he is capable of transmitting to them. From the outermost satellite [mean-
ing J-IV] his apparent diameter exceeds that of the sun, as seen by us, some
eightfold, and his apparent size, therefore, exceeds the sun's more than
sixtyfold (1896 ed., pp. 153ff).

In December 1904 J-VI was discovered.

The discoverer was Charles Dillon Perrine, using the Crossley reflector, at Lick Observatory, and he found it on one of the very first
plates exposed for the purpose of hunting down faint satellites of
Jupiter. While he was still checking the orbit of J-VI in January 1905,
Perrine found J-VII, as he reported in the *Publications of the Astronomical Society of the Pacific* (vol. XVII, 1905). Both of them were so
far from Jupiter that they needed about 260 days for one orbit around
their primary, whereas the periods of the "old satellites" were expressed
in terms of a few days and hours (see table, page 00).

In 1908 Greenwich Observatory started checking up on the orbits
of J-VI and J-VII, and Melotte, while photographing them, discovered
J-VIII. It moved in a still larger orbit, needing 750 days to complete
one circuit of its primary. Its orbit was also quite eccentric and strongly
inclined to the orbital plane of the Galilean satellites, and in addition
the satellite moved in its orbit in a direction opposite to that taken by
all the others. It was a "retrograde" satellite..

Six years later a new name was added to the list of astronomers who
had made discoveries in the Jovian system, that of Seth B. Nicholson.
He described the beginnings of his career as a satellite discoverer in
the *Smithsonian Report for 1940*:

In 1914, while a graduate student at the Lick Observatory, I was assigned
the task of photographing the distant satellites of Jupiter to see how closely
they were following their calculated paths. A ninth satellite was found (*Publications of Astronomical Society of the Pacific,* vol. XXVI, 1914) on photographs of the eighth, just as, some years before, the eighth had been found
by Melotte near the sixth and seventh. The period of the ninth satellite is
almost the same as that of the eighth and it also revolves in a retrograde
direction.

JUPITER'S SATELLITE FAMILY
(listed in order of nearness to the planet)

NO.	NAME	YEAR OF DISCOVERY	DISCOVERER	MEAN DISTANCE FROM PLANET (MILES)	ORBITAL PERIOD (DAYS)	DIAMETER (MILES)
V	Amalthea	1892	Barnard	112,600	0.50	100
I	Io	1610	Galilei	261,800	1.77	2,300
II	Europa	1610	Galilei	416,600	3.55	2,000
III	Ganymede	1610	Galilei	664,200	7.15	3,200
IV	Callisto	1610	Galilei	1,169,000	16.69	3,200
VI		1904	Perrine	7,114,000	250.33	100
VII		1905	Perrine	7,292,000	260	40
X		1938	Nicholson	7,350,000	260	15*
XII		1951	Nicholson	13,000,000	625	20*
XI		1938	Nicholson	14,000,000	700	15*
VIII		1908	Melotte	14,600,000	739	40
IX		1914	Nicholson	14,700,000	758	20*

* Approximation.

Satellites VIII and IX are so far from Jupiter that their motions are greatly disturbed by the gravitational attraction of the sun, and their paths around Jupiter do not even approximate closed curves. The computation of their positions is therefore a difficult task and it has been necessary to observe them frequently to prevent their being lost. In the past 20 years, whenever Jupiter has been near the earth, they have, therefore, been photographed many times and such photographs have always been examined for additional satellites, but none has been found.

In July and August, 1938, Nicholson conducted a photographic search for any still undiscovered satellites which, in such a well-explored area, obviously would be small and faint. They could also be assumed to be quite far from Jupiter, and hence slow-moving. As seen from the earth their movement would consist mainly of the movement of Jupiter around the sun. For this reason, while one-hour exposures were taken, the telescope was guided to follow the planet, so that a faint satellite would register on the plate. As has been explained, fixed stars would produce short lines and so would planetoids, since they move faster than Jupiter. Only round dots would deserve further investigation.

Satellites J-VI, J-VII, J-VIII, and J-IX produced dots on the plates, one result being the first complete orbit computation for J-IX, but so did five "unknowns." Three of these could be identified as planetoids which happened not only to be in the line of sight but also to have a rate of motion rather close to that of Jupiter. The other two were new satellites of Jupiter. They were designated J-X and J-XI, and their discovery was announced in *Publications of the Astronomical of the Pacific* (vol. 50, 1938).

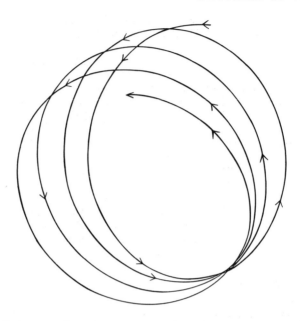

A so-called varying ellipse; Jupiter's outer small satellites are in orbits of this type

Nicholson refrained from giving them names; he pointed out in his article in the *Smithsonian Report* that the system of numerals was established and convenient and even "makes it possible to foretell the name of the next satellite, should another be discovered. It will be J-XII."

He was a better prophet than he knew. A twelfth satellite was dis-covered—by Nicholson, on September 29, 1951.

During the preceding two nights, Dr. Nicholson had been taking photographs for the purpose of checking the orbits of J-IX, J-X, and J-XI. Ephemerides for these satellites were at his disposal; the one for J-IX had been published by Dr. Samuel Herrick of the University of California in Los Angeles, while the other two had been sent to him by Dr. P. Musen of the Cincinnati Observatory. During the first night only one photograph, of the position for J-XI, was obtained, then the sky became overcast. During the following night, with better weather, pictures of J-IX, J-X, and J-XI were taken, plus a few others for the field between J-X and the planet.

To understand what follows it must be kept in mind that the satel-lites were labeled as to their calculated positions. When Dr. Nicholson identified J-IX, say, he did so because J-IX appeared where it was supposed to appear. J-X was similarly identified; it was very close to its computed position. But to the west of this position—in the direction of the planet—there was a new object. It was most likely a new satellite, J-XII. It also was a very faint object; its magnitude was 19, about the same as that of J-X. A good many possible mistakes could be eliminated by the magnitude. J-X and the new object were equally faint; J-IX is somewhat brighter than J-X and J-XI a bit brighter than J-IX. There was no problem about J-VI, J-VII, and J-VIII (the latter was not actually observed) because their magnitudes are around 16. The fact that planetoid No. 1003, Lilofee, was approximately in the line of sight did not matter either, since its brightness is magnitude 13, positively brilliant compared to J-X.

As soon as Dr. Nicholson felt sure of his discovery he sent the information to Harvard, which distributed it as Harvard Announcement Card (usually referred to as HAC) No. 1147, dated October 8, 1951. Since Dr. Musen had supplied the ephemeris for J-X, Dr. Nicholson wrote to tell him that the moon had been located almost precisely in the spot computed. As it happened, Dr. Musen had already received HAC No. 1147. He at once realized that the "new" satellite announced by Nicholson must be J-X, traveling in its computed orbit, but 20 days behind schedule. He was about to report this to Harvard as a correction of HAC No. 1147, when he received Nicholson's letter saying that everything was fine with J-X. He wrote to Nicholson instead. Nicholson measured the plates and found that the "J-X" he had photographed, though in the right place, was moving in the wrong direction and could not, therefore, be J-X. Then Dr. Musen informed Harvard that the newly discovered J-XII was actually J-X behind schedule. This news was incorporated in HAC No. 1152, dated October 25. HAC No. 1154, dated October 30, then informed astronomers that the object believed to have been J-X was really J-XII. HAC No. 1155, dated November 8 gave better positions for the new object (Nicholson had exposed new plates on November 2, as soon as *our* moon got out of the way), and HAC No. 1160-1161, dated November 21, gave J-XII's orbital elements and a first ephemeris.

To summarize what actually happened, J-XII, occupying the position computed for J-X, was mistaken for it, since J-X was elsewhere at the time and the magnitudes of the two were about the same. J-X, on the other hand, being in an unexpected position, was taken for a new object.

There have been no subsequent new developments on the Jovian system, except for the rediscovery of J-VIII, which had been "lost" in 1941. It could have been found again by a really thorough computation, using all the cases in the past where it had been observed, but the job was much too laborious for a human computer. By 1954 Univac was available and the machine, after sufficient preparation, in 2½ hours computed ten slightly different possible orbits for J-VIII. Dr. Nicholson found it on January 25, 1955. Since the machine computation is for 10-day intervals extending to 1980, J-VIII is highly unlikely to get lost again.

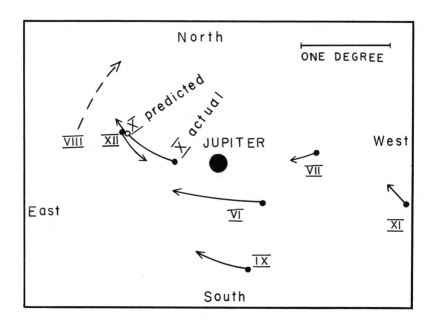

Chart showing the discovery of J-X

15

SATURN

S A T U R N, like Jupiter, has no history of discovery, since it has been known for as long as humanity has records. But it was probably the last of the naked-eye planets to be recognized as a planet. All the others have a conspicuous feature of some kind. Mercury is conspicuous by being sometimes present and sometimes not; Venus's glare cannot possibly be overlooked when it is in the sky; Mars shines as a red star at two-and-a-quarter-year intervals; and Jupiter is noteworthy for its brightness for very many nights running. But Saturn, the most beautiful sight in the heavens when seen through a telescope, is not very impressive to the naked eye. It is fairly bright, but so are many stars. And though its brightness can vary considerably, this again to the naked eye, is not too conspicuous, since there is not always a star of steady brightness nearby for comparison. And since it needs nearly 29½ years to complete one orbit around the sun it does not move fast among the fixed stars.

Still it was known to be a planet as far back as the beginning of writing.

Mythologically speaking, Saturn was the god of agriculture. The name is related to both the noun *satus* (seed corn) and the verb *serere* (to sow). Why the planet Saturn should have been identified with agriculture is a question which classicists have not been able to answer. There certainly was no obvious connection, like that of the identification of red Mars with blood and war. But a recent astronomical work [1] provides an interesting hint. The name for the planet Saturn most often used by the Assyrians was *lubadsagush,* which, since *lubad* meant "old sheep," has to be translated as "oldest of the old sheep." Alexander thinks that this name was applied because Saturn moves so slowly among the stars. Possibly this slow movement accounts for its Latin name too; it may have reminded skywatchers of the slow gait of plowing oxen or grazing cattle.

As long as all astronomy was naked-eye astronomy, only Saturn's

[1] *The Planet Saturn* by Arthur Francis O'Donel Alexander (London: Faber & Faber, 1961; New York: Macmillan, 1962).

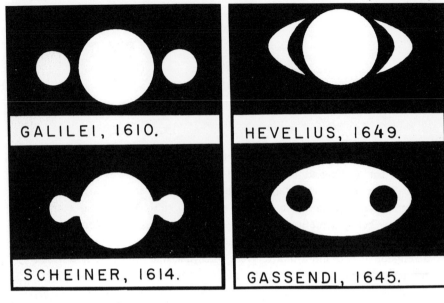

GALILEI, 1610.   HEVELIUS, 1649.

SCHEINER, 1614.   GASSENDI, 1645.

Drawings of the appearance of Saturn before the nature of the ring was recognized

movement could be studied. Tycho Brahe did try to make a naked-eye estimate of its apparent diameter, an attempt that strikes one in retrospect as a deed either of arrogance or of madness. Of course the estimate was completely wrong.

Even after the telescope was invented, Saturn's body was neglected—its rings and moons claimed all the attention. However, Saturn's distance from the earth,[2] is so great that the early telescopes, which were good enough to show the rings and the larger moons, could not show fine detail of the planet's surface, or rather of its atmosphere.

About 1645 Francesco Maria Grimaldi, S.J.—not to be confused with his contemporary Giovanni Francesco Grimaldi, a painter called Il Bolognese—succeeded in making a very good estimate of the difference between the polar and equatorial diameters of the planet. He arrived at the figure of $\frac{1}{12}$ for the flattening. Such pronounced flattening indicated a rapid rotation on its axis. Giovanni Domenico Cassini tried to establish the period. As one of the drawings he made of Saturn indicates, he could see the belts of the planet, but he could only perceive a general impression. The markings in the belts were too faint for his instrument and he could not find any definite value for the period of rotation. Saturn's belts were seen by other astronomers

---

[2] It can never be closer than 744 million miles; the greatest possible distance is 1028 million miles.

too, according to the *Philosophical Transactions* (vol. 59). Charles Messier, on March 28, 1766, "perceived on Saturn's globe two darkish belts; they were indeed extremely faint, and difficult to be discerned, directed, however, in a right line parallel to the longest diameter of Saturn's ring."

Concentration on the rings seems to have continued for the first three quarters of the eighteenth century. Even William Herschel, who was the first to find Saturn's period of rotation, began by looking at the rings. However, his first report on Saturn, in *Philosophical Transactions* (vol. 80), though devoted mainly to the rings and to the discovery of two new satellites of Saturn (Nos. 6 and 7), contains quite a number of remarks on belts seen on the planet's body. In June 1780 Herschel saw a large and apparently not well-defined spot in the belts, which moved a considerable distance from one night to the next. Herschel concluded soon that the belts and the dusky spot were atmospheric phenomena, pointing out that the presence of a large and dense atmosphere was also indicated by the way in which Saturn's moons were occulted by the planet. They did not slide smoothly behind the planet and wink out, as would be the case with a planet without an atmosphere or with a fairly negligible one. Instead, they lingered for a long time. Herschel said to his sister, *"sie kleben am Planeten,"* which may best be rendered as "they look as if they were glued to the planet."

On September 14, 1789, when the view of Saturn's rings was very nearly edge-on, Herschel measured the polar and equatorial diameters and found the flattening to be very nearly $\frac{1}{11}$—Grimaldi had done well with a far poorer instrument.

The paper which Herschel read before the Philosophical Society in January 1794 was almost exclusively devoted to his determination of the period of rotation of the planet. His method consisted in taking two observations in which the belts had looked alike, under the assumption that he had then seen the same area of the belts in or very near the center of the planet, and trying to find a figure for the rotation which would account for this result. Herschel had found a period of rotation of about 10½ hours for the rings; consequently he had to consider only periods shorter than 10½ hours for the rotation of the planet. His first result was that Saturn had rotated 79 times between two equal appearances of the belt, which meant that one rotation took 10 hours, 15 minutes, and 40 seconds. Two other observations involving equal appearances gave a period of rotation of 10 hours, 16 minutes, and 51 seconds. After that he made another good observation which agreed with an earlier one; between these two observations, he calculated, there had been just 100 rotations of the planet, providing a period of 10 hours, 16 minutes, and 0.4 seconds.

In addition to his valuable contributions to the knowledge of Saturn, William Herschel also contributed an excusable mistake, which has been nicknamed the "square-shouldered figure of Saturn." In 1805 and 1806 the flattening of the planet in its polar areas appeared to be not gradual but rather abrupt. It looked as if Saturn were not a flattened spheroid, but something for which there is no proper term but which may be described as a "bulging cylinder," bulging both around the circumference and at top and bottom. He spent much effort trying to find out at what latitude the curvature suddenly changed.

Although astronomers knew that it is impossible for a large planet, especially one with an extensive atmosphere, to have such a shape, they hesitated to say so. In the first place, the report had come from William Herschel. It took as much courage to assume that Herschel could have made a mistake (in observation, that is; interpretation is another matter) as it did to deny that the first Cassini had seen a moon of Venus. In the second place, other observers, including Herschel's son, had observed the same effect.

During the years 1830–1832 Friedrich Wilhelm Bessel took an extensive series of measurements (reported in *Astronomische Nachrichten,* vol. 12), partly to check on the difference of polar and equatorial diameters, partly to establish whether there were any such discontinuities in the curvature. Bessel measured the equatorial diameter seventy times and the polar diameter sixty-eight times and concluded that the discontinuity must be an optical illusion. When the rings were edge-on the curvature appeared perfectly smooth. On a later occasion (in 1848) the Reverend Robert Main, who worked at Greenwich Observatory, and who had not read Bessel's report, repeated these observations and arrived at the same conclusion. "Square-shouldered Saturn" appeared when the rings were fairly wide open; the illusion was compounded of the position of the rings, the brightness of the equatorial zone of the planet, and the shading of the polar areas. But it is an interesting sidelight that William F. Denning, observing in 1880, saw the "square shoulders" very clearly. Of course he knew that the effect was an optical illusion, but no amount of refocusing of his instrument, and no amount of telling himself that this was only an illusion, enabled him to avoid seeing this appearance, any more than the knowledge that the moon at the horizon has the same diameter as the moon overhead can convince your eyes that it is not bigger when it is low.

Spots on Saturn are not as common as they are on Jupiter and as a rule they are quite faint. But on December 7, 1876, a bright equatorial spot developed, which proved to be a long-lasting phenomenon. Asaph Hall in Washington, D.C., observed it and followed it for sixty-one rotations. The period of the spot was 10 hours, 14 minutes, and 23.8 seconds. Hall could check his own observations with those of no less than five different American observers, though not all of them had followed the spot for as long as Hall had. But the ephemeris stated that, "according to Sir William Herschel," the period of Saturn was 10 hours and 28 minutes.

How a discrepancy of about 13 minutes per rotation can make an observer's life miserable can be seen by a little simple arithmetic. The mistake obviously amounts to 7 times 13 or 91 minutes for seven rotations of Saturn. Seven rotations of Saturn happen to be just about the same as three rotations of the earth. An observer who wants to check on something specific three days after a first observation will be thrown off by 1½ hours by such an error. Hall, after satisfying himself that his much shorter period was correct as far as the planet's equator was concerned, then took the trouble of tracing how the figure "according to Sir William Herschel" had found its way into the ephemeris. By patient checking he found that Herschel had never given that figure. It had come from Pierre Simon de Laplace. Moreover, it referred, *not* to the planet, but to the rings!

One other thing that Asaph Hall worked on with respect to Saturn was another determination of the planet's mass. He found it to be ⅟₃₅₀₀ of the mass of the sun.[3]

More spots appeared in 1893 and 1894; they were carefully observed by Camille Flammarion and E. M. Antoniadi as well as by observers in England. It was most surprising, therefore, when in 1896 E. E. Barnard claimed that all the spots must have been optical illusions— he had, he said, used a bigger instrument than the observers in France and England and had been unable to see any spots at all. But the English and French observers supported one another. Antoniadi said that Barnard, in spite of his larger instrument, was simply not an experienced observer of fine detail on planetary surfaces. It has also been suggested that Barnard might have been misled semantically. The European planetary men knew that Saturn's spots were areas which

[3] This calculation had been done previously by others: according to the 1726 edition of Newton's *Principia* the figure read 1/3021; Bouvard, in his *Astronomical Tables of 1821,* had given the value of 1/3512; Leverrier, in 1876, calculated 1/3530, and W. Meyer, in 1881, found it to be 1/3519. Bouvard and Leverrier had based their calculations on the perturbations of Saturn on Uranus, and all others had utilized the periods of revolution of the moons.

did not differ too strongly in intensity from the surrounding areas. Barnard might have looked for well-defined "spots" like sunspots or Jupiter's Red Spot.

The somewhat humorous conclusion of this particular story is that, in June 1903, Barnard announced the discovery of a spot on Saturn which has even been named "Barnard's white spot."

But aside from this interlude the history of Saturn during the latter part of the nineteenth century and the first half of the twentieth century is virtually a carbon copy of the history of Jupiter. H. C. Vogel's paper on the spectra of the planets of 1874 stated that Saturn's spectrum differed slightly from that of the sun in the same manner that Jupiter's did, therefore indicating a small and undetermined percentage of intrinsic light coming from Saturn.

Logically, Agnes M. Clerke, in her *Popular History of Astronomy During the Nineteenth Century* (London, 1902), could state:

It is likely that Saturn is in a still earlier stage of planetary development than Jupiter. He is the lightest of his size of all the planets.[4] In fact, he would float in water. And since his density is shown, by the amount of equatorial bulging, to increase centrally, it follows that his superficial materials must be of a specific gravity so low as to be inconsistent, on any probable supposition, with the solid or liquid states. Moreover, the chief arguments in favour of the high temperature of Jupiter apply, with increased force, to Saturn; so that it may be concluded, without much risk of error, that a large proportion of his bulky globe, 73,000 miles in diameter, is composed of heated vapours, kept in active and agitated circulation by the process of cooling.

The "cooling process" which took place was not precisely what Miss Clerke and her contemporaries had in mind. Instead of being the slow cooling of an actual planet, over millions of years, it was Dr. Harold Jeffreys' article showing that all the cooling that was possible had already occurred.

Rupert Wildt made a model of Saturn as well as of Jupiter. His figures were: a central solid core with a diameter of 28,000 miles, surrounded by an ice shell 6000 miles thick and overlaid by an atmosphere 16,000 miles deep. While Wildt's idea of solutions of metallic sodium in solid ammonia, which would look gray at the temperature of Saturn's atmosphere, explained rather satisfactorily why Saturn does not show the colors observed in Jupiter's currents, his model of the planet did not find much approval. The main, and most pertinent, criticism was that this would give Saturn far too much hydrogen, more

---

[4] The figures for the mean density of Saturn now given in handbooks vary between 0.69 and 0.71.

by a good percentage than Jupiter had under the same set of assumptions. Since the outer planets must have had a common origin they had to consist of the same elements, not only in kind but in quantity.

Afterward Ramsey and Miles applied the reasoning they had used for Jupiter to Saturn and calculated various models, of which the one called S_2 was approved by Jeffreys. In the S_2 model Saturn has eighteen atoms of hydrogen for every atom of helium, with 17 per cent of the planetary mass concentrated in a central core. One interesting speculation which emerged is that the central cores of Jupiter and of Saturn may be about equal in mass; the differences between the two planets would then all be attributable to the layers surrounding the central cores.

To avoid repetition it may be stated that the reasoning used for Jupiter and Saturn applies also to Uranus and Neptune. (It does not apply to Pluto for reasons explained in Chapter 18). The outer planets are frozen gas giants, of about the same composition as the sun, but too small to generate in their interiors the pressures and temperatures needed to start atomic reactions.

THE MOONS OF SATURN

The planet Saturn was high in the sky in northern Europe in the spring of 1655. Christiaan Huygens, using his self-designed telescope, of which he recorded that it was 12 feet in length and had a magnifying power of 50 times, took advantage of this opportunity and on March 25, 1655 noticed a star which he thought might be a satellite of that planet. He followed it for several months, to make sure that it was a satellite. During this time he not only became convinced that his original suspicion had been correct, he also determined the period of revolution around the planet as being 16 days. He published his discovery in a pamphlet with the simple and direct title *De Saturni luna observatio nova,* printed at The Hague in 1656.

It was the satellite now known as Titan, but Huygens did not name it; he referred to it as *Luna Saturni* (Saturn's moon). A few years later, in 1659, in his second report devoted to the Saturnian system, he unfortunately began having philosophical ideas. He wrote that one should rejoice in the discovery of this satellite, for now the number of bodies going around the sun has grown to twelve (counting the planets from Mercury to Saturn, the earth's moon, the four Galilean moons of Jupiter, and Saturn's moon), and twelve is such a perfect number that one could believe it was the number intended by the Supreme Architect. Perhaps he was thinking of the twelve tribes of Israel, the twelve disciples of Christ, and the twelve signs of the zodiac. Whether this idea actually prevented him from looking for additional satellites of Saturn, as has been asserted, is one of the insoluble puzzles of history. In any event he did not discover any of the others.

A second moon of Saturn was found on October 25, 1671, by Giovanni Domenico Cassini, then in the service of Louis XIV in Paris. It was the one now named Japetus, a body about 1000 miles in diameter. On December 23, 1672, Cassini found another one, Rhea, which is slightly larger than Japetus, and Cassini's report, as published in the *Philosophical Transactions* (vol. XII, p. 831), stated that its period of revolution was 4 days, 12 hours, 27 minutes. After announcing the new moon, Cassini reported a further discovery concerning the moon he had found in 1671. This moon was visible only when to the west of its planet and could never be found when east of the planet. Cassini firmly declared that this could not have anything to do with varying distance from the sun, which did not change enough to matter. Hence the "diminution and augmentation" of that moon had to have another cause. He drew the only possible conclusion: "It seems that one part of his surface is not so capable of reflecting to us the light of the Sun which maketh it visible, as the other part is. . . ." At a later date the moon was seen east of Saturn, and Cassini (*Mémoires de l'Académie des Sciences,* 1707, p. 96) said he had made his statement too hastily and withdrew it.

It was the withdrawal which was made too hastily. William Herschel went on record about a century later saying that there was no other possible explanation than the one made by Cassini. Modern measurements have shown that about one-half of Japetus or a little less reflects only 20 per cent as much light as does the other portion. Very likely the brighter portion is covered with frozen gases which are missing on the darker portion.

There is a minor episode connected with Cassini's second discovery. Because of it the number of bodies going around the sun had been increased to fourteen, and the ruler of France was Louis XIV. Cassini did not fail to bring this to le Grand Monarque's attention and Louis XIV was sufficiently impressed to have a commemorative medal struck.

A dozen years later Cassini spoiled his own argument by discovering (on March 21, 1684) two more satellites of Saturn, the ones now named Thetys and Dione. Louis XIV was still on the throne; his re-action is not known. Cassini may have been somewhat worried about the fact that the royal number fourteen was no longer represented in the heavens, because he mentioned in print—where the King would be likely to hear about it— that all five moons of Saturn had been discovered under the patronage of Louis XIV; this applied even to the discoveries by Huygens, who had lived in Paris for twenty years, though he was not a subject of Louis XIV. Cassini suggested that the satellites of Saturn should be known collectively as the "Louisian Stars" (*Sidera Lodoicea*). Fortunately this name was not considered even temporarily outside of France.

While enlarging and enriching the Saturnian system with his dis-coveries, Cassini stuck to his own rule of numbering satellites, calling the one closest to the planet No. 1, but this in time created problems. His own first satellite discovery had been farther from Saturn than Huygens' *Luna Saturni,* hence Huygens' moon became S-1 and Cas-sini's S-2. But all of the three satellites which Cassini found later were inside the orbit of Huygens' S-1. Cassini had to renumber for his dis-covery of 1672, and again for his two discoveries of 1684. If that had been all, astronomers probably would have grown used to Cassini's final numbers. But on August 28, 1789, William Herschel entered in his journal (later printed in *Philosophical Transactions,* vol. 80): "Saturn with 5 stars in a line, very beautiful. The nearest of the five is probably a satellite, which has hitherto escaped observation. It is less bright than the others. What makes me take it immediately as a satellite is its exactly ranging with the other four and with the ring. The ring is very bright and extremely slender. . . ."

It was indeed a new satellite—the satellite Enceladus—closer to the planet than any of the others. According to Cassini's system it should be S-1, and the others would have had to be renumbered once more. Before anybody got around to doing this, William Herschel on Septem-ber 8 and 14, saw another object which also seemed to be a satellite. Another observation on September 17 (now regarded as the date of discovery) made it certain. The new satellite was the one now named Mimas. Since it was still closer to Saturn it became the new S-1.

This ended the numbering problem for a little more than half a cen-tury, but not permanently. In 1848 another satellite of Saturn was found, at a distance which proved to be between that of Huygens' moon and that of Cassini's first discovery. This was the satellite now called Hyperion and it was actually discovered twice. On October 16 of that year, William C. Bond, using the 15-inch refractor of Harvard Observatory, noticed a small star situated in the plane of Saturn's rings. This could be coincidence, but it was also suspicious and deserved checking. On September 18 William Lassell in England had noticed the same small star in that suspicious position. During the following night both observers were sure that the small star followed Saturn, instead of being left behind by Saturn as a fixed star would have been. It had to be a new moon of Saturn. Actually both Bond and Lassel should be named as discoverers—neither knew of the other's work—but since Bond noticed the new moon two nights earlier it is usually listed as his discovery.

This new moon should then have taken the number of Cassini's first discovery (after three renumberings), while Cassini's first would have moved up one number. What made life complicated for everybody was that, if one checked old journals or books, one had to stop to figure out just which satellite was meant by, say, S-3 in a given case.

Sir John Herschel, in 1858, decided that something had to be done about satellite nomenclature. Jupiter's moons presented no problem, then, because only the four Galilean moons were known, but the Saturnian system presented nothing but problems. Only names would help. Herschel suggested a list of mythological Titans, the list now in use (see table below). It is of some interest that the names of the satellites of Saturn were proposed by a man who with all his contributions to astronomy, had not discovered a single one of them!

One more name was added to Sir John's list before the nineteenth century ended. On August 16, 1898, William H. Pickering announced

SATURN'S SATELLITE FAMILY
(according to distance from the planet)

NAME	YEAR OF DISCOVERY	DISCOVERER	MEAN DISTANCE FROM PLANET (MILES)	ORBITAL PERIOD (DAYS)	DIAMETER (MILES)
Mimas	1789	W. Herschel	115,000	0.94	370
Enceladus	1789	W. Herschel	148,000	1.36	460
Tethys	1684	Cassini	183,000	1.89	750
Dione	1684	Cassini	234,000	2.74	900
Rhea	1672	Cassini	327,000	4.52	1,150
Titan	1655	Huygens	759,000	15.94	3,550
Hyperion	1848	Bond	920,000	21.28	300
Japetus	1671	Cassini	2,210,000	79.33	1,000
Phoebe	1898	Pickering	8,034,000	550.48	200
Themis(?)	1905	Pickering	(existence doubtful)		

the discovery of moon number nine, orbiting Saturn much farther away than any of the others. Pickering suggested the name of Phoebe, in mythology one of Saturn's sisters. Phoebe, from the outset, was remarkable on three counts. It was much farther from the planet than any of the other moons— the orbital period of the up-to-then outermost satellite, Cassini's Japetus, is 79⅓ days, that of Phoebe 550 days; it was the first satellite to be discovered photographically; and it was the first to be discovered from an observatory in the southern hemisphere, the Harvard observatory near Arequipa in Peru.

As time went on, another remarkable fact was added. There had been four "discovery plates," exposed around the middle of August 1898. In July 1904 Pickering had succeeded in obtaining more pictures and had determined three more positions from them. On September 12 of the same year E. E. Barnard succeeded in seeing Phoebe through the large refractor at Yerkes Observatory, thus offering one more position. A. C. D. Crommelin, computer at the Royal Observatory, Greenwich, went to work on five positions of Phoebe and announced his results in the *Journal of the British Astronomical Association* (vol. 15, 1905). Phoebe's orbit was not only much larger than any of the other Saturnian satellite orbits, it was also quite different. All the other satellites revolved very nearly in the plane of Saturn's orbit around the sun. And it was *retrograde*. Since this was before the four retrograde minor moons of Jupiter were discovered, it was considered unique (and not quite believable) that a planet should have satellites going in both directions.[5]

The orbit of Phoebe was finally established with the aid of sixteen plates taken by P. J. Melotte of the Royal Observatory in 1907. Another set of pictures taken one year later at the same observatory did not produce any major corrections.

Phoebe may have the additional distinction of being the only satellite in our solar system with a period of rotation differing from its period of revolution. Cassini guessed in 1705 that all satellites may behave the way our moon does, namely that one of their hemispheres points permanently at their primary. E. M. Antoniadi (*Journal of the British Astronomical Association,* vol. 45, 1935) reported that the tidal forces of Saturn must have accomplished this result with Japetus, but that Phoebe was too far away to have its rotation, provided it has any, annulled by Saturn.

The lapse of six years between Pickering's first and second sets of pictures of Phoebe had been caused by the fact that Saturn, during those years, had been in Scorpio and Sagittarius, where there are far

[5] Crommelin did suggest that Phoebe might be considered a captured planetoid but he considered this a very slender probability. Still, there is no other, though of course it is much easier to believe that the retrograde and highly inclined Jovian satellites are such captures, especially since Jupiter is so close to the planetoid belt.

too many stars in the background for such work (see Chapter 18). After measuring the 1904 plates, Pickering thought that he had use for the name Themis—another of Saturn's sisters. He announced the discovery in 1905; it was supposedly the tenth Saturnian satellite in order of discovery, but the seventh as to distance from the planet, fitting between Titan and Hyperion. From the thirteen images measured, the following orbital elements were deduced: mean distance from planet 908,000 miles; orbital period 20.85 days; eccentricity 0.23; and inclination to the ecliptic 39°. These figures do not usually appear in catalogues, for "Themis" was never seen again and is believed to have been a mistake, though it is hard to imagine that an astronomer of Pickering's experience could have been deceived by a planetoid moving at about the same rate as the planet. Of course, such a mistake might have been made, in which case an astronomer with sleuthing instincts might try to determine which planetoid masqueraded as "Themis." To keep the history of astronomy believable to outsiders, let us hope that it was not the planetoid of the same name.

Titan, first discovered of Saturnian satellites, has other distinctions besides priority and size. It is large enough that observers have tried to see whether they could discover markings on its surface, despite the long distance. The results were such that they could be ascribed to optical illusion, comparable to the "markings" on Venus. As late as 1940, astronomers at the Pic-du-Midi observatory reproduced such observed markings, several drawing a light equatorial area with shaded poles, others drawing a dark equatorial belt with lighter poles.

While this work remained inconclusive, Gerard P. Kuiper, during the winter of 1943-44 established that Titan possesses an atmosphere. This had been suspected for some time; in 1925 I attended a lecture on measurement methods given in Berlin by Jan P. Gramatzki, during which he mentioned incidentally that Jupiter's large moons might have atmospheres and Titan almost certainly did.

Kuiper proved it by taking spectrograms which were published in the *Astrophysical Journal* (vol. 100). The atmosphere was found to contain methane, as do the atmospheres of Jupiter and of Saturn. At the temperature assumed for Titan the ammonia would be frozen, but a trace of it seemed to show.

The two major factors in deciding the question of whether a relatively small body can hold an atmosphere are, first, the size, or rather the mass, of the body—the more massive, the better the chance, and secondly, the temperature, which is determined by the distance from the sun—the lower the temperature, the greater the probability. Kuiper established a simple formula which results in a figure by which the stability of an atmosphere can be judged. (It is assumed, of course, that the body started out with an atmosphere.) The figures for the smaller planets and larger satellites run as follows: earth 11.3, Venus 9.5, Triton 6.3 or 6.6, Mars 5.7, Titan 5.3, Ganymede 4.3 or 4.5, Callistro 3.4 or 3.8, Io 3.5, Europa 3.1, Mercury 2.9, and our moon 2.4. These figures agree nicely with observation. We know that Mars still has an atmosphere and that our moon does not. Kuiper thinks that the boundary line lies between Titan and Ganymede, at about 5; if the figure on his scale is above 5, the body, by virtue either of its high mass or its low temperature, can hold an atmosphere. If the figure is below 5, it cannot.

THE RINGS OF SATURN

During the summer of 1610 Johannes Kepler received a letter from Galileo in which Galileo said that, in addition to the discoveries described in the *Sidereus Nuncius,* he had made another one which he did not wish to describe yet, but for which he wanted to establish his priority by the anagram

smaismrmilmepoetalevmibunenugttaviras.

As has been mentioned, Kepler tried to solve the anagram with Martian satellites in mind, but had no success.

He learned what the jumble of letters was supposed to mean from another letter by Galileo, written to the Ducal Tuscan Ambassador at Prague, Guiliano de' Medici. Galileo wrote that Saturn, when seen through a telescope, showed shapes that seemed to change but the sphere of Saturn looked as if it were flanked on either side by smaller spheres, "like two servants supporting an old gentleman." He asked the ambassador to tell the Imperial Mathematician Kepler that the anagram he had sent him was to be read: *Altissimum planetam tergeminum observavi,* "I have seen the uppermost [outermost] planet triple."

Naturally he supposed the two lesser spheres to be large satellites which should revolve around the planet. As he continued to observe, it became clear that they did not revolve; the three bodies kept their relative positions to each other. His surprise and dismay increased when, late in 1612, Saturn suddenly presented itself as a single sphere like Jupiter. "What is to be said about so strange a metamorphosis? Are the two lesser stars consumed after the manner of the solar spots? Have they vanished or suddenly fled? Has Saturn perhaps devoured his own children?"

What had happened was that Saturn had assumed the "edge-on" position in which the thin rings disappear. In modern telescopes they can still be seen even when enormously foreshortened—they then appear as a straight line—but Galileo's telescope was too weak to show the foreshortened phase; as far as he was concerned they simply disappeared for months. Since Galileo did not understand the phenomenon, his prediction that they would reappear must have been based mainly on hope. Of course the two "lesser spheres" did become visible again. But then they began to change shape. They were no longer spheres. Galileo still did not know what he was seeing, but he continued to observe and to sketch. One of his sketches, made in 1616, is so accurate that Professor Giorgio Abetti [6] remarked that if Galileo had seen Saturn like that on his first observations he would probably have understood what he was seeing.

The list of other astronomers who observed Saturn between Galileo's announcement and, say, the year 1650, is a virtually complete roster of all the early observers. There were the Germans Christoph Scheiner, S.J., and Johannes Hevelius of Danzig, the Frenchman Pierre Gassendi, and a whole assembly of Italians: Giuseppe Biancani, Giovanni Batista Riccioli, Francesco Fontana, and Francesco Grimaldi. Like Scheiner, all the Italians were Jesuit fathers, with the exception of Fontana who was a lawyer during daylight hours. And none of them had a telescope good enough to show that Saturn had rings. To most of them it looked as if the planet had handles, like the handle of a teacup. Since the Latin word for "handle" is *ansa,* the appendages of Saturn were discussed under the name of *ansae.* This term is used as a label even now, not that it is correct or even good, but it is picturesque in its connotations and has the advantage of simplicity.

Hevelius, though he saw Saturn as a single sphere, as a triple sphere, and as a sphere with ansae, never got away from the idea that the "handles" were real, though he did not attempt to explain their nature. This was tried by the Frenchman Giles Personne de Roberval, whose explanation was quite logical for his time. Saturn had a torrid zone along its equator which produced vapors which streamed out from the planet. If the vapors were small in quantity they were transparent enough not to be seen; Saturn then appeared in "single phase." If the vapors were large in quantity, they produced the "triple phase" or appeared as ansae. Sir Christopher Wren tried a similar theory, postulating an elliptical corona for the planet. He tried to work out an axis and a period of rotation for this corona which would satisfy the observa-

[6] *History of Astronomy,* p. 109.

tions and even built a model,[7] but he never published this work because
the truth became known before he was finished.

Though Galileo was the first to see the rings of Saturn, their acknowledged discoverer is Christiaan Huygens, because Huygens was the first
to understand what he saw. He also had a better telescope, which is an
additional point to his credit, since he had invented both the compound
eyepiece and a superior method for grinding lenses. Huygens thought
that he had discovered the true nature of the ansae when he wrote his
report on the discovery of Titan in 1656. But he was not yet completely
certain and like Galileo he resorted to an anagram to protect his priority.
His book on Saturn's moon contains this sequence:

aaaaaaa	ccccc	d	eeeee	g	h
iiiiiii	llll	mm	nnnnnnnnn		
oooo	pp	q	rr	s	tttt uuuuu

The solution, which nobody possibly could have found (except, perhaps, after it became known what discovery Huygens was protecting)
was published by him in 1659, in his book *Systema Saturnium*. It read:
*Annulo cingitur, tenui plano, nusquam cohaerente, ad eclipticam in-
clinato* (Encircled by a ring, thin and flat, nowhere touching, inclined
to the ecliptic).

It was not difficult to anticipate objections, all of which would be

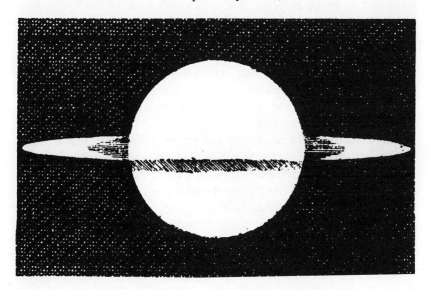

Huygens' drawing of Saturn's ring, from his *Systema Saturnium*

[7] According to Alexander's *The Planet Saturn*, chapter 4.

based mainly on the novelty of a ring. Huygens expected others to argue
either that bodies in space were spheres (a "perfect" shape) and that
no other than the perfect shape was possible; or, more simply, that nobody had ever seen a ring before, hence there couldn't be such a thing.
Huygens' answer to these objections, given in advance, was that the
idea of the ring was based on the evidence of his eyes and was not
an imaginary concept like the epicycles of the early astronomers, which
nobody had ever seen in the sky, and that a ring-shaped body could
rotate around its center just as well as a solid body. But in the main
Huygens relied on an explanation of everything that had been observed,
and on prediction: the ring would disappear in July 1671, in March
1685, and in December 1700. He lived to see the first two of his predictions come true, though his timing was only approximately correct.

The reception of the announcement was mixed. Some people, among
them Sir Christopher Wren, declared at once that they thought this the
proper solution. Others, including Huygens' personal friend Ismael Bullialdus (Boulliau), objected on the grounds that a ring could never
completely disappear; they failed to grasp the idea of a sufficiently thin
ring and presumably thought of something like a wedding ring. Riccioli
is said to have considered writing a pamphlet against the theory but did
not actually do so, possibly because he learned that another astronomer
was going to attack Huygens. The attack was made by the Italian Eustachio Divini, but the actual writing was done by the Frenchman Honoré
Fabri, S.J., because (according to A. F. O'D. Alexander) Divini was a
poor Latinist. The pamphlet appeared in August 1660 as a "Short Anno-
tation to the Systema Saturnium" (*Brevis Annotatio in Systema Saturnium*). It not only attacked the idea of a ring around the planet, it also
attacked Huygens' method of building telescopes, and, for good measure,
the concept of a moving earth.

After having denied practically everything, Divini said that it was a
special conceit of Huygens to claim that only a freely rotating ring
could explain the observed phenomena. Other theories could do so too,
he wrote, and as for himself he preferred the one worked out by Father
Honoré Fabri. This assumed four very large satellites of Saturn, two
bright and two black. What Huygens believed to be just space in the
interior of one of the ansae was actually a black satellite, partly covering
a bright one. The proof was to be found in the fact that the dark area
inside an ansa was blacker than the sky around Saturn. Discounting the
minor fact that this just isn't true, Fabri had the problem of keeping all
of his four satellites, both black and bright, "behind" Saturn all the time;
they could not be permitted to cross in front of the planet because this

would be visible. In order to avoid objections with regard to Titan, Fabri admitted that Huygens had discovered that satellite but declared in the same breath that it was not really a satellite, because it moved behind Saturn instead of orbiting around it. Having committed himself this far he, of course, had to say that the four satellites of Jupiter did not circle their planet either.

Huygens' answer [8] was short and to the point. Fabri's "juggling act" with four balls could not explain the observations; his satellite was in a true satellite orbit; besides, his own observations had been confirmed by an English observer (William Ball, 1656), who had written him a letter about it. Divini and Fabri, in 1661, wrote one more pamphlet against Huygens (increasing the number of their hypothetical satellites to six), to which Huygens wisely did not reply. In 1665 Fabri, in a pamphlet written under his own name, agreed that Huygens was correct; he had been convinced by observations through one of Campani's telescopes, which was far superior to those he had used before. But he insisted that the plane of the earth's equator and the plane of Saturn's rings were parallel and that, "therefore" the Copernican system could not be correct!

The existence of the ring established, the next problem was to explain its nature. Huygens had considered it solid since it looks that way to the eye and he was, in general, more concerned with its position than with its nature. But he did have a mistaken argument for the ring's solidity— the fact that, from time to time, the ring became invisible for several months. Although he considered the possibility that the ring might be too thin to be visible when edge-on to the earth, he rejected this idea and explained the invisibility as the result of seeing the unilluminated side of the ring, with the sun shining on its opposite side. This implied a solid and opaque ring, or rather the other way round: if it was opaque it had to be solid.

While Huygens and Fabri were fighting, others made a few discoveries. The two telescope-makers Divini and Campani noticed that the outer section of the ring was a little less bright than the inner section. Several observers confirmed Huygens' statement that the ring cast a shadow on the globe of the planet.

Cassini took the next step in 1675, after having discovered the satellites Japetus and Rhea. He noticed that "the breadth of the ring was divided into two parts by a dark line, apparently elliptical but in reality circular, as if into two concentric rings, the inner of which was brighter

[8] *Brevis Assertio systematis Saturnii sui,* 1660.

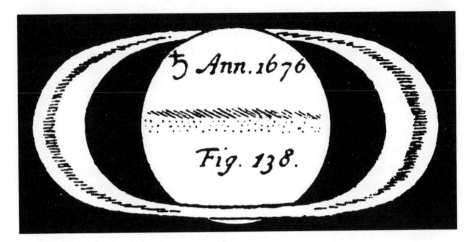

Drawing of Saturn by Giovanni Domenico Cassini, showing the division named after him

than the outer one." [9] This was the discovery of what has been known ever since as "Cassini's Division." (It was also the discovery which made astronomers begin to speak of Saturn's rings in the plural, though for many years "ring" was still used by those who considered Cassini's Division merely a black line.) Cassini did not state in words whether or not his division produced two rings of equal width, or not, but a drawing he made at the time shows that he saw the inner ring wider than the outer ring.

Cassini also expressed an opinion on the nature of the rings. According to Antoniadi, he thought them to be swarms of tiny satellites, too small to be seen separately, moving with differing velocities. He expressed this view in 1705; his son, Jacques Cassini, echoed it in 1715. Although the Cassinis, *père et fils,* had intuitively grasped the truth it was a long time before the correctness of their views could actually be proved.

William Herschel never agreed with the Cassinis. In fact, for quite a long time he stubbornly spoke of "the ring," which he considered solid. Of course he saw Cassini's Division; in fact his superior telescope showed it better than any other telescope had ever done, but he considered it prudent to regard it as a surface marking of some kind. His attitude was that at that time—(1778)—he had seen only the northern

[9] The quotation is from a letter written by Cassini in August 1676, printed in *Philosophical Transactions* (vol. XI, p. 689). A nineteenth century move in England to give the credit to the English astronomer William Ball, a contemporary of Christiaan Huygens, and to speak of "Ball's Division" (as R. A. Proctor did) was proved mistaken by W. T. Lynn and Professor John C. Adams, both also English. The mistake originated from a commentary on one of Ball's drawings of Saturn, made ten years before Cassini announced his discovery. Ball himself never claimed to have seen the division.

plane of the ring and would wait until the southern plane presented itself to his view. This implied a wait of about eleven years. In the meantime he was not idle. He established, first, that the "black belt," as he called it, did not change either its width or its position. He also called attention to the extreme thinness of the ring, comparing its nearly edge-on view with the diameter of the satellites; since his figures for the latter were too large, he also overestimated the thickness of the ring.

Because he believed the ring to be solid he had the problem of explaining why it could be seen when the sun shone on its other side. He said that this might be light reflected from the body of the planet, analogous to our seeing our moon by reflected earthlight. As for the occasional bright spots he noticed on "the ring," in 1778 he thought they might be mountains, shining brightly in the sunlight. But later, he changed his mind, evidently with a sigh of relief. Mountains, to be visible at the distance separating Saturn and the earth, would have to be incredibly tall. But in 1789 Herschel observed one such bright spot until "one of these supposed luminous points was kind enough to venture off the edge of the ring and appeared in the shape of a satellite." This, of course, immediately raised the question of whether all the luminous spots reported by various observers might not be just Saturn's satellites, having merged with the nearly edge-on ring.

In 1778 Herschel, deferring judgment, had said that the final proof of whether the "black belt" was a gap would consist in seeing a star through the gap. That event occurred, though not until long after Herschel's death. But by 1791, after observing the other face of the ring, Herschel himself came to the conclusion that it was a gap: "I think myself authorised to say that the planet Saturn has two concentric rings, of unequal dimensions and breadth, situated in one plane, which is probably not much inclined to the equator of the planet."

Herschel's previous position had not agreed with a mathematical investigation by Pierre Simon de Laplace which had been published in 1785 as *Théorie des Attractions des Sphéroïdes et de la Figure des Planètes*. It was one of the memoirs which make up the story of knowledge, but as regards Saturn's rings the Marquis de Laplace advanced a strangely complicated notion. He began by pointing out that the ring, in order to stay in place at all, had to rotate, else it would break up and fall into the planet. He then showed that the inner portions of the ring would have to rotate faster than the outer portions, in fact that a given small area of the ring would have to rotate with precisely the speed it would have if it were a satellite at that distance from the planet. In a solid ring this would lead to stresses and strains which could not be absorbed by the strength of the material. To these stresses others, caused by the gravitational pull of the planet, would be added. The whole argument reads as if Laplace were building it up to confirm mathematically the idea of the Cassinis. One expects him to start the next paragraph with the statement that, therefore, the rings are possible only in a broken-up condition; that we see, as Cassini put it, *"un essaim de petits satellites"* ("a swarm of tiny satellites"). But instead Laplace, citing Cassini's Division as proof that there is more than one ring, went on to say that all his objections apply only if Saturn's ring is taken to be one solid ring of the dimensions that can be calculated from the observations, or even two rings as shown by Cassini. The objections would not apply to a system of a large number of very narrow rings. Hence Saturn's ring system must consist of two wide ring systems each of which, in turn, was composed of a large number of very narrow rings.

Herschel had convinced himself that Cassini's Division actually was a division and he admitted that the periods of revolution of the two rings were not the same, though the difference was probably small. But that was as far as he would go, and he never changed his opinion again.

Laplace's conclusion implied, of course, that there must be other divisions in addition to Cassini's. If so, these probably could be seen and the astronomers of the first part of the nineteenth century resolved to find them.

Naturally, when looking for divisions in the ring, one could not help seeing "lucid spots" in the ring when they appeared. Johann Schröter and Karl Harding (who was at that time Schröter's assistant) observed some in 1802 and 1803; Heinrich Schwabe in 1833 and 1848; and the American father-and-son team, W. C. and G. P. Bond, in 1848. Their verdict was as unanimous as it was surprising: the bright spots did *not* move. They stayed in one location, not only for hours, but for days and even months. Bond even stated that his criterion for distinguishing bright spots from satellites which coincided with the rings was that the satellites moved, the spots remained immobile. This, of course, makes Herschel's 1789 result a mystery. The stationary luminous spots are evidently purely optical effects caused by the relative positions of Saturn, the rings, the sun, and the earth. But in view of Herschel's observation one may have to assume that there are also bright spots, apparently much rarer than the stationary ones, which do follow the rotation and which could be local particle clusters.

But now for the "finer divisions."

Volume IV (for 1830) of the *Memoirs* of the Royal Astronomical Society contains a paper on this particular problem by Captain Henry

Kater, who was the vice president and treasurer of the society. The observations were made beginning in 1825; the paper was read to the society on May 14, 1830. On December 7, 1825, Captain Kater had noted: "I fancied that I saw the outer ring separated by numerous dark divisions, extremely close, one stronger than the rest, dividing the ring about equally . . . I have little doubt, from a most careful examination of some hours, that that which has been considered the outer ring of Saturn consists of several rings. The inner ring decidedly has no such appearance." He made very similar notes for January 16 and 17, 1826, but noted on January 22, 1828, that "no trace of division in the outer ring could be perceived." At the end of his paper, Captain Kater stated that Professor Quetelet in Paris, using a telescope with a 10-inch aperture and achromatic lenses, had seen a division in the outer ring in December 1823. Kater also quoted a statement that "Mr. Short" had seen the outer ring as three or four concentric rings in about 1870. Since Kater, in a careful search, could find no direct reference for this observation, he concluded that Lalande, who reported it, might have learned about it in a conversation with Short.

The problem with the finer subdivisions in the outer ring was, first, that they were very rarely seen, and, second, that different observers saw them in different places, subdividing the outer ring either in the middle, or nearer its outer edge, or nearer its inner edge. Only one ever received a name; Encke's Division, after Professor Johann Franz Encke, whilom director of the Urania Observatory in Berlin from which Neptune was later discovered. Professor Encke first saw the division on April 25, 1837. Next time he saw it, on May 28, he could make micrometric measurements, placing his division one-third of the width of the outer ring, counting from its inner edge. Heinrich Schwabe in Dessau, Germany, observed Saturn for thirty days in August and September 1841 and saw Encke's Division four times during that period.

But William Lassell and the "eagle-eyed" Reverend William R. Dawes, using the same telescope alternately, saw a division in the outer ring on September 7, 1843, and both placed it one-third of the way from the outer edge, stressing that it was visible on both ansae. In November 1850 Dawes saw a part of that division, and the next day he received a letter from Lassell who claimed to have seen the division on November 21, two days before Dawes saw it. The situation turned into a case quite similar to that of the "canals" of Mars half a century later. On fine nights the division of the outer ring was suddenly there, on other nights only Cassini's Division showed. One observer stated that the degree of blackness of Cassini's Division was an indicator of the visibility of other divisions; if Cassini's Division did not look deep black nothing else would be visible.

During the winter of 1854-55 Dawes repeatedly saw a fine but clear line in about the middle of the outer ring, and Father Angelo Secchi, during the same winter, saw a fine line in the outer ring which he compared to a fine pencil line, a term later used by many other observers. The Germans usually called this Encke's Division, even though it was not in precisely the position measured by Encke.

While the search for subdivisions, though not entirely unsuccessful, did not yield any definite results, a new discovery grew out of it: Ring C, more usually called the "crepe ring," inside the inner ring. Though the final discovery is ascribed to specific observers—not less than five, the Bonds, father and son, Charles W. Tuttle, Lassell, and the Reverend Dawes—it is certain that it had been seen for quite some time by various astronomers.

Captain Kater's paper contains a note he wrote on November 30, 1825: "The exterior ring of Saturn is not so bright as the interior, and the interior is less bright close to the edge next the planet. The inner edge appears more yellow than the rest of the ring and nearer in colour to the body of the planet." Kater also quoted a statement by Wilhelm Struve in Russia, that: "[the inner ring], toward the planet seems less distinctly limited, and to grow fainter, so that I am inclined to think that the inner edge is less regular than the others." Struve's observation was made in 1826. And in 1838 Johannes Galle saw the crepe ring, too, as reported by Encke: "The inner edges of the first ring [Encke counted the rings from the inside out] fade away gradually into the dark interval between the ring and the sphere. It seemed . . . that the ring extends over nearly half the space towards Saturn's sphere. . . ." [10] Dawes remarked later that Galle must have seen the dark line on Saturn's body which is caused by the crepe ring, because he drew it, but that he evidently failed to realize at the time what it was he drew.

The reports now regarded as "the" announcements of the discovery of the crepe ring were written by William C. Bond (in *Astronomical Journal,* vol. II and by Dawes in the *Monthly Notices* of the Royal Astronomical Society (vol. XI, which also contains the confirmation by Lassell). The period of observation by the various discoverers was spread out over a little less than one month. The Bonds started early in November and reached their conclusion on November 15, the Reverend Dawes was delayed by bad weather in England until the end of November, and Lassell's confirmation came on December 3, 1850.

[10] *Verhandlungen der Berliner Akademie der Wissenschaften,* 1838.

The discovery was mainly a matter of realizing what they had seen and others before them had also seen, more or less clearly. W. C. Bond gave the credit for explaining what had been seen to Charles W. Tuttle: ". . . the idea was suggested by Mr. Tuttle of explaining the penumbral light bordering the interior edge of the bright ring . . . as well as the dusky line crossing the disc . . . by referring both phenomena to the existence of an interior dusky ring, now first recognized as forming part of the system of Saturn. This explanation needed only to be proposed to insure its immediate acceptance as the true and only satisfactory solution of the singular appearances. . . ."

The name "crepe ring" was coined more or less accidentally by Lassell in a letter to the Astronomer Royal, written on December 3 after he had seen the ring through Dawes's telescope. Otto Struve, the son of Wilhelm Struve, then suggested calling it Ring C, following the custom, already used by some astronomers, of counting Saturn's rings from the outside inward, but using letters instead of numbers.

By then it was time to think about the nature of the rings once more. The same volume of the journal that contained W. C. Bond's report on the discovery of the innermost ring also contained an investigation into the nature of the rings by his son G. P. Bond. The younger Bond began by summarizing all the attempts to find minor divisions in the rings, both those which had had some success and those which were completely unsuccessful, even though bigger telescopes had been often used for the latter. Bond did not try to discredit Encke's Division and others like it as optical illusions. The fact that sometimes something had been seen and other times had not been seen indicated to him that the rings themselves were changing. But if this were true, they could not be rigid, whether one believed, with Herschel, in two (now three) rings or, with Laplace, in a multitude of them. Bond concluded that the rings had to be fluid, in which case the particles near the inner edge of the rings could easily flow past those which had a slower period of revolution. Of course local disturbances would take place and, when they did, would appear as minor divisions, but this would not endanger the stability of the rings.

Bond's hypothesis of fluid rings was seconded five years later by the American mathematician Benjamin Peirce who had started his investigation by checking Laplace's conclusion. His reasoning ran about as follows: the number of rings suggested by Laplace was too small, or rather, the average width of Laplace's rings was too large, so that much narrower and therefore more numerous rings would be neeeded. But then the stability of the system would be endangered, more or less in direct proportion to the number of rings assumed, leading to a collapse of the whole. Since Saturn still had its rings they could not be solid and were probably fluid, as suggested by G. P. Bond.

It was another two years before the final step was taken.

In 1855, the year Professor Peirce published his work, Cambridge University announced a prize—the so-called Adams Prize Essay—for a work dealing with the problems of Saturn's rings, and specifically with what their nature must be to render them stable and at the same time explain their appearance. The prize was won in 1857 by James Clerk Maxwell with an *Essay on the Stability of Saturn's Rings.* Maxwell showed first that solid rings of the Laplace kind were not completely impossible, but they would have to be of such unequal mass distribution that the rings would not look the way they do, and even with these assumptions the system would be very easily disturbed; hence the idea of solid rings had to be rejected. As for fluid rings they only appear to avoid the difficulties, as the various gravitational fields to which the rings are subjected would cause a fluid ring (which lacks any internal strength) to break up into a number of (fluid) satellites. Hence "the only system of rings which can exist is one composed of an indefinite number of unconnected particles, revolving round the planet with different velocities according to their respective distances."

Maxwell's mathematical analysis had finally confirmed Cassini's early hypothesis. And Maxwell's analysis, in turn, was later confirmed by the spectroscope.

The remaining problems were: to explain Cassini's Division and the smaller divisions, either temporary or just difficult; to establish the nature of the particles forming the rings; and to explain, if possible, why there are rings at all. The explanation of the gap between the two main rings was fairly simple. The gaps in the belt of Minor Planets had been explained by the American astronomer Daniel Kirkwood in 1866 (see Chapter 13). One year later Kirkwood himself expanded his theory to include the gaps in Saturn's rings. A particle moving around Saturn in 11.3 hours has a period which is half that of Mimas, just about one-third of that of Enceladus, a quarter of that of Tethys, and one-sixth of that of Dione. Such a particle would be subject to very strong disturbance by not less than four of Saturn's satellites. A particle with that orbital period would be moving in Cassini's Division and would obviously not remain there for very long.

Cassini's broad gap is the result of the combined action of four satellites with a little assistance from two more: Rhea, which has an orbital period nine times that of a particle in the division, and Titan, even though its period is thirty-three times that of the hypothetical particle. Of course the particles which once moved in the division must now be elsewhere; it is usually assumed that the brightness of Ring B at the edge of Cassini's Division is caused by its being crowded with particles that originally filled this gap.

Kirkwood's calculations were especially interesting with regard to Encke's Division, which had been seen either inside or outside the middle of Ring A.[11] Dividing the outer ring into one hundred parts for the purpose of expressing distances in percentages, Kirkwood found that at 39 per cent (counting from the outside inward) the period of a particle equals three-fifths of the orbital period of Mimas, while at 57 per cent the period of a particle would be two-fifths of the orbital period of Enceladus. Most Saturn observers are now agreed that Encke's Division is not a true gap but merely a thin region, an area not completely devoid of orbiting particles. The fact that it often cannot be found might be due to relative positions between the rings and the observer, but it might also be due to a real "filling up." It is possible that Encke's Division has a periodicity of some kind.

The gap between Ring B and the crepe ring—a gap that many observers say does not exist—was explained by Kirkwood as due to the fact that a particle in that gap would have one-third of the periodicity of Mimas. Later on, Kirkwood's idea was repeatedly reworked by others, Crommelin, for one, and found to be correct.

There were still a number of minor mysteries, both old and new, to be cleared up. E. E. Barnard utilized the favorable years of 1894 and 1895 to check on a statement which had cropped up periodically, namely that the rings of Saturn were not concentric to the center of the planet. Barnard disproved this completely and emphatically. The rings were not eccentric with regard to the planet, but their positions often created the optical illusion that this was the case.

Some fourteen years later Barnard had to check on a new report. During 1907–1908 the French astronomer Georges Fournier reported that, outside the rings, he had seen a very faint luminous area—*"une zone lumineuse très pâle."* In that faint area he had spotted[12] fast-moving

---

[11] Dr. M. Wilhelm Meyer, who spent many years in Italy for reasons of health and who observed with Schiaparelli, mentioned in a popular book written near the end of his life that he and Schiaparelli could establish that Encke's Division changes its position. The wording of his statement is such that it may mean that they saw Encke's Division one night in one place and another night in another place but it may also mean that the shift of position was actually seen. I have been unable to find a formal report on these observations.

[12] *". . . on aperçoit dans la zone lumineuse de petits corpuscules lumineux qui se meuvent trés vite."*

tiny luminous points—something never seen, or at least never reported, by anyone else. One year later, E. Schaer, a Swiss astronomer working at the Geneva Observatory, reported that he had seen a dusky ring *outside* Ring A. Schaer, at the time, was not yet acquainted with Fournier's observation. Several observers in England confirmed the existence of Schaer's outer crepe ring. And, in addition, Percival Lowell reported that he, in 1907, had observed "thick spots" in the rings which he called "tores," borrowing a botanical term meaning thickenings.

As for Fournier's "little luminous bodies" Antoniadi suggested that they might have been "extra-planar particles," that is, particles outside the normal plane of the rings. Fournier agreed. Lowell's "tores," not seen by anybody elsewhere, might conceivably have been the same thing. But Schaer's external crepe ring was not found when Barnard looked for it in 1909 and has not been seen since. However, it seems somewhat unjust simply to write off Schaer's statement and the corroborating statements by British observers. Possibly the rings were disturbed in 1907 and 1908 by extraneous bodies, causing ring particles to assume more eccentric orbits for a while and thus temporarily producing an outer crepe ring. A collision of major particles inside the ring might have had the same result.

This brings us to the question of the size of the particles composing the rings, and this question, in turn, is tied up with the thickness of the rings. But before these questions can be discussed, a lucky chance observation, which has some bearing on these problems, must be reported. On February 9, 1917, Saturn's rings (but not the planet itself) occulted a seventh-magnitude star in Gemini. The occultation had not been predicted and by pure good luck was observed by two men in England, John Knight and Commander Maurice A. Ainslie. The relative motions were such that the star was first covered by Ring A, was then seen through Cassini's Division (just as William Herschel had hoped would happen one day), and was then covered again by Ring A.

Knight, who observed the beginning of the rare spectacle, watched how the star "ate its way into the outer ring" but never completely disappeared. It could be seen all the time even though there were moments where it was only "something extra" in the ring. Shortly before 10 p.m. it appeared clearly in Cassini's Division and Knight could see it through the division until 10:25 when the seeing became bad. But at about 10:15 Commander Ainslie, working in another observatory and at the time, unaware of Knight's observation, picked up the star while it was still shining through Cassini's Division. Ainslie then watched it being covered by the A ring and could watch it until it reappeared from behind the

ring at 11:10. Ainslie said that if the star's brightness when clear of the
rings is designated as 100, it was of that brightness or very nearly so
while in Cassini's Division, and of a brightness of 25 when seen through
the A ring. But twice, while it was covered by the A ring, its brightness
increased to about 50, once for 10 to 15 seconds and again for about 5
seconds.

This proved once more the existence of two "thin spots" in the ring;
for the star's location during the longer of the two bright periods, Ainslie used the term Encke's Division.

Now this observation could be used to make an estimate of the size
of the particles. Obviously the particles composing the ring could not be
larger than the ring's thickness, which is the reason the over-all thickness
of the rings entered into the discussion. At first there had been very considerable leeway. William Herschel, in 1789, had stated that the thickness of the ring was not more than one-third of the diameter of the
satellite Rhea, which would mean less than 280 miles. Sir John Herschel
in 1813 revised his father's estimate downward a little. The rings had
disappeared during an "edge-on" period, and Herschel, knowing the
power of his telescope, felt that he would have seen the rings even edge-
on if their thickness were 250 miles or more. Fifteen years later G. P.
Bond, using precisely the same reasoning but having a better telescope,
arrived at a thickness of less than 42 miles and Barnard in 1891 still
estimated "less than 50 miles."

The really drastic revision was announced in 1908, in the *Astrophysical Journal* (vol. 27) by Professor Henry Norris Russell of Princeton
Observatory, who said that the thickness of the rings could not be greater
than 13 miles. Dr. Louis Bell in 1919 reduced this figure to "less than 10
miles." None of the particles composing the ring could therefore be more
than 10 miles in diameter and the diameter was probably much less.

After Ainslie's observation Dr. Crommelin could make a better estimate. A star's light had been dimmed by a curtain of particles moving at
the rate of about 16 miles per second. If these particles, seen from earth,
had looked about as large as the star, a definite flickering of the star
image should have been the result. The problem was the diameter of the
star image. Stars, even in the largest telescopes, show as points without
a measurable diameter; neither the actual diameter of the star nor its
actual distance, enters into the discussion. What had to be determined
was the size of a body which at the distance of Saturn from earth would
look as large as that star did. Dr. Crommelin pointed out that a luminous
body under those circumstances would have to have a diameter of less
than half a mile. This being the relationship, particles of, say, a quarter-

mile in diameter would have caused flickering. Since no flickering was observed the particles of Saturn's ring must be much smaller.

After a star had been seen through Ring A, nobody really doubted that a star could also be seen through Ring B. But still, it had not actually been done and planetary observers were much interested when, in January 1920, an occultation of a star by Saturn was predicted for March 14 of the same year. But on the night of March 14 the weather all over Europe was horrible, and at the time of the occultation the Western Hemisphere had daylight. Only one good observation was made, by W. Reid at Rondebosch, near Capetown in South Africa. But Reid was so sure that his European colleagues must be doing well that he did not even make a formal report, he only wrote an article for the local newspaper. However, even that established that the star (of magnitude 7.3) could be seen through Ring B; there was one "momentary flicker."

During the discussion of this observation by the Saturn Section of the British Astronomical Association, the belief was expressed (probably for the first time) that the rings of Saturn might be like enormous sheets of cirrus clouds, in that the particles composing them might be ice crystals.

The view that Saturn's rings are mainly ice crystals has found more and more support as time went on. All the ice crystals would of course be minute in size, but there is no reason to assume that Saturn's rings consist of ice crystals only. Fragments of different natures and different sizes might well be present. All that can be said definitely is that very large particles, a quarter of a mile or more in diameter, are so unlikely that their existence can be denied. But otherwise it has been impossible to establish an "average size" for them. The problem probably cannot be solved by observation from earth.

But while the nature of the rings is now clear—separate orbiting particles ranging in size from single ice crystals, numerous, to an unknown though not very large upper limit—the cause of the rings is still a mystery. Once a ring has formed around a planet it can become stable and continue to exist. But why a ring should be formed is a question for which there is no definite answer.

16

URANUS

On a chilly evening in the year 1781 the diameter of our solar system was doubled by the discovery of a new planet orbiting the sun about 800 million miles farther out than Saturn, then thought to be the most distant of the planets.

Of course the fact that the size of the solar system had been doubled did not become immediately apparent. It was not even immediately apparent that the body was a new planet, the first to be discovered since antiquity. In fact, its discoverer, Sir William Herschel, put "Account of a Comet" at the head of the communication which he sent to the Royal Society. Herschel's account (as published in the *Philosophical Transactions,* 1781) is remarkable for its utter simplicity; nothing unnecessary is said, nothing necessary is left out:

On Tuesday the 13th of March, between ten and eleven in the evening, while I was examining the small stars in the Neighbourhood of H Geminorum, I perceived one that appeared visibly larger than the rest; being struck with its uncommon magnitude, I compared it to H Geminorum and the small star in the quartile between Auriga and Gemini, and finding it so much larger than either of them, suspected it to be a comet.

I was then engaged in a series of observations on the parallax of the fixed stars, which I hope soon to have the honour of laying before the Royal Society; and those observations requiring very high powers, I had ready at hand the several magnifiers of 227, 460, 932, 1536, 2010 etc. all which I have successfully used upon that occasion. The power I had on when I first saw the comet was 227. From experience I knew that the diameters of the fixed stars are not proportionally magnified with higher powers, as the planets are; therefore I now put on the powers of 460 and 932, and found the diameter of the comet increased in proportion to the power, as it ought to be, on a supposition of its not being a fixed star, while the diameters of the stars to which I compared it were not increased in the same ratio. Moreover, the comet being magnified much beyond what its light would admit of, appeared hazy and ill-defined with these great powers, while the stars preserved that lustre and distinctness which from many thousand observations I knew they would retain.

Herschel, needless to say, waited eagerly for the next clear night when he could check up on his "comet." On March 19 he noted: "The Comet's apparent motion is at present 2¼ seconds [of arc] per hour. It moves according to the order of the signs [of the zodiac] and its orbit declines but very little from the ecliptic."

On March 28: "The diameter is certainly increased, from which we may conclude that the Comet approaches to us."

And finally, on April 6: "With a magnifying power of 278 times the Comet appeared perfectly sharp upon the edges, and extremely well defined, without the least appearance of any beard or tail."

Could it be a planet?

Herschel hesitated; in his native language mistakes are "committed" instead of being merely "made"; rather wait than be caught in a hasty assertion! It was actually A. J. Lexell who, in midsummer 1781, announced that Herschel's comet was a new planet, moving in a nearly circular orbit 19 Astronomical Units from the sun. But it was Herschel's privilege to name it. On this subject, he wrote:

> The first consideration in any particular event, or remarkable incident, seems to be its chronology: if in any future age it should be asked, *when* this last-found Planet was discovered? It would be a very satisfactory answer to say, "In the Reign of King George the Third." As a philosopher then, the name of *Georgium Sidus* presents itself to me, as an appellation which will conveniently convey the information of the time and the country where and when it was brought to view. Best, as a subject of the best of Kings, who is the liberal protector of every art and science;—as a native of the country from whence this Illustrious Family was called to the British throne; —as a member of that Society, which flourishes by the distinguished liberality of its Royal Patron;—and, last of all, as a person now more immediately under the protection of this excellent Monarch, and owing everything to his unlimited bounty;—I cannot but wish to take this opportunity of expressing my sense of gratitude, by giving the name *Georgium Sidus* to a star which (with respect to us) first began to shine under his auspicious reign. —By addressing this letter to you, SIR, as President of the Royal Society, I take the most effectual method of communicating that name to the Literati of Europe, which I hope they will receive with pleasure.

The "Literati of Europe" did not receive the suggestion with pleasure; to them the name of *Georgium Sidus* was merely a breach with the tradition of classical learning. In the British Nautical Almanac the planet was listed as the "Georgian" until 1850, but everywhere else Johann Elert Bode's suggestion to name it Uranus was quickly accepted. Not only was it classical, therefore neutral; it was also logical, since the mythological Uranus was said to be one of the originators of astronomy, as well as the father of Saturn, who in turn was the father of Jupiter.

These developments did not progress as rapidly as it sounds when told in retrospect. The possibility that the object might be just a comet lingered for a few years. The French astronomer Alexandre-Gui Pingré, in his *Cométographie, ou Traité Historique et Théoretique des Comètes,* published in 1784, listed Uranus as "Première Comèt 1781" and began the section on it with the words: *"Cette Comète ou Planète (car il n'est pas encore décidé si elle est l'une ou l'autre) fut découverte en Angleterre."* In English: "This comet or planet (for it has not yet been decided whether it is the one or the other) was discovered in England." But Pingré then stated that Anders John Lexell had calculated a nearly circular orbit at a distance of 18.9283 Astronomical Units; Pingré probably did not want to risk leaving such a big comet out of his listing, if it turned out to be one.

Since Lexell had calculated a nearly circular orbit, which in itself spoke in favor of a planet, there was one more possibility of a cross check. Uranus is large enough to be visible with the naked eye if you know precisely where to look; it then appears as a very faint star near the limit of visibility. But this makes it a conspicuous object in even a small telescope; possibly earlier astronomers had listed it as a star. Bode started looking for such earlier listings and found two almost immediately. One was an observation made in 1690 by John Flamsteed, the first Astronomer Royal; he listed it in his *Historia Celestis* as "a star of the sixth magnitude"; the second was in one of the star charts prepared by the German astronomer Johann Tobias Mayer, who died in 1762. Spurred on by Bode's success, other astronomers continued to search; one, Burchardt, by name, found four more observations by Flamsteed, one for April 2, 1712, and three others for March 4, 5, and 10, 1715.

The record was held by the French astronomer Pierre Charles Lemonnier, who, before his death in 1799, began an examination of his own charts and found that he had seen Uranus three times, each time carefully entering its position as a fixed star. Alexis Bouvard, who later published the first comprehensive tables on the motions of Uranus, also went through Lemonnier's papers and found ten more observations of Uranus, four of them on consecutive nights! One of Lemonnier's observations, discovered by Bouvard, was written on a stained paper bag which had originally contained hair powder. If Lemonnier had spent about two hours of daytime comparing his own charts he would surely have discovered the planet. He obviously did not. Bouvard accused Lemonnier of carelessness. Arago, somewhat later, when he was director of the Paris Observatory, declared, "Lemonnier's records were the *image* of chaos!"

In the meantime the planet itself was being carefully observed. Herschel himself announced that his new planet had satellites, six of them.

Here he made a mistake, four of his six satellites being merely small fixed stars. The two true satellites he discovered are those now named Titania and Oberon. Two others, Ariel and Umbriel, were found by William Lassell in 1851. To everybody's surprise a fifth moon—which was named Miranda—turned up in 1948; it was discovered photographically on February 15 of that year (and confirmed on two plates on March 1) by Gerard P. Kuiper at McDonald Observatory in Texas.

Uranus, meanwhile, presented astronomers with still another surprise. Since Jupiter and Saturn rotate rapidly on their axes it was at least probable that Uranus did the same. If so, it should show a noticeable flattening at the poles. Herschel himself stated that he had seen this; he was right, even though some later observers failed to notice the phenomenon. But they were right too, a fact which was connected with the nature of the surprise which was to come. The first hint came from observations of the orbits of the Uranian satellites. In most cases the planes of satellite orbits are more or less the same as those of the solar orbits described by their planets. But it soon became clear that the satellites of Uranus had orbital planes which were very nearly vertical to the orbital plane of their planet.

URANUS'S SATELLITE FAMILY

NAME	YEAR OF DISCOVERY	DISCOVERER	MEAN DISTANCE FROM PLANET (MILES)	ORBITAL PERIOD (DAYS)	DIAMETER (MILES)
Miranda	1948	Kuiper	80,800	1.41	150
Ariel	1851	Lassell	119,100	2.52	600
Umbriel	1851	Lassell	165,900	4.14	400
Titania	1787	Herschel	272,000	8.71	1,000
Oberon	1787	Herschel	364,000	13.46	900

Strange, satellites usually are more or less above the equators of their planets. Nobody then knew why this is so (and even now we aren't too sure), but the fact was indisputable. Then the interesting idea arose that the satellites of Uranus still might be above the equator of their planet, that the planet's equator had a peculiar position. Possibly the axis of Uranus was in the plane of its orbit. At first this idea did not even sound reasonable, as the axes of the other planets are more or less upright on their orbits and do not coincide with the orbital plane. It was Buffham in England who was the first to bring evidence that this strange assumption actually was correct. The axis of Uranus differs by only 8 degrees from the planet's orbital plane. And its moons do orbit over its equator.

Once this fact was known, the discrepancies in the statements of ob-

servers as to the flattening of the poles of Uranus could be explained. It
has often been said that the rotation of Uranus could be compared to a
ball rolling on the ground. This is a proper simile only at times, for as
Uranus goes around the sun the position of its axis does not change, but
always points to the same place in the sky. Hence for two sectors of the
orbit the simile is reasonably correct, for the other two sectors it is
wrong. But whether or not the comparison is correct, the over-all result
is that observers sometimes see Uranus in such a way that the planet's
equator bisects the disk more or less accurately, in which case the flattening of the poles can be seen. But at other times one of the planet's poles
will be more or less in the center of the disk, and then the flattening
will naturally not be visible; even a football will look perfectly round
when seen from the proper angle.

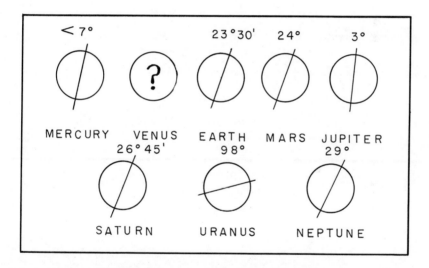

Position of the axes of the major planets

Uranus, seen through a good telescope on a good night, looks pale
green. Under exceptional conditions (and if the position of the planet is
favorable) a lighter band at the planet's equator can be seen. Occasionally observers in different countries—e. g., Professor W. H. Haas
and Dr. A. G. Smith in the United States and Günter D. Roth and others
in Germany—have seen white spots, which helped to establish the period
of rotation.

One unsolved problem, in addition to that of the nature of the white
areas, is that Uranus as a whole seems brighter at some times than at

others. Some difference in brightness is to be expected depending on whether we happen to have an equatorial or a polar view, since the cross section of the planet during a polar view is obviously somewhat larger. But even if this factor is taken into account, plus the relative distances between the earth and Uranus at the moment, there still are variations in brightness. They might be due to activities in the atmosphere of the planet, but we probably will have to wait for a view of Uranus from a space station or from a lunar observatory before more can be said.

17

NEPTUNE

FOLLOWING the example of many writers of modern mystery stories, who provide a cast of characters on the well-founded assumption that the reader would get lost otherwise, I shall begin this chapter with a list of the people most involved. They are, in alphabetical order:

Adams, John Couch, an Englishman (1819–1892), who became Professor of Astronomy at Cambridge in 1858

Airy, Sir George Biddell, another Englishman (1801–1892), Astronomer Royal from 1835 to 1881

Arago, Dominique François Jean, a Frenchman (1786–1853), sometime Minister of War of the Second Republic, also director of the Paris Observatory

d'Arrest, Heinrich Ludwig, a German (1822–1875), who became a professor at the University of Leipzig in 1852

Challis, John, another Englishman (1803–1882), astronomer

Galle, Johann Gottfried, another German (1812–1910), astronomer at the Urania Observatory in Berlin

Leverrier, Urbain Jean Joseph, another Frenchman (1811–1877), who became director of the Paris Observatory in 1854, succeeding Arago

In addition to the human beings involved, the cast includes the planet Uranus and an unknown planet.

As has been mentioned in the preceding chapter, the actual discovery of Uranus was followed by the realization that the planet had been seen earlier without being recognized as a planet. This looked like a boon to the mathematicians engaged in the problem of expressing the observations of the apparent position of the planet in the sky in terms of its orbit around the sun. These "ancient observations," as they called them, could be used as a convenient cross check which should make life simpler. In reality almost the opposite result obtained. Alexis Bouvard, who published tables on the orbit of Uranus in 1821, after about forty years of more or less continuous observation, had to say in his foreword:

> The construction of these tables involves this alternative: if we combine the ancient observations with the modern, the former will be sufficiently

well represented, but the latter will not be so, with all the precision which their superior accuracy demands; on the other hand, if we reject the ancient observations altogether, and retain only the modern, the resulting tables will faithfully conform to the modern observations, but will very inadequately represent the more ancient. As it was necessary to decide between these two courses, I have adopted the latter, on the ground that it unites the greatest number of probabilities in favor of the truth, and I leave to the future the task of discovering whether the difficulty of reconciling the two systems is connected with the ancient observations, or whether it depends on some foreign and unperceived cause which may have been acting upon the planet.

Bouvard's last line is a rather strong hint of what he had in mind. The words "foreign and unperceived cause" could just as well have been "unknown and so far unseen planet." Bouvard used the more careful terminology because he did not wish to exclude any other possibility. The other possibility which he may have had in mind was that the well known inverse-square law of the pull of gravitation had not yet been checked over really long distances. It could be said without much hesitation that the inverse-square law applied from the sun to Saturn. Beyond that, considering the orbits of some comets, it would be reasonable to wonder whether, if the distance were great enough, some corrective factor might not be needed.

So one could speculate on what might happen to the inverse-square law over a distance of, say, 1 light-year, or one could assume that the inverse-square law held true regardless of distance and look for the other factor that ruined the calculations for the orbit of Uranus. Since Uranus was a major planet that had just been discovered, nothing stopped anyone from assuming still another unknown planet. If there was one, it could produce the perturbations of the orbit of Uranus, and its position could perhaps be calculated from these perturbations.

Decades of practical experience have taught me that a nonastronomer usually does not know just how to visualize such a "perturbation." Astronomers, though they know precisely what perturbations mean to them, usually don't know how to explain them, because they think of them in mathematical symbols. But the problem is neither difficult to understand nor very difficult to explain if one starts out with a simplified picture.

Let us imagine that our earth is the only known planet going around the sun. To simplify things some more let us also assume that its orbit is circular. Hence the earth would not only need one year to complete one orbit around the sun, it would also move with uniform velocity: the *radius vector* would sweep over equal angles in equal times. Now let us assume the existence of a second planet with an orbit larger than that of the earth. Naturally it would need more than one year to complete one orbit, but let us assume circularity for that second orbit too.

As long as the earth and the other planet are in their orbits in opposite quarters nothing much would happen. But as the faster earth caught up with the other planet their gravitational attractions would begin to act upon each other. The earth, being "behind" the slower outer planet, would tend to hold it back. This pull would hardly change the orbit, but it would influence the orbital velocity of the outer planet. It would move a little more slowly than if the earth did not pull from behind. Since gravitational pulls operate both ways, the pull of the outer planet will increase the orbital velocity of the inner planet, the earth. In time the earth will reach a position in which the two planets, as seen from the sun in the center, lie along the same line. Then the earth moves ahead of the outer planet, but the mutual pulling still goes on. Now, however, it has the result that the inner planet, the earth, is slowed down, while the velocity of the outer planet increases.

If you observe that a planet moves somewhat more slowly than would be expected for a while and then suddenly moves somewhat faster than called for, you know that a planet inside the orbit of the planet under observation is responsible. If a planet first moves faster than it should and then loses velocity, a planet outside its orbit is responsible.

In the case of real planets the complicating factors are, first, that the actual orbits are elliptical, so that the orbital velocity is not uniform to begin with, and second, that there are several planets. The planet Mars is subject to the pulls not only of the earth but also of Venus and of Jupiter. Uranus would be subject to perturbations from Jupiter and Saturn, plus those of an unknown planet, if there was one, outside its orbit.

Bouvard had of course taken Jupiter and Saturn into account.

Enter now John Couch Adams, age twenty-two, student of astromony and mathematics at Cambridge. During his summer vacation in 1841 he made a note to himself which was found among his papers after his death. It reads:

> 1841, July 3. Formed a design in the beginning of this week, of investigating, as soon as possible after taking my degree, the irregularities in the motion of Uranus, which are yet unaccounted for; in order to find whether they may be attributed to the action of an undiscovered planet beyond it; and if possible thence to determine the elements of its orbit, etc. approximately, which would probably lead to its discovery.[1]

[1] Adams probably did not know that he was not the first to suspect a planet beyond Uranus. The Reverend T. J. Hussey, Vicar of Hayes in Kent, had made the same suggestion in 1834, and in 1840 Friedrich Wilhelm Bessel of Königsberg

Not quite two years after this memorandum was written, Adams had obtained his degree, received a college fellowship, and started his work on Uranus, in addition to other duties, of course. Before the actual calculations could be started, a few assumptions had to be made. What was the plane of the orbit of the unknown planet? Adams decided to begin with the assumption that it was the same as that of the orbit of Uranus. What should be assumed as the size of the unknown planet? Well, let's say about the same as Uranus. And its distance from the sun? That one was easy; according to the Bode-Titius rule, a planet beyond Uranus should be at about 39 Astronomical Units. Since the rule had held true from Mercury to Uranus there was no reason to disregard it for the next planet.

Adams started by assuming a circular orbit for the unknown planet. This, he knew, was almost certainly not the case, but he wanted to see whether the discrepancies in Uranus's orbit could be explained at all by a planet farther away. Satisfied that such an assumption could explain the problem, he asked Professor John Challis to obtain the observed "errors in longitude" for him. Challis wrote to Sir George Biddell Airy, the Astronomer Royal, who immediately dispatched the data that had accumulated at Greenwich. Airy must have been nagged by the problem himself because he did far more than was requested. Adams, via Challis, received not only the data for the period 1818–1826, but also everything that the Greenwich Observatory had been able to do with the observations from 1754 to 1830.

It is not reported whether Adams needed some time to recover from the sudden sight of such an overwhelming mass of data; at any event he set to work again, with the same assumptions as before, but with an elliptical orbit. He finished in September 1845 and handed Challis a paper predicting the position of the unknown planet for October 1, 1845. We now know that his position was correct within 2 degrees, and if anybody had taken the trouble to point a telescope in the right direction during the first week in October of that year the new planet would have been found. Challis could have done it—at least he had the authority and the means—but instead he gave Adams a letter of recommendation and praise to the Astronomer Royal.

What followed was a series of mishaps that would sound utterly unconvincing if anybody had invented it. Adams traveled to Greenwich,

---

had stated in a lecture that "one man, namely my young friend Flemming, has worked his way through the problem." Bessel was not quite correct; his young friend, Friedrich Wilhelm Flemming, died during the same year at the age of twenty-eight, leaving his calculations unfinished. The work he had done was published in 1850.

armed with Challis's letter of introduction and a summary of his work. But the Astronomer Royal was in France, busy with something which the records call the "Cherbourg breakwater investigation." Told after his return about the attempted visit he wrote to Challis, saying "Would you mention to Mr. Adams that I am very much interested with the subject of his investigations and that I shall be delighted to hear of them by letter from him?"

Adams apparently felt that a letter implied delay and he was naturally anxious to have his calculations put to the test by observation. He made another trip to Greenwich—on October 21, 1845— but again the Astronomer Royal was not at home. He was in London, attending a meeting of the Railway Gauge Commission. Adams left his card, with a message that he would permit himself to call again later. The card was taken to Mrs. Airy; Sir Harold Spencer Jones [2] states that the message was not delivered to her. This, considering the training and habits of English servants, seems highly unlikely—it is far more probable that Mrs. Airy, who gave birth to her son Osmond only a week later, forgot all about it. In any event when Adams called again, while the Astronomer Royal was having dinner, he was not admitted, nor was there any message for him. Adams obviously felt that he had been deliberately snubbed, but he maintained some measure of outward calm and left his paper with the servant, for the Astronomer Royal to read at his leisure.

Airy did receive the paper and read it. He had no idea that the young man had been turned away from his house, probably assuming that the paper had arrived by mail. Airy then wrote two letters, one to Adams and one to Challis. In the letter to Adams, after the usual acknowledgement, he inquired whether Adams's work covered not only the errors in longitude (i.e., the position of the planet in the sky) but also the errors in the length of the *radius vector,* the distance of Uranus from the sun. Adams felt that this was a trivial question, since the length of the *radius vector* is completely unimportant for visual observation if you have the correct position. He did not reply.

In the letter to Challis, Airy was somewhat more explicit about his thoughts. "There is no *a priori* reason for thinking that a hypothesis which will explain the error of longitude will also explain the error of radius vector," he wrote. After continuing at some length, he ended by

[2] The whole case has been written up in detail twice, both times under the title *John Couch Adams and the Discovery of Neptune,* once by Sir Harold Spencer Jones, then Astronomer Royal, in 1947 (The University Press, Cambridge, England), and once by Professor W. M. Smart of Glasgow University, whose version appeared in *Nature* (November 9, 1946) and in *Popular Astronomy* (June 1947).

saying that Adams's theory could be false, "NOT from any error of Adams's BUT from a failure of the law of gravitation. On this question therefore turned the continuance or fall of the law of gravitation." In short, Airy ignored the possibility of discovering a new planet in his concern with finding or not finding an error in Newton's laws. One gets the impression that he was looking for such an error: the discovery of the need for a corrective factor for Newton's equations, especially if made by Airy, would have been infinitely more important.

True, but Airy's preoccupation with a theoretical question prevented action as far as the unknown planet itself was concerned. This probably would not have mattered too much if Greenwich had been the only astronomical observatory in the world and the Airy-Challis-Adams circle the only astronomers. In time some night work would probably have been done at the observatory.

But during the same year in which Adams made his fruitless calls on Airy, the director of the Paris Observatory, Dominique Arago, talked to his younger friend and protégé Leverrier about the orbit of Uranus. Leverrier is generally admitted to have been as brilliant a mathematician as Adams. Personally he thought himself more brilliant, and he may even have been right. What counted, however, was that he was eight years older and already had a number of publications to his credit; moreover, Leverrier and his nominal superior Arago were in steady personal contact while Adams had not yet even met Airy. Leverrier went to work at once and during that year (1845) brought Bouvard's work up to date, showing that the irregularities increased as time went by. But in his first paper he did not discuss either an unknown planet or the need of correcting the law of gravitation. He dealt only with established facts, unpleasant as they were to an astronomer.

Leverrier's second paper—they were all published in the *Comptes Rendus*—came in June 1846. Nothing he wrote could explain the irregularities of Uranus, except the existence of a planet beyond Uranus. Like Adams, he followed the Bode-Titius rule for the distance; unlike Adams, he assumed that the unknown planet moved in the plane of the ecliptic. Like Adams, he gave a probable position, which differed from the one given by Adams by just one degree! Two brilliant mathematicians, both arrived at the same solution at about the same time. But one published; the other did not. No doubt Adams was perturbed; Leverrier did not even know that he had a competitor. In June 1846, Airy wrote to Leverrier about an explanation for the errors in the length of the *radius vector*. Leverrier replied immediately, saying that his theory accounted for these errors "automatically." He also asked Airy whether the Royal

Observatory at Greenwich could not make a search for his unknown planet, "in which case I will supply full details." Airy had not told him that a younger (and unpublished) English mathematician had already done the work.

Before Leverrier's letter arrived in England, Airy (having read the *Comptes Rendus*) told the Board of Visitors of the Royal Observatory that the discovery of a new planet seemed to be in the near future. By July 9 he said that the situation was becoming "desperate" (his own term) and wrote to Challis, requesting that Challis use the Northumberland telescope at Cambridge for a search for the new planet. Challis agreed, but he had somehow convinced himself that it would be a long and tedious search. He saw no reason for special hurry and did not actually start observing until nearly three weeks later, on July 29.

Then things moved like a somewhat irregular timetable.

On August 31 Leverrier presented his third paper to the Academy at Paris. In it he gave the position for the unknown planet and pointed out that it should show a disk 3 seconds of arc in diameter, which should make it easy to tell it from a fixed star.

On September 2 Adams sent another set of calculations to Airy.

On September 18 Leverrier wrote to Galle in Berlin, asking if the Prussian Observatory would oblige him by looking for the new planet at heliocentric longitude such-and-such in or near the ecliptic.

The letter was received on September 23. Galle had to ask permission of Encke, the director of the observatory. Encke said, *"Tun wir doch den Herren in Paris den Gefallen"* ("Let us oblige the gentlemen in Paris"), and since the weather seemed promising Galle decided to start the same night. At that point a student, young d'Arrest, made a suggestion. The observatory had been preparing a star chart (one of a series called Bremiker's charts) and d'Arrest said that it would be useful to check whether a Bremiker chart was already in existence for the area of the sky pointed out by Leverrier. The particular chart would be labeled *Hora XXI*. Chart *Hora XXI* had been completed earlier during the year; the only reason why it had not been mailed to observatories elsewhere was that the next chart was nearly finished and the director had decided to mail both of them together to save postage.

In the evening Galle took his place behind, or, more accurately, under the telescope, d'Arrest sitting some distance away at a table with the chart, illuminated by a shaded lantern which would not shine into Galle's eye. Galle called out the stars in his field of view, and d'Arrest checked them off on the chart. When Galle announced a star of the eighth magnitude in such and such a position, d'Arrest immediately replied, *"Nicht auf der Karte"* ("Not on the chart"). The new planet had been discovered, within about one hour of the start of the search. Of course a few more observations were needed to make sure that it actually was a planet but by the end of September there was no longer any doubt.

Both Berlin and Paris were jubilant. Arago called Leverrier's work "one of the most magnificent discoveries of astronomical theory, one of the glories of the French Academy." Berlin was not precisely modest either. Maybe the score had been written elsewhere, but they had put on a magnificent performance without any rehearsals.

What had happened in England?

When the news of the discovery came in from the continent Challis stopped his "long search" and added up his results. He had made a total of 3150 observations of stars. Four of them had been the new planet and Challis had failed to notice the fact! Evidently he had been neither enthusiastic nor very careful. When reproached, as of course he was, he confessed that he had simply lacked confidence in the results of such theoretical work as Adams's. He also explained that he had been very busy with mathematical work on some comet observations—a poor excuse, as this could have been done just as effectively a year later.

Challis, as a matter of fact, might still have discovered the new planet independently, even though later than Galle. On the night of September 29 he checked 300 stars and found that only one of them had a disk, all the others being dimensionless points, which is how fixed stars appear in the telescope. If he had observed the disklike object for about three hours he would have detected the planet's motion, but he decided to check it during the following night. However, on September 30, the moon was in the way, something that a keen observer should have thought of in advance. On October 1 he learned that Galle had discovered the planet a week earlier.

The Astronomer Royal, needless to say, was in a dark mood. Challis's lack of interest had deprived England of the honor of having discovered the new planet. And Airy may very easily have blamed himself too. If he had not been preoccupied with a possible improvement in theory, he could have ordered a search after receiving Adams's resumé in 1845.

While Airy was probably trying to justify the way things had turned out, Sir John Herschel tried to remedy the situation. Leverrier received all the acclaim, of course, and nobody could say that he did not deserve it. But Adams deserved some acclaim too. He had done the same work, with equal competence. It was only bad luck that had prevented his

THE PLANET NEPTUNE, ACTUAL ORBIT AND ORBITS
CALCULATED BY LEVERRIER AND ADAMS

	ACTUAL ORBIT		LEVERRIER'S CALCULATION		ADAMS'S SECOND APPROXIMATION	
YEAR	LONGITUDE	RADIUS VECTOR (A. U.)	LONGITUDE	RADIUS VECTOR (A. U.)	LONGITUDE	RADIUS VECTOR (A. U.)
1800	226° 4′	30.30	231° 34′	33.57	238° 9′	34.90
1810	247° 20′	30.28	251° 10′	32.80	256° 39′	33.92
1820	268° 52′	30.23	271° 28′	32.35	276° 5′	33.25
1830	290° 31′	30.55	292° 8′	32.29	295° 54′	32.96
1840	312° 17′	30.06	312° 36′	32.63	316° 10′	33.11
1850	334° 12′	29.96	332° 25′	33.32	335° 50′	33.67
1860	356° 14′	29.87	351° 17′	34.26	354° 39′	34.57

name from being mentioned in print. Sir John wrote a letter which appeared in the October 3 issue of *Athenaeum*. The latter described Adams's work and stated that the positions deduced by Leverrier and Adams were nearly the same.

The French were properly indignant. Now, after the event, somebody comes along and claims to have done the same work at least a year earlier! Since the letter was signed by Sir John Herschel, the French could not dismiss the whole thing. To their minds Herschel had probably just tried to do a compatriot a favor, but the paper in question was most likely only a crude essay—they more or less took the by no means unreasonable position that Mr. Adams's work, if it had been good and thorough, would have been published.

To confuse the confused issue some more, Challis started writing letters too: he did not want to be left without any glory at all. In a letter dated October 5, he told Arago that he had observed the planet on September 29, "in conformity with the suggestions of Leverrier." Not a word about all the discussions he had had with Adams. Then Airy wrote to Leverrier direct on October 14, stating that an English mathematician had done similar work, but "the English investigations, as I believe, were not so extensive as yours. They were known to me earlier than yours." This would have been harmless by itself (disregarding the slur upon Adams's work, probably caused by the fact that Airy, no matter what he said, had not paid enough attention to Adams), if the letter had not contained the sentence: "If in this I give praise to others I beg that you will not consider it as at all interfering with my acknowledgement of your claims. You are to be recognized, without doubt, as the real predicter of the planet's place." It almost sounds as if Airy was happy to get rid of all the responsibility by saying "Oh, well, it was a French discovery."

While the French were fully justified in saying that Leverrier was the hero of the hour because his work had actually led to the discovery, some French editors clearly went too far. The newspaper *Le National* uncovered a "plot" by Herschel, Challis, and Airy to steal the discovery from Leverrier by inventing "the myth of calculations said to have been made by one Mr. Adams."

In such an atmosphere even the normally pleasing task of naming the discovery became a subject for controversy. Leverrier had first suggested the name Neptune and had said that he was in agreement about this with the Bureau of Longitudes. (But later no record could be found at the Bureau of Longitudes; it was obviously Leverrier's own idea and he was fully justified in assuming that any name he might give would be officially approved.) But then Arago suggested naming the new planet after its discoverer. Obviously Leverrier and Arago had conferred about this, because Leverrier offered a "trade": he had finished a memoir about the motions of Uranus in the text of which the planet is called Uranus, but the paper was presented to the Academy under the title "Researches on the Motion of the Planet Herschel (formerly Uranus)." The idea was of course to give planets the names of their discoverers, making the practice retroactive to Herschel's discovery of Uranus.

Even though this would have honored an English astronomer, English astronomers were aghast. "Think," one of them said to Airy, "how awkward it would be if the next planet should be discovered by a German, by a Bugge, or Funk, or your hirsute friend Boguslawski!"

Leverrier defended the choice of his own name: there was Comet Encke, Comet Halley, and so forth, why not Planet Leverrier? Moreover, Arago had used the term Planet Herschel for Uranus decades before. But the combined opposition of English, German, and Russian astronomers won out: Neptune was the name first proposed and Neptune it remained.

Adams did finally receive the recognition due him. He succeeded Challis as director of the Cambridge Observatory. Queen Victoria offered him a knighthood, but he begged off. He also refused the offer of Prime Minister Gladstone to make him Astronomer Royal, to succeed Airy.

But now back to astronomy proper.

After Uranus had been discovered it turned out that the planet had been seen repeatedly before. Had the same thing happened with Neptune? Diligent search turned up one instance only, an entry in Joseph Jérôme de Lalande's *Histoire Céleste*. The chart for May 10, 1795, showed a star which doesn't exist but which, as far as position is concerned, could have been Neptune. A check of the original manuscript of the work revealed that Lalande had first observed this star on May 8. Upon checking it once more on May 10, Lalande saw that the earlier entry showed the wrong position, so he corrected it for May 10. The "mistake," of course, had been the movement of Neptune in two days.

The next discovery connected with Neptune was made on October 10, 1846, when the English astronomer William Lassell found Neptune's large moon, later called Triton. Lassell also thought for a while that Neptune had a ring like Saturn's, though much fainter, but nobody else ever saw it.

The next problem was the determination of the orbit of Neptune. Both Leverrier and Adams had found that the Bode-Titus rule did not apply as strictly as it did to all the other planets. The perturbations from a planet 39 Astronomical Units away did not work out well, as such a planet would be too slow moving. They both reduced the assumed distance by 5 A.U., and later observations showed that the actual distance was about 30 A.U. The first tables for Neptune were published in Russia in 1855 by Kovalski. In 1865 Simon Newcomb of the U.S. Naval Observatory in Washington published *Investigation of the Orbit of Neptune, with General Tables of Its Motion."* (Washington, Smithsonian Institution, 1865) and twenty years later Asaph Hall published a short monograph on the *Orbit of the Satellite of Neptune.*

And in the same year the *Astronomischen Nachrichten* (No. 2698, 1885) carried a note by David P. Todd, entitled "Telescopic Search for the Trans-Neptunian Planet." The hunt for the next planet was on.

Before proceeding with that search, however, the discovery of another satellite of Neptune must be mentioned. It happened in 1949, more than a century after the discovery of the planet itself. The discoverer was Professor Gerard P. Kuiper, and the instrument the 82-inch reflector of McDonald Observatory in Texas. The second satellite of Neptune, which was named "Nereid" by Kuiper, is small, with an estimated diameter of 200 miles or less and a very elongated orbit. Careful photographic work by George Van Biesbroeck in 1957 established that the orbit had an eccentricity of 0.749, which means that its farthest point (should it be called apo-Neptunion?) is 6 million miles from the planet, while the peri-Neptunion is only 0.9 million miles. The time required to complete one orbit was established as 359.881 days. And Nereid moves in its orbit in a direction opposite to that of the motion of Triton.

All of which, interestingly enough, has some bearing on the problem of the planet outside the orbit of Neptune.

18

PLANET X

On September 30, 1846, one week after Galle had actually found Neptune, Leverrier, in a letter to Alfred Gautier in Geneva, declared that the new planet might not be the outermost planet of our solar sysem. Other astronomers had the same thought, partly for the sheer joy of anticipating another discovery, which anyone might make, and partly because a quick and easy calculation shows that the gravitational field of our sun is powerful enough to hold a planet at a distance of four to eight times the distance of Neptune.

In addition to the general considerations of probability, there were a few specific indications. After Lassell had discovered the larger satellite of Neptune, and its revolution around its primary had been observed often enough for a thorough mathematical analysis of its orbit, Simon Newcomb of the U. S. Naval Observatory announced a discrepancy. The mass of Neptune, calculated from the perturbations of Uranus, came out as $1/19,700$ that of the sun. But its mass as calculated from the motion of Triton was $1/19,380$ that of the sun.

It seemed as if the perturbations of Uranus which had led to Leverrier's "planet of and for calculation" were actually caused by two planets, Neptune and an unknown one. But this discrepancy, taken by itself, was not enough to work out an orbit for the unknown half of the "calculation planet." After all, Leverrier, in order to make his calculations at all, had had to assume the mass *and* the orbit of his unknown planet. The *actual* orbit was not quite what Leverrier—or Adams, for that matter—had assumed. Neptune might still account for all the perturbations. Consequently the problem was up to the observers for some time to come. The movement of Neptune had to be observed carefully and its actual orbit established, for several purposes. One was to check the perturbations on the orbit of Uranus caused by the actual (as distinct from the calculated) Neptune. The other was to determine whether Neptune's own motion could be fully accounted for by the gravitational influences of Jupiter, Saturn, and Uranus.

If Neptune's orbit could not be fully explained, or if Neptune's gravitational field did *not* account for the Uranus "residuals" (as astronomers call unaccountable differences between calculation and observation), it might be possible to repeat the performances of Leverrier and of Adams from these residuals. The reason the "residuals" of Uranus were chosen, when Neptune obviously must be closer to the supposed unknown planet, was that by, say, 1880, Uranus had been observed for more than one full revolution, not even counting the "ancient" observations, whereas Neptune had been under actual observation for only about 20 per cent of its orbit. Any mathematical attack still had to start with the motion of Uranus, but Neptune's influence was now added as a known factor.

But a strange interlude came first.

It had originated at the U.S. Naval Observatory, during the summer and early fall of 1850. A member of the staff, James Ferguson, had been following the motions of the planetoid Hygeia, which had been discovered a year earlier. Ferguson measured the distance of Hygeia from nearby stars with well-established positions, using a device called a filar micrometer. It consisted of a metal plate holding four very fine wires, all oriented in the east-west direction. Three of the four wires were fixed. The observer moved the whole plate until a star was bisected by one of the fixed wires. Then he moved the fourth, movable wire until it bisected the object under observation, in this case, Hygeia. The angular distance of Hygeia from the reference star could then be calculated from the distance of the movable wire to the fixed wire which had been used.

Ferguson's report on the motion of Hygeia appeared in the *Astronomical Journal* of January 18, 1851. Among its readers was an English astronomer named J. Russell Hind, later one of the outstanding English astronomers of the nineteenth century, but then just beginning his career. Hind, checking Ferguson's report against star charts, noticed that a reference star which Ferguson had designated as k on October 21, 1850, was not shown. This was not too surprising; charts were still quite incomplete and it was often necessary for one astronomer to determine another astronomer's reference star from its position with reference to still other stars. But, more important, Hind could not find star k in the sky. He wrote to Washington.

The director of the Naval Observatory at that time was the famous Matthew Fontaine Maury, who is known all over the world as the "Father of Oceanography" and to many Americans also as the man who ruined a most promising career by resigning from the Navy in order to join the Confederacy. Maury checked Hind's report and admitted that the star "is not now to be found where it then was." And he drew the logical conclusion: "I infer that it is probably an unknown planet." He directed Ferguson to start a search and had the observation journals for October 1850 carefully checked. His conclusions ended on a note of regret: ". . . had there been sufficient force at the Observatory for the immediate reduction [of Ferguson's observations] they would then have revealed to us the character of the star."

Evidently Maury felt that his observatory had missed discovering a new planet, though he did not quite say so. Hind, however, in a letter to the editor of the *Astronomical Journal* (November 13, 1851), declared that the object's motion clearly showed that it must be a planet beyond Neptune. Assuming a circular orbit to account for the observed motion, that planet was 137 A.U. from the sun with a period of revolution of 1600 years. But Hind added a note of puzzlement. He was a devoted planetoid hunter, and he happened to have spent the last three years carefully mapping precisely that area of the sky, but Ferguson's star *k* was not on his own chart either. However, he was quite willing to give Ferguson full credit.

In the meantime Ferguson was hunting his "planet," presumably with hope alternating with despair. By now it would have entered the region of Sagittarius with the Milky Way as background. Nobody who has not seen this region through a powerful telescope can imagine the task of trying to find a single pinpoint of light in the crowded masses of other pinpoints of light. A look at a good photograph helps to visualize the difficulties—it is like trying to locate one street lamp, a slightly different street lamp, while flying over a city like Philadelphia or New York. Ferguson gave up after four months. The case was completely forgotten by most astronomers until about two decades later (in 1879) when a belated explanation was offered.

The German-born astronomer Christian Heinrich Friedrich Peters, had come to the United States as a political exile in 1854, at the age of forty-one, and four years later had become the director of the Hamilton College Observatory at Clinton, New Jersey. Professor Peters was a planetoid hunter with forty-eight discoveries (plus two comets) to his credit. Naturally he was interested in unknown planets. Moreover he was making a very accurate star chart of the region of the zodiac and Ferguson's star *k* troubled him. Could Ferguson have made a mistake of some kind? Peters began checking on this possibility by reviewing Ferguson's methods and instrumentation. When he read about the micrometer he began to wonder—could Ferguson have become confused about which one of the three fixed wires he had used for measurement?

This possibility could be fairly easily reconstructed; Peters found that if wire No. 2 had been used instead of wire No. 1, there was a star in

the proper position, star No. 36,613 in Lalande's catalogue. He wrote
to Washington where the original records were kept and Aspah Hall
went over them. It became clear that Ferguson *had* used wire No. 2
and, in eight cases, had recorded it accordingly. In three other cases
he had recorded that he used wire No. 1. Later, when he was making
the calculations, he had simply assumed (possibly trusting his memory
without checking his own records) that he had always used No. 1. But
in reality he must always have used No. 2, because, if he did use No.
2, there was no missing planet.

By sheer coincidence, during the same year, 1879, in which Peters
demolished Ferguson's unknown planet, another astronomer added another hint as to the existence of a planet beyond Neptune. This was
Camille Flammarion, who, ten years earlier, had founded the Société
Astronomique de France.

As has been explained in Chapter 7, the comets seem to be permanent
members of the solar system, though at the enormous distance of half a
light-year or more. Once in a while one of them, for still unknown
reasons, approaches the sun; then it may become a "member of the inner
circle," which occurs when it passes a major planet that changes the
very long comet orbit into a shorter orbit, with a major axis of the
order of magnitude of planetary distances from the sun. As has also been
explained, the aphelion of the new orbit then falls in the vicinity of the
orbit of the planet which brought about the so-called capture. Usually,
but not in all cases, the new aphelion of the comet is somewhat farther
from the sun than is the aphelion of the capturing planet.

Hence a planet beyond Neptune might betray its existence by one or
several comets with aphelia beyond Neptune. Camille Flammarion not
only called attention to this possibility, but even suggested two comets
that might be captives of the unknown planet, namely, Comet 1862 III
with an orbital period of about 120 years and an aphelion 47.6 A.U.
from the sun, and Comet 1889 III with a somewhat longer orbital period
and with its aphelion at a distance of 49.8 A.U. The unknown planet,
Flammarion stated later (in *Astronomie Populaire,* edition of 1890, p.
601), probably moved at a distance of 45 A.U.

As many astronomers have pointed out since, Flammarion never
followed up his own suggestion in detail. However, the inference that
he did not consider his suggestion worthwhile is not necessarily correct.
He may have intended only to call the attention of other astronomers
to the possibility of finding an unknown planet by checking on comet
orbits.

Only one year after Flammarion's original suggestion, Professor

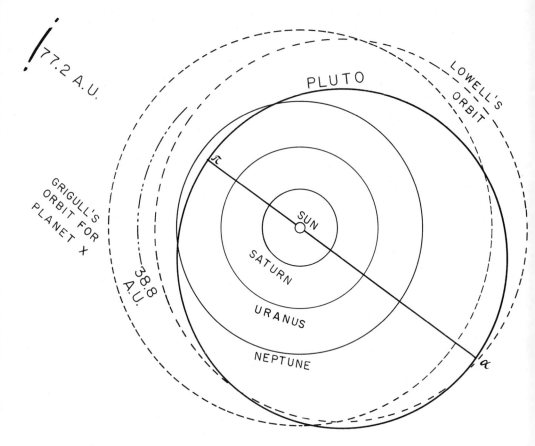

The predictions for the orbit of Planet X

George Forbes published a memoir concerning the aphelia of comet orbits and their association with planet orbits in the *Proceedings of the Royal Society of Edinburgh* (1880, x).

By about 1900 five comets with aphelia beyond the orbit of Neptune were known. They offered one line of approach. And the continuing observations of Uranus and of Neptune offered another one. Both were utilized.

Professor Forbes in 1900 published a prediction of the unknown planet. He put his "Trans-Neptune" at a distance of about 100 A.U. with an orbital period of 1000 years. Since the trans-Neptunian planet had to produce perturbations of the orbits of Uranus and Neptune it had to be quite large if it was that far away; hence Forbes assumed that its mass was larger than that of Jupiter. Others pointed out immediately that even a planet as large as Jupiter probably would no longer be visible in a telescope at a distance of 100 A.U. Its illumination by the sun would be so feeble that it simply would not have much light to reflect.

During the next five years several astronomers and mathematicians published their own ideas of what might be found in the outer reaches of our solar system. A mathematician of the Paris Observatory, Gaillot, assumed two trans-Neptunian planets, one at a mean distance of 45 A.U., the other at 60 A.U. The American astronomer Thomas Jefferson Jackson See—often called T.J.J.—even predicted three trans-Neptunian planets: the first one, which he called "Oceanus," at 41.25 A.U. with an orbital period of 272 years; then a "trans-Oceanus" at 56 A.U. with an orbital period of 420 years; and finally one beyond "Trans-Oceanus" at 72 A.U. with a period of 610 years. The German astronomer Dr. Theodor Grigull of Münster, in a paper on a trans-Neptunian planet published in 1902, assumed a planet of about the size of Uranus at a distance of 50 A.U. with an orbital period of 360 years. He called his "Hades." Grigull based his work mainly on the orbits of comets with aphelia beyond Neptune's orbit, with a cross check on whether the gravitational pull of a body thus assumed would produce the observed "residuals" of Uranus. As an example of the method he later (after the discovery of Pluto) published an article in which he applied it to Neptune:

We have, for example, comet 1852 IV with an orbital period of 61.73 years. Its aphelion is 29.4 A.U. from the sun, at a distance where a planet is possible. The comet passed perihelion in 1852, which means that half an orbit earlier it passed its aphelion. That would have been in 1821; earlier aphelion passages took place in 1759, 1697, 1636 and so forth. The heliocentric longitude of its aphelion is 224°. If we knew when this comet was captured, the problem would be solved. But let us go on: Comet 1846 IV has an orbital period of 75.71 years, its aphelion is at 35 A.U. and 270° heliocentric longitude. It passed its aphelion in 1808, 1732, 1657 and so forth. Now if we compare the aphelion passages of these two comets we find two years reasonably close to each other, 1636 and 1657. The time interval is 21 years, the distance between the aphelia 46°. If we assume that the unknown planet had captured both comets in these years and had been moving in its orbit somewhere near the comet aphelia, the mean orbital motion of a planet at this distance would be 2¼°. Well, where would the planet Neptune (assumed to be still undiscovered) be in 1930? Since 1636 and 1657, respectively, 294 and 273 years have passed, the motion of the planet since then would be 9/4 that many degrees which gives us 661.5° and 614.25°. To these figures we have to add the longitude of the aphelia and we obtain 885.5° and 884.25°, or, simplified, 165.5° and 164.25°.

There is a known total of five comets [with such orbits], namely, comet

1812 with a period of 71.56 years and aphelion at 273°, assumed captured in 1490; comet 1815 with a period of 74 years, assumed captured in 1704 with aphelion at 329°; comet 1847 V with a period of 72.2 years, assumed captured in 1667, with aphelion at 260°. Calculating for the capturing planet we find its positions as follows:

Comet 1812	183°
Comet 1815	117.5°
Comet 1846 IV	164.25°
Comet 1847 V	131.75°
Comet 1852 IV	165.5°

The mean of these positions for the year 1930 is 152.4° and the planet Neptune actually passed this longitude near the end of March 1930. Considering the large spread of the single values this result might be called a coincidence, but it shows the way. The other values for Neptune which could be derived from the same calculation are a period of 160 years and a mean distance of 29.47 A.U., the true values are 165 years and 30 A.U." [1]

Grigull had, as stated, assumed an orbital period of 360 years in 1902. Later (in the journal *Das Weltall*, 1921, p. 114) he wrote: "Let us assume a little more flexibility for the orbital period, if it is 330 years we find the probable position [for 1920] at 72°, for an orbital period of 310 years at 99°. As with the other planets it can be assumed that the angle of inclination to the ecliptic is small." [2]

The two most carefully worked out predictions for the Trans-Neptune were both of American origin. They were William H. Pickering's *A Search for a Planet Beyond Neptune (Annals Astronomical Observatory, Harvard College,* vol. LXI, part II, 1909), and Percival Lowell's *Memoir on a Trans-Neptunian Planet* (Lynn, Mass., 1915). Though concerned with the same subject they used entirely different approaches and incidentally got different results. Professor Pickering, in order to avoid the endless tedious calculations required, had invented a graphical method. (One is tempted to say that he foresaw the device now known as an analog computer, though Pickering did not use that term and did the work "by hand," without the aid of a computing machine.)

Percival Lowell, on the other hand, used the strictest methods of computation possible. Since he had read Pickering's work he could express his deprecating opinion of it and point out how much more accurate his own admittedly tedious method was. Reading Lowell's *Memoir* now, one is struck by the general acidity of his tone; this hardly seems the same man who ten years earlier had written about Mars with

---

[1] Translated from Dr. Grigull's article in the weekly *Die Grüne Post* (August 10, 1930); this periodical, now defunct, was a general magazine, not an astronomical journal, published in Berlin.

[2] Grigull's planet, assuming the 310-year period, would have been at 109° in 1930. Pluto was found in that year at 108°; hence Grigull was somewhat justified in considering himself one of the "predicters" of Pluto.

so much enthusiasm and pleasantness. Perhaps the attacks against his Martian theories were the cause of such entries as: "After excellent analytical solutions, values of the quantities involved are introduced on the basis apparently of the respect due to age. Nautical Almanacs abet the practice by never publishing, consciously, contemporary values of astronomic constants; thus avoiding committal to doubtful results by the simple expedient of not printing anything not known to be wrong."

But behind this show of irascibility there was an obsession for precision; after having calculated "Planet X" (as he called the Trans-Neptune, with Leverrier's residuals, he decided that Leverrier's late work was not exact and did all the calculations over again using Gaillot's residuals.

All this happened long enough ago that we can now note with some

PICKERING'S PREDICTION FOR 1909

Longitude	105° 8′	Mass (Sun=1)	1:168,000
Mean distance	51.9 a.u.*	Mass (Earth=1)	2.0
Period	373.5 years	Right ascension	7h 47min
Mean annual motion	0° .964	Declination	+21°

Diameter (if density like Neptune's)	0″.8
Visual magnitude (albedo like that of Neptune)	11.5
Visual magnitude (albedo like that of Mars)	13.4

* Pickering noted that a Professor Todd, in 1877, had predicted a trans-Neptune planet at a mean distance of 52 a.u., but Todd never explained what methods he had used to arrive at this result.

amusement that Pickering's despised graphical method at least gave definite positions, while Lowell's painstaking work always resulted in a choice of two positions, depending on whether a certain factor was assumed to be 0 degrees or 180 degrees. Thus Lowell had to state that the longitude of Planet X for July 1914 was either 84 degrees or 262.8 degrees and its perihelion either 19.6 degrees or 203.8 degrees.

Lowell, before he had embarked on his full-scale mathematical investigation, had tried to find Planet X by a photographic search during the years from 1905 to 1907. His method was a kind of reverse of that introduced by Professor Max Wolf at Königsstuhl Observatory for finding planetoids. The planetoid hunt was performed by exposing a plate for several hours, following the fixed stars. For the obviously slow-moving Planet X this would not work, so Lowell took a picture of a region of the sky with a three-hour exposure and then photographed the same region three days later. In three days even Planet X would have moved some distance so that its image on the second plate would not be in the same spot as its image on the first.

Of course, this is not quite as simple as it sounds. Such a pair of plates may register dozens of "shifts" which have nothing at all to do

with Planet X. The first plate may show a star image in a spot where
the second plate shows nothing. This could be either a tiny flaw in the
emulsion, which often looks starlike, or a variable star which happened
to be at maximum brightness during the first exposure and at minimum
brightness (not registering at all) during the second exposure. Also
there may have been quite a number of objects which have clearly
moved during the interval between exposures, such as small comets,
both known and unknown, or planetoids which happen to be in such a
position that their motion is not fast enough to leave short lines. Comparing the plates, therefore, begins with an elimination of the variable
stars while the objects which did move have to be identified one by one.
After everything identifiable has been checked off, three categories still
remain: new comets, hitherto unknown planetoids, and, just possibly,
the predicted planet.

Lowell's plate pairs covered the region of the ecliptic all around the
sky, each plate pair being centered on a spot about 5 degrees from the
earlier plate pair. Hundreds of planetoids turned up and some ten
dozen comets. But not Planet X.

The second search was begun in 1914, mainly by C. O. Lampland,
director of Flagstaff Observatory. By then Lowell's mathematical work
had been finished though not yet published;[3] Lowell obviously delayed
it in the hope of being able to announce the actual discovery. In May
1914 he wrote to Lampland from Boston: "Don't hesitate to startle me
with a telegram 'Found.' " And in December he wrote again: "I am
giving my work before the Academy on January 13. It would be thought-
ful of you to announce the actual discovery at the same time."

The second search was terminated by Lowell's death on November
12, 1916.

A third search was begun in 1919, this time based on Pickering's
work. It was carried out at Mount Wilson Observatory by Milton Humason, who also used the method of the plate pairs. But Humason's
search did not turn up anything suspicious either, much to Pickering's
disappointment, of course.

When Lowell made his first search he had to use a magnifying lens
to compare his plate pairs. But a few years later the firm of Carl Zeiss
in Jena developed an instrument for this precise purpose. It acquired
the name of "blink comparator," and it is based on the physiological
fact that the human eye does not respond without delay—the Germans
call this delay "optical inertia." Both plates of a given pair are inserted

---

[3] Lowell read his *Memoir* to the American Academy of Arts and Sciences on
January 13, 1915; the printed version appeared three months later.

in the instrument and illuminated from below. Both images are viewed through the same magnifying eyepiece and are matched so that, to the observer, the stars of the left-hand plate are in precisely the same position as those of the right-hand plate. The actual work consists of shifting the illumination rapidly from the left-hand plate to the right-hand plate. If both plates were precisely alike this would look to the eye like a steady image. But if one object on the plate has moved between exposures it appears to jump back and forth between two positions. After a little practice with the instrument, such a jumping object stands out as if there were nothing else on the plates.

The search which resulted in the discovery of Pluto was carried out with a blink comparator, and the man who did the "blinking" was a young astronomer named Clyde W. Tombaugh, who had joined the staff of Lowell Observatory in January 1929. Two months later he began working with the 13-inch photographic refractor.

Tombaugh has told the story of his discovery repeatedly; the following is taken from his article "Reminiscences of the Discovery of Pluto," published in the March 1960 issue of *Sky and Telescope*.

As the autumn of 1929 came the perfected technique of observing and blink examination had settled into routine. When the plates were well matched and reasonably clean of spurious images, I would carry out six or seven hours of actual blinking each day. In Pisces and Aries, each plate recorded some 50,000 stars, and a pair could be examined in three days. These plates were a delight to scan, with hundreds of images of beautiful spiral galaxies.

The number of star images gradually increased as the Milky Way was approached. The plates of eastern Taurus and western Gemini contained up to 400,000 stars each! These had to be examined in small groups of only a dozen stars at a time. For very rich regions, it was necessary to use narrow rectangular diaphragms to limit the maze of stars. Therefore, the speed of examination decreased as these rich star regions were encountered, and the work with the blink comparator began to fall behind schedule.

In February 1930, after struggling through the Taurus plates, I skipped over to those in eastern Gemini, where the stars were less thickly packed. The entire length of the latter constellation had been photographed by the end of January that year. I chose three plates centered on Delta Geminorum, taken January 21st, 23rd, and 29th, respectively, but bad seeing made the first of these unacceptable for blinking.

I placed the other two in the comparator and began blinking the east half from the south end. By 4:00 P.M. on February 18th, one fourth of the plate area had been blinked. Upon turning to a new eyepiece field two thirds of a degree east of Delta, I suddenly spied a 15th magnitude object popping in and out of the background. Just 3½ millimeters away another 15th magnitude image was doing the same thing, but appearing alternately with respect to the other, as first one plate and then the second was visible through the eyepiece.

"That's it!" I exclaimed to myself. The change in position—only 3 or 4 millimeters in 6 days—was much too small for an ordinary asteroid near opposition. But were the images real or spurious? At once I laid out the 8-by-10 inch plates that had been taken by our Cogshell camera simultaneously with the 13-inch exposures. Although nearly at its limit of visibility, there were the images exactly in the same respective positions!

With mounting excitement I got out the January 21st plates and quickly checked them with a hand magnifier. Even though the 13-inch plate was a sorry one, there was the image displaced about 1 milimeter east of the January 23rd position, and it was confirmed on the 5-inch exposure. Any possibility of the phenomenon being a pair of variable stars was now ruled out. Next, I measured the displacements with a millimeter scale. The object was retrograding about 70 seconds of arc per day. This seemed to be it!

Dr. Lampland was in his office across the hall. At 4:45 P.M. I told him that I had found something, and he came and sat down at the comparator. Then I went to the director's office to inform Dr. [V. M.] Slipher, who hurried down the hall to the comparator room. (The other staff member, E. C. Slipher, was not in the building.) The two astronomers repeated the same checks for their satisfaction. The air was tense with excitement.

We looked through the window. The sky was very cloudy—no chance of getting a recovery plate that evening. Dr. Slipher stressed that no announcement should be made until observational confirmation was completed during the next few weeks. . . .

The next night, February 19th, was clear and another one-hour exposure of the Delta Geminorum region could be taken. I developed the plate and left it on the drying rack to be ready for blinking the next morning with one of the discovery pair. Although three weeks had elapsed, the new image was quickly found about one centimeter west of the January 29th position. . . .

As the weeks passed, the motion of the object conformed perfectly to that expected of a trans-Neptunian planet. It was decided to announce the discovery on March 13, 1930, which was the 75th anniversary of Percival Lowell's birth and the date of Uranus' discovery 149 years earlier. Late on that night of the 12th, director V. M. Slipher sent a telegram to the Harvard Observatory clearing house for official distribution.

The message sent to Harvard and distributed from there stated only that the systematic search for a trans-Neptunian planet had resulted in the discovery of a fifteen-magnitude object at proper rate of motion west of Delta Geminorum. The precise position for March (R.A. 7^h 15^m 50^s, Decl. $22°6'49''$) was given. This was followed by a circular from the Lowell Observatory, signed by V. M. Slipher, stressing the low visual magnitude, the apparent lack of a disk, and the yellowish color. The circular ended:

Thus far our knowledge of it is based largely upon its observed path and its determined rates of motion. These with its position and distance appear to fit only those of an object beyond Neptune, and one apparently fulfilling Lowell's theoretical findings. While it is thus too early to say much about this remarkable object and much caution and concern are felt—because of the necessary interpretations involved—in announcing its discovery before its status is fully demonstrated, yet it has appeared a clear duty to science

to make its existence known in time to permit other astronomers to observe
it while in favorable position before it falls too low in the evening sky for
effective observation.

It is no exaggeration to say that every observatory interrupted whatever it happened to be doing to check on the new planet. Confirmation
of the findings of Lowell Observatory was quick and unanimous. Letters
and telegrams with suggestions for a name poured in at Flagstaff; the
ones seriously considered were Pluto, Minerva, and Cronus. Minerva
was out because that name had been used for one of the larger planetoids. The choice fell on Pluto because Pluto's mythological brothers
Jupiter and Neptune were already planets. Also, the letters P and L
(which, intertwined, made up the symbol for the planet) happened to
be Percival Lowell's initials. The suggestion, which had been transmitted
by a professor of astronomy at Oxford, had come from an eleven-year-
old girl.

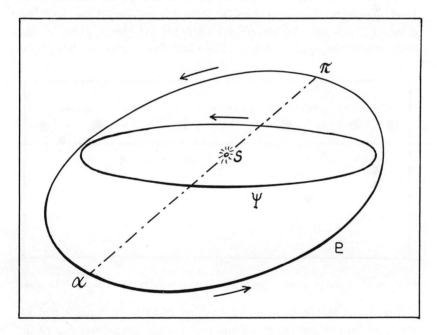

Orbits of Neptune and Pluto, showing their relative positions in space

There was no doubt that Tombaugh had discovered a new planet.
But was it Lowell's Planet X? The more time elapsed the graver the
doubts became.

The orbit was the first surprise. Until Pluto was discovered, Mercury
had been the planet with the strongest inclination to the ecliptic, namely

7 degrees. The inclination of Pluto was 17 degrees; only comets and a few planetoids showed such strongly tilted orbital planes. Moreover the perihelion was actually closer to the sun than Neptune's; the new planet was farther from the sun than Neptune is only most of the time—from about 1970 to 2000, it will be closer to the sun.

ORBIT OF PLUTO:
LOWELL'S PREDICTION AND THE FIRST ORBIT COMPUTATIONS

	LOWELL	NICHOLSON AND MAYALL	F. ZAGAR
Orbital period (years)	282	249.2	248.9
Eccentricity	0.202	0.2461	0.2472
Longitude of perihelion	204°.9	222° 23' 20"	222° 29' 39"
Perihelion passage	1991.2	1889.75	1888.4
Inclination	about 10°	17° 6' 58".4	17° 6' 50".8
Perihelion (A.U.)	34.31	29.86	29.80
Aphelion (A.U.)	51.69	49.35	49.36
Semi-major axis (A.U.)	43.0	39.60	39.58

The high inclination was one of the reasons for the failure of the 1905 search, as Pluto was then far from the ecliptic. It was largely a matter of luck that Tombaugh searched for the planet when he did; in the intervening quarter-century Pluto had drawn closer to the ecliptic.

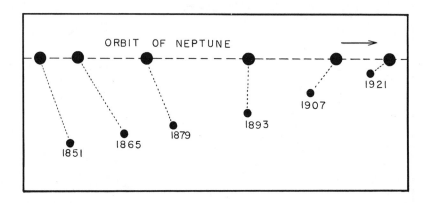

Pluto's positions relative to the ecliptic; diagram made prior to the discovery of the planet

Next came the problem of establishing Pluto's size. Lowell had assumed in his calculations that Pluto had a mass seven times that of the earth. If that was correct, Pluto should be about three magnitudes brighter than it turned out to be. But the fact that it did not show as a disk indicated that it could hardly be larger than the earth. This did not produce a reasonable picture no matter how you look at it. There had been a nice orderly arrangement of the solar system: small and dense planets near the sun (small and dense, according to recent ideas, because the sun heated them so much that they could not hold their original enormous atmospheres), large and light planets farther away from the sun, retaining their original gaseous components. Why suddenly a small and dense planet so far from the sun? And if Pluto was the size of the earth *and* had Lowell's mass of seven times that of the earth, its average density would be about 38 times that of water. There is no element as dense as that. To be sure, the core matter of stars is much denser, but Pluto was no star.

Then, twenty years after its discovery, Gerard P. Kuiper succeeded in measuring the visual diameter of Pluto. Calculating the true diameter from the visual diameter and the distance, he found it to be 3600 miles. With Pluto so much smaller than the earth the problem of its density became even more vexing. There was an ameliorating factor; observations of perturbations traceable to Pluto made since the discovery showed that Lowell's value for the mass had been much too high; the mass that could be assigned from the perturbations was about the same as that of earth. However, with its diameter so drastically reduced, the average density (for a mass about the same as that of earth) came out even higher: 60 times that of water! [4]

It became necessary either to conclude that the discovery of Pluto had been incredible coincidence—that Lowell's calculations had somewhere gone awry but nevertheless a small planet happened to be in an orbit somewhat similar to the one calculated—or to find some way of saving Lowell's figure of "seven times earth" and reconciling it with the observations. One explanation was the concept of "specular reflection" ("specular" is derived from the Latin *speculum,* meaning "mirror"). Dr. A. C. D. Crommelin, one of the first to compute Pluto's orbit, had advanced this thought as early as 1936, but at that time there was not sufficient reason to dwell upon it. After the measurements of the diameter by Kuiper and Humason it was revived and amplified by Dinsmore Alter, the director of the Griffith Observatory at Los Angeles.[5]

The theory is as follows: Pluto is so far from the sun that all of its once-extensive atmosphere has condensed and lies frozen on the ground, thus making the planet mirror-smooth. This mirror-smooth sphere would reflect the very feeble sunlight in the same manner as did those balls

[4] If you make the calculation the other way round, assuming Kuiper's diameter with a density like that of earth (5.5 times that of water), you obtain a mass of only 1/10 of that earth, in which case its perturbations on the orbit of Uranus would be negligible, and the whole basis of Lowell's calculations is removed.

[5] Article by Alter, Bunton, and Roques, in *Publications of the Astronomical Society of the Pacific,* vol. LXIII (1950).

of mirror glass which some fifty years ago were favored as garden decorations. The diameter measured by Kuiper and Humason would be the diameter of the reflection. The actual planet would be dark against a dark background—in other words, it would not show. One might obtain a 3600-mile reflection from a planet 20,000 miles in diameter, and such a planet could have a mass seven times that of earth without leading to impossible density figures.

It sounded interesting, but not quite convincing.

If Pluto only had a satellite (which would logically be named Proserpina, for Pluto's mythological consort, even though there is of course a planetoid by that name), its period of revolution would establish Pluto's true mass. But even a large satellite of Pluto would be invisible. Let us for a moment assume that the true diameter of Pluto to be actually 20,000 miles. A large satellite would certainly not be larger than, say, our moon, and with the 3600-mile Pluto as hard to see as it is, the chances of seeing a 2100-mile moon would be nil. Since there was no hope of seeing a satellite, astronomers at least tried to establish Pluto's period of rotation. In 1955 Merle F. Walker and Robert Hardie (of Lowell Observatory) took a large number of photoelectric measurements, looking for variations in brightness. One year earlier Dr. Walker had carried on similar observations from Mount Wilson while Kuiper had done the same in 1953 at McDonald Observatory in Texas. Combining the observations, the probable length of the Plutonian day could be ascertained as 6.39 earth-days, an unusually long period of rotation for a planet.

This was the figure Kuiper needed to crystallize a suspicion: Pluto was certainly in a planetary orbit but it had not been a planet originally. It was a run-away moon of Neptune.[6] All the moons in the solar system have periods of rotation equal to the orbital periods around their planets. While a 6.39-day period of rotation is impossibly long for a planet far from the sun, it is an entirely reasonable period for a satellite; Pluto, after having somehow escaped from Neptune, simply went on spinning at the same rate it had had while it was one of Neptune's moons. The same event (whatever it was) which detached Pluto from Neptune also

---

[6] The same suggestion had been made as early as 1936 (in *Monthly Notices of the Royal Astronomical Society*) by R. R. Lyttleton, who showed that such a runaway orbit might have resulted from a very close approach of Pluto (then still a moon of Neptune) and Neptune's large moon Triton. Dr. Kuiper's statement about the nature of Pluto was originally part of a lecture on the origin of the solar system, delivered at the Royal Canadian Institute at Toronto and published in the *Journal of the Royal Astronomical Society of Canada* (1956, Nos. 2, 3, and 4.). Kuiper did not agree with Lyttleton on the mechanism of the detachment of Pluto.

influenced Neptune's small moon Nereid and produced its very long orbit but Nereid either did not escape or else was recaptured.

The demotion of Pluto from a full-fledged planet to a runaway moon in a planetary orbit explained everything—the nature of the orbit, the period of rotation, even the small mass, now taken to be about one-thirtieth of that of the earth. But this small mass certainly could not cause the residuals upon which Lowell had based his work. Hence Pluto could not be Planet X.

During the period when the motion of Pluto was being established, and while Pluto was firmly believed to be Planet X, the astronomers at Lowell Observatory were aware, of course, that others had predicted additional trans-Neptunian planets. And since the search for Pluto had developed the researchers' skill, it was agreed at the observatory that they would look farther. Plates were taken all around the ecliptic and for a considerable distance from it and Tombaugh continued his blinking. As he reported later:

During my share of Lowell Observatory's long-continued searching for trans-Neptunian planets, about 90 million star images were examined in 7000 hours at the blink comparator. Nearly 4000 asteroid images were marked on the plates, 40 percent of them new, while 1807 variables were noted and 29,548 galaxies were counted. One new globular cluster and six galactic star clusters were by-products of the search. Only one comet was found, on a pair of plates taken a year earlier. It seems safe to conclude from the Lowell surveys that no unknown planet beyond Saturn exists that was brighter than magnitude 16½ at the time of search (*Sky and Telescope,* op. cit.).

There is no reason to doubt Dr. Tombaugh, but Planet X is still needed. The "X" now stands not only for "unknown" as in Lowell's calculations, but for the Roman numeral ten, since Pluto is now the ninth planet. In 1942 Dr. Robert S. Richardson concluded from the delay in the latest appearance of Halley's comet that there might be another planet at about the same distance from the sun as Pluto, but in a more regular orbit. But since the delay of Halley's comet can also be explained in other ways, this prediction is now generally disregarded. If there is a Planet X it is more likely to be in an orbit like the one worked out by Grigull in 1902.

In 1950 Dr. Karl H. Schuette of Munich reviewed again the comets with aphelia beyond Neptune and established two "families"; the Pluto Family with five known members and the Trans-Pluto Family with eight known members. The Trans-Pluto Family is clearly divided into two groups, one of three comets with aphelia at about longitude 24 degrees, and another of four comets with aphelia at about longitude 154 degrees, and an eighth member, with an orbit far away from the others.

As the table in the Appendix shows, the aphelia of the Pluto Family range from 47.6 to 59 A.U.; the aphelia of the Trans-Pluto Family from 75.3 to 89.1 A.U. With the exception of the first member of the latter group—the one discovered by C.H.F. Peters in 1857—all have aphelia a few astronomical units beyond 77.2 A.U., which is the next planetary distance beyond Neptune in the table of the Bode-Titius rule. Hence Schuette felt that 77 A.U. is the most likely distance for the planet which is responsible for the existence of this family of comets. Under the simplest assumptions the longtitude of its perihelion would be at about 100 degrees. Since all the comets in question show a high inclination, the orbit of the planet is probably strongly inclined too. This might explain why it was not found in the continuation of Tombaugh's search after the discovery of Pluto.

Or perhaps it is just too faint. But the existence of the Trans-Pluto comet family strongly suggests that it is there.

PART III

APPROXIMATE INFINITY

Wenn nun die Fixsterne ein System ausmachen, dessen Umfang durch die Anziehungssphäre desjenigen Körpers, der im Mittelpunkt befindlich ist, bestimmet wird, werden nicht mehr Sonnensystemata, und, so zu reden, mehr Michstrassen entstanden sein, die in dem grenzenlosen Felde des Weltraums erzeuget worden?

But if the fixed stars form a system the circumference of which is determined by the gravitational power of the body in the center, would there not be more such systems of suns, so to speak more Milky Ways, which originated in the limitless area of outer space?

—Immanuel Kant, *Allgemeine Naturgeschichte und Theorie des Himmels (General Natural History and Theory of the Heavens)*, 1755

19
PARALLAXES AND PARSECS

THE astronomers before Copernicus, not to mention Copernicus himself, were mainly occupied with "saving the phenomena," and the astronomers from Kepler to Herschel considered it their main task to establish the facts about the solar system. The astronomers of the nineteenth century, however, worked in two fields simultaneously. As Part II of this book shows, they did an incredible amount of detail work on the bodies of the solar system, but at the same time they looked beyond the solar system, to the stars.

The fundamental problem was to find the distance between the star nearest to us, the sun, and another star, *any* other star. This looked very much like a repetition of two earlier problems, that of finding the size of the earth and then that of finding the earth's distance from the sun. Once the distance between two points on earth had been definitely established, it had been a relatively simple matter to calculate the size of the home planet. Likewise, once the distance between the earth and another planet had been found for a given moment it had been only a matter of mathematical tedium to find all the other distances.

Reasoning by analogy, if a method could be developed to find the distance to one other star, the distances to the others could also be established, presumably by using the same method.

The main difficulty was to find a starting point.

All that astronomers had to work with was one assumption and one fact. The assumption was made first by the Arabs: it was that all stars were of the same size and therefore their apparent brightness or faintness was caused by distance only. The fact, which had been discovered by Dr. Halley was that a few of the brightest stars had slightly changed their positions in the sky since Ptolemy's time. This discovery went excellently with the assumption—only some of the brightest stars had moved, which showed that they were the nearest stars. It seemed to prove two things, one that the stars were actually at different distances and that something moved, either the stars, or our sun, carrying the planets along. But in order to arrive at a conclusion of some kind an additional clue was needed. Sir William Herschel reasoned that an apparent shift of a star position might be caused by the movement of the earth around the sun. Between the dates of January 2 and July 4, the earth moves one-half of its orbit around the sun. An observer observing a region of the sky during the first week of July is 186 million miles from the point from which he had been observing during the first week in January. This should cause the nearer stars to look as if they had shifted position against the background of more distant stars. This annual shift would be the clue needed.

Herschel next reasoned that such a shift should show up most clearly if pairs of stars were observed, preferably a very bright star which was next to a faint star. The assumption was still that the apparent brightness was a function of the distance. Of course the faint star next to a bright star was not "near" it by any means; the two just happened to lie in about the same line of sight as seen from earth.

The logical thing to do was to make a careful catalogue of such star pairs and then check their relative positions at regular intervals. When Herschel began his work on this catalogue (of which the discovery of Uranus was an unexpected by-product), he was interested only in constructing a catalogue which would enable an observer to check on a probable shift in position—the parallax as astronomers call it—and he paid no attention to a loud and generally unpleasant discussion about such star pairs which was then going on in continental Europe.

The fact that some stars were very close to each other had been noted earlier; the oldest observed example was Mizar—the center star in the Big Dipper's handle, Zeta Ursae majoris—with little Alcor next to it. Giovanni Battista Riccioli had marked this pair of stars as something unusual in 1650. Gottfried Kirch in Berlin, who had been an assistant of Johannes Hevelius for a while, had measured the angular distance between Mizar and Alcor in 1700; James Bradley had repeated the measurement in 1755. Hevelius himself in 1659 had found two more close pairs, Alpha Capricorni and 61 Cygni. The first of these two had been measured by John Flamsteed in 1690, while James Bradley had measured 61 Cygni in 1753. During the same year the Abbé de Lacaille had measured the angular distance between the two components of Alpha Centauri. Before that, in 1719, Bradley had found two more pairs, Gamma Virginis and Alpha Geminorum.

But while the visual closeness of these pairs of stars had been noted with interest, nobody had wondered whether, at least in some cases, the two stars of a pair might not actually be close to each other in space. The first man to express doubt that the visual closeness was accidental only was Johann Heinrich Lambert in Berlin. Though Lambert was not a professional astronomer—at his death in 1777 he had the title of Chief City Architect *(Oberbaurat)*—he influenced astronomical thinking in the German-speaking countries by his *Cosmological Letters* which appeared in Augsburg in 1761. In these "Letters" he wrote about the motions which such star pairs would have to describe if Sir Isaac Newton's law of gravitation applied to them. He concluded that Newton's law would apply, but he doubted that these stars were actually close neighbors, though he made no decision in the matter.

Only a few years later, in 1767, the *Philosophical Transactions* carried an article by the Reverend John Michell with the somewhat wordy title "An inquiry into the probable parallax and magnitude of the fixed stars, from the quantity of light which they afford us, and the particular circumstances of their situation." He pointed out that it was most improbable that the appearance of certain star groups such as the Pleiades and the known star pairs should all be due to accidents of position. One of the facts that spoke in favor of actual physical proximity was that the components of such star groups and also of some star pairs were about equally bright. Of course many fainter and presumably more distant stars were visible in the vicinity, but at least the bright ones had to be at about the same distance from us; hence they had to be more or less as close to each other as they seemed.

Nobody seems to have paid much attention to the article by the Reverend John Michell, but a lecture by Christian Mayer delivered in 1777, the year of Lambert's death, created a discussion. Christian Mayer, professor of mathematics in Heidelberg and Court Astronomer in Mannheim, was a Jesuit, as was his assistant Johann Metzger. The two had done for several years what William Herschel was to do soon afterward: they had looked for bright stars with faint stars next to them. They had found nearly a hundred such pairs and had concluded that the faint stars were planets of the bright stars. In his lecture Mayer reported on their observations and offered his conclusion. Naturally the local newspaper, the *Mannheimer Zeitung,* had sent one of its editors to report the lecture of the Court Astronomer and the paper carried a long article about it. Father Hell in Vienna read the article and shook his head— these two had made an elementary mistake. Father Hell, like all scientists, did not like mistakes, and he was especially opposed to mistakes made by Jesuits, which brought disgrace on the Order.

He wrote an article in a Viennese journal (the *Wiener Diarium*) in which he pointed out that Mayer's "satellites of the fixed stars" were just optical illusions, explaining them as he had the "satellite of Venus," as reflections of the image of the bright star from the observer's eye back into the telescope. Mayer was insulted at being accused of such an elementary mistake—after all, he *was* Court Astronomer. He replied twice, first in German in 1778 under the title "Thorough Defense of the New Observations of Satellites of Fixed Stars," and a year later in Latin. He insisted, first, that he had not made a mistake, and second, that he had a right to extend the use of the word *comes* (companion or partner) to the fixed stars. Father Hell wrote a reply to Mayer and Nikolaus Fuss, a Swiss working in St. Petersburg as an assistant to Leonhard Euler, joined in with some *Réflexions sur les satellites des étoiles* which appeared in St. Petersburg in the original French in 1780 and in 1785, two years after Mayer's death, was reprinted in German in the *Berliner Jahrbuch*.

Of course Father Hell and Professor Mayer were both wrong. The objects that Mayer had seen were not illusions, but neither were they planets of other suns; we now know that planets of other suns cannot be seen with optical instruments operating through our atmosphere.

With this controversy raging, it was only prudent of Herschel to ignore all implications and just make a catalogue. It was presented to the Royal Society in 1782 under the title of *Catalogue of Double Stars;* it listed 269 objects.

Herschel arranged his double stars in six classes according to the angular distance between the two stars. The sixth class, of 66 objects included those between 1 and 2 minutes of arc apart; the fifth class of 51 objects had an angular distance of between ½ and 1 minute of arc; the fourth class of 44 objects were 15 to 30 seconds of arc apart; the third class of 46 objects were separated by only 5 to 15 seconds of arc; the second class of 38 objects had an angular distance of 5 seconds of arc or less; and the first class, finally, consisted of 24 objects which could be separated only by his most powerful instruments. Many other men, after this accomplishment, might have decided that their work was done. Herschel considered it just a beginning. Only two years later he followed it with another list of 434 objects and additional communications brought the total number to 846.

While Herschel had refrained from joining the debate about Christian Mayer's "satellites of fixed stars" he could not help drawing conclusions of his own. There were too many such objects to be explained by optical accident, though that had been his original opinion. Some time between 1782 and 1784 he reconsidered. If there actually were *Doppelsterne (double stars)*,[1] they should show relative motions around

[1] Herschel usually thought in German about astronomical matters, partly because he always discussed them with his sister Caroline, who was an astronomer

each other. Originally he had intended to look for a shift of the brighter star in quest of stellar distances, now he began to look for relative motions. The search culminated with his report of 1803 entitled "Account of the changes that have happened during the last 25 years in the relative situation of double stars." By then there was no doubt left; double stars, nowadays usually called binaries, do exist.

Herschel had found changes in relative position of the two bodies of binaries ranging all the way from 5 to 51 degrees; there could be no doubt that the smaller of such a pair was in orbit around the larger one, or else, if they were roughly equal in size, that they moved around their common center of gravity. Of course there are some "visual binaries" but their number is not large.

Though Herschel had made his systematic "sweeps" of the sky for the sake of double stars and for the ultimate purpose of finding the distance to one or several stars he could not help coming across all kinds of curious things which had already been listed by Messier. Of course he noted everything he saw with the greatest of care and an assembly of his notes produced, in 1786, a *Catalogue of one thousand new Nebulae and Clusters of Stars*. Here Herschel used a subdivision into eight classes: class I, bright nebulae; class II, faint nebulae; class III, very faint nebulae; class IV, planetary nebulae (so called because in the telescope they show a disk similar to the disk of a planet), class V, very large nebulae; class VI, compressed rich star clusters; class VII, compressed clusters of small and large stars; and, finally, class VIII, coarsely scattered clusters. The division, as is apparent, was based on appearance; it was not yet orderly in our sense. Herschel's work in astronomy was somewhat similar to that of Konrad Gesner of Zurich in zoology, a comprehensive and diligent listing of what was known—or, in Herschel's case, what could be seen—which provided the material for later studies and understanding.

Beginning students in astronomy and interested laymen tend to think that Herschel's overwhelming position in the astronomical world of the early nineteenth century is due to the fact that he "was the first to build a big telescope." Of course Herschel did build the first really large telescope. At Slough, near Windsor, where he had settled, Herschel, with financial aid from George III, began the building of his most famous instrument, with a tube 40 feet long and a speculum metal mirror 58 inches in diameter. The work took from 1785 to 1789 and in 1795

---

in her own right. She was elected a member of the Royal Astronomical Society for her own work on comets and her assistance on her brother's catalogue of nebulae.

Herschel himself published a detailed and enthusiastic description. The foundation consisted of masonry and heavy beams upon which rested a wooden structure like two inverted V's, holding the tube between them. The mirror end of the tube was protected by a wooden house; at the open end of the tube there was a wooden cage for the observer. Herschel's big telescope, like most of the telescopes he made after his first few attempts, was of his own design. His first one had been of Sir Isaac Newton's design, using a small plane mirror in the tube to catch the image formed by the main mirror and to reflect it into the magnifying eyepiece. Herschel, while checking a mirror he was making, noticed that one could just tilt the main mirror so that its image would not fall into the center line of the tube, but at its rim near the open end. This way the small plane mirror could be eliminated. The enormous tube could be raised and lowered by the observer by means of a system of ropes and pulleys. Herschel, in his description of the instrument, told how he had observed Saturn with it for many hours.

But the simple fact was that the "big one" was not often used. It was too awkward to handle in the days before electric servomotors and the image was not as good as expected; in all probability the mirror was slightly distorted by its own weight. Most of Herschel's important work was done with a 20-foot telescope with an aperture of 19 inches; still a very large instrument for its time. The important factor, however, was Herschel's diligence and experience.

Herschel's work on the binaries had some additional consequences. Remember that the original assumption had been that all stars are of the same size and brightness, varying only in distance. This assumption had to be dropped; two stars which obviously formed a binary were of very different brightness (and sometimes of different color, too), making it clear that stars, like planets, came in different sizes. And still another conclusion had to be drawn, namely, that stars, whether binaries or not, had motions in space. But if this was so then our sun, being a star, might logically be expected to have motion too. Herschel realized at once that the motion of our sun would appear as an apparent motion of other stars, like the apparent motion of distant houses and trees to a traveler in a train. Naturally Herschel was intrigued by the question about which point of the sky was the "apex," as he called the point toward which the sun moved. He concluded that the apex must be located in the vicinity of the star Lambda Herculis.

But in spite of his enormous contributions to astronomy in general and to the knowledge of the stars in particular, Herschel never did what he had set out to do; he did not find the distance between the sun and another star.

The one who first succeeded in doing this was Friedrich Wilhelm Bessel (1784–1846), who, like Herschel, had come to astronomy not only from outside astronomy but from outside science in general. He was, as a young man, a clerk in the office of a merchant in Bremen and, just as Kepler intended to become a good pastor, Bessel intended to become a successful merchant. In his day that implied overseas travel and Bessel began to prepare himself for such travel, partly by learning the languages he was likely to need, partly by studying navigation.

Navigation is one of the practical applications of astronomy and it was logical for Bessel to start reading works on astronomical theory and practice. Personal influences were added: Dr. Olbers lived in Bremen and Schroeter in Lilienthal was not far away. Largely for the purpose of trying his skill, Bessel took a set of 200-year-old observations, namely the observations of Halley's comet by Thomas Harriot in 1607, and "reduced" them, which means that he calculated the orbit from the observations which noted where the comet had been in the sky at a given time. Bessel's paper was published and received warm praise from both Dr. Olbers and the Baron von Zach. As for Bessel, he had discovered what really interested him; it was the niceties of precise astronomical calculations. Using James Bradley's observations he succeeded in deducing the errors of Bradley's instruments from the observations themselves, allowing for such factors as aberration in the atmosphere, etc. This highly refined astronomical detective work was far more satisfying than waiting for cargo ships to come into port and trying to derive a profit from carefully timed buying and selling. He gave up his mercantile career and became Schroeter's assistant in Lilienthal.

In 1810 he received a call to an area which to most Germans in those days was practically the Far East—to Königsberg in East Prussia, where Immanuel Kant had died six years earlier. The old Albertus University, founded in the days of the Teutonic Knights, was to have an observatory and Bessel, then aged twenty-six, had been chosen as its director. Actual observing had for the time being to wait or be carried out only as a hobby. A new observatory was to be organized and new instruments had to be installed. There were probably waiting periods; the meridian telescope, for example, which he installed in 1820, came from Munich, where G. von Reichenbach had started a precision workshop for scientific instruments in 1804.

On weekday evenings Bessel often gave popular lectures, as was customary with most famous scientists at the time. He told his audience of merchants, ship's captains, army officers, civil servants, and local nobility, who had come to town to attend the lecture, what the real job of an astronomer was, namely the finding of sources of error before they could do any harm. The vertical pillar which carries the instrument, he would explain, is not really vertical but only approximately so. Find out how much it is off, and in which direction. The axis of the telescope around which it is elevated or lowered forms an angle of 90 degrees to the optical axis of the tube, but again it is not precisely 90 degrees; nor are the steel bearings of the axis precisely circular. The gradations on the circles are not precisely equal to each other. The first job, then, is to find out where and by how much the instrument is imperfect. "Every instrument is really made twice, first by the artisan in steel and brass and then by the astronomer on paper, by way of a list of corrections which his investigation established . . . for the astronomer can measure more precisely than the instrument maker can build."

To facilitate computation of necessary corrections and to produce uniformity of usage, Bessel began publication of his *Tabulae Regiomontanae* (Königsberg Tables) in 1830.

Then he attacked the problem of stellar distances.

It is self-evident that measuring the distance to another star is the more likely to succeed if you pick a fairly near star. But how could one tell which star was relatively near? Before Herschel, the brightest star in the northern sky, Sirius, would have seemed to be the nearest. But Herschel's work on binaries had shown that stars had different intrinsic brightness; the brightest star *might* still be the nearest, but not necessarily. Similarly a star which showed a large proper motion was likely to be nearer, just as a car traveling along a nearby highway at 60 miles per hour seems to be going faster than one traveling at the same rate farther away. But this was not certain either; different stars might move at different speeds and they could not be assumed to move at a right angle to our line of sight. A star might actually move quite fast, but nearly along the line of sight (toward us or away from us) and then it would, in spite of its high speed, seem motionless. Another uncertain way of judging, or rather guessing, was provided by the binaries. If a binary was "open," meaning that its two components looked fairly far apart, it might be near. But again, who could assume that the actual distance between the two components was the same, or nearly so, for all binaries? In fact, Newton's law proved that the distances would vary considerably; if the two components were close to each other the period of revolution would be short, if they were far apart, the period of revolution would be long. And Herschel's long list contained wide variations in durations, from years to centuries.

The ideal would have been a very bright, very open binary of known period of revolution with a high proper motion. But there was no such binary in the northern sky. Bessel settled for a faint open binary with high proper motion, the star which was No. 61 in Flamsteed's list of those comprising the constellation of the Swan. One reason for choosing 61 Cygni was that some faint stars which showed no motion at all and which could therefore be presumed to be far distant, were, optically speaking, nearby. Bessel began his observations in 1837 and in 1838 the *Astronomischen Nachrichten* (Nos. 365 and 366) carried his report on *"Bestimmung der Entfernung des 61. Sterns des Schwanes"* (Determination of the Distance of the 61st star of the Swan.) Bessel gave the round figure of 600,000 astronomical units, or about 60 million million miles.

If Sir William Herschel had still been alive he would, no doubt, have been greatly pleased to see that the work he had started had been brought to a conclusion. His sister Caroline did live to see it, and his son, Sir John Herschel, was president of the Royal Astronomical Society, when, in 1841, its gold medal was awarded to Bessel for the discovery. He wrote Bessel at that time: "I congratulate you and myself that we have lived to see the great and hitherto impossible barrier to our excursions into the sidereal universe—that barrier against which we have chafed so long and so vainly—almost simultaneously overleaped at three different points. It is the greatest and most glorious triumph which practical astronomy has ever witnessed."

The "three points" referred to the fact that measurements of the distances of two other stars had also been published. Just two months after the publication of Bessel's result, the *Memoirs* of the society (XI, 1839) carried a paper "On the Parallax of Sirius and of Alpha Centauri" by Thomas Henderson. Henderson, a Scotsman born at Dundee, had a career fairly similar to Bessel's. He had been a solicitor's clerk in his home town, discovered an interest in and an aptitude for astronomy, and had been appointed director of the observatory at the Cape of Good Hope. And from there he could observe what Bessel did not have in the northern sky, a bright open binary with high proper motion: Alpha Centauri. Henderson gave the distance as about 200,000 astronomical units. The distance was later found to be about 260,000 A.U., but the triple system of Alpha Centauri—a reddish star known as Proxima Centauri describes a very large orbit around the bright binary—is the star system nearest to our own.

Actually Henderson had made his observations before Bessel began to observe 61 Cygni, but he had delayed the mathematical work until after his return to Edinburgh where he became Astronomer Royal for Scotland.

And in the same year (1839) Wilhelm Struve in Russia published, as an appendix to a larger work, a *"Disquisitio de parallaxi alpha Lyrae"* in which he showed that Alpha Lyrae (Vega), must be 800,000 A.U. distant. Struve's was the least accurate of the three determinations, since the true distance is about double that, but Vega, being much farther away, was a more difficult subject than the others.

The general attitude in 1841 was one of great optimism. "The barrier has begun to yield, it will speedily be prostrated," wrote Sir John Herschel in his letter to Bessel. Everybody thought that as soon as enough specialized observations could be made, the distances of at least the brighter stars would be marked alongside their names on the star charts. The next star to yield was Sirius (by way of a correction of Henderson's work), but no further results of importance could be claimed for decades to come. It so happens that the brightest stars, suspected to be near because they are bright are *not* necessarily near. The lists of the twenty-two nearest and the twenty-two brightest stars have only three names in common: Alpha Centauri, Sirius, and Procyon. Sir John Herschel's "barrier" was not single, as later astronomers were to learn. Bessel, Henderson, and Struve had breached the first barrier only, that of the distances of stars which produce a parallax with the diameter of the earth's orbit as a base line.

In these first determinations the distances were still expressed in astronomical units, a large yardstick, but too small for stellar distances. The changeover to the light-year—the distance traveled by light during one year or 5.88 million million miles—came later in the century. Then the now familiar figures began to emerge: 4.3 light-years for the distance to Alpha Centauri, 8.7 light-years for the distance to Sirius, 10.4 light-years to Procyon, and 10.7 to 61 Cygni. But simultaneously another unit came into use, the distance of 3.259 light-years. This other unit was more useful, not because it was somewhat longer, but because it was more logical. The parallax of Alpha Centauri was a little less than 1 second of arc which worked out to the 4.3 light-years mentioned. If Alpha Centauri produced a shift of 1 second of arc it would be at a distance of 3.259 light years; hence this distance producing a *par*allax of one *sec*ond became the *parsec*. No star happens to be 1 parsec from us, but the unit is useful; if a star shows a parallax of $\frac{1}{10}$ of a second of arc its distance is 10 parsecs, or 32.59 light years; the star Pollux very nearly qualifies, as it is about half a light-year closer than 10 parsecs.

This 10-parsec distance is utilized for a specific purpose. As has been said repeatedly, brightness and distance unfortunately have no simple relationship. Nor do they have any kind of relationship for which an expression can be devised. Canopus, for example, the second brightest star, is at least 200 parsecs distant, while Proxima Centauri (which now is on "our" side of its long orbit and therefore actually nearer than Alpha) is so dim that it cannot be seen at all with the naked eye. It follows that Canopus must be enormously bright when seen from a certain distance, while Proxima Centauri, seen from the same distance, would still be dim. The standard distance picked for comparing different stars is 10 parsecs, and our own sun, seen from 10 parsecs away, would have a magnitude of 4.8; this is referred to as the "absolute magnitude," though "standardized magnitude" would be a more correct term.

Once the absolute magnitude of a star has been established its brightness can be compared with that of the absolute magnitude of another star. If one has an absolute magnitude of 8.0 and the other one has an absolute magnitude of 3.0, they differ by five magnitudes. Five magnitudes is the same as a brightness ratio of 100 to 1, hence the *intrinsic brightness* (also called "actual brightness" or "true luminosity") of the star of absolute magnitude 3.0 is 100 times that of the star of absolute magnitude 8.0. This could be expressed in millions of candle-power, but can be visualized better by a comparison with our sun: the luminosity of Sirius is 26 times that of our sun, that of Procyon 5.5 times that of our sun, and that of Proxima Centauri $\frac{1}{10}$ of one per mille of our sun.

The elder Herschel, whose largest telescope did not come up to his expectations, must inevitably have speculated about—and probably discussed with Caroline—what the astronomical instruments of the future might be like. Whatever his hopes may have been in his old age, they were probably realized in the half century after his death, when several new groups of instruments came into being. Most of these stemmed from the work of the gifted Bavarian Joseph Fraunhofer, who advanced from the beginnings made by the Englishman John Dollond.

Dollond, who was born in 1706, when Sir Isaac Newton was at the height of his fame, and was originally a silk weaver, became interested in optics because of Newton's work. Sir Isaac, you remember, invented the reflecting telescope named after him to avoid the rainbow fringes produced by a single lens. Dollond, experimenting, found that different kinds of glass behave differently when it comes to producing color fringes. They do not all have the same index of refraction, to use the technical term. By combining lenses of two kinds of glass, called crown and flint glass, respectively, Dollond produced lens systems which magnified but had only a very slight color fringe.

In 1752 Dollond founded an optical workshop in London which

quickly became famous and which, after his death in 1761, was continued by his son Peter and his nephew George Huggins (who later changed his name to Dollond). The Dollond instruments were the best of their time; if they were not perfect it was mainly because glass makers were still unable to produce batches of unvarying quality. The flint glass especially was not uniform; it was almost impossible to find even a 4-inch disk completely without striations.

But the art of glass-making improved, and by 1806, when Joseph Fraunhofer took employment with von Reichenbach in Munich, he could get perfect flint-glass disks from his friend P. L. Guinand in Switzerland. (One of Guinand's solutions to the problem had been to select perfect pieces of glass, even if small, heating them until they became soft, and squeezing them into large disks.) Fraunhofer soon became the head of the optical division of the firm which, in 1817, was separated from the instrument-making section and became the Optical Institute at Munich. Fraunhofer's main objective was to measure precisely the optical qualities of various kinds of glass. There he encountered the problem that the yellow light, for example, which he used to measure the qualities of the glass, could not be either exactly identified or duplicated from one case to another. He used a prism for dispersing a shaft of sunlight into the rainbow-colored band called a spectrum and noticed a number of fine black lines going across the spectrum. At first he blamed the glass; then he wondered whether the lines might be due to diffraction; but by 1817 he had convinced himself that they were real and that they always appeared in the same places. Of the total of 500 lines he counted, he picked out eight which he labeled with the letters A to H for the purpose of identifying light of a certain color. Fraunhofer's lines did their first useful work as markers for specific "wavelengths," to use a modern term.

Fraunhofer also designed a new kind of telescope, distinct from others not only because of superior lenses but with a new and perfectly balanced mounting. Moreover, he added graduated circles for the reading of angles, and, most important, the clockwork drive which made the telescope follow the stars, compensating for the rotation of the earth.

In 1820 Fraunhofer built a 24-centimeter (about 9-inch) telescope of this type for Struve's Dorpat observatory, which did wonders for Struve's work on double stars.[2] The next larger instrument of Fraun-

[2] The binary Gamma Virginis has an orbit which is so oriented that the two stars very nearly coincide as seen from earth. When it was first investigated, in 1780, the two components were 5.7 seconds of arc apart but were gradually closing up. In 1836 Gamma Virginis was a single star to all telescopes except Fraunhofer's Dorpat refractor, which showed it elongated. The binary was widest open in 1920, with an angular distance of 6.2 seconds of arc. It will be "single" again in 2016.

hofer's design was not supervised by Fraunhofer himself, who had died at a comparatively early age in 1826, but by his successor Merz. It was the 38-centimeter (15-inch) refractor ordered by Czar Nicholas I for the new Pulkovo Observatory.

Of course Fraunhofer, who pioneered all this, had competitors. There were Troughton, and later Grubb, in England, and Steinheil in Germany, and soon an American, Alvan Clark in Washington, whose lenses became famous all over the world. Part of their fame was due to a lucky accident; Clark's first large lens (18 inches in diameter) was tested by his son in 1862 and in the test Sirius was seen to have a tiny white companion. Nobody could possibly guess then how important the "Companion of Sirius" would become in the future (see Chapter 21); for the moment it proved the superiority of Clark's lenses. Later the moons of Mars were discovered with a Clark lens.

But just at the time that the Companion of Sirius was discovered "Fraunhofer lines" acquired new importance.

The line which Fraunhofer had called the D line was an especially pronounced double line in the yellow section of the solar spectrum. Several scientists—Sir George Gabriel Stokes in Cambridge, Anders Jöns Ångström in Upsala, and Jean Bernard Léon Foucault in Paris (inventor of the Foucault pendulum which directly shows the earth's rotation, and also of the gyroscope)—had noticed that the D line could be produced by heating sodium. Did this indicate that there is sodium in the sun? If so, an absolutely undreamed-of possibility existed: a chemical analysis could be made of an inaccessible body.

Only about a quarter-century earlier (in 1835) the French philosopher Auguste Comte had published a book which was still fresh in everybody's memory. In this *Cours de philosophie positive* Comte had written that astronomers could determine "the shapes, distances, sizes and motions" of planets and stars, "whereas never, by any means, will we be able to study their chemical composition [or] their mineralogic structure. . . ." He had also said that "every notion of the true mean temperature of the stars will necessarily always be concealed from us." The scientists proceeded with much pleasure to show that Comte's categorical statements had been as wrong as Hegel's before him.

While the fundamental discovery—that the presence of specific lines depended on the presence of specific chemical elements—was made by several scientists, the development of spectrum analysis is associated with the names of the physicist Gustav Adolf Kirchhoff and the chemist Robert Wilhelm Bunsen.

Kirchhoff, with Bunsen's aid on the chemical aspects, evolved the theory by making the distinction between absorption lines and emission lines. To continue with the double D line: if sodium is heated enough to send out light it will just look yellow to the eye. But when the light is sent through a prism it will produce the yellow double line. This is an emission line. When light emitted by a luminous body (for example our sun) passes through the sun's atmosphere which also contains sodium vapor, the double D line, which was originally present, is absorbed by the sodium vapor, so that the solar spectrum produced in the observatory shows the double D line as a black line. To check what the black absorption lines represented it was first necessary to produce them as emission lines from known elements, such as hydrogen, magnesium, iron, calcium, and so forth. When the emission lines of the elements could be matched with black lines in the solar spectrum Kirchhoff concluded that these elements were present, as gases, in the outer atmosphere of the sun. His fundamental publication on these findings appeared in Berlin in 1862-63.[3] The new science progressed so fast that only twenty years later Heinrich Kayser published a fairly complete instruction book on the use of the new tool.

In the meantime Anders Ångström had replaced Kirchhoff's arbitrary scale for determining the positions of the lines with a scale of the wavelengths of light, measured by a unit one ten-millionth of a millimeter in length, now known as the Ångström unit.

The usefulness of new science founded by Kirchhoff and Bunsen was not restricted to astronomy; it helped to discover and to identify unknown elements on earth which existed in such small quantities that they had escaped detection by the usual chemical means. Kirchhoff and Bunsen themselves discovered two such elements, cesium and rubidium; Sir William Crookes discovered thallium with the aid of the spectroscope, and F. Reich and H. T. Richter discovered indium. The spectroscope has remained a tool of chemists for the detection of traces of impurities, and atomic physicists use it for the same purpose, but its most important use was in discovering the chemistry of the stars.

Another new idea, which was developed between Fraunhofer's time and that of Kirchhoff and Bunsen, was what we now call the Doppler principle, named after the Austrian physicist Christian Johann Doppler, (1803–1853). Doppler had been intrigued by the fact that the two components of a binary could have different colors and had also wondered about the orbital motions of binaries. In a book on binaries, in 1842, he first stated his principle: if the distance between an observer

---

[3] *Untersuchungen über das Sonnenspectrum und die Spectren der chemischen Elemente* (Investigations of the Solar Spectrum and the Spectra of the Chemical Elements).

and a constant source of vibrations, such as a light-emitting star, changes, then the frequency of the vibrations received by the observer will deviate from the true value. If the distance is increasing, the number of vibrations received per second will decrease; if the distance is decreasing the number will increase.

This principle, properly applied, makes it possible to detect motions which had seemed to be undetectable, namely, the motion of a star along the line of sight. Motion away from the observer appears as what is now called the "red shift" (toward the red end of the spectrum), while motion in the direction of the observer appears as a "blue shift."

The colors of some stars also intrigued another scientist, the papal astronomer, Father Angelo Secchi (1818–1878). The different colors of stars led him to suggest a classification of stars based on their probable surface temperature. In his first grouping, he had four classes. The first he called "white-blue stars," with Sirius as the best-known example. The second class was the yellow-white stars, exemplified by our sun and by Capella. The third was that of the orange-red stars, with Betelgeuse as the main example. And finally there was a class of "blood-red stars."

The nineteenth century extended astronomy into the realm of the fixed stars, beginning with William Herschel's attempt, as he called it, at "unfixing" them. It brought a whole arsenal of new tools: improved telescopes, the spectroscope, and the photographic camera. It also brought a first attempt at stellar classification and a number of theories of stellar evolution which will be discussed later.

20

THE NEAREST STAR

INCREDIBLE as it may sound, it is a historical fact that astronomical observers for nearly two centuries neglected the brightest object in the sky, namely the nearest star—our sun.

After the initial flurry about spots on the sun's immaculate body, interest in the sun subsided. The existence of the sunspots was acknowledged and it was known that they were always near the sun's equator, both north and south of it. The spots indicated a period of rotation of just about 25 days. These few facts constituted the sum total of the knowledge about the sun up to the end of the eighteenth century. The efforts expended on the Venus transits were concerned with the distance to the sun, not its nature. Once the distance was established, the diameter—860,000 miles—could be easily calculated.

During the whole of the seventeenth century, the sun was observed by only a very few men. Johannes Hevelius was one of them; his *Selenographia* contains an appendix on observations of the sun for the years from 1642–1645. The few observations by others from that period were not even preserved. The manuscript volumes of Georg Christoph Eimmart, of his daughter Clara and of his pupil Johann Philipp Würtzelbauer burned up in a fire in a Russian monastery, while the notebooks of Heinrich Siverus in Hamburg simply disappeared after his death in 1690.

However, all astronomers knew that the number of sunspots was variable, and the question of whether some rule was discernible must have come up, for the *Mémoirs* of the Parisian Academy declared in 1713, *"Les temps de l'apparition des taches ne sont nullement réglés"* "The times of the appearances of the spots do not follow any rule."

Christian Horrebow in Copenhagen—his father Peter had been Ole Römer's assistant and later successor—seems to have been the first to doubt the opinion of the French astronomers. His diaries—saved from a burning building in 1807—contain entries which he made in 1775–76 which show that he had observed the sunspots since 1738. The key sentence reads in translation: "Astronomers have shown little zeal in observing the sunspots frequently, no doubt because they believed that it would not lead to anything of interest in astronomy and physics. But it may be hoped that diligent observation might establish a periodicity. . . ." If Horrebow had published his thoughts they might have influenced younger men, but they remained buried in the diary until they were published as a historical item in the *Astronomische Nachrichten* in 1859 (Nos. 1185 and 1893). By that time somebody else had found the periodicity Horrebow hoped for.

Its discoverer was Heinrich Schwabe, a pharmacist in Dessau who had started making systematic observations in 1826, following the advice of his friend Harding. Schwabe, for some time, paid attention to the sunspots only secondarily; he hoped to catch a transit of a planet inside the orbit of Mercury. But he kept careful records all the time and a number of years later he made a tabulation which showed a definite periodicity. He then wrote to Carrington in England, "I may compare myself to Saul, who went out to seek his father's ass, and found a kingdom."

While Schwabe was elated with his discovery, the majority of astronomers remained unimpressed. A few stated bluntly that Schwabe's suspected periodicity of "about 10 years" was probably just an accident; others declared more cautiously that a set of observations extending over only 18 years was too short to draw definite conclusions.

But less than a decade later a most surprising corroboration of Schwabe's work came from Great Britain, where Major General Edward Sabine had been tabulating something entirely different. On March 18, 1852, Sabine submitted to the Royal Society a report entitled "On Periodical Laws Discernible in the Mean Effects of the Larger Magnetic Disturbances," in which he pointed out that his periods of magnetic disturbances ran parallel to Schwabe's sunspot maxima.

In retrospect one should have expected General Sabine's report to prove the point and open up several new perspectives. In reality things were, as usual, more complicated. For one thing, Sabine's report was not printed at once and its title was unlikely to catch an astronomer's eye.

But two astronomers, neither aware of the other's efforts and both ignorant of Sabine's discovery, found a related report. The astronomers were Alfred Gautier in Geneva and Rudolf Wolf in Zurich. The report was on a study of the daily variations of the magnetic compass published in 1846 by Johann Lamont, who was born in Scotland but worked in Munich. Lamont had found a periodicity which looked so smooth that he tried to express it in a series of sine equations. Both Gautier and Wolf realized that Lamont's and Schwabe's periods went together. Wolf then decided to try to extend Schwabe's sunspot tabulation backward to the time of Galileo and the invention of the telescope. He wrote to all astronomers and other well-known scientists requesting information about any chance reports on sunspots before 1826 which might be found in private diaries and observers' journals.

Wolf soon learned of the existence of General Sabine's report. He also learned that the great Michael Faraday had never heard of it, though Alexander von Humboldt had. Quite a number of observations which would otherwise have been forgotten were found and published. Wolf, after battling endless detail, announced that there were nine sunspot maxima per century, the average period being 11 $\frac{1}{9}$ years. Curiously enough, Wolf's most vehement opponent was Lamont himself, while the Scottish astronomer John Allan Broun spent much effort trying to prove that the period of the deviations of the magnetic needle was 10.45 years and "therefore" the sunspot maxima must have the same period.

The next step was taken by Professor Elias Loomis of Yale with a research paper published in New Haven in 1870. The title, though long, clearly stated what Loomis had found: "Comparison of the mean daily range of the magnetic declination with the number of auroras observed each year and the extent of the black spots on the surface of the sun." Here was still another parallelism; a tabulation of the auroras showed the same general periodicity.[1] *A Tabulation of Observed Aurorae* by Hermann Fritz of Zurich was published in Vienna, in 1873. The same author then wrote a large work specifically devoted to the auroras: *Das Polarlicht* (Leipzig, 1881). But this was not the first large work on the subject. The *Traité physique et historique de l'aurore boréale,* written by Jean-Jacques Dortons de Mairan (secretary of the Parisian Academy) had been published a century and a half earlier, in 1731.

In spite of the neglect of the sun by astronomers between 1620 and 1750—when it was far more interesting to hunt for new satellites—some speculations were written down. Mairan tells, for example, that the first Cassini suspected that the zodiacal light was brighter when the sunspots were numerous. Several Italians speculated on a connection between sunspots and weather; Riccioli's *Almagestum novum* noted that the sun was without spots from the middle of July to the middle of September 1632, "a period of unusual drought," but that the spots were numerous in June 1642 when it was unusually cold in Italy.

[1] The name *Aurora borealis* was coined by Pierre Gassendi on the occasion of a conspicuous one on November 12, 1621. The first report on an antarctic aurora *(Aurora australis)* was that of Captain James Cook (February 20, 1773), while the first good description of a northern aurora came from the pen of the zoologist and physician Konrad Gesner of Zürich. The date of that aurora was December 27, 1560 (old style); the book, written in Latin, was published under the penname of Conrado Boloveso Fridemontano.

Along with speculations about possible effects of the spots ran others about the nature of the sunspots. That they were just dark clouds had been Galileo's first thought, while Simon Marius had spoken vaguely of "slag."

Since nobody knew anything about the constitution of the sun and it was generally assumed to be a dark body, its luminosity had to be explained by a special quality of its atmosphere which received the name of "photosphere." A sunspot, then, must be an interruption of the luminous photosphere. But what kind of an interruption? Cassini reasoned that the photosphere might show a phenomenon comparable to high and low tides; the photosphere would be uninterrupted and the sun therefore without spots when the "tide" was high. But at "low tide" the higher mountains of the sun's body began to show as dark spots. Christoph Scheiner had had a similar but more indirect idea: the photosphere was parted when the volcanoes on the sun's surface were active; gases rising from those volcanoes would produce more or less circular holes in the luminous top layer.

For some time Cassini's idea prevailed; peaks of tall mountains reaching through the photosphere were easier to visualize; besides, the peaks of the Alps made a convenient example. But late in the eighteenth century the theory of holes in the photosphere gained the upper hand. Alexander Wilson, a professor of astronomy at Glasgow, in a paper on "Observations on the Solar Spots" (*Philosophical Transactions,* 1774), which was awarded a prize by the Royal Academy in Copenhagen, showed that the shape of the spots agreed with the concept of holes rather than with the idea of mountain peaks. It was probably this paper which prompted Sir William Herschel to give some attention to the sun. Herschel's report "Observations Tending to Investigate the Nature of the Sun" appeared in the *Philosophical Transactions* in 1801. He was in full agreement both with tradition and with Alexander Wilson. The sun was a dark body and the spots were holes in the photosphere. As for the influence of sunspots on the weather, Herschel stated that harvests seemed to be bigger in the years with many sunspots.

The idea that the sunspots are holes in the photosphere is essentially correct; the mistake was the assumption that the dark area in the center of the sunspot is the sun's dark and cool surface. The spots look black by contrast only and would be very bright if they could be seen separately in the sky. But while the older Herschel was mistaken about the nature of the sun, he succeeded in giving the best one-sentence description of its appearance (aside from the spots) as seen through a powerful telescope with eye-protecting dark glasses. *"Die Sonne sieht wie*

Reissuppe aus," he said to his sister Caroline—"The sun looks like rice soup." Technically this is the sun's "granulation," but very modern photographs, taken from balloons hovering in the lower stratosphere, only bear out his description.

It was mainly work done by Sir John Herschel—during his famous stay in South Africa—which forced a revision of the concept of the sun. When the sun was only 12 degrees from the zenith at noon on December 31, 1838, he conducted a carefully worked out experiment in which a precisely known amount of water was heated for 10 minutes by a beam of sunlight of known diameter. The results of this experiment enabled him to calculate the amount of energy received from the sun by the earth.[2] He expressed this energy in terms of melting ice, stating that the amount of heat received at the earth's surface, with the sun in the zenith, would melt 1 inch of ice in 2 hours and 12 minutes. The figure was incredibly large and in order to make it clear to his students just what it meant, Professor C. A. Young of Princeton University played around with it in a very interesting manner: [3]

Since there is every reason to believe that the sun's radiation is equal in all directions, it follows that, if the sun were surrounded by a great shell of ice, one inch thick and 186 million miles in diameter, its rays would melt the whole in the same time. If, now, we suppose this shell to shrink in diameter, retaining, however, the same quantity of ice by increasing its thickness, it would still be melted in the same time. Let the shrinkage continue until the inner surface touches the photosphere, and allowing for atmospheric absorption, the ice-envelope would become more than a mile thick, through which the solar fire would still thaw out its way in the same time."

The opening clause of this quotation will strike most readers as an entirely superfluous precaution, but Professor Young had a reason for it. Because Sir John Herschel had derived such a large figure for the energy coming from the sun, and others who had repeated his measurements had unhesitatingly increased the amount by nearly 50 per cent, the idea had been voiced that radiant heat was an "action between masses." If you have metallic spheres charged with static electricity the sparks will jump between those spheres only. The thought was that the sun sends radiant energy *only* in the direction of some other mass able to receive it.

[2] This is now called the "solar constant," defined as the energy received by a surface exposed at right angles to the sun's radiation just outside the earth's atmosphere when the earth is at its mean distance from the sun. The value of the solar constant is 1.94 calories per square centimeter per minute (or 1.07 B.T.U. per square yard per second).

[3] Quoted from *The Sun* by C. A. Young, London, 1895 ed., p. 288. The book was first published in 1881.

Of course it doesn't work that way. As Professor Young wrote: "The energy radiated from a heated globe is found to be alike in all directions, and wholly independent of the bodies which receive it, nor is there the slightest reason to suppose the sun any different in this respect from every other incandescent mass." He could also have pointed out that the concept of radiant energy as an "action between masses" would have reduced the energy emission of the sun only if a distance limit had also been introduced. If the interaction could take place over *any* distance "receiving masses" ranging from comparatively near large planets to very distant interstellar gas and dust, could be found somewhere in space all around the celestial globe.

That the fantastic energy output could not be the result of ordinary oxidation could be shown by simple calculations. If the whole sun consisted of anthracite, a layer 20 feet in thickness would have to be burned every hour to account for the energy release, and the whole sun would be consumed in somewhat less than 5000 years. It would not even have lasted through the "age of the world" as derived by theologians who added up the generations of the Old Testament for this purpose.[4] Chemical combustion could not account for it, though as late as 1882, Dr. C. W. Siemens (a member of the family of German industrialists who had settled in London) tried to imagine such a possibility. What other sources of heat were there?

One of the great discoveries of the nineteenth century was the "law of the conservation of energy," proposed in 1842 by Julius Robert Mayer, who, after spending years at sea as a ship's doctor, settled in Heilbronn as the City Physician. Mayer stated that energy could never vanish, that it was indestructible. It might appear in various forms— as motion, as heat, or as visible light—and it could be transformed from one into another, as, for example, the heat of the steam in a steam engine was diminished by pushing the piston but then appeared as mechanical motion. But the sum total of all the energy in the universe remained constant. At the same time James Prescott Joule in Manchester—like Hevelius he was a brewer—designed experiments for finding what is now called a "conversion factor," the determination of how much mechanical work was equivalent to a unit of heat. (The answer was that 1 kilogram-calorie, the heat which raises the temperature of 1 kilogram of water by 1° C., is equal to 425 kilogram-meters, the energy required to lift 425 kilograms 1 meter.)

Mayer then reasoned that if heat can produce mechanical motion,

[4] E.g., Rabbi Shemayah Hillel and, somewhat later, Archbishop James Ussher.

stopping mechanical motion will produce heat, and the sun's heat might easily be maintained by a steady flow of meteorite impacts. In principle this is a possible explanation.

The next step was to find out how many meteorites were needed to support the observed amount of energy released from the sun. The result was a curious coincidence: about the mass of the earth every century would be needed. Two objections could be raised immediately. One was that such a high concentration of meteoric matter near the sun should be observable. The other was even more serious: such an increase in the mass of the sun would cause the orbital velocities of the planets to increase. An increase of the sun's mass of 1/100 of an earth mass per year would shorten the orbital period of the earth by nearly 2 seconds per year. This would have been discovered, at the latest, at the time of Kepler. Leverrier's amused comment that he did not believe that *"le Soleil déjeune et dine des Astéroïdes"* ("the sun breakfasts and dines on asteroids") becomes understandable in the light of these figures.

The German physicist Hermann von Helmholtz, though he admired Mayer because of the law of the conservation of energy, realized almost at once that Mayer's explanation could not be correct. He admitted that meteorite impacts might contribute to the heat of the sun, but they could not be its main source. It occurred to him that extrasolar material was not needed; the heat could be produced by the material of the sun itself. He stated his "contraction theory" for the first time in 1854 and continued to work on it for a long time. Like Friedrich Wilhelm Bessel and Alexander von Humboldt, Helmholtz liked to deliver popular lectures; in one of them, delivered in Berlin in 1871, he gave a fine over-all picture of his conclusions:

If the mass of the sun had once been diffused in space and had then been condensed—that is, had fallen together under the influence of mutual gravitational attraction—the resultant motions were destroyed by friction and collision with the production of heat. The new world formed by such condensation must have acquired a reservoir of heat, not just of considerable but of colossal magnitude. Calculation shows that . . . the temperature might have been raised to 28 million degrees [centigrade] if such quantity of heat could ever have been present in the sun at one time. This cannot be assumed, for such an increase in temperature would be a great obstacle to condensation. It is probable that a great deal of this heat, while being produced by condensation, was radiated into space before the condensation was complete. But the heat which the sun could have developed by its condensation would have been sufficient to account for the current rate of expenditure for not less than 22 million years in the past. And the sun is by no means as dense as it can become . . . the density of the sun, owing probably to its enormous temperature, is less than a quarter of the mean density of the earth. We may, therefore, assume that the sun will still continue in its condensation. Even if it only attained the density of the earth—though it will probably become far denser in the interior owing to the enormous pressure— this would develop heat sufficient to maintain for an additional 17 million years the same intensity of sunshine as that which is now the source of all terrestrial life.

Hermann von Helmholtz was satisfied with his own theory until his death in 1894. But for the last ten years of his life his theory was no longer acclaimed by others without reservation. The idea was still fine, but the figures were wrong. Astronomers now had better figures for the energy release of the sun, and they were considerably larger than those Helmholtz had used. If one tried to account for these larger figures by the contraction theory, the sun would shrink to an extent which should be measurable. In any event the sun would keep shining at the present rate for only 7 million instead of 17 million years. And *all* the representatives of two other sciences—geology and paleontology—declared unanimously that 22 million years of sunshine in the past was simply not enough. Geologists were fond of quoting from Luke 19:40, "if these [the disciples] were silent, the very stones will cry out." The stones of the geologists, real stones, required a much longer time for their formation; the stones of the paleontologists, fossils, showed a process of evolution which could not possibly have taken place in some 20 million years. The most conciliatory geologists asked for 100 million years of continuous sunshine; the more enthusiastic of the paleontologists wanted about 250 million years. They might themselves have been surprised if they could have learned that their successors of only half a century later calmly took 4000 million years to be the *minimum* age of the earth's crust.

Helmholtz's contemporary, Sir William Thompson (later Lord Kelvin) investigated both Mayer's theory and Helmhotz's in the course of his long scientific career—he held the chair of Natural Philosophy at the University of Glasgow for fifty-three years. At one time he conceived a variant of Mayer's impact theory which had the fate of being featured in popularizations for decades. The annual impact of meteorites was not enough to keep the sun going. Probably the radiation of the sun weakened, but if one assumed resistance to the motion of the planets by interplanetary gas the planets would finally reunite with the sun one by one. Each planetary impact would make the sun flare up again, for varying periods of time depending on the mass of the planet. Assuming that the sun, each time, resumed its current strength, the planet Mercury, for example, would fuel it for 6 years and 219 days. The assumed consumption of the whole solar system made the following table:

Mercury	6 years, 219 days	Jupiter	32,254 years
Venus	83 years, 326 days	Saturn	9,652 years
Earth	95 years, 19 days	Uranus	1,610 years
Mars	12 years, 259 days	Neptune	1,890 years

The disappointing total is less than 46,000 years!

Sir William Thompson then turned to the contraction theory, which held greater promise.

One factor which might provide a clue as to the origin of the sun's heat was the surface temperature of the sun, and many astronomers, especially Father Angelo Secchi and Professor Samuel Pierpont Langley, had expended much work and ingenuity in an effort to discover it. The figures derived by the various researchers, as Dr. M. Wilhelm Meyer resignedly remarked in 1900, had "in common that they all lie between zero and infinity. . . ."

According to Professor Young, "Secchi originally contended for a temperature of about 18,000,000° Fahrenheit (though he afterward lowered his estimate to about 250,000°); Ericsson puts the figure at 4,000,000° or 5,000,000°; Zöllner, Spoerer and Lane name temperatures ranging from 50,000° to 100,000° Fahrenheit, while Pouillet, Vicaire, and Deville have put it as low as between 3,000° and 10,000° Fahrenheit."

One of those who put the temperature quite low—at about 3,000° C. or around 5,500 F., was the Dr. Siemens already mentioned. Siemens also looked for a means of replenishing the sun's energy, one which was continuous as well as unobservable. The hypothesis he advanced in 1882 amounted to a chemical *perpetuum mobile* on a cosmic scale. There was water vapor in space, as well as carbon compounds, all of which would be decomposed into their elements by solar radiation. These elements, hydrogen, oxygen, carbon, and so forth, would be drawn into the sun, there to recombine, releasing heat while doing so. The simple elements would enter the sun at its poles; the recombined elements would be thrown off at the equator, intercepting sunlight and decomposing again.

Today a minimum of half a dozen objections would occur to any physicist in as many seconds; then, *one* main objection was voiced. To provide the amount of gases required to keep the sun's fires burning in such a literal sense, the interplanetary gas would have to be quite dense. Siemens had estimated a maximum density of 1/2000 of the density of our atmosphere at sea level. Others pointed out quickly that about 1/200 of the sea-level density of our atmosphere would be required. But the observed motions of the planets and especially of the smaller comets did not permit an assumption of a density of even 1/20,000.

No doubt there was some gas in space, but the amount was at least a million times too small to make the theory workable.

In contemporary commentary on Dr. Siemens' idea, one can discern a clear note of regret. The impact theory had not worked. The contraction theory had grown doubtful, to say the least. And now the new theory, based on ideas never before tried, collapsed as soon as it was proposed. It was all thoroughly unsatisfactory.

That Antoine Henri Becquerel's chance discovery, made in 1896, that uranium compounds fogged securely wrapped photographic plates, might have a bearing on both the age of the earth and the heat of the sun was something nobody could have predicted.

21

STARS, CLUSTERS, AND

GALAXIES

THE proper words to introduce a chapter on the history of the investigation and understanding of the stars around us were written over a century ago by Alexander von Humboldt in his *Kosmos*: "Just as we, in our forests, see the same species of tree in all stages of growth and derive from their simultaneous existence the impression of gradual development, we also recognize in the garden of the worlds in space the various stages of the gradual development of the stars."

In this sentence the aged scientist expressed a thought that was still resented by many of his contemporaries, namely that the stars are not eternal.

However, astronomers had by that time developed a classification according to age. There were brightly shining blue-white stars like Sirius, evidently vigorous young stars at the peak of their power. The next type, the yellow-white stars of which our sun was a good example, were somewhat older, still shining vigorously but slowly aging. Much of their original heat had been radiated away and the replacement process, whatever it was, had not been quite able to make up for the loss. The orange-colored stars, typified by Betelgeuse, were evidently still older, while the deeply red stars were so old as to be feeble, just barely able to still shine. Logic demanded that there should be a fifth class, the stars that no longer shone. But logic was not needed; Bessel in Königsberg had already proved the existence of a "dark star."

Interestingly enough, it was a close neighbor of the bright star Sirius. Sirius had been well observed and Bessel, in 1834, assembled the observations and saw that its motion was not a straight line; it seemed to be wavelike. To make certain, Bessel had his assistants measure the precise position of Sirius at regular intervals, and ten years after his first suspicion he was sure that Sirius was a binary. The wavelike motion could be explained only by the assumption that Sirius and another star moved around their common center of gravity, taking 50 years to complete a full revolution. Since "Sirius B," as it soon came to be called, could not be found even with the best telescopes it had to be a non-luminous star.

The fact that the "Companion of Sirius" was later discovered did not at first influence the reasoning; it only proved that Sirius B was not yet completely dark. Because of its close proximity to the very bright Sirius A its own brightness could not yet be measured. Somewhat later the masses of the two could be determined, Sirius A being about 2½ times the mass of the sun, and Sirius B about 95 per cent of the sun's mass.

But of course the stars could not have begun as stars of the type of Sirius A. They began as unformed nebulosities, the type of sky object which had caused Messier to make his catalogue and which had intrigued Sir William Herschel. Immanuel Kant had been the first to assume that suns and planetary systems began as unformed matter which filled all space, and forty-one years later, the Marquis de Laplace had worked out a similar concept with more detail in his *Exposition du Système du Monde* (Paris, 1796). The two systems were actually quite different—Kant had postulated completely unformed matter, chaos, while Laplace began with a *rotating* nebula with a dully glowing sun in the center—but nineteenth-century writers considered them the same and started speaking of "the" Kant-Laplace Theory. Though French authors often objected to this designation, probably because it implied that the Prussian Kant had been the predecessor of the Frenchman Laplace, the habit of speaking of the combined theory has persisted to this day. The essence of both theories is that a nebula was taken to be an unborn star, even though different theorists introduced differences of detail.

It is worth mentioning that one passage in Kant's *General Natural History and Theory of the Heavens* (p. 103 of the first edition, Königsberg, 1755) makes it quite clear that Kant, not an observer himself, considered some of the nebulosities described by others to be "other Milky Ways," distinct from those which might condense into suns and solar systems. In making this distinction Kant proved himself to be at least a century ahead of his time.

The two leading examples, though Kant did not mention them by name, was the Great Nebula in Andromeda, first mentioned by Simon Marius, and the Great Nebula in Orion, first mentioned by Johann Baptist Cysat. The Andromeda nebula was observed with special attention by Messier, by Sir William Herschel, by the Earl of Rosse,[1] and by

[1] William Parsons, the third Earl of Rosse, used the famous "Leviathan of Parsonstown," a Newtonian refractor with a mirror 6 feet in diameter and a

G. P. Bond, who wrote a special *Account of the Nebula in Andromeda* in 1848. Herschel and Lord Rosse, and later Bond, agreed that the Andromeda nebula could be "partially resolved," that is, that the stars composing it could be seen separately in some areas. Bond counted 1500 individual stars, but most astronomers reserved judgment as to whether those 1500 stars were part of the nebula or faint and distant stars positioned in the line of sight. At the beginning of the twentieth century the nature of the Andromeda nebula was still under debate. Spectrograms gave a continuous spectrum like that of the sun, and hence were evidence that the "nebula" was a distant cluster of stars. But photographs agreed with the pictures that had been drawn to explain Laplace's hypothesis of the formation of a solar system; they showed several concentric rings, not all complete, surrounding a near-spherical central mass. The spectroscopic findings were correct; the telescope used for taking the photographs was simply not powerful enough. We now know that the Andromeda nebula is another galaxy, in fact our neighbor in space.

The Orion nebula was first pictured by Huygens in his *Systema Saturnium,* 1659, though not well. The first good picture was drawn by Sir John Herschel at the Cape of Good Hope; an even better one was by Lord Rosse. In the case of the Orion nebula one can discern progress from the titles of the publications. The early ones are general: William Lassell's *Observations of the nebula of Orion* (1854); *Observations de la grande nebuleuse d'Orion* (1862) by Otto Struve in collaboration with Liapounov; and Father Secchi's *Sulla nebulosa di Orioni* (1868). But in 1882 Edward Holden, later director of the Lick Observatory, published a *Monograph on the central parts of the nebula in Orion,* and since then the titles have become even more specific. The Orion nebula is actually gas, and part of our galaxy, though about 1900 light-years distant.

Gradually it became clear which "nebulosities" actually deserved that name and belonged to our galaxy, and which were other galaxies, enormous aggregations of stars like our own. At first these were called "extragalactic nebulae," then "island universes," and finally just galaxies. (The term "metagalaxy" means the observable universe with all the known galaxies in it; Harlow Shapley carefully refers to the observable universe as "the inner metagalaxy.") These galaxies are mostly spirals, megaparsecs distant. A few objects outside our galaxy have irregular shapes, including the two Magellanic Clouds, which are comparatively near.

---

focal length of 52 feet, which he built at Birr Castle in 1845. It was mostly used for Messier objects.

The nebulosities belonging to our galaxy are divided into three types. Those of the first type, which include the one in Orion are called Irregular Nebulae. Their color is usually faintly blue or green and they are usually illuminated by stars shining inside them. In the case of the Pleiades not much gas is left between the stars, but the connection between the stars of the Pleiades cluster and the nebula is obviously intimate, suggesting that such nebulosities may form star clusters as well as single stars.

The second type has the rather misleading name of Planetary Nebulae. The nebulae have nothing to do with planets but because they are more or less circular, in a small telescope they look like planets. The center of a planetary nebula is normally occupied by a star which makes the gas visible. The Dark Nebulae, the third type, are not illuminated by stars inside them but are seen because they blot out the light of objects farther distant than they are. Naturally they show up best when they blot out a section of the Milky Way. Some of these dark nebulae are probably only about 100 parsecs away from us; they are believed to consist wholly or mainly of dust.

To complete the listing of the objects which are not stars, the globular clusters must be mentioned; of all the objects at stellar distances they are both the strangest and the most wonderful. The globular cluster in Hercules (M-13 in Messier's catalogue) is a typical example, although more than a hundred are now known. A very large number of stars, more than 100,000, form a sphere in the center of which they are so densely packed that their distances from one another may be less than 1000 star diameters. The dense inner portion of a globular cluster is surrounded by a rapidly thinning star field which shares the cluster's motion, if any. When the clusters were first identified as a special, *very* special, kind of object, they were assumed to be outside the galaxy. Some astronomers classed them as equals with the spiral galaxies and called them spherical galaxies. Considering them as being outside the galaxy was correct, but they are not a special type of galaxy; they belong to our own, even though they are separated from the galactic lens.[2]

The clusters inside our galaxy are much smaller both in volume of space occupied and in the number of stars; they are called open clusters. The Pleiades are a typical example. There is probably no reason to make a distinction between an open cluster and a moving cluster, as is often done (for example in Norton's *Star Atlas*). A moving cluster is defined as a group of stars which show a close relationship by moving in the

[2] A few true "spherical galaxies" were discovered later.

same direction with equal or nearly equal velocities. Their common motion probably points to a common origin, which most likely also holds true for the open clusters. In short, a "moving cluster" is probably an "open cluster" that is near us. There is one that is so wide that we are passing through it right now: the Ursa Major cluster, which consists of all but two stars of the constellation Big Dipper (Beta, Gamma, Delta, Epsilon, and Zeta Ursae Majoris), Sirius, Delta Leonis, Beta Eridani, Beta Aurigae and Alpha Corona Borealis. To locate all these stars in the sky you have to look in opposite directions, since our solar system is passing through the cluster. But our sun is *not* a part of it; it is moving in a different direction.

The classifications and explanations reported in the last few pages were mainly the work of the twentieth century, though the actual discoveries had of course been made earlier. But along with a legacy of lists of nebulosities and other useful data the twentieth century also inherited a number of individual strange cases, all of which required closer investigation and, if at all possible, explanations as well.

Let's begin with one that has already been mentioned, Bessel's dark Companion of Sirius, which then turned out not to be dark after all.[3] As has been reported, the mass of the faint Companion was found to be nearly equal to that of our sun. If it had also had the sun's luminosity there would have been no problem. But its luminosity was found to be only 1/10,000 of that of Sirius A, which has a luminosity 35½ times that of our sun. The luminosity of a star depends on two factors: its surface area, that is to say its size, and its surface temperature; a hotter star will look brighter than a cooler star of the same size. The figures derived for Sirius A were quite reasonable. It was hotter at the surface than our sun and also somewhat larger, with a diameter of about 1,330,000 miles, compared to the 865,000 miles of our sun.

But the figures for Sirius B were *not* reasonable. It was difficult to see; hence it evidently was both smaller than the sun and of a lower surface temperature. The assumption that its surface temperature was half that of the sun—one could not go much lower without making it literally dark—resulted in a diameter of 180,000 miles. But its mass was nearly equal to that of the sun; its average density would have to be 150 times that of water, *twenty-two* times as high as the densest metal known! This made no sense. Better measurements were required, and in 1915, when Sirius A and Sirius B were about as far apart as they can be as seen from Earth, Dr. W. S. Adams of Mount Wilson Ob-

---

[3] The same happened to the "Companion of Procyon," also detected by Bessel and later seen.

servatory made them. For those who had expected a "sensible" solution things moved from bad to worse. Sirius B was not one of the feeble deep-red stars, as had been both expected and hoped since it would then have a reasonable size and density. Dr. Adams found that Sirius B had a higher surface temperature than our sun, radiating almost four times as much energy from each square foot of its surface.

But if it radiated that strongly and still had only 1/360 the luminosity of our sun it was not just small, it was tiny. Calculation, no matter how often repeated and checked for slipped decimal points, gave a diameter of approximately 24,000 miles, just three times that of earth. In volume it was smaller than our large outer planets! But with a mass 95 per cent of the sun's, its average density became 65,000 times that of water.

This was impossible. But it was evidently the case. Hence there had to be an explanation. There was one, but not in 1915.

Another enigma, or set of enigmas, inherited by the twentieth century, is the variable stars, stars of changing brightness. They violate a concept that the classical astronomers had taken for granted, namely that any star had a given brightness. If stars did not shine with the same brightness night after night, Hipparchos could never have conceived his scheme for arranging stars by magnitudes.

The first man to notice the changes in brightness of the star Algol was Gemiano Montanari of Padua, who published a report about it in 1672. Sixty years later, Maraldi, as well as Christfried Kirch, noticed it, but the credit for the first thorough investigations is given to John Goodricke of York. Goodricke was deaf and dumb and he died very young— at not quite twenty-two—but his eyesight was good; it may have been his disabilities which led him to astronomy. His report appeared in the *Philosophical Transactions* for 1783:

The first time I saw it vary was Nov. 12, 1782, between 8 and 9 o'clock at night, when it appeared of about the 4th magnitude; but the next day it was of the 2nd magnitude, which is its usual appearance. On December 28, I perceived it to vary again thus; at $5\frac{1}{2}^h$ in the evening, it was about the 4th magnitude, as on the 12th of Nov. but at $8\frac{1}{2}^h$ I was much surprised to find it so quickly increased as to appear of the 2nd magnitude.

Goodricke established that the interval from minimum to minimum is about 15 minutes less than 69 hours and that Algol is fainter than second magnitude for 7 hours. He concluded by saying:

If it were not perhaps too early to hazard even a conjecture on the cause of this variation, I should imagine it could hardly be accounted for otherwise than either by the interposition of a large body revolving around Algol, or some kind of motion of its own, by which part of its body, covered with spots or such like matter, is periodically turned towards the earth.

Sir William Herschel did not at first like the explanation of a periodic eclipse by a dark and large body revolving around Algol, but after he made his own studies on binaries, he admitted that Goodricke was probably right. Researches in recent decades have fully confirmed Goodricke's conjecture, with the slight correction that the other star is not dark but faintly luminous. But, of course, a weak lamp placed in front of a bright lamp will dim the bright one; Algol was the first example of what is now called an "eclipsing variable."

Two years after his observations of Algol, Goodricke found another variable, the star labeled *delta* in the constellation of Cepheus. He established the time interval from maximum brightness to the next maximum as 5 days, 8 hours, and 37½ minutes (the modern value is 5 days, 8 hours, 47 minutes, 27 seconds). He noticed that Delta Cephei behaved differently from Algol. Algol stayed bright for quite some time, dimmed for 7 hours, and then returned to its normal brightness. Delta Cephei did not remain at the same brightness at any time. It reached its brightest (apparent magnitude of 3.3, as established later) and then immediately began to fade, dimming steadily until, after not quite 4 days, the lowest point (apparent magnitude slightly above 4.6) was reached. Then it brightened again, but needed only 1 day to return to full brightness. Then the cycle started over again.

All attempts to explain such a change by an eclipsing dark companion failed utterly. If the change was caused by an eclipse the light curve would be symmetrical; that is to say, the return to full brightness should take as long as the dimming to the faintest stage. Minor differences could have been accounted for by tricky orbits of the two stars around each other. There was the theoretical possibility of a triple system— one bright star, one dimmer star, and one almost dark— but to the best of my knowledge nobody then tried to work out the details of such interplay. And while improved and larger telescopes finally enabled astronomers to see the "dark" companions of other stars, Delta Cephei stubbornly remained single.

The spectroscope, instead of being helpful, only made things more mysterious. At its brighest Delta Cephei showed itself as belonging to spectral class F_4; at its dimmest it was spectral class G_6. Now class F_4 means that the surface temperature is about 7000° C., while G_6 corresponds to a surface temperature of about 5000° C. The star not only changed its brightness, which was annoying enough since it could not be explained, it also changed its *type*. To use a zoological comparison, it was as if it changed from giraffe to okapi and then back again to giraffe. If there were such an animal some zoologists would be utterly fascinated by it and devote all their time to the puzzle, while others would try to ignore it by concentrating on other animals. Both these attitudes could be found among astronomers sixty and seventy years ago. Some exerted much ingenuity trying to find an explanation, while others were visibly annoyed by the existence of the variable stars and advocated doing "something useful" until more was known.

Most of the credit for lengthening the lists of variable stars belongs to Friedrich Wilhelm Argelander, a pupil of Bessel. Argelander, his assistants, and his pupils were hard-working astronomers themselves; in addition, Argelander broadened the basis in 1844 by an *Aufruf an die Freunde der Astronomie* (Appeal to the Friends of Astronomy). He urged interested laymen to acquire telescopes and to assist the professional astronomers by making such observations as could be performed effectively with small instruments and for which observatories could not spare the time, since the bigger instruments were needed for more difficult work. Many of the groups of amateur astronomers of today can, ultimately, be traced to the example of the first such groups stimulated by Argelander. Because of this work a total of 225 variable stars were known in 1889.

The next problem was how they should be classified. Edward Charles Pickering, the fourth director of the Harvard College Observatory, suggested in 1881 (in *Proceedings of the American Academy of Arts and Sciences,* vol. XVI) that five classes should be established. His first consisted of "new" or "temporary" stars which showed an enormous increase in brightness, but only once (as far as was then known). The second, named after Mira Ceti, showed a pronounced change in brightness and a long interval between changes. The third class was that of stars with only minor and irregular fluctuations (possibly explained by very pronounced "sunspot" maxima). The fourth class was short-period variables of the Delta Cephei type, and the fifth class variables of the type of Algol.

Pickering's scheme was not well received in Europe. Rudolf Wolf took the position, for example, that the Algol-type stars should not be called variables at all, since the star did not change brightness but merely was eclipsed—just as "visual binary" is not a true binary but only looks like a double star because the two stars are nearly in the same line of sight. Other astronomers rejected the inclusion of the novae, assuming these to be the result of a collision between faint or dark stars.

Though custom still retains the Algol-type stars among the variables, their special nature is usually stressed.

In the standard catalogue published in 1919 by Gustav Müller and Ernst Hartwig, there were 131 variables of the Algol type, which are in reality common stars occulted now and then by others. The Beta Lyrae type, regularly varying in mostly small periods between two equal maxima and two unequal minima, numbered 22 stars. The continuously changing stars of short period, called "Cepheids" after Delta Cephei, accounted for 169 items. The largest number, more than 600, were strongly variable red stars with periods of the order of one year, called "Mira type" after the first discovered "wonderful star of the Whale" (Pannekoek, *op. cit.*, p. 436).

By the time Müller and Hartwig compiled their catalogue one very long step had been made toward the solution of many stellar riddles. As has so often happened in the history of science the step was made by two people independently. In this case both Ejnar Hertzsprung [4] of Potsdam and Henry Norris Russell of Cambridge arranged the better-known stars in the form of a diagram which is now known as the Hertzsprung-Russell diagram. Both began their work just before the outbreak of the first World War. Both compared the absolute magnitudes of the stars with their spectral classes, which are actually designations of the surface temperatures.

Probably both entered our sun on the diagram first, at the point where the lines for absolute magnitude (4.8) and for special class (G) intersect. This produced a dot not quite in the center of the diagram. Sirius, of stellar class A and greater absolute magnitude, made a dot to the left and somewhat higher up than the sun. As the entries progressed it could be seen that very many stars fitted the diagram along a line indicated by the positions of Sirius and the sun, running diagonally from the upper left to the lower right. This line, which became known as the Main Sequence, began at the top left with very hot stars of great luminosity and ended at bottom right with cool red stars of spectral type M and very low luminosity.

That there was any pattern at all might be counted as the first surprise. But others followed. That the M-type red stars fitted at the bottom of the Main Sequence looked quite logical. But a number of M-type stars, though cool, proved to be quite luminous and produced a cluster of dots near the upper right-hand corner of the diagram. Since they were cool their high luminosity could be accounted for only by very large size and they logically came to be called the Red Giants. The faint red stars at the bottom of the Main Sequence were labeled Red Dwarfs. The Companion of Sirius with its strange characteristics did not fit into the Main Sequence either. It was hotter than the sun, which placed it

---

[4] In 1909 Hertzsprung surprised himself and the scientific world by discovering that Sirius keeps pace with the Ursa Major stars.

farther to the left in the diagram. But its luminosity was far less, which made it slide down. Stars like Sirius B ended up in the lower left-hand corner and came to be called White Dwarfs.

As for the cepheids, they belonged on about the same vertical line as the sun, but were higher up in the diagram, to the left of the Red Giants.

Still farther to the left, but at the same level as the cepheids, was another group of variables. These greatly resemble the cepheids, but while the cepheids all have periods of more than one day, these variables, first found in the globular clusters, have periods of less than one day, in some cases of only a few hours. Hertzsprung suggested that only cepheids with a period longer than one day should have that name. Harlow Shapley agreed that the subdivision, though arbitrary, should be made "merely as a convenience." He suggested the label "cluster-type variables," even though "there is at present no evidence of real differences between the two classes." The term now used is "cluster variables," which is slightly misleading, since these stars do not exist only in globular clusters, but have also been found inside the galactic lens.

All this was indubitably interesting; the question was what conclusions could be drawn from the arrangement. The very large number of stars along the diagonal called the Main Sequence indicated that these were the "normal" stars, as the majority is usually considered the norm. That the others were in some way unusual had been obvious all along; the Hertzsprung-Russell diagram showed why. They were either too hot or too cool for their size, or, like the cluster variables and the cepheids, did not stay in one spot in the diagram. In a carefully drawn diagram the cepheids should be represented as short lines, varying in length to show the degree of fluctuation, and the Main Sequence stars, the giants, and the dwarfs as dots.

Because of their habit of changing from bright to dim and back again, Sir James Jeans on one occasion called the cepheids "lighthouse stars." It was a prophetic designation if there ever was one; the cepheids became the guide stars of stellar astronomy.

In 1912 Henrietta S. Leavitt published a tabulation of twenty-five cepheids in the Lesser Magellanic Cloud. Many more variables in the Cloud were known, but the minima and maxima of these twenty-five had been measured. The one with the shortest period had one of 1.253 days; twenty had periods ranging from 1¾ to 13½ days; and four had longer periods: 16.75, 31.94, 65.8, and 127 days respectively. The tabulation proved what had been only suspected: a relationship between the period and the magnitude. The longer the period, the brighter the star.

The reason the very difficult investigation of the cepheids in the Lesser Magellanic Cloud was needed to prove this relationship is really quite simple. The cepheids in our "stellar neighborhood" are, naturally, at greatly varying distances, and the unfortunate fact is that even the nearest cepheid [5] is too far away for measuring its distance by the method Bessel had successfully used.

But the Magellanic Clouds are far enough away so that the position of individual stars in the Cloud does not matter, just as the distance between any of the inhabitants of Chicago and of Cape Town can be considered to be the same, regardless of where in the two cities an individual happens to be. Over a distance as great as that, a star in the Cloud which *looked* brighter than another star in the Cloud evidently *was* brighter.

If there happened to be a cepheid—even one—at a distance that could be measured by the method of Bessel, Henderson, and Struve— and with modern instruments that method could be applied for as much as 100 light-years—the cepheids would have provided a fine distance scale in our own galaxy. The distance to every star would not have been measurable then, but it could have been found wherever a cepheid pulsates—a term to be taken literally as first advocated by Harlow Shapely in the *Astrophysical Journal* in 1914. But since no cepheid is near enough to be subjected to the classical method for distance measurement the size of our own galaxy remained a puzzle for a number of decades even after Miss Leavitt's tabulation was made.

While Sir William Herschel had tried to visualize the shape of our island universe, he had not made a guess about its dimensions. The first astronomer to try was Jacobus Cornelis Kapteyn who began a survey of the Milky Way in 1906. Photographing it in sections he carried out a star count. Disregarding those stars which were obviously nearer and just projected against the background of the Milky Way, he assumed that all the far and dim stars were of the same size and he then calculated how far away they had to be to appear as tiny dots of light on the plate.

In the course of his work, Kapteyn must have thought often of the example used in the schoolbooks of his native country to explain the appearance of the Milky Way. The example—it is usually credited to Immanuel Kant, but I failed to find the original source—runs as follows: Take a large silver coin, a Thaler piece (a five-gulden piece in Kapteyn's case), and imagine that you can see the silver molecules composing

---

[5] It happens to be Polaris, with a period of 4 days. But the variation is only about 10 per cent of its average brightness and therefore invisible to the naked eye. The estimated distance is 800 light-years.

the coin. Then imagine yourself small enough to be an inhabitant of one of these silver molecules, one located near the center of the coin and about halfway through its thickness. If you looked in the direction of the face or the back of the coin the silver molecules would seem to be scattered over the sky. And since these molecules would be comparatively near to you, they would look quite bright. But in the direction of the rim of the coin there would be so many that to your view they would coalesce into a distant silvery haze. Obviously, if your home molecule was not near the coin's center, the silvery haze would be denser in one direction and not so dense in the opposite direction.

Kapteyn's photographs and star counts seemed to confirm this example. The brightness all around, and the relative crowding, were about the same, indicating that our solar system was near the center of the whole. And then, as had been noted back in 1600, "the *via lactea* runs through the middle of the heaven's roundness," which simply meant that our solar system is also near the halfway point of the thickness of the galaxy. Kapteyn's conclusions were that the galaxy has a lenticular shape 23,000 light-years in diameter and with a maximum thickness of 6000 light-years in the center. The only disturbing fact was the distribution of the globular clusters. One should expect them to be evenly distributed, in which case, seen from the center, every section of the sky should contain about the same number. But the globular clusters crowded together in one direction; more of them could be counted in the constellations Sagittarius and Scorpio than in all the other areas taken together. This *might* indicate an off-center location for us. On the other hand, they might just happen to be unevenly distributed.

All the progress made up to 1920 can be summed up by a description of a debate on "The Scale of the Universe," which took place at the National Academy of Sciences in Washington, D.C., on April 26, 1920.[6] The two speakers were Harlow Shapley, then thirty-four years old and a member of the staff of Mount Wilson Observatory, and Heber D. Curtis, then director of the Allegheny Observatory. Both had devoted much time to investigations of the Milky Way and of star clusters. Shapley, had made calculations of the distance of globular clusters based on Miss Leavitt's work, from which globular cluster M-13 (in Hercules) seemed to be 36,000 light-years away.

Shapley opened the debate. Since the distance to M-13 had been determined he could estimate the distances of the other globular clusters by assuming that they were of about the same size as M-13 so that their

[6] Published in the *Bulletin* of the National Research Council, vol. 2, part 3, 1921.

apparent size was an indicator of their distance. The globular clusters formed a kind of halo around the lens-shaped body of the galaxy, the geometrical center of the halo being also the center of the galaxy. Then the diameter of the galaxy had to be about 300,000 light-years and our sun was *not* near the center, but about 50,000 light-years away from it.

As regards the spiral nebulae Shapley did not (then, that is) think that they were comparable to the galaxy. His argument ran as follows: If object M-31, better known as the Andromeda nebula, were comparable in size to our galaxy it would have to be 10 million light-years distant. But novae had been observed in this spiral. The logical assumption would be that the novae of the Andromeda spiral are the same as those in our own galaxy; then the Andromeda spiral would have to be much closer than 10 million light-years and would be *much* smaller than our galaxy. If the novae in the Andromeda spiral were assumed to be much more luminous than our novae, this would introduce an unknown factor. The necessary conclusion, therefore, was that the spiral nebulae, like the globular clusters, were systems outside the galactic lens, and smaller than our galaxy. Even then there was still a riddle: the "zone of avoidance." No spirals had been found in or near the Milky Way, the edge of our own galaxy. For some reason there did not seem to be anything outside the *edge* of our galaxy.

Heber D. Curtis agreed that the globular clusters were outside our galaxy and he also agreed with Shapley's figures for the *relative* distances of the clusters. But he doubted the actual distance derived by Shapley (and he did not trust any calculation based on cepheids). M-13 was probably about 3600 light-years away (one tenth of Shapley's figure) and all the other distances shrank to the same extent. Hence the size of the galaxy in Curtis's picture agreed well with Kapteyn's estimate. But Curtis accepted the spirals as objects comparable to our galaxy. Shapley had stated in earlier papers, Curtis said, that the nearer spirals were probably 20,000 light-years away. Accepting "the general principle of approximate equality in size for celestial objects of the same class," the distance to M-31 would be about half a million light-years and the novae in it would have an absolute magnitude at maximum of minus 4, which agreed well with the absolute magnitude of minus 3 of four novae *of known distance* in our own galaxy. If we accept the spiral nebulae as systems like our galaxy and of about the same size, there is an easy explanation for the zone of avoidance. Many spirals show a dark lane along their edge (this, of course, can be seen only on such spirals that happen to present edgewise views to us), a lane indicative of obscuring matter. Most probably our own galaxy is also surrounded by such a ring of obscuring matter which simply blots out distant spirals in its area.

We now know that both disputants were partly right. Curtis was correct in considering the spirals other galaxies; Shapley was more nearly correct as far as dimensions were concerned. Both made the mistake of thinking that the space outside the Milky Way galaxy is perfectly transparent. It is not; there is a small amount of light-absorbing interstellar matter present and the glare of M-13 is weakened by absorption as well as by distance. Hence the latest distance determination puts M-13 at about 25,000 light-years, 11,000 light-years closer than Shapley's figure. The diameter of our galaxy has been reduced even more; it is now given as 100,000 light-years. The reason Kapteyn had obtained a smaller figure was that he thought he could see (and photograph) the whole galaxy. Kapteyn's figure was correct for the portions which could be seen, but large sections are obscured to our view by interstellar matter, a fact not then known.

Kapteyn was also right in placing the solar system in the approximate center of "his" galaxy, that is, of the area that can be observed visually. It is now known that we are located in one of the spiral arms of our galaxy, approximately 30,000 light-years from the true center.

For many years the distance to the Andromeda galaxy was given as 750,000 light-years, one and a half times as far as Curtis had estimated. The 750,000-light-year distance to the Andromeda spiral had been the direct outcome of the 100-inch telescope on Mount Wilson. When, in 1924, Edwin Powell Hubble took photographs with the then new instrument the outer arms were definitely resolved into stars, cepheids among them. And this other galaxy, now definitely proved to be one, also had its outer halo of globular clusters. But while the Andromeda spiral was definitely a galaxy—and all the other spirals had to be accepted as galaxies, too—it seemed somewhat smaller than ours. This should have made astronomers suspicious but apparently it didn't until 1942 when Walter Baade went after the Andromeda galaxy once more with the 100-inch telescope. He had an advantage which Hubble lacked: the second World War was on and Los Angeles was blacked out.

This time the inner portions of M-31 could be resolved. Baade saw to his great surprise that the bright stars of the central core were reddish while those of the spiral arms were bluish. Different kinds of stars were predominant in the two areas. Baade called the stars of the spiral arms Population I because they had been discovered first, and the stars of the central portion Population II.

The difference between the two stellar populations turned out to be profound, but it took years of work—and the 200-inch instrument on Palomar Mountain—to establish the facts. The underlying reason for the difference seems to be the presence of dust in space. In the spiral arms there is a great deal of dust and as a consequence the stars of Population I are of many ages. Some are apparently quite young, possibly recently condensed; others are somewhat older, like our sun and Sirius. And some seem to have been rejuvenated, stars which have moved through dust clouds, sweeping up matter and emerging as Blue-White Giants. But the Population II stars have dust-free surroundings and seem to be more or less the same age.

Nobody had ever before differentiated between Population I (in dusty space) and Population II (in virtually dust-free space). Hence nobody had taken into consideration that the stars in the globular clusters and the Magellanic Clouds were Population II. Cepheids occur in both populations but could one assume that the Population I cepheids were the same as those of Population II? Baade then began to compare the Population I cepheids in the spiral arm of our galaxy where the sun is located with cepheids in globular clusters, the nearest accessible Population II cepheids. The ones in the Magellanic Clouds are farther away and the ones in the center of our galaxy (which would be the nearest) are obscured by interstellar matter, dust of the spiral arms. The result of his studies was that Miss Leavitt's period-luminosity curve was still good for Population II cepheids, but it did not apply to Population I cepheids. The cepheids of the dusty regions are between four and five times as bright for the same period of fluctuation.

What had gone wrong was quite simple.

The distance to the Andromeda galaxy had been based on the cepheids in its spiral arms, and these had been compared to cepheids in the globular clusters. But cluster-cepheids are Population II; the cepheids in the dusty arms of the Andromeda galaxy are the far brighter Population I cepheids. To appear as dim as they did, the Andromeda galaxy had to be farther away, about 2 million light-years. The other spirals, with distance estimates based on the distances of nearby spirals, also had to be about three times as distant as had previously been thought. Of course the dimensions had to be increased, too. If the Andromeda galaxy was 2 million light-years distant instead of 750,000, it had to be larger than had been thought. It is, therefore, not smaller than the Milky Way galaxy, but actually somewhat larger.

None of these corrections applied to our Milky Way galaxy. Its extent had been based on the corrected distances of the globular clusters, which were not changed.

While Shapley, Curtis, Hubble, and Baade were working on our galaxy and others, another puzzle much nearer home was also solved, namely the source of the sun's heat. It proved to be a problem for the physicist, which explains why the "pure" astronomers of the past could not solve it.

Let us recall some dates: in 1842 Mayer had published his law of the conservation of energy, stating that the sum total of the energy in the universe was unchanging. In 1896 Becquerel discovered what came to be called radioactivity. And in 1905 Albert Einstein stated a new law, namely the equivalence of mass and energy.

This could be called an extension of Mayer's law. Energy had been considered indestructible. Most physicists and all chemists were certain that matter was equally indestructible, although nobody's name is specifically attached to this statement. Now Einstein's equation said that matter could conceivably be destroyed, but it then had to appear as energy. It now was the *sum* of energy and matter in the universe which was unchanging, but matter might be converted into energy and energy might be condensed into matter.

Beginning in about 1920, astronomers were suggesting that the energy of the sun was probably due to "atomic transformations." But this was only a theoretical concept. Nobody knew whether such transformations actually occurred, and in 1925 some physicists were still saying cautiously that "the release of atomic energy, *if* it existed, would probably require as much energy to bring about as would be released." But by 1930 there were theoretical papers stating that if four hydrogen atoms could be fused into one helium atom the problem of the sun's energy supply would be solved.

The theoretical work on the fusion reaction made it clear that this reaction could conceivably take place in the interior of a star, where enormous pressures could be expected to produce the necessary temperatures. It was not something that might be accomplished in a laboratory, but laboratory research might be expected to produce information that would lead to an understanding of the atom's structure. And in the course of such experimentation Enrico Fermi, in 1934, accomplished the fission of uranium. Fission had *not* been predicted by theory; hence neither Fermi nor his fellow researchers knew just what caused their instruments to show sudden releases of energy. By 1940 a few physicists knew what had occurred not only in Fermi's laboratory but also in the laboratory of Otto Hahn and Fritz Strassmann. They also realized what the outcome of this knowledge could be, which is why, probably for the first time in history, scientific knowledge was kept secret.

The first fission (uranium) bomb was exploded on July 16, 1945, near Alamogordo in New Mexico. Most physicists, as soon as the facts became known, predicted the fusion (hydrogen) bomb; the temperature need to start the fusion reaction could be supplied by the explosion of a fission bomb.

Inside a star the necessary heat is provided by pressure.

The formation of the concept of fusion energy was like the discovery of inertia by Sir Isaac Newton three and a half centuries earlier. A long missing fundamental fact had at last been found; understanding replaced speculation; verifiable theory took the place of uncertain hopes. The life history of a star could be described. Interestingly enough the beginning of this life history is still what Helmholtz thought it to be. We still believe that a star begins as a condensation of gas and dust, condensing by mutual attraction which is helped along to some extent by the radiation pressure of the other, already existing, stars. The very tenuous gas ball, the proto-star, begins to glow for the reasons Helmholtz had advanced a century ago. But when the temperature at the core of the proto-star has grown hot enough the fusion reactions begin to work. The proto-star has acquired a new heat source and is, strictly speaking, no longer a proto-star. It has promoted itself to the status of a true star.

At that moment, according to George Gamow [7] and C. Critchfield, there are two possibilities. The first is that the internal heat expands the star to enormous size, with a diameter comparable to the diameter of the earth's orbit. If this happens, a Red Giant is the result. The other possibility is that the star stays at the bottom of the Main Sequence, gradually growing hotter and brighter. The reason for its increase in heat and luminosity is explained by the so-called shell source model. It works as follows: the fusion of hydrogen atoms into helium atoms (more precisely: hydrogen nuclei into helium nuclei) first takes place in the center of gravity of the star which is also its geometrical center. At the prevailing temperatures the helium nuclei produced no longer react but begin to accumulate. Hence a spherical core of helium forms in the star's center and the fusion reaction takes place on the surface of that core. As the helium core grows larger, its surface grows larger too, and the rate of hydrogen consumption and that of heat production both increase. The interesting result—which is also the precise opposite of what had been thought prior to the discovery of atomic energy—is that an older star will shine more brightly.

---

[7] Gamow has explained much detail for which there is no room here in *The Creation of the Universe* (New York: The Viking Press, first published in 1952 and revised in 1961).

As the reacting surface grows quite large compared to the over-all size of the star, instabilities may occur. Larger amounts of hydrogen will be fused simultaneously and if the amounts are large enough a nova outbreak could result.

A star which has used up its hydrogen and blown away its outer layers in a nova explosion will be hot enough for all its atoms to have lost their electron shells. Then the nuclei will be packed so tightly that superdense matter results, turning the star into a White Dwarf like the Companion of Sirius.

This much is reasonably certain, but there is much debate on fine points, often from viewpoints as different as those expressed in the debate between Shapley and Curtis. One is tempted to say that these debates, if they grow hot enough, are likely to lead to a fusion of the various points of view. But nobody can predict how.

22

LIFE IN THE UNIVERSE AND
THE CONCEPT OF THE
ECOSPHERE

"I HAVE chosen that part of Philosophy which is most likely to excite Curiosity; for what can more concern us, than to know how this World which we inhabit, is made; and whether there be any other worlds like it, which are also inhabited as this is?"

This sentence (in John Glanvill's translation of 1688) is from the preface of a once-famous book. First published in France in 1686, it was *Entretiens sur la Pluralité des Mondes* (Conversations about the Plurality of Worlds), by Bernard le Bovier de Fontenelle, a nephew of Corneille. Bernard de Fontenelle was not quite thirty years old when he wrote this work and it made him famous. It is a bit surprising that he never revised it, though he lived to be a hundred, from 1657 to 1757. But he let it be reprinted and translated into other languages in its original form.

At the time de Fontenelle wrote, the term "philosophy" was often used to designate facts and concepts which we would call "science," and "philosophical thoughts" meant what we would call "scientific speculation." But in this case the word "philosophy" does mean philosophy; up to de Fontenelle's time everything said and written about life on other worlds or the "plurality of worlds" was truly philosophical speculation. The "plurality of worlds" was argued for and against with verve and sometimes with venom, but the purpose of the arguments was not to find the truth but to prove a point, and the scientific facts on which the arguments should have been founded simply were not known. I even have the feeling that the facts, if anybody had known them, would have been pushed aside as irrelevant by many of the disputants.

But while de Fontenelle was correct in calling his book "philosophy," the words "plurality of worlds," had already changed their meaning. To de Fontenelle the term meant about the same as it does to us; the problem of whether there might be life on another planet. But that was not its original meaning. When the Aristotelians made slighting remarks about the Pythagorean concept of the plurality of worlds they had something entirely different in mind.

When Metrodorus of Chios, one of the leading philosophers of the atomistic school during the fourth century B.C., remarked: "It seems absurd that in a large field only one stalk should grow and in an infinite space only one world exist," he did not have the habitability of Mars or Venus in mind. He meant to reinforce the opinion of his predecessor, Demokritos the Abderite, who had stated: "The ordered worlds are boundless and differ in size: in some is neither sun nor moon: in others both are greater than with us, and in yet others more in number. The intervals between the ordered worlds are unequal, here more and there less; some worlds increase, others flourish, and others decay. They are destroyed by colliding one with another. Some ordered worlds are bare of animals and plants, and of all water."

This statement [1] provides a hint as to what the Greek philosophers meant when they spoke of "the world." It was not the earth, nor was it the "universe" in our sense. It was the artificial universe of Aristotle and Hipparchos—now often called the Ptolemaic system—consisting of a central earth, with sun and moon and planets going around it and a spherical star-ornamented enclosure for the whole. Since the discussion dealt with something that does not actually exist, there is no need to go into much detail.

While the Atomists and the Pythagoreans were willing to believe in an infinity of worlds, and the Pythagoreans and a few other philosophers also considered the moon earthlike in nature, the Aristotelians took a diametrically opposed point of view. The moon could not be earthlike, because all "earth" was concentrated in the center of the universe, that is, the planet Earth, and the universe had to be finite and unchanging. Needless to say, Aristotle's dictum dominated all philosophy for many centuries, partly because Aristotle gradually came to be the prime authority, partly because in this particular case he was in full agreement with Plato, and partly, finally, because the idea of a plurality of worlds seemed to be in opposition to Scripture. It is interesting that a germ of doubt arose from a theological concept. How could God's Plenitude be reconciled with just one world? Although he does not

---

[1] Unfortunately the wording has come down to us only at second or third hand, and in excerpts too brief to follow the reasoning very far. Many of the early ideas are known to us only through a book called *Philosophumena* (a "refutation of all heresies") by the early ecclesiastical writer Hippolytus (died c. 235 A.D.). For a discussion of the growth and changes of the ideas involved, see Dr. Grant McColley's "The Seventeenth-Century Doctrine of a Plurality of Worlds," in *Annals of Science*, vol. I (1936), no. 4.

use the term, it must have been thought of this kind which caused St. Augustine to write:

> Mankind should not attempt to understand the infinite extent of space or time existing before creation. Those who imagine infinite time before the world, during which they cannot believe that God did nothing, likewise suppose infinite space outside the world. If they do not cause Deity to rest and not work in this space, they must adopt Epicurus' dreams of innumerable worlds, with this difference: he forms his worlds by the casual coagulation of atoms, but they make all that exists from the handiwork of God. (*De Civitate Dei,* lib. XI, chap. 5.)

All the important names of the late Middle Ages sided with Aristotle and St. Augustine. Among these were Vincent of Beauvais (died c.1264 A.D.), the author of the *Speculum naturale*; Albert von Bollstädt, known as Albertus Magnus and called the *Doctor universalis* (died 1280 A.D.); St. Thomas Aquinas, the *Doctor angelicus* (died 1274 A.D.); and finally the *Doctor mirabilis* Roger Bacon (died 1294 A.D.).

I did not list the dates of the deaths of these eminent scholastics and theologians merely for the sake of completeness. Both Albertus Magnus and Roger Bacon were still alive, when, in 1277, Pope John XXI granted authority to Etien Tempier, bishop of Paris, to condemn the proposition that God could not create a plurality of worlds.[2] As Dr. McColley says: "The power of God definitely overshadows the physics of Aristotle," after this condemnation of a laboriously fashioned attitude. And Richard of Middleton gave the proper theological answer to the statement of the Aristotelians that the heavy earths would come together and collide if there were several; he simply told them that the earths would stay where God put them.

This sudden and admittedly dramatic change must not be misinterpreted to mean that the Church had enthusiastically joined the philosophers who believed in a plurality of worlds. It was merely an official statement that God's Plenitude made such a belief admissable. Many still preferred to believe in one world only.

After Copernicus and Kepler the whole aspect changed; perhaps it became easier to believe in a plurality of worlds because "worlds" were no longer whole "universes" in the Aristotelian sense. With the earth considered a planet among planets the question was simply whether the other planets should be considered "earthlike." The answer, for those who considered the earth a planet, was almost automatically, "Of course."

Since nobody apparently could imagine an uninhabited earth, the

---

[2] *Quod prima causa non posset plures mundos facere.*

acceptance of the other planets as "earthlike" included the acceptance of inhabitants.[3] The first goal of speculations about inhabitants was our moon, and it seems only fitting that such speculations were started by Kepler himself. This statement can be made even though the moon had been supplied with inhabitants by earlier writers. Plutarch had put the souls of the dead on the moon. Lukian of Samosata (usually called Lucian) in 160 A.D. had put large and fantastic armies there but had prefaced his work with the proper warning: "I write of things which I have neither seen nor suffered nor learned from another, things which are not and never could have been, and therefore my readers should by no means believe them." Only a century before Kepler, Lodovico Ariosto, in his *Orlando furioso*—the first 40 cantos appeared in 1516— had described an inhabited valley on the moon. But all these earlier works had been fiction. Kepler speculated.

The book in question was *Somnium* (Sleep), which Kepler worked on, in between bigger and more urgent labors, for decades. It was not printed during his lifetime; Jakob Bartsch, his son-in-law, prepared it for the printer after Kepler's death but also soon died himself, and Kepler's son Ludwig undertook to have it printed. It finally appeared in 1634.[4] In the *Somnium* the moon is called *Levania* (from Hebrew *lebana* or *levana*), and the earth appears as *Volva*; hence all seleites fall into two classes, the *subvolvani,* who have the earth in the sky, and the *privolvani,* who never see the earth.

After describing the sky as seen from the moon, especially sunrise and sunset and the appearance of the earth in the lunar sky, Kepler started speculating about the life forms:

Everything produced by the soil of Levania and everything which runs about the surface is monstrously large in size. Growth is very rapid, and everything is very short-lived because of enormous body mass. The Levanians have no safe and secure established dwelling, but instead wander about their world in troops during the day. When their water is drawn to the

[3] The only exceptions are the planets in the book *Iter ecstaticum coeleste* (Ecstatic Voyage) of Athanasius Kircher, S. J., which was printed in 1656. Kircher was of course obliged to accept the earth as the center of the world and to consider that creation had been restricted to earth. Hence his other planets are not only uninhabited but without any life—their landscapes are shaped in accordance with astrological and (occasionally) mythological concepts. But he considered them solid bodies, not tenuous lights in the sky.

[4] The full title was *Joh. Keppleri Mathematici olim imperatorii SOMNIUM seu Opus posthumum de astronomia lunari.* It was reprinted in Latin in Frankfurt in 1870 as volume VIII of *Joannis Kepleri Astronomia Opera Omnia* and soon after translated for the first time into German by Dr. Ludwig Günther and published in 1898 in Leipzig as *Kepler's Traum vom Mond.* The only English translation is that of Everett F. Bleiler which appeared in a science-fiction anthology called *Beyond Space and Time,* edited by August Derleth (New York: Pellegrini & Cudahy, 1950).

other side of the globe, they follow it, partly on foot, for they have legs longer than a camel's, partly by wing, and partly by means of ships. When a halt of several days is necessary, they crawl into holes and caves, picking whatever type of cave is most suited for their biological needs. . . . [The mention of ships makes it clear that Kepler had intelligent (among other) life forms in mind.]

The bark of trees or the hide of animals, or what corresponds to it, forms the larger part of the body mass. It is spongy and porous, and when one of the creatures is surprised by the heat of the day, the external portion of the fur becomes singed and hard and drops off when evening comes again.— Everything the soil produces (and there is naturally very little upon the ridges of the mountains) comes into existence and perishes during the same day. The vegetation is thus renewed each day. Snake-like forms prevail on Levania. It is marvelous the way they bask in the sun at mid-day, never straying far from their protecting caverns, so that they can retreat into them rapidly, if necessary. . . . Scattered around the landscape, far and wide, are piles of things shaped like pinecones, whose external scales are singed by the heat of the day. At night, or in the remoter shadows, however, these cones produce living creatures.

Most of this must have been written before Kepler received his copy of Galileo's *Sidereus Nuncius,* since reading it caused him to elaborate on his own ideas. In a letter to Father Paulus Guldin, S.J., in St. Gallen, Switzerland (not dated, but mentioning a telescope which was a present from Guldin brought to Kepler by Father Nicolaus Zuccus, S.J., in 1623), Kepler wrote:

Those hollows of the moon first seen by Galilei are, as I show, portions below the general level, like our oceans. But their appearance makes me judge that they are swampy for the greater part. It is there where the Endymionides find the sites for their fortified cities which protect them against the swampiness as well as against the heat of the sun, possibly also against enemies. They do it in the following manner: in the center of the chosen site they put a stout pole to which they attach ropes, their lengths depending on the size of the fortress to be built; the longest [rope] measures five German miles [about 20 statute miles]. Then they walk to the periphery of the future wall which is marked by the end of the rope. Then they amass to pile up the wall, the width of the moat is one German mile at least, the excavated material is, in some cities, taken from the interior only, in others partly from the inside, partly from the outside, building a double wall with a very deep moat in the middle. Every wall returns into itself, forming a circle, because it is given by the distance of the end of the rope from the center post. . . . Whenever the inhabitants feel annoyed by the power of the sun those who live near the center move into the shadow of the outer wall . . . following the shadow for fifteen days they wander about and by this means endure the heat.

This was of course one of the cases in which Kepler was wrong, but it shows how the concept of a solid body in the sky automatically led the thinking people of the seventeenth century to the concept of life and inhabitants.

Two English works [5] soon followed, at least the first of them visibly influenced by the *Somnium*. This fictional work, Bishop Francis Godwin's *The Man in the Moone,* published in 1638. Kepler's influence can be traced by the nationality of the hero and by a mistake. In naming the hero Domingo Gonzales, Bishop Godwin played along with one of Kepler's jokes. In the *Somnium* demons carry the traveler from the earth to the moon, but they have trouble if the earthling is too heavy; hence the demon tells Kepler: "Germans are not suitable, but we have no objection to lean Spaniards." The mistake was this: the hero travels at the rate of 50 leagues (or about 175 miles) per hour and the trip to the moon takes twelve days. This works out to 50,000 miles, the figure given by Kepler. But Kepler meant the then customary German miles (he said so) and 50,000 German miles is about right for the distance from the earth to the moon. Bishop Godwin's figure of 50,000 English miles is far too small.

The other English book, *The Discovery of a World in the Moone* by Bishop Wilkins, is not fiction but philosophical speculation. Its first printing appeared within a few months of *The Man in the Moone.* The book is divided into thirteen "propositions." Since the work unlike Bishop Godwin's has been out of print for centuries, and the original is difficult to find, these "propositions" are listed here; to a modern reader they represent a summary of the book itself:

(I)   That the strangenesse of this opinion [the one stated in the title] is no sufficient reason why it should be rejected, because other certaine truths have beene formerly esteemed ridiculous and great absurdities entertayned by common consent.

(II)   That a plurality of worlds do's not contradict any principle of reason or faith.

(III)   That the heavens doe not consist of any such pure matter which can priviledge them from the like change and corruption, as these inferiour bodies are liable unto.

[5] The full title of Bishop Godwin's book was *The Man in the Moone:/* or / *A Discourse of a Voyage thither* / By / Domingo Gonzales / *The Speedy Messenger.* A French translation appeared in 1648 under the title *L'Homme dans la Lune,* ou, *le Voyage chimérique fait au Monde de la Lune, par* Dominique Gonzalès, *aventurier espagnol.* A German translation, repeatedly reprinted, appeared in 1650 under the title *Der fliegende Wandersmann.* The original English was reprinted in 1937 as Smith College Studies in Modern Languages, xix, no. 1, and again in 1950 in Derleth's anthology *Beyond Time and Space.*
    The full title of Bishop Wilkins's book was *The Discovery / of a World / in the / Moone, / or / A Discourse / Tending, / To Prove, / that 'tis probable there / may be another habitable / World in that Planet* (London, 1638). The second printing is the same as the first; the third printing of 1640 contains an additional chapter dealing with the possible invention of a "flying chariot." The French book *Le Monde dans la Lune, divisé en deux Livres: le premier prouvant que la Lune peut être un Monde: le second que la Terre peut être une plânète,* by le Sieur de la Montagne (Rouen, 1655) is simply a translation of Wilkins's book, though his name is not mentioned. Another French edition (properly credited) appeared in London in 1640, a German translation in 1713.

(IV)   That the Moone is a solid, compacted, opacous body.

(V)   That the Moone hath not any light of her owne.

(VI)   That there is a world in the Moone, hath beene the direct opinion of
         many ancient, with some moderne Mathematicians, and may prob-
         ably be deduced from the tenents of others.

(VII)   That those spots and brighter parts which by our sight may bee dis-
         tinguished in the Moone, doe shew the difference betwixt the Sea
         and Land in that other World.

(VIII)   That the spots represent the Sea, and the brighter parts the Land.

(IX)   That there are high Mountaines, deepe vallies, and spacious plaines
         in the body of the Moone.

(X)   That there is an Atmo-sphaera, or an orbe of grosse vaporous aire,
         immediately encompassing the body of the Moone.

(XI)   That as their world is our Moone, so our world is their Moone.

(XII)   That tis probable there may bee such Meteors belonging to that
         world in the Moone, as there are with us.

(XIII)   That tis probable there may be inhabitants in this other World, but
         of what kinde they are is uncertaine.

The last "proposition" is pervaded by an optimistic attitude which now
sounds prophetic. Some philosophers and theologians, Bishop Wilkins
wrote, have speculated that the Paradise may be in the moon, an idea
about which the Bishop is doubtful. He mentioned it only, he said,

to shew the opinion of others concerning the inhabitants of the Moone, I
dare not my selfe affirme any thing of these Selenites, because I know not
any ground whereon to build any probable opinion. But I thinke that future
ages will discover more; and our posterity, perhaps, may invent some meanes
for our better acquaintance with these inhabitants. . . . I doubt not but that
time who is still the father of new truths, and hath revealed unto us many
things which our Ancestours were ignorant of, will also manifest to our posterity, that which we now desire, but cannot know.

Omitting the works of fiction by Cyrano de Bergerac and by several
English authors,[6] Bernard de Fontenelle represents the next milestone.
The book purports to record the discussions between de Fontenelle and
the Countess D————s at her country seat during one week and is
therefore subdivided into five "evenings." (I have not checked whether
de Fontenelle actually spent a week with the young and beautiful
countess; I prefer to believe that it is true.) After the first "evening,"
which was spent in demolishing the classical geocentric system with
much enthusiasm and levity and explaining the heliocentric system of
Copernicus, de Fontenelle says: "In the Morning, I sent to the Countess's
Apartment, to know how she had rested, and whether the Motion of the

[6] The literary aspect has been treated fully by Marjorie Hope Nicolson in a
number of works, especially in *A World in the Moon* (Smith College Studies in
Modern Languages, XVIII, no. 2, 1936) and *Voyages to the Moon* (New York:
Macmillan, 1948).

Earth had not disturb'd her? She answer'd, she began to be accustom'd to it, and that she had slept as well as Copernicus himself."

The second "evening" is devoted to the moon. De Fontenelle loses no time in getting to the question of whether it may be inhabited.

Well, Madam, *said I*, Since the Sun, which is now immoveable, hath left off being a Planet, and the Earth, which turns round him, is now become one, you will not be surprized when you hear that the Moon is an Earth too, and that she is inhabited as ours is. I confess, *said she,* I have often heard talk of the World in the Moon, but I always look'd upon it as Visionary and meer Fancy. And it may be so still, *said I*. I am in this case as People in a Civil War, where the uncertainty of what may happen makes 'em hold intelligence with the opposite Party; for tho' I verily believe the Moon is inhabited, I live civilly with those who do not believe it; and I am (as some honest Gentlemen in point of Religion) still ready to embrace the prevailing Opinion, but till the Unbelievers have a more considerable Advantage, I am for the People in the Moon.

Continuing in this style, de Fontenelle informed his countess about the earlier ideas about the moon, from Plutarch to his present. The discussion of the moon also occupies the third "evening" since de Fontenelle used the opportunity to discard a number of general arguments against the plurality of worlds.

On the fourth "evening" the inhabitants of Mercury and Venus are discussed. The Countess thinks that it "is easie eniuogh to guess at the Inhabitants of Venus; they resemble what I have read of the Moors of Granada, who were a little black People, scorch'd with the Sun, witty, full of Fire, very Amorus, much inclin'd to Musick & Poetry, and ever inventing Masques & Turnaments in honour of their Mistresses." The author, on the grounds that Venus is closer to the sun than the earth and therefore "receives a more vigorous and active influence," agrees, but adds, "Granada in all its Glory, was a perfect Greenland to it; and your gallant Moors, in comparison with that People, were as stupid as so many Laplanders."

Coming to Mercury, de Fontenelle states that the length of its day was not known but assumes it to rotate very fast because it is so small. Its inhabitants "are yet nearer to the Sun, and are so full of Fire, that they are absolutely mad; I fancy they have no Memory at all . . . make no reflections, and what they do is by sudden starts, and perfect haphazard; in short, Mercury is the Bedlam of the Universe."

"Mars," de Fontenelle continued, "hath nothing that I know of, his Day is not quite an hour longer than ours, but his Year is twice as long as our Year; he is a little less than the Earth; and the Sun seems not altogether so large and so bright to him, as it appears to us; but let us leave Mars, he is not worth our stay." However, the Countess is not quite satisfied with this quick rejection, and after a discussion of Jupiter and its four moons (all assumed to be inhabited), she asks whether Mars has any moons. Bernard de Fontenelle has to reply that it apparently does not but that something may take the place of a moon during the night.

You have seen the Phosphorus . . . how it receives and imbibes the rays of the Sun, and what a great light it will cast in a dark Place: Perhaps Mars hath many great high Rocks, which are so many natural Phosphorus's, which in the day take in a certain provision of light, and return it again at night. . . . Besides, there is a kind of Bird in America, that yields such a light, you may read by it in the darkest night [de Fontenelle meant the large luminous beetles of South America] and who knows but Mars may have great flocks of these Birds, that as soon as it is night, disperse themselves into all parts, and spread from their wings another day.

The fifth and last "evening" is devoted to the explanation that the other stars in the sky are suns, each one probably with a planetary system. It is interesting that de Fontenelle explains the comets as errant planets from other solar systems. Their tails are dismissed as optical illusions, but he avoids explaining just how such an optical illusion can come about.

A little more than 250 years after its first appearance, a stern astronomer characterized de Fontenelle's book as a "piece of Gallic fluff" and had several harsh things to say about it. He forgot how much time had elapsed since its publication and that it had been intended as a popular book in the first place; I also suspect that he had not read it carefully. All the astronomical facts given by de Fontenelle are accurate for his time. Some of his explanations could still be used in popular articles. The fact that Johann Elert Bode translated it into German shows that the book was valued highly in its time. And it is historically important as a proof that late in the seventeenth century it was taken for granted that a planet would be inhabited, mainly "because it is there."

Hard on the heels of the *Entretiens sur la pluralité des mondes* followed another work on the inhabitants of the planets, also speculative of course, but containing more restrained, more "scientific" speculation. Christiaan Huygen's *Kosmotheoros*,[7] which was published posthumous-

---

[7] Its full title was *Kosmotheoros, sive De Terris Coelestibus, earumque ornatu, Conjecturae* (The Hague, 1698). The first English translation (the translator is not named) appeared in Glasgow four years later under the title *Cosmotheoros: or, Conjectures concerning the Inhabitants of the Planets.* The second and enlarged English edition, published in London in 1722, bears the title: *The Celestial Worlds Discovered, or, Conjectures Concerning the Inhabitants, Plants and Productions of the Worlds in the Planets.*

ly. Huygens, in contrast to de Fontenelle, swiftly discarded our moon. It cannot be inhabited because "it has no seas, no rivers, nor clouds, nor air and water." Huygens, though primarily a physicist, used what we would now call a biological approach. In order to be habitable, a planet must, first of all, have liquid water "because water is needed to partake of nutrition." It also must have air "to carry sound to their ears." He then set down a list of thoughts. The size of the "inhabitants" (at first he used the word to mean life in general) has nothing to do with the size of the planet—see the wide range of sizes of the living things on earth. The "inhabitants" must have eyes and ears—in short, senses—in order to bring pleasures (or warnings) to them. As regards "inhabitants" in the stricter sense of intelligent beings, Huygens first defined what characterizes an intelligent being. "Men differ from beasts in the study of Nature," he declared, and then went on to list requirements for intelligent beings: (1) "they must have geometry and arithmetic and writing," (2) "they must have hands to make things," (3) "they must have feet to move around," (4) "they must have houses for protection from weather," and (5) "they must be upright to free their hands for the making of things." But since a rational soul could inhabit many different shapes "it follows not that they have the same shape with us."

The *Kosmotheoros* did not find as many readers as de Fontenelle's book, and the readers it did find said remarkably little about it, possibly because Huygens had said everything that could be said at the time. One man who was much impressed by it was Immanuel Kant, who in 1755 wrote a *General Natural History and Theory of the Heavens, or, an Attempt on the Constitution and the Mechanical Origin of the Whole Universe, discussed on Newtonian Principles.*[8] He concluded his discussion of the origin and construction of the universe with a chapter entitled "On the Inhabitants of the Heavenly Bodies."

College students who have had to read portions of Kant's *Critique of Pure Reason* may be surprised to learn that Kant had a well-developed sense of humor. But his enjoyment of humor is evident in the chapter mentioned above, in which he quotes the following paragraph from the *Kosmotheoros*: "Those creatures which inhabit the forests on the head of a beggar had always considered their habitat as an enormous sphere and believed themselves to be the crown of creation until one day one of them, endowed with a subtler soul by heaven, a small Fontenelle of

---

[8] The original title of the first edition read *Allgemeine Naturgeschichte und Theorie des Himmels, oder, Versuch von der Verfassung und dem mechanischen Ursprunge des ganzen Weltgebäudes nach Newtonischen Grundsätzen abgehandelt* (Königsberg und Leipzig, 1755).

his race, happened to see the head of a nobleman. At once he called all the more intelligent companions of his area and told them with great pleasure: we are not the only living things in all Nature, see, there is another land inhabited by other lice!" This quotation led Kant to philosophize about the arrogance of people in thinking that creation has taken place for their sake. Still, he concluded: "However, most of the planets are certainly inhabited and those which are not, will be at some time."

The nineteenth century, then, began with a well-established background of a philosophical inclination toward inhabited planets. Those who still felt that everything had to have a purpose (one of the roots of astrological thinking, incidentally) considered that Venus and Mars existed for the sake of their inhabitants just as the earth existed for the sake of mankind. Those who rejected such a line of reasoning as simple-minded were still willing to accept inhabitants as a logical consequence of the existence of a suitable planet.

This attitude suggested, first, that one should be alert for signs of habitation, if they could be found. The astronomer Franz von Paula Gruithuisen (already mentioned Chapters 10 and 11) thought that certain lunar formations looked like ruins; it seemed to him that the moon was no longer inhabited but had been at one time in the past.

At about the same time, near the end of the first half of the nineteenth century, the Danish-born astronomer Peter Andreas Hansen slowly began to formulate an idea which he submitted to the Royal Astronomical Society a decade later. It was published by the society in its *Memoris* (XXIV, 1854).

Hansen had been interested in gravitational phenomena, and one of his papers, on the mutual perturbations of Jupiter and Saturn, was rewarded with a prize by the Berlin Academy in 1830. Another, on the disturbances of the orbits of comets, received a prize from the Paris Academy in 1850. In the meantime he had spent many years on the theory of the orbit of our own moon. Early in this work suspicion arose in his mind that the theory did not work out perfectly because there was a missing factor. By about 1852—after the Royal Astronomical Society had awarded him a gold medal for the second time—he thought he had found the answer. The moon was not a sphere. Of course most planets are not spheres but spheroids, being flattened at their poles by rotation, but that was not the kind of nonsphericity which accounted for the discrepancies in the case of the moon. Hansen concluded that the moon had to be slightly egg-shaped, with the narrow end always pointing toward the earth. The deviation from the true sphere was probably only 20 miles or so but it meant that the visible portion of the moon was 20 miles above the line where it would be if the moon was a true sphere.

The conclusions that could be drawn from this concept were varied as well as amazing. Of course we could not detect any atmosphere or any water since we were looking at a twenty-mile high plateau. If a portion of the earth jutted out to a distance of 20 miles its surface would also be waterless and without atmosphere. Consequently the far side of the moon did not have to resemble the near side at all. The far side might have an atmosphere and it might have water. It could be a wet jungle. We now know that even if the moon did have such an egg shape, its gravitational field is too weak to hold an atmosphere or open water. But the theoretical knowledge we can bring to bear on this problem did not exist at that time. It was a fascinating idea and it is more than mildly surprising that fiction writers did not make more use of it.

Hansen died in 1874, and his theory did not survive him for long. Several astronomers, one of them Professor Simon Newcomb in Washington, D.C., started special programs to check on the shape of the moon, and by 1900 it was clear that the shape was not what Hansen had thought it to be.

During Hansen's lifetime something else had happened that had at first no connection with astronomy. This was the publication of Charles Darwin's *Origin of Species* in 1859. The concept of organic evolution added another line of thought. The more complex and more recent life forms were the offspring of simpler life forms of the past, and logic demanded that this reasoning be carried back to very simple life forms at a very early age of the earth. But even the simplest life forms must have come from somewhere.

Did one now have to return to the old idea of spontaneous generation, an idea everybody had considered safely dead and buried? The reason scientists thought of it as "safely" dead was that the earlier ideas, held even by learned men had been so ridiculous. Mice were, or so it had been asserted, the product of mud or of discarded clothing. Fleas formed in the dust of an ill-kept house; eels were generated in wet pieces of grass sod when the March sun shone upon it. Late in the eighteenth century there had been scientific crusades against such beliefs, under the battle cry of *Omne vivum ex ovo* (All life comes from eggs), or *Omne vivum e vivo* (All life comes from living [matter]). All examples of spontaneous generation ever mentioned by anybody were thoroughly disproved. The slogans held true even for life forms visible only under the microscope; after all, the very visible success of the idea of sterility in the operating room was based on the assumption that bacteria caused sickness and not the other way around. But now organic evolution demanded that spontaneous generation had taken place somewhere and at some time, even if only once. That we had life on earth could not very easily be denied.

The necessity of spontaneous generation at one point had to be reluctantly admitted. But one did *not* have to assume that it had taken place on earth; the problem could at least be pushed further into the past and literally farther away if one looked at the possibility that life on earth had arrived from space. The oldest and most primitive fossils which paleontologists could point out were not really simple. There were strangely formed crustaceans; there were impressions on sandstone which might have been made by a stranded jellyfish at the seashore when that sandstone was still sand. There were worms, or spoor where a worm had crawled—either explanation was possible. There was something that looked like a fossilized clump of hairlike algae. But nothing really simple, nothing that looked as if it could have been "the beginning." Paleontologists said, of course, that what had gone before was too soft to fossilize and in all probability microscopic in size, too. But maybe the simplest and earliest forms that could be found were the earliest and simplest that had ever lived *on earth.*[9]

Now these earliest-known life forms had two things in common. They were quite small individually, even though the hairlike algae might have existed in numbers large enough to make half an ocean look like green scum. And they were all marine or at least aquatic life forms. These facts seemed to open up a possibility which was worked out by the astronomer M. Wilhelm Meyer in the form of popular lectures and magazine articles from 1895 to about 1905. Supposing, he said with one eye figuratively on the planetoids between Mars and Jupiter, supposing a medium-large, earth-sized planet with an atmosphere, oceans, and abundant life is destroyed by some catastrophe. The reason for the catastrophe is unimportant; the planet does explode. Then what would happen?

Its atmosphere would most likely be dispersed in space; the liquid interior would contract into a multitude of "drops" of all sizes and, after radiating its heat away, would solidify. Some of the old continents might form oddly shaped chunks, taking up their individual orbits

[9] For the last thirty years the idea of spontaneous generation on earth has been quietly accepted by scientists. Because of a better knowledge of organic chemistry, spontaneous generation does not look as incredibly difficult now as it did in, say, 1880.

around the sun. All land life would perish, killed by the heat of the planetary explosion, suffocated by the lack of atmosphere. Just possibly we might, one day, find a meteorite from that planet containing a fossil, but it would already have been a fossil when the planet perished. But what about the former oceans of that planet? The explosion would throw them into space where they would contract into spheres of varying sizes, just like the lavalike material from the interior of the planet. And like the molten rock of the interior they would radiate their heat away and solidify; they would freeze into large spheres of water, still containing numerous samples of all the life forms which had inhabited these oceans. But some of these creatures, especially those of small size and relatively primitive organization, might stay alive, become dormant, ready to come to active life again when the chunk of ice which harbored them entered the atmosphere of another planet, a planet with bodies of water but yet without life. Possibly creatures like crabs might not themselves survive, but their eggs might, to hatch in the waters of another planet.

Paleontologists admitted that this *might* have happened but were not enthusiastic. Other astronomers felt that Dr. Meyer had left the confines of his own science and were reluctant to follow him. But the speculation contained one hint which belonged in the field of astronomy; it certainly would do no harm to look at meteorites to see whether they contained something that might be a fossil from another planet.

One man had already done so.

I am looking at a beautifully bound leather-backed folio volume which indicates by its virtually perfect condition that it has not been read often. It was published in Tübingen in 1880, apparently at the author's expense, and is entitled *Die Meteorite (Chondrite) und ihre Organismen*—The Meteorites (Chondrites) and Their Organisms. The author was one Dr. Otto Hahn and as the title of his book indicates he thought that he had found fossils in meteorites. He had obtained meteorites of the type called chondrites, which are stony meteorites with a typical crystalline structure, from eighteen different falls. He had sectioned these meteorites and ground the slices so thin that they were semitransparent and could be looked at with a microscope. Of the more than 400 specimens he prepared he selected 142 to be pictured in his book, in beautiful and expensive heliogravure.

Looking at the photographs—they are considerably enlarged—one is surprised at first glance by what they show. One picture looks like a piece of brain coral, another evidently shows a part of the "stem" of a sea lily (crinoid), and still another might be a portion of a sponge. But in most cases the resemblance of the picture to Dr. Hahn's caption is very slight and in a large number of cases there is no resemblance at all. Dr. Hahn, however, declared triumphantly that he had made a great discovery: the chondrites were not just pieces from a fossil-bearing stratum of another planet; they had been *built* by organisms, like a terrestrial coral reef.

Unfortunately he was just deceiving himself. He should have been suspicious from the very outset because his "fossils" were so tiny. He himself said that the largest of them measured 3 millimeters—about ⅛ inch—in diameter; all others were much smaller. Everybody but the proud father of the discovery realized at once that the resemblances were accidental similarities in the structure of the chondrites. A paleontologist or two may have been quietly sympathetic, for just at that time a few "fossil mosses" which had been carefully described and scientifically labeled also turned out to be purely mineral structures which had never been alive.

Soon after the turn of the century a new concept was added by Svante Arrhenius, the Swedish chemist who won the Nobel Prize in 1903. M. Wilhelm Meyer's colleague and compatriot Richter had said that large chunks of frozen ocean were not needed to start life on earth; a few bacterial spores hidden in a meteorite might do it. Arrhenius pointed out that the spores did not really need a meteorite as a carrier. Spores of bacteria are even harder to kill than bacteria in their nondormant form; cold does not harm them, nor do electric fields, and they seem to be immune, if this term is permitted in this connection, to ultraviolet light. In short, bacterial spores, floating freely in space, would probably stay alive. But if they did float freely in space, the pressure of sunlight would move them, even against the sun's gravitational pull. (A few years later the Russian physicist Pyotr Nikolayevitch Lebyedev—he died in 1911—proved experimentally that light pressure did move the spores of some terrestrial plants.)

Svante Arrhenius calculated the optimum size for a body to be pushed through space by radiation pressure, the size at which radiation pressure would best overcome gravity. Anything as large as a grain of sand would follow the pull of gravity, though opposing radition pressure might slow it down a little. A single molecule would also follow the pull of gravity. But in between these two there is a size at which light, figuratively speaking, gets an especially good grip on the body; Arrhenius stated that the optimum size was 100 million molecules which would be, if spherical, a body of 0.00016 millimeters in diameter. That happens to be the average size of bacterial spores. Arrhenius assumed that spores

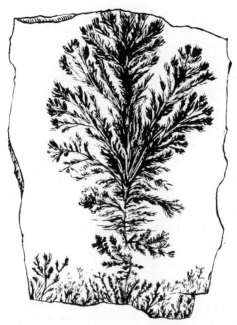

Once classified as a fossil moss, this object, shown in actual size, was later recognized as being the result of mineral deposits in a crack in limestone. The error was even more natural since this particular limestone (from Solnhoften in Franconia) is rich in true fossils. Objects such as this are now called dendrites

which had been carried to the limits of a planetary atmosphere by some means might be thrown out of the atmosphere by electrical repulsion. Then they would be moved by radiation pressure from the sun. If the spore left our atmosphere it would be pushed to the orbit of Mars in just 20 days and to the orbit of Jupiter in about 80 days.

Now, said Arrhenius, we can assume that any planet which bears life is continually losing spores which are forced to travel through space under the light pressure of some sun; we have to assume, therefore, that life spores can be found anywhere in space inside the galaxy, ready to start life on any planet which is ready to receive life.

From the Greek words for "everywhere" and for "seed," he coined the term "panspermy" for this concept. And ever since, whenever an epidemic starts anywhere newspaper articles appear in which somebody is quoted as having said that the organisms responsible for this epidemic probably came from space.[10]

In 1932, fifty-two years after the publication of Hahn's book, an

[10] Some space research projects have the capture of cosmic dust as one of their goals. Such samples may help decide whether there are dormant but viable spores in space.

American scientist, Professor Charles B. Lipman, who then taught at the University of California at Berkeley, claimed that he had succeeded in connecting meteorites with the transfer of life from planet to planet. He made no reference to Hahn's book, but he might have said that he had gone further than Hahn who had merely looked for fossils; Lipman stated [11] that he had found live bacteria. Of course, no meteorite has ever been caught in midair; they are picked up from the ground, often years after the fall, so that they have had plenty of time to become contaminated with terrestrial bacteria. Soil experts have stated that uncultivated sandy soils contain an average of 100,000 bacteria per gram (there are 28 grams to the ounce) while the number in cultivated garden soils is ten to fifteen times as large. An uncontaminated meteorite, therefore, is an impossibility, and while sterilizing a piece of rock is simple (by heating it red-hot), the process would probably destroy all bacteria whether on the outside, in surface cracks, or inside the stone.

In a letter to Sharat Kumar Roy [12] Lipman described his technique for sterilizing meteorites:

This [the removal of the terrestrial soil bacteria] was attempted by first washing the surface of the specimen thoroughly with soap and hot water with the aid of a sterile brush. The specimen was then rinsed in distilled water, dried with a paper towel and placed in a solution of bactericide . . . a 30 per cent solution of H_2O_2 was used for periods varying generally from three to six hours. After the exposure of the specimen to the bactericide for the desired period, it was transferred to 95 per cent alcohol for half a minute to a minute, grasped with sterile tongs and exposed to a large gas flame until the alcohol had all burned away and for a few seconds more. In the early experiments it was then quickly thrown into a sterile iron mortar and crushed and the powder distributed with a sterile spoon into several flasks of sterile media. In the later experiments, however, the specimen was dropped directly from the flaming procedure just described into a wide-mouthed flask containing one of the best adapted media in sterile condition. In such media the specimen remained for periods varying from two or three weeks to four or five months. . . . Everything used in the experiments was sterilized by the most drastic means. Glassware and tongs were heated for twenty-four hours or more at 165° centigrade (330° F.). The mortars were heated at the same temperature for several days. Liquid and solid media were sterilized in the autoclave two or three times before using, each exposure being from one to three hours at 20 pounds steam pressure. . . .

In spite of all this, bacterial growth appeared in the media (Peptone soil extract, Peptone coal extract, etc.) after some time, and Lipman felt justified in considering the forms extraterrestrial, even though, in his

[11] *Novitates* of the American Museum of Natural History, nos. 588 and 589, 1932.

[12] See vol. VI, no. 14, Dec. 12, 1935, of the "Geological Series" of the Chicago Natural History Museum, then the Field Museum.

own words, "they were similar to forms common on our earth and probably identical with some."

From 1933 to 1935 Sharat Kumar Roy (then Assistant Curator of Geology at the Field Museum) repeated the experiments, using meteorites from the same falls Lipman had used. Again bacterial growth appeared, but it could be identified as *Bacillus subtilis* and *Staphylococcus albus,* well-known terrestrial species with the habit of showing up where unwanted. The conclusion was inevitable that Lipman had not succeeded in removing contamination from his meteorites.

The story did not end then and there, however, even though various geologists and astronomers wrote articles that such a search was and must be futile. Sir James Jean's assertion that the earth was the only life-bearing planet in the universe was still believed in some quarters.

Naturally, after Lipman's mistake everybody became very careful. But in spite of this extra caution several groups of scientists have gone on record during 1961 as having found evidence of alien life in meteorites. The meteorite in question—it sometimes seems as if Nature indulged in heavy-handed jokes—was a chondrite!

It was the Orgueil chondrite, so named because it had fallen, in the presence of many witnesses, on May 14, 1864, near the town of Orgueil, France. Since it had been seen to fall it was recovered very soon; the meteorite had shattered into half a hundred known fragments; the largest, about the size of a human head, is now in Paris. A chemical analysis was made soon after recovery of the fragments which resulted in the label "carbonaceous chondrite," a rare form of chondrite with a much higher percentage of carbon than the usual 0.15 per cent. But at that time chemical analysis could only establish that carbon was present and in what percentage. Methods now available permit counting the number of carbon atoms in a molecule, and Douglas J. Hennessy, Warren J. Meinschein, and Bartholomew Nagy used these methods in investigating a fragment of the Orgueil chondrite. And then they announced that they had come across a trace of former life.

The number of carbon atoms per molecule in the fragment was usually 19 and 21, and only occasionally 18, 20, or 22. Molecules containing 19 or 21 carbon atoms happen to be typical for substances such as the wax on an apple's skin, the resinous covering of a palm frond, or, to give an everyday example, butter. The discovery amounted to finding a fossil in a meteorite, except that the fossil was not obvious to the eye but had to be established by advanced chemical analysis.

The announcement of the discovery produced the reactions one could have predicted, ranging from pleased acceptance to complete scepticism.

"Probable contamination" was the first objection, though the three scientists insisted that the interior of the meteorite had been well sealed. Dr. Egon T. Degens, geologist at the California Institute of Technology, ran a series of tests which consisted of boiling a ground-up meteorite first in water, then in alcohol, then for 10 hours in dilute sulfuric acid, and after that for 22 hours in hydrochloric acid. After all that, he still could extract chemicals characteristic of living organisms. His conclusion was that contamination is so probable that there can never be any proof that organic matter found in a meteorite is *not* of terrestrial origin. Another objection was that substances with 19 or 21 carbon atoms per molecule might be formed without the aid of a living organism, even though no such substances are at present known.

Less than a month after the announcement about possible traces of life in the Orgueil carbonaceous chondrite came an announcement that living organisms had been obtained from another carbonaceous chondrite, one that fell at Murray, Kentucky, in 1950. The two scientists who reported the find were Dr. Frederick D. Sisler, microbiologist with the U. S. Geological Survey, and Dr. Walter Newton, chief of the germ-free laboratories at Bethesda, Maryland. They had sterilized their meteorite with hydrogen peroxide and bichloride of mercury and finally with ultraviolet light. Then the meteorite was crushed in a sterile mortar and the dust injected into germ-free laboratory rats and put into Peptone solution in sterile flasks. There was no reaction in the rats, but the solution in the flasks grew cloudy. The cloudiness was caused by microorganisms which looked like twisted rods, or, to quote Dr. Sisler's statement to a press conference, "like sausages you might have twisted, thrown on the floor and jumped on." Two facts were definite: the twisted rods were organisms (they reproduced) and they were not identical with any known form. But since the meteorite had been on earth for a decade, nobody, including Dr. Sisler, would insist that they are of extraterrestrial origin.

But, as was noted earlier, the question of bacteria going into or coming from space is no longer as important as it was when Svante Arrhenius evolved his theory. Then the origin of living matter was thought to be impossibly difficult—and a few popular books still maintain that this is the case— but we now know that a spontaneous generation is not only thinkable but even likely under the conditions a young planet will provide.

I have referred to "spontaneous generation," because it is an entrenched term, but the word "spontaneous" is quite misleading. Even the origin of life has to be conceived as a gradual process which might have taken any amount of time, from days to centuries, and even an observer on the spot probably could not say which moment in the process has to be considered *the* moment. As scientists visualize the process now, our earth had progressed to the point where the surface was cool. There can be—and therefore is—disagreement on the question of the maximum temperature of our planet during its formation; it depends on which theory you favor. But there is agreement on the assumption that the temperature was too high to permit water to assume its liquid phase. After the temperature had receded to below the boiling point of water the vapor which had been in the atmosphere began to condense. The first result was a planet with a generally cool crust and with all depressions filled with water—warm water by present day standards. The atmosphere, then as now, consisted mainly of nitrogen, but it did not contain any oxygen. All the oxygen which might originally have been present had been used up chemically, reacting with the metals present but mainly reacting with the then abundant hydrogen to form water.

The gaseous compounds one would expect to find in such an atmosphere would be: water vapor (H_2O), methane (CH_4), ammonia (NH_3), carbon dioxide (CO_2), and sulfur dioxide (SO_2). The most important of these for the purpose of producing life would be the methane, the ammonia, and liquid water; the only additional thing needed is energy in the form of an electrical discharge, lightning. As has been shown experimentally by Dr. Stanley L. Miller, a mixture of methane and ammonia will form organic compounds when subjected to an electrical discharge. Today such organic compounds would be eaten up by micro-organisms, but micro-organisms did not exist at the time under consideration. The compounds could accumulate in a closed body of water (in the open ocean they would probably be dispersed), undergoing additional chemical reactions, and slowly building up to more complicated organic compounds, to semiliving and, finally, to living things which would then subsist, at first, on the simpler compounds. Because of this the whole process has been nicknamed "the soup that ate itself," which is an amusing term, though in reality one part of the soup ate the rest of it.

The requirements for the origin of life, as they now appear, are fairly simple: the common light elements, static electricity, a nonoxidizing atmosphere, and liquid water. Once life has acquired a good foothold, or roothold, on a planet, the main requirement for its continued existence is that the water is liquid. Now this condition depends mainly on the distance of a planet from its sun. An earthlike planet orbiting our sun at a distance of 20 million miles would have all of its water in its atmosphere as water vapor all the time, and the normal life processes cannot take place under such conditions. An earthlike planet orbiting the sun in the orbit of Jupiter would have all of its water permanently frozen, which also excludes active life.

There is, then, around every sun an area with the geometrical shape of a spherical shell, inside of which the water on a planet would be normally liquid. This spherical shell has received the name "ecosphere," a term constructed by analogy with the classical Greek term *oikumene,* which meant the "habitable world." The ecosphere of a star is that volume of space in which a planet could bear life. In our solar system Venus is too close to the sun to be in it. Mars is near the outer edge of our sun's ecosphere, while the earth is about in the middle.[13] A planet situated at the outer edge of the ecosphere—in our solar system somewhat farther from the sun than Mars is—might furnish the proper conditions for life around its equator only. Unfortunately the term "equatorial planet" has been coined for this condition. While the term itself may be claimed to be logical, it unfortunately conveys the impression that the whole surface of the planet is equatorial, that is to say tropical. Conversely, planets at the inner edge of their star's ecosphere have been labeled "polar planets" because life could exist only near their poles.

The distance of the inner edge of the ecosphere from the center of the star would, of course, depend on the nature of the star. If the star is a Blue-White Giant the inner edge of its ecosphere would be quite distant, with a good chance that the ecosphere contained several planets. If it is a feeble star, the inner edge of the ecosphere might be relatively near its surface, and all its planets would probably be outside the ecosphere. This reasoning indicates that life is more likely to exist on planets of a medium-bright star like our sun, or a brighter star like Sirius, than on planets of a dim star.

But there is still another consideration. The volume of the ecosphere has been defined as that volume at which the water of a hypothetical planet would be in its liquid phase most of the time. This implies that the ecosphere is "valid" only for life of the type found on earth, life with a chemistry based on carbon. Isn't it conceivable that there might

[13] A first inkling of the concept of the ecosphere, if you will, can be found in de Fontenelle, where the Countess says: "I am sure we have one great convenience in the situation of our World; it is not so hot as Mercury or Venus, nor so cold as Jupiter or Saturn; and our Country is so justly plac'd, that we have no excess either of Heat or Cold. I have heard of a Philosopher, who gave thanks to Nature that he was born a Man, and not a Beast, a Greek, and not a Barbarian; and for my part I render thanks that I am seated in the most temperate Planet of the Universe, and in one of the most temperate Regions of that Planet."

be types of life with a chemistry which does not require liquid water and that these therefore might thrive in a different temperature range?

Life with a chemistry based on silicon, instead of carbon has been a favorite speculation of many writers, both in science and in science fiction. Chemists who had time to spare or who could obtain research grants for such activities have actually produced a number of organic compounds which have silicon atoms in the molecules where carbon atoms would normally be, one of the notable accomplishments being the synthesis of the silicon equivalent of formic acid. These experiments have made one thing clear: in our own temperature range some of the silicon compounds would be too active, and others too stable, to be useful in living tissue. Recently Dr. Isaac Asimov, who is a science writer, a science-fiction writer, and a professor of biochemistry, has toyed with such possibilities and found that silicon would actually be serviceable only if a great many other unlikely conditions were fulfilled too, and at a very high temperature range, to boot. Life forms based on fluorocarbons, with liquid sulfur taking the place of water in an appropriately hot environment, or life forms based on a nitrogen chemistry, with liquid ammonia taking the place of water in a sufficiently cold environment, actually appear to be more likely than silicon life.

The reason biologists and astronomers always specify "life as we know it," (i.e., based on carbon) is that possible chemistries at different temperature ranges have not been sufficiently investigated to provide useful information.

Restricting ourselves to the type of life we know, we can hope that future astronauts will find plant life on Mars, with animals as a borderline possibility. And observers of our moon have said on occasion that certain faint but definite color changes could be explained if they could assume a kind of very tough vegetation clinging to some areas of the lunar landscape.

In addition, two exceptional places outside the ecosphere offer possibilities. One is the twilight belt of Mercury, where the temperature range at least should be favorable in spots. The other is, strangely enough, a possible surface sea on Jupiter, as was pointed out by Carl Sagan, a professor of astronomy at the University of California, in the journal *Radiation Research*.[14] The atmosphere of Jupiter might produce a very strong "greenhouse effect" (see Chapter 10).

As Professor Sagan put it:

The amount of methane and ammonia spectroscopically identified above the cloud layer will be essentially opaque in the far infrared part of the spectrum.

[14] Vol. 15, August 1961, p. 189f. The paper was first presented at the Panel on Extraterrestrial Life, Armed Forces–National Research Council, Committee on Bio-Astronautics.

If Jupiter has a surface which is opaque to visible light, this surface will be heated by light penetrating through the cloud layer and will emit in the infrared. But because of the absorptive properties of the atmosphere, this infrared radiation emitted from the surface will be unable to escape to space . . . and the temperature of the Jovian atmosphere will increase sharply with depth below the visible cloud layer. It is possible that temperatures near room temperature or above prevail deep in the atmosphere of Jupiter. From cosmic abundance considerations there must be water on Jupiter. . . . The standard explanation of the absence of spectroscopically detectable amounts of water is simply that it is frozen out; the temperature of the cloud layer is approximately 140° Kelvin (equal to *minus* 207° Fahrenheit or *minus* 92° centigrade). But if warmer temperatures prevail beneath the cloud layer, the possibility arises that water or ammonia seas exist on Jupiter.

The existence of an ocean on Jupiter depends on two factors which are not known. The surface of the planet must be opaque to visible light; well, it would be hard to imagine a surface that isn't. And visible light must be able to reach the surface; in other words, the cloud layer must be such that visible light can pass through it. The whole problem hinges on this latter condition.

If there is a surface ocean it is virtually certain that life forms exist in it. To quote Professor Sagan once more:

From atmospheric simulation experiments it is clear that simple organic molecules must be produced in the atmosphere . . . by solar ultra violet light or atmospheric electrical discharges. . . . The Jovian atmosphere is known to be convective, and these molecules will be carried below the visible cloud layer.

This theoretical reasoning applies in principle to the outer planets, but in reality it probably applies only to Jupiter. Jupiter, roughly five times as far from the sun as the earth is receives only $\frac{1}{25}$ of the solar radition per square mile that the earth receives. If conditions for producing the greenhouse effect are good, that much radiation can build up in time to temperatures above the freezing point of water. But Saturn, at 9.5 A.U., receives a little less than $\frac{1}{90}$ of the solar radiation the earth gets, and that, in all probability, is not enough. Saturn's surface temperature may well be higher than has been believed, but in all probability it is still far below freezing point.

The greenhouse effect, therefore, might produce "pockets" of life-sustaining temperatures even outside the ecosphere of a star. Even if Jupiter's cloud layer should be too dense to permit any radiation to pass, the reasoning might well apply to similar planets of other suns.

It is, therefore, a mistake to state flatly that only Mars looks favorable for life; a more proper statement would be that, of the probably life-bearing planets, only Mars is accessible. Other stars have ecospheres too—with planets in them.

EPILOGUE: THE SEARCH
FOR OTHER CIVILIZATIONS

In the late evening hours of April 11, 1960, an 85-foot radio telescope located in Deer Creek Valley in West Virginia was activated for the first time. It was a United States Government project with Dr. Frank Drake in charge and was officially known as Project Ozma. Its purpose was to tune in, if possible, on radio broadcasts of another civilization.

Two stars which may have planets, Tau Ceti and Epsilon Eridani, were the special targets. There were no results and after a number of months the search was discontinued, but not because Dr. Drake or anybody else had come to the conclusion that there were no broadcasts to intercept. The conclusion was that equipment now available is not yet sufficiently sensitive for the purpose. And it is quite possible that any place on the earth's surface, no matter how remote from the centers of our cities, is a poor base for such a search. Both our own civilization and our ever-active atmosphere produce too much static, and the number of broadcasting artificial satellites also increases all the time. The proper place for Project Ozma II might be the place Beer and von Mädler considered the ideal location for an optical telescope—the far side of our moon.

Project Ozma did not succeed.

But it has a firm place in the history of science: it was the first systematic search for other civilizations. Dr. Otto Struve, formerly director of the Yerkes Observatory as well as of the National Radio Astronomy Observatory at Green Bank, West Virginia, even stated that this attempt marked an astronomical revolution. During lectures * at the Massachusetts Institute of Technology in 1959—that is, before Project Ozma became active—he said:

"Astronomy has had three great revolutions in the past four hundred years. The first was the Copernican revolution that removed the earth from the center of the solar system and placed it 150 million kilometers away from it; the second occurred between 1920 and 1930, when, as

* Published under the title *The Universe* by the Massachusetts Institute of Technology Press, Cambridge, Mass., in 1962.

a result of the work of Harlow Shapley and R. J. Trumpler, we realized that the solar system is not at the center of the Milky Way but about 30,000 light years away from it, in a relatively dim spiral arm; the third is occurring now . . . this is the revolution embodied in the question: Are we alone in the universe?"

To the layman this has been very much *the* question for nearly a century. The layman, who during the decades from 1880 to 1910 read the papers and magazines for news from Schiaparelli in Milan, was not interested in hearing that the period of rotation of the planet Mars had been more accurately determined. He wanted an answer to his question (poorly phrased from the astronomical as well as the biological point of view): "Are there *people* on Mars?"

The layman also regretted that an idea of the great Carl Friedrich Gauss had never been carried out.

Gauss, at one time during his career—I have not been able to find the original source, and therefore I don't know the genesis of this concept— evolved the thought of marking the earth with a symbol which would proclaim far into space that this planet was inhabited by reasoning beings. The mark had to be such that it could not be mistaken for a natural formation. Gausse suggested the geometrical figure that is used to demonstrate what we call the Pythagorean theorem—the triangle with one 90 degree angle and a square constructed on each one of its three sides. One could construct this figure, Gauss mused, in a locality like Central Siberia, picking an area which was essentially flat and several hundred miles in diameter. The lines of the figure could be formed by dark pine forests while the interior of the three squares might be seeded with a type of vegetation providing a good color contrast—for example, wheat or rye, which would look light green in one season and bright yellow in the next one. The yield of grain would also pay for the work.

This idea of Gauss's, and a similar one advanced by von Littrow in Vienna, would have served only for interplanetary signaling; by now everybody is agreed that if there are signals to be received, or to be transmitted, they would be interstellar signals. Unfortunately a sphere with our sun in the center and with a radius of 16 light-years contains only about forty stars, one of which is our sun. The probability that quite a number of these stars have planets is quite high, and, to quote Otto Struve: "The probability is also great that a few of these outer planets have some form of life. But the probability that any of them have intelligent life at the present time is vanishingly small. The probability that even if intelligent life now exists outside the solar system, but closer to us than 20 light years, any artificial radio signals are reaching us now is even smaller. But it is not zero. . . ." (Op. cit. pp. 158-59).

One problem is that we cannot be certain which of these comparatively near stars have planets. Two of them—both binaries, 61 *Cygni* and *70 Ophiuchi*—are known to have invisible and presumably dark companions, but since the masses of these dark companions work out to more than ten times the mass of Jupiter there may be some doubt of whether they can be called "planets." German astronomers refer to them tentatively as *dunkel Nebensonnen,* which might be translated as "dark auxiliary suns," leaving open the possibility that they might even be faintly luminous. To detect true planets of other suns is impossible at the moment, as Struve has pointed out: "If we imagine ourselves on our nearest stellar neighbor Alpha Centauri . . . the sun would appear as a fairly bright star, perhaps like the well-known star Capella, but the planet Jupiter, about 4 seconds of arc away, would be completely lost in the glare of the brilliant sun and would not be recognizable except on long photographic exposures with the largest existing telescopes if the glare of the sun could somehow be eliminated, which, of course, cannot now be accomplished" (Op. cit., p. 9).

But a combination of new techniques and observations from space (without our own atmosphere also getting in the way) might tell us one day that Alpha Centauri, Sirius, and Altair, all of which are within that 16-light-year radius, actually do have planets.

Only three decades ago this possibility was roundly denied by scientists as important as Sir James Jeans and Sir Arthur Eddington. At the time it was believed that a planetary system could form only if there was a very close encounter between a single star and a binary. Since such encounters would obviously be rare, Sir James Jeans concluded that "the chance is about a hundred thousand to one against [a star's] being surrounded by planets." And Sir Arthur Eddington added the "sounding words" which others had produced in the past on similar occasions: "Not one of the profusion of stars in their myriad clusters looks down on scenes comparable to those which are passing beneath the rays of the sun."

The belief in the uniqueness—or near-uniqueness—of the planetary system was anthropocentrism's last line of defense.

It now seems probable that the stars of the Main Sequence at least do have planets as a rule, though exceptions are always possible.

The customary estimate for the number of stars in the Milky Way galaxy is 30,000 million, and the three stellar classes, F, G, and K are believed to comprise about 60 per cent of the total. Although an accurate count is impossible because of interstellar dust, the figure of 18,000 million sun-type stars in our own galaxy cannot be far off the mark. Hence the assumption that there are at least 18,000 million planetary systems in our galaxy would be considered reasonable by most astronomers.

But now let us make a series of absolutely unreasonable assumptions, with the purpose of reducing the numbers involved to the smallest possible size. First we'll assume that the distances of these planetary systems from their primaries are such that only once in a hundred cases a planet revolves in the ecosphere of its sun. That assumption still provides 180 million planets which could bear life. Further assuming that only one out of a hundred planets which can bear life actually does bear life, there could still be 1.8 million planets with life forms on them. A somewhat less unreasonable assumption is that one out of every hundred planets with life is, at the present moment, inhabited by beings with an intelligence comparable to *Homo sapiens*. Even this assumption provides our galaxy with 18,000 planets which are "inhabited," in the sense in which Percival Lowell claimed Mars to be inhabited; in reality there are likely to be many more. Statistically, this means that one planet of one of the forty suns within a distance of 16 light-years from us, might be the dwelling place of another civilization.

The search for other civilizations still has a chance to succeed—but only if we improve our equipment and move it out from under the blanket of our atmosphere.

APPENDIX

CHRONOLOGICAL LIST OF GREAT ASTRONOMERS FROM PYTHAGORAS TO RECENT TIMES

(Living astronomers are not included)

GREEKS AND ROMANS

DATES	NAME OR NAMES	ACTIVE IN
580(?) B.C.–500(?) B.C.	PYTHAGORAS (of Samos)	Southern Italy
429 B.C.–348 B.C.	PLATO (Aristokles)	Athens
409 B.C.–356 B.C.	EUDOXOS (of Cnidos)	Athens
384 B.C.–322 B.C.	ARISTOTLE (of Stagyra)	Athens
280 B.C. *fl.*	ARISTARCHOS (of Samos)	Alexandria
230 B.C. *fl.*	ERATOSTHENES (of Cyrene)	Alexandria
180(?) B.C.–125(?)B.C.	HIPPARCHOS (of Nicea)	Rhodes
4(?) B.C.–A.D. 65	SENECA (Lucius Annaeus)	Rome
A.D. 23–79	PLINY THE ELDER (Gaius Plinius Secundus)	Rome
A.D. 120(?)–190(?)	PTOLEMY (Claudius Ptolemaeus)	Alexandria

ARABS

805–886	*Albumazar* (abu-Ma'shar Ja'far ibn-Muhammad)	Baghdad
836–901	*Tobit* (Thâbit ibn-Qurra)	Damascus(?)
840 *fl.*	*Alfraganus* (abu-al-'Abbas Ahmad al-Farghâni)	Transoxiana
850(?)–929	*Albategnius* (abu-'Abdullâh Muhammad ibn-Jâbir al-Battânî)	Rakka
903–986	*Alsufi* ('Abd al-Rahmân ibn-'Umar, called al Sûfi "the Wise")	Baghdad
1075 *fl.*	*Arzachel* (ibn-al-Zarqâla)	Toledo
1126–1198	*Averroës* (abu-al-Walîd Muhammad ibn-Ahmad ibn-Rushd)	Morocco and Seville

SACROBOSCO TO HERSCHEL

1160?–1240?	SACROBOSCO (John of Holywood)	Paris
1394–1449	ULUGH BEG (Grandson of Tamerlane)	Samarkand
1397–1482	Paolo dal Pozzo TOSCANELLI	Florence
1423–1461	Georg von PEURBACH (Purbach)	Vienna
1436–1476	REGIOMONTANUS (Johannes Müller)	Nuremberg
1473–1543	Nicholas COPERNICUS (Koppernigk)	Thorn and Frauenburg
1483–1553	Girolamo FRACASTORO	Verona
1495–1552	APIAN (Peter Bienevitz)	Ingolstadt
1546–1601	TYCHO BRAHE	Hveen and Prague

1562–1647	LONGOMONTANUS (Christian Severin)	Hveen and Copenhagen
1564–1642	GALILEO Galilei	Tuscany
1564–1617	DAVID FABRICIUS	Frisian islands
1570–1624	SIMON MARIUS (Mayr)	Ansbach
1571–1630	JOHANNES KEPLER	Prague, Linz and Ulm
1575–1650	Christoph SCHEINER	Rome and Neisse (Silesia)
1587–1615	JOHANNES FABRICIUS (son of David)	Frisian islands and Emden
1588–1657	Johann Baptist CYSAT	Lucerne
1598–1671	Giovanni Battista RICCIOLI	Bologna
1600–1660	LANGRENUS (Michael Florent van Langren)	Brussels
1611–1687	Johannes HEVELIUS (Hewelcke)	Danzig
1625–1712	Giovanni Domenico (Jean Dominique) CASSINI	Paris
1629–1695	Christiaan HUYGENS (Huyghens)	The Hague
1635–1703	Robert HOOKE	London
1642–1727	Sir Isaac NEWTON	London
1644–1710	Ole RÖMER	Paris and Copenhagen
1646–1719	John FLAMSTEED (first Astronomer Royal)	Greenwich
1656–1742	Edmond HALLEY (second Astronomer Royal)	London and Greenwich
1657–1757	Bernard le Bovier de FONTENELLE	Paris
1679–1764	Peter HORREBOW	Copenhagen
1688–1768	Joseph Nicolas DELISLE	Paris
1693–1762	James BRADLEY (third Astronomer Royal)	Oxford and Greenwich
1700–1764	Nathaniel BLISS (fourth Astronomer Royal)	Greenwich
1711–1796	Alexandre-Gui PINGRÉ	Paris
1713–1762	Nicholas Louis de LACAILLE	Paris and Cape of Good Hope
1723–1762	TOBIAS MAYER	Göttingen
1728–1777	Johann Heinrich LAMBERT	Berlin
1730–1817	Charles MESSIER	Paris
1732–1807	Joseph Jérôme le Français de LALANDE	Paris
1732–1811	Nevil MASKELYNE (fifth Astronomer Royal)	Greenwich
1736–1813	Joseph-Louis LAGRANGE	Berlin and Paris
1738–1822	SIR WILLIAM (Friedrich Wilhelm) HERSCHEL	Slough

NINETEENTH CENTURY TO RECENT TIMES

1745–1818	Johann Hieronymus SCHROETER	Lilienthal
1746–1826	Giuseppe PIAZZI	Palermo
1749–1822	Jean-Baptiste Joseph DELAMBRE	Paris
1750–1848	CAROLINE HERSCHEL (sister of William)	Slough and Hannover
1749–1827	Pierre Simon, Marquis de LAPLACE	Paris
1754–1832	FRANZ Xaver, Baron VON ZACH	Gotha
1756–1827	Ernst Florens Friedrich CHLADNI	Breslau
1758–1840	Heinrich Wilhelm Mathias OLBERS	Bremen
1765–1786	John GOODRICKE	York
1765–1834	Karl Ludwig HARDING	Bremen and Göttingen
1767–1836	John POND (sixth Astronomer Royal)	Greenwich
1774–1862	Jean Baptiste BIOT	Paris
1777–1855	Carl Friedrich GAUSS	Göttingen

1781–1840	Joseph Johann von LITTROW	Vienna
1784–1846	Friedrich Wilhelm BESSEL	Königsberg
1789–1859	William Cranch BOND	Harvard
1791–1865	Johannes Franz ENCKE	Berlin
1792–1871	SIR JOHN HERSCHEL (son of William)	Slough and London
1793–1864	Friedrich Georg WILHELM STRUVE	Dorpat
1794–1874	Johann Heinrich von MÄDLER	Berlin and Dorpat
1795–1864	Peter Andreas HANSEN	Gotha
1799–1875	Friedrich Wilhelm ARGELANDER	Helsingfors and Bonn
1799–1880	William LASSELL	Liverpool
1800–1867	LORD ROSSE (William Parsons, third Earl of Rosse)	Parsonstown
1801–1892	George Biddel AIRY (seventh Astron. Royal)	Greenwich
1811–1877	Jean-Joseph Urbain LEVERRIER	Paris
1812–1910	Johann Gottfried GALLE	Berlin and Breslau
1816–1893	RUDOLF WOLF	Zürich
1818–1878	Angelo SECCHI	Rome
1819–1892	John Couch ADAMS	Cambridge, England
1819–1905	OTTO Wilhelm STRUVE (son of F. G. W. Struve)	Pulkovo
1822–1875	Heinrich Ludwig D'ARREST	Berlin and Copenhagen
1824–1914	Sir William HUGGINS	London
1825–1865	George Phillips BOND (son of W. C. Bond)	Harvard
1826–1873	Giovanni Batista DONATI	Florence
1829–1907	Asaph HALL	Washington, D.C.
1834–1906	Samuel Pierpont LANGLEY	Pittsburgh
1834–1908	Charles A. YOUNG	Washington, D.C.
1835–1909	Simon NEWCOMB	Washington, D.C.
1835–1910	Giovanni Virginio SCHIAPARELLI	Milan
1836–1920	Sir Joseph Norman LOCKYER	London
1837–1882	Henry DRAPER	New York
1837–1888	Richard Anthony PROCTOR	London and New York
1842–1925	(Nicolas) Camille FLAMMARION	Paris
1846–1919	Edward Charles PICKERING	Harvard
1848–1925	Johann PALISA	Vienna
1851–1922	Jacobus Cornelis KAPTEYN	Gronigen
1855–1916	Percival LOWELL	Flagstaff, Arizona
1857–1923	Edward Emerson BARNARD	Yerkes Observatory
1858–1938	William Henry PICKERING (brother of E.C.)	Harvard Observatories
1858–1920	LUDWIG STRUVE (son of O. W. Struve)	Kharkov
1863–1932	MAX (Franz Joseph Cornelius) WOLF	Königstuhl Observ.
1868–1938	George Ellery HALE	Yerkes and Mount Wilson
1877–1946	SIR JAMES Hopwood JEANS	London
1882–1944	SIR ARTHUR Stanley EDDINGTON	Greenwich
1889–1953	Edwin Powell HUBBLE	Mount Wilson
1891–1963	Seth Barnes NICHOLSON	Mt. Wilson
1893–1960	Walter BAADE	Hamburg and Palomar
1897–1963	OTTO STRUVE (son of Ludwig Struve)	Yerkes (and others)
1900–1960	Sir Harold Spencer JONES	Cape of Good Hope and Greenwich

NOTE ON RADIO ASTRONOMY

A nitrogen-oxygen atmosphere, as ours is, happens to be opaque to most wavelengths of the electromagnetic spectrum. The main exception is the range of wavelengths which we call visible light, but our atmosphere is almost transparent to a band of radio wavelengths. Astronomers call these radio waves which can penetrate to the ground the "second window"—the first one being visible light—and a new branch of astronomy operates by receiving them.

The discovery of the existence of this second window, which could have been deduced theoretically, was based on an accident. In 1932 Karl Jansky, a physicist with the Bell Telephone Laboratories, engaged in a study of static. He found that even when there was no static his equipment produced a faint hiss much of the time. The strength of this hissing sound was not uniform and Jansky noticed after a while that a maximum occurred daily but not precisely at the same time every day. The time lag was significant, since it amounted to 4 minutes. The normal day is 24 hours, from one noon—the time the sun is highest in the sky—to the next. But the interval between the meridian passages of the same star is 23 hours, 56 minutes. Getting a noise maximum at the same time of every "sidereal day" indicated that the source of the radio noise was somewhere among the fixed stars.

After Jansky's discovery had been published (and publicized), a radio amateur, Grote Reber of Wheaton, Illinois, decided to build special equipment for the purpose of tracing the source of the noise discovered by Jansky. He built a 31-foot parabolic-dish antenna, the world's first radio telescope. (It has been preserved and now stands at the entrance of the National Radio Astronomy Observatory at Green Bank, West Virginia.) Reber found that there was not just one source of radio noise in the sky, but many. Evidently many stars emitted radio waves along with visible light and heat. In some cases the radio source could be identified with a star which was optically visible; in some cases the noise originated in a place where no star could be seen. These optically visible sources were dubbed "radio stars." In reality, as we now know, many of these are not stars but nebulosities.

During the second World War the beginning science of radio astronomy received a boost from an unexpected direction. The invasion of the European mainland had already taken place when, one day, a number of radar sets began to emit a loud and steady noise. The cause was first thought to be a German radar-jamming device, and for this reason the fact was kept secret. But a later study proved that all the sets which had been "jammed" had pointed in the direction of the sun at the time. Our sun qualified as a radio star, though it is not a very powerful one.

After the end of the war radio telescopes were built in many countries, with Great Britain and Australia leading. The best radio telescope is a parabolic-dish antenna like the one built by Grote Reber. But this also happens to be the most expensive type. The largest fully stearable dish at present is the one at Jodrell Bank in England. A less expensive type consists of antennas placed on the ground in a cross-shaped pattern. The largest of these is now nearing completion in the Soviet Union; naturally it has been nicknamed the "red cross."

Radio astronomers have a few advantages over optical astronomers. They can work in daytime, since light does not interfere with the reception of radio waves. Similarly a radio telescope can operate through a cloud cover which forces the optical observatories to give up for the night. But not all the advantages are with the radio telescopes. Because radio waves are so long, the instruments must be enormous. Reber's first dish antenna may be compared with a portable telescope, it was so small. The work is also complicated by the fact that we have no organ sensitive to radio waves as the eye is sensitive to light rays. The radio waves gathered by the dish must first be amplified and then translated into a form which our senses can perceive—either into noise that can be heard in an earphone or into lines drawn on a strip of paper by a recording apparatus. Moreover, while an optical telescope can take a picture of a region in the sky with an exposure time of a few hours, a radio telescope may take weeks to "scan" the same area.

Radio astronomy is, at the moment, at about the stage which optical astronomy had reached at the time of Sir William Herschel—the mapping stage.* Because the work is still in progress no comprehensive works on results exist yet, nor are they likely to be written for a quite a number of years to come.

* For further detail see *Radio Astronomy* by J. H. Piddington (New York: Harper, 1961), and *Radioastronomie* by Erich Krug (Stuttgart: Frankische Verlagshandlung, 1962).

UNITS OF DISTANCE

Astronomical unit (A. U.) = 93,003,000 miles = 149,500,000 kilometers

	LIGHT-YEARS	A. U.	MILLION MILLION*	
			MILES	KILOMETERS
Light-year	1	63,290	5.88	9.463
Parsec	3.259	206.652	19.16	30.840
Dekaparsec	32.590	2,062,650	191.60	308.400

(Kiloparsec = 1000 parsecs, megaparsec = 1,000,000 parsecs)

* The term "billion" should be avoided wherever possible, since billion means 1,000,000,000 *only* in the United States. Elsewhere 1,000,000,000 is a milliard, and 1,000,000,000,000 a billion.

THE BODE-TITIUS RULE

The so-called Bode-Titius Rule was first published by Johann Daniel Titius (1729–1796) in the German edition of Bonnet's *Contemplation de la Nature*, which was edited by Titius. The formula as given by Titius read: $0.4 + 0.3 \cdot 2^n$ where n took, in succession, the values — 0, 1, 2, 3, 4, 5, and so forth. The rule is now usually given in the form of a table.

								ACTUAL DISTANCE A. U.
4 + (0 • 3)	:	10	=	0.4	Mercury	0.39
4 + (1 • 3)	:	10	=	0.7	Venus	0.72
4 + (2 • 3)	:	10	=	1.0	Earth	1.00
4 + (4 • 3)	:	10	=	1.6	Mars	1.52
4 + (8 • 3)	:	10	=	2.8	Ceres	2.77
4 + (16 • 3)	:	10	=	5.2	Jupiter	5.20
4 + (32 • 3)	:	10	=	10.0	Saturn	9.54
4 + (64 • 3)	:	10	=	19.6	Uranus	19.19
4 + (128 • 3)	:	10	=	38.8	Neptune	30.07
4 + (256 • 3)	:	10	=	77.2	——	?
4 + (512 • 3)	:	10	=	154.0	——	?

THE FIRST 100 PLANETOIDS
DISCOVERED BETWEEN 1801 AND 1868

NO.	NAME	YEAR AND DATE	DISCOVERER	MAGNITUDE WHEN CLOSEST TO EARTH
1	Ceres	1801, Jan. 1	Piazzi	7.4
2	Pallas	1802, March 28	Olbers	8.0
3	Juno	1804, Sept. 1	Harding	8.7
4	Vesta	1807, March 29	Olbers	6.5
5	Astraea	1845, Dec. 8	Hencke	9.9
6	Hebe	1847, July 1	Hencke	8.5
7	Iris	1847, Aug. 13	Hind	8.4
8	Flora	1847, Oct. 18	Hind	8.9
9	Metis	1848, April 26	Graham	8.9
10	Hygeia	1849, April 12	de Gasparis	9.5
11	Parthenope	1850, May 11	de Gasparis	9.3
12	Victoria	1850, Sept. 13	Hind	9.7
13	Egeria	1850, Nov. 2	Hind	9.7
14	Irene	1851, May 19	de Gasparis	8.6
15	Eunomia	1851, July 29	de Gasparis	8.6
16	Psyche	1852, March 17	de Gasparis	9.6
17	Thetis	1852, April 17	Luther	10.1
18	Melpomene	1852, June 24	Hind	9.3
19	Fortuna	1852, Aug. 22	Hind	9.8
20	Massalia	1852, Sept. 19	de Gasparis	9.2
21	Lutetia	1852, Nov. 15	Goldschmidt	10.1
22	Kalliope	1852, Nov. 16	Hind	9.8
23	Thalia	1852, Dec. 15	Hind	10.5
24	Themis	1853, April 5	de Gasparis	10.8
25	Phocaea	1853, April 7	Chacornac	10.5
26	Proserpina	1853, May 5	Luther	10.5
27	Euterpe	1853, Nov. 8	Hind	9.7
28	Bellona	1854, March 1	Luther	10.1
29	Amphitrite	1854, March 1	Marth	9.0
30	Urania	1854, July 22	Hind	9.9
31	Euphrosine	1854, Sept. 2	Ferguson	11.0
32	Pomona	1854, Oct. 26	Goldschmidt	10.6
33	Polyhymnia	1854, Oct. 28	Chacornac	11.8
34	Circe (Kirkeia)	1855, April 16	Chacornac	11.5
35	Leukothea	1855, April 19	Luther	12.2
36	Atalante	1855, Oct. 5	Goldschmidt	12.0
37	Fides	1855, Oct. 5	Luther	10.4
38	Leda	1856, Jan. 12	Chacornac	11.4
39	Laetitia	1856, Feb. 8	Chacornac	9.5
40	Harmonia	1856, March 31	Goldschmidt	9.2
41	Daphne	1856, May 22	Goldschmidt	10.5
42	Isis	1856, May 23	Pogson	10.4
43	Ariadne	1857, April 15	Pogson	10.0
44	Nysa	1857, May 27	Goldschmidt	9.8
45	Eugenia	1857, June 26	Goldschmidt	10.7
46	Hestia	1857, Aug. 16	Pogson	10.6
47	Aglaia	1857, Sept. 15	Luther	11.2
48	Doris	1857, Sept. 19	Goldschmidt	10.9
49	Pales	1857, Sept. 19	Goldschmidt	11.0
50	Virginia	1857, Oct. 4	Ferguson	11.7

NO.	NAME	YEAR AND DATE	DISCOVERER	WHEN CLOSEST TO EARTH
51	Nemausa	1858, Jan. 22	Laurent	9.8
52	Europa	1858, Feb. 4	Goldschmidt	10.3
53	Kalypso	1858, April 4	Luther	11.5
54	Alexandra	1858, Sept. 10	Goldschmidt	10.9
55	Pandora	1858, Sept. 10	Searle	10.8
56	Melete	1858, Sept. 10	Goldschmidt	11.3
57	Mnemosyne	1859, Sept. 22	Luther	10.7
58	Concordia	1860, March 24	Luther	11.6
59	Elpis	1860, Sept. 12	Chacornac	10.9
60	Echo	1860, Sept. 5	Ferguson	11.1
61	Danaë	1860, Sept. 9	Goldschmidt	11.0
62	Erato	1860, Sept. 14	Förster	12.3
63	Ausonia	1861, Feb. 11	de Gasparis	9.9
64	Angelina	1861, March 5	Tempel	10.5
65	Cybele	1861, March 9	Temple	11.0
66	Maja	1861, April 10	Tuttle	12.2
67	Asia	1861, April 17	Pogson	11.2
68	Leto	1861, April 29	Luther	10.5
69	Hesperia	1861, April 29	Schiaparelli	10.7
70	Panopaea	1861, May 5	Goldschmidt	10.9
71	Niobe	1861, Aug. 13	Luther	10.7
72	Feronia	1861, May 29	Peters	11.2
73	Klytia	1862, April 7	Tuttle	12.0
74	Galatea	1862, Aug. 29	Tempel	11.8
75	Euridike	1862, Sept. 22	Peters	11.6
76	Freia	1862, Oct. 21	d'Arrest	12.0
77	Frigga	1862, Nov. 12	Peters	11.1
78	Diana	1863, March 15	Luther	10.6
79	Eurynome	1863, Sept. 14	Watson	10.5
80	Sappho	1864, May 2	Pogson	10.6
81	Terpsichore	1864, Sept. 30	Tempel	11.8
82	Alkmene	1867, Nov. 27	Luther	11.2
83	Beatrix	1865, April 26	de Gasparis	11.3
84	Klio	1865, Aug. 25	Luther	11.3
85	Io	1865, Sept. 19	Peters	10.9
86	Semele	1866, Jan. 4	Tietjen	12.4
87	Sylvia	1866, May 16	Pogson	11.9
88	Thisbe	1866, June 15	Peters	10.8
89	Julia	1866, Aug. 6	Stephan	10.1
90	Antiope	1866, Sept. 1	Luther	11.6
91	Aegina	1866, Nov. 4	Borelly	10.8
92	Undina	1867, July 7	Peters	10.9
93	Minerva	1867, Aug. 24	Watson	10.8
94	Aurora	1867, Sept. 6	Watson	11.3
95	Arethusa	1867, Nov. 23	Luther	11.3
96	Aegle	1868, Feb. 17	Coggia	11.4
97	Klotho	1868, Feb. 17	Tempel	10.6
98	Ianthe	1868, April 18	Peters	12.7
99	Dike	1868, Oct. 10	Borelly	13.7
100	Hekate	1868, July 11	Watson	11.9

THE STELLAR CLASSES

(in order of decreasing surface temperature)

Type O.   *Wolf-Rayet Stars* (greenish-white). Massive fast-moving stars of very high surface temperatures (35,000° K., 62,000° F.) in Milky Way and Magellanic Clouds. This is Father Secchi's Type V. Example: Gamma Velorum.

Type B.   *Orion Stars,* also called Helium Stars (bluish). Very large stars, mean density $\frac{1}{10}$ of our sun. Helium lines prominent in spectrum, surface temperatures 25,000° K., 44,000° F. Secchi's Type I. Examples: Delta and Zeta Orionis, Beta Crucis.

Type A.   *Sirian Stars,* also called Hydrogen Stars (white). Helium lines absent in spectrum, hydrogen lines intense, surface temperatures 11,000° K., 20,000° F. Second most numerous class (most numerous is K); examples: Sirius, Alpha Andromedae, Beta Carinae.

Type F.   *Sirian-Solar Stars,* also called Calcium Stars (yellow-white). Hydrogen lines less intense, calcium lines prominent, other metallic lines present. Majority of known binaries are of this type. Surface temperatures 7500° K., 12,200° F. Examples: Canopus, Gamma Bootis.

Type G.   *Solar Stars* (yellow). Hydrogen lines still less intense, many fine lines of other, including metallic elements. This is Secchi's Type II. Surface temperatures 6000° K., 10,000° F. Examples (in addition to our sun): Capella and the brighter of the Alpha Centauri binary.

Type K.   *Arcturian Stars,* also called Red-Solar Stars (orange-yellow). Faint hydrogen lines, hydro-carbon lines. Includes very large but tenuous (density $\frac{1}{10,000}$ of sun) Red Giants. Most numerous type of stars in our galaxy. Surface temperatures 4200° K., 7000° F. Examples: Arcturus, Alpha Ursae Majoris.

Type M.   *Antarian Stars* (orange). Spectra similar to that of sun, but with heavy calcium and titanium oxide bands. Giants of the M-type show only half the density of the giants of the K-type. Secchi's Type III. Surface temperatures: 3000° K., 4900° F. Examples: Antares, Betelgeuse, Mira.

Type N.   *Carbon Stars* (deep orange-red.) Spectra resemble those of comets, due to carbon compounds. Secchi's Type IV. Surface temperatures 2600° K., 4200° F. Examples: U Hydrae, 19 Piscium.

The original classification was alphabetical, but the classes C, D, E, and H have been dropped as being redundant. Type P is the designation of gaseous nebulae; Type Q is the designation of novae. Types R and S were formerly members of Type N. Type R (orange-red) looks like Type N visually but photographs more brightly due to more blue and violet in the visible spectrum. Type S (red) consists mostly of long-period variables, showing complicated spectra with bright hydrogen lines.

NOTE ON ASTRONOMICAL FANTASIES

During the last 150 years a number of bizarre statements about astronomy have been advanced by people who referred to themselves either as "philosophers" or as "reformers." These "astronomical fantasies," as they are best called, differ from wrong guesses by professionals in that they were not advanced as theories or hypotheses which can be dropped or modified on the discovery of new facts.

On the contrary, and this is one of their characteristics, they were proclaimed as "the truth" by their fabricators. Another characteristic of these astronomical fantasies is that their originators invariably address themselves to the public, instead of to the logical forum for the judgment of a new hypothesis—the scientists in the field. The final characteristic of an astronomical fantasy is the lack of astronomical knowledge (most especially of knowledge in the fields of physics and mathematics) which is apparent immediately.

What was probably the first of these fantasies was known, in its time, as "Symmes' hole" because it originated with a printed letter from the former army captain John Cleves Symmes, which was sent to all members of Congress, the governors of the then existing states, and to a number of learned societies and individually famous men. The letter, dated "St. Louis, Missouri Territory, April 10, A.D. 1818," read as follows:

To All the World:

I declare the earth is hollow and habitable within; containing a number of solid, concentrick spheres; one within the other, and that it is open at the poles twelve or sixteen degrees. I pledge my life in support of this truth, and am ready to explore the hollow, if the World will support and aid me in the undertaking.

Two documents were attached to this letter. One was the announcement of a book (which never happened) and the other a certificate of sanity! Symmes' picture of the earth was that of a hollow shell, between 1000 and 1500 miles in thickness and with two large spherical openings around the poles which Symmes called the "verges." Though circular and parallel to each other the verges were not centered on the poles; the line from the center of one verge to the center of the other formed an angle of 12 degrees with the earth's axis. Since the poles were not in the center of the verges, their rims were located at different latitudes in different places. The 2000-mile-wide northern verge was highest over Europe, with the Svalbard Archipelago on or near the edge. Consequently, the verge was at its lowest latitude in northeastern Siberia, so that an expedition to the interior of the earth would most conveniently reach its goal by traveling to eastern Siberia first. As for the southern verge, it was larger, with a diameter of about 3000 miles; and one of the proofs of its existence was what was known as the Magellanic Clouds. They were sunlight glinting on the ice of the verge seen across the verge by captains who had come close to it, on the other side, without knowing about it, of course.

Symmes spent the time from 1818, the year that his letters were mailed, to 1829, the year he died, lecturing on his theory. Though he spoke mainly about the earth and the marvels that would be found in the interior, he said that other planets must be built on the same plan, since hollow concentric spheres were the "natural shape" assumed by all matter which is left to itself.

It is a historical fact that the Russian government, which was thinking about an expedition to eastern Siberia, offered Symmes a post with that expedition. But Symmes died before the expedition was organized and apparently the plan was then abandoned for other reasons.*

Another astronomical fantasy was advanced in 1869 by another American, Cyrus Reed Teed, who was professionally a physician. Claiming that "the truth" had been revealed to him when he was a boy, he wrote books on "Koreshan Universology" which are easily the most nonsensical books ever written. Eliminating the gibberish which is ninety-five per cent of the whole statement of Cyrus—or "Koresh"—his thesis boiled down to the claim that we live *on the inside* of a rocky shell with a wall thickness of only about 100 miles. Consequently: "the sun, moon, planets, and stars are not large bodies as they are supposed to be but are focalizations of force. . . ." Teed, who had also claimed to be immortal, died in 1909, but in Florida a colony of the cult he founded is still in existence.

Symmes had offered his honor as an officer and a gentlemen as guarantee of the truth of his teachings, and Teed simply claimed "revelation." Both "methods of proof" made life fairly simple for scientists. All they had to do was to pay no attention.

But the *Welteislehre* (World Ice Doctrine) of the Austrian engineer Hanns Hörbiger and the German amateur astronomer and high-school teacher Philipp Fauth was not such a simple matter. They started out with a book which could not be overlooked: large size, 772 pages printed in two columns, and 212 illustrations, most of them diagrams in drafting-room style. Ostensibly written by Fauth—but with long sections written by Hörbiger—the book bore the title *Hörbigers Glacial-Kosmogonie* (Kaiserslautern, 1913) and a subtitle which reads in English: "A new cosmogony of the universe and of the solar system, based on the realization of a constant battle of a cosmic Neptunism against an equally universal Plutonism, prepared with consideration of the latest results of all the exact sciences and supported by personal knowledge and experiences." The contents, however, were much less stilted than one would suspect from the title; it was almost, but not quite, a popular book.

It happened to come out less than a year before the outbreak of the first World War. Some professional journals ran short reviews saying, in effect, that the concepts presented were so new that critical examination would require more time than was, at the moment, available.

* While Symmes was still alive, a satirical novel, *Symzonia* by "Capt. Adam Seaborn," appeared, which claimed to have made the trip through the interior. Apparently Edgar Allan Poe's unfinished *Arthur Gordon Pym* was building up to a similar voyage. An otherwise unknown W. F. Lyons in 1868 published an adaptation of Symmes' idea (minus the other concentric spheres inside the main sphere and with much smaller verges) in a book entitled *A Hollow Globe,* without once mentioning Symmes!

Hanns Hörbiger, after the war, stated that he had received the first in-spiration late one evening in September 1894. He was a young engineer then, specializing in machinery used in coal and ore mining, and after work he often looked at the sky, especially the moon, through his portable tele-scope. He saw the lunar mountains which can look so blinding white next to the dark plains of the maria. Suddenly he had the thought that the white lunar mountains consisted of ice. The "recognition" of the lunar surface features as piled-up ice was his first intuition, to use his own words. The second intuition came in a dream a few weeks later; he saw himself in space, looking at the moon which was suspended on a silver thread, swing-ing like a gigantic pendulum. The silver thread lengthened and the swings became longer and longer until the thread broke. "When I woke up," he wrote later, "I knew that Newton had been wrong and that the sun's gravita-tional pull ceases to exist at three times the distance of Neptune." This statement was typical for Hörbiger, who never, for a single moment, doubted the validity of his own thoughts. If anybody pointed out that this or that assertion did not work out mathematically, he had a standard reply: "Calcu-lation can only lead you astray," which was a strange attitude for an engineer.

Between 1894 and 1912 Hörbiger worked out his theory, largely in cor-respondence with Fauth, and when the book was ready he would proudly say that his theory was the only one which explained *all* the facts of Nature, astronomy and geology, cosmogony and meteorology.

This is what the theory said:

Many millions of years ago, in the constellation Columba, as seen from our current position in space, there was an enormous reddish star, the Star Mother. The diameter of that giant star was on the order of 350 mil-lion miles, and its over-all density was 10, so that the mass of the Star Mother was at least 300 million times that of our sun. An enormous dead star, water-soaked to its core and frozen all the way through, slowly ap-proached the Star Mother. Compared to her it was small, but it was still about 40,000 times as massive as our sun. It struck the Star Mother in a vertical fall and, after friction against the matter of the Star Mother had reduced its velocity, it sank toward the Star Mother's center until it came to rest in layers of the same density as the intruder. There the water-soaked frozen body was slowly changed into a steam bomb by the heat of the Star Mother's body. Nothing happened as long as the weight of the outer layers could contain the explosive force. But then a triggering event occurred, possibly another collision. The deeply imbedded body exploded with great violence, and a very large quantity of matter was ejected from the body of the Star Mother, consisting in the main of the body of the intruder, but carrying other star material along. The explosion happened to point in the direction of the constellation Lyra, and the ejected matter plunged in that direction with a velocity of about 2000 miles per second in the beginning. The gravitational pull of the Star Mother was quickly overcome and after-ward the ejected masses began to revolve around their common center of gravity. Our sun came into existence at the center, accompanied by at least eighteen planets.

Since all space is filled with traces of hydrogen gas (but Hörbiger had rather massive traces in mind, not what astronomers mean nowadays when they use the same term), no orbit can be really stable. The hydrogen, in the first place, slows down the motion of the solar system as a whole, and also makes the orbits of the planets shrink. Since the planes of the orbits of the planets are nearly at a right angle to the motion of the sun in space, one has to imagine that each planet moves around the surface of a very long tapering cone. The apex of each cone lies along the projected path of the sun's motion. Hence, one by one, the planets will be swallowed up by the sun. In fact, six small planets which once moved inside the orbit of Mercury (when Mercury's orbit was much bigger) have already been swallowed up, each planet, by being consumed, renewing the energy of the sun.

But the ejected matter not only formed the solar system as we see it now, with a few additional planets; much more matter was torn from the body of the Star Mother than is accounted for by the sun and the planets. Much of this matter was gas—to be specific, free oxygen— and during the intervening millions of years this oxygen has combined with the hydrogen in space to form water or, because space is so cold, ice. And it is this ice in space which we see as the Milky Way. Astronomers formed a mistaken opinion about the nature of the Milky Way because a number of real stars are so located that they shine through the ice ring. Moreover, some of the ejected matter formed minor suns, like our own but much smaller, which are also in the ice ring or somewhat beyond it.

The ice ring, then, plus a few dozen tiny suns, is actually a part of our solar system—but it must not be considered a part in the same sense that, say, Uranus is a part. Uranus is still in the sun's gravitational field and therefore in orbit around the sun. The ice ring is farther away than three times the distance to Neptune; hence it is not under gravitational influence of the sun. It travels with the solar system since it had the same origin and has been slowed down by the space hydrogen at the same rate. But single ice blocks from the ice ring fall behind for various reasons and are then caught by the sun's gravitational field. The impact of such an ice block produces a sunspot. But the ice naturally evaporates and a stream of water vapor is ejected into space from the funnel of the sunspot. The vapor then freezes into "fine ice" which travels outward from the sun, and which explains the brightness of Mercury and Venus—they are covered with "fine ice." Earth is too far from the sun to receive much "fine ice." When it does, we see cirrus clouds in the sky.

The outer planets receive virtually no "fine ice" any more, but they intercept many of the ice blocks from the ice ring, which is the reason why they grew to their enormous size.

Earth was a special case in two respects. It does not receive much "fine ice" and it only rarely intercepts an ice block. If it does, we get hail storms traveling for scores of miles in a straight line. But earth was special also in having undergone a growth process. There had been five small planets outside the earth's orbit, all of which were captured, one by one, by the earth, as their orbits shrank. Each one of these moons was broken up by the earth's gravitational force and the pieces descended on the earth to form its major geological layers. The once independent planet Luna was captured about 12,000 years ago. The capture process was accompanied by a major flood which drowned Atlantis; the memory of this flood is preserved in countless legends. And the break-up of the moon which preceded Luna (Hörbiger called it the Tertiary Moon) took place late enough to be dimly remembered, leading to legends about battles of gods in the sky and *Götter-dämmerung*.

Add to all this that meteors are not what astronomers think but are ice blocks passing the earth and glinting in the sunlight, and you have the "explanation" for literally everything in one "gigantic, monolithic and self-consistent view of the world."

After the first World War, Hörbiger hopefully waited a few years for the praise that was sure to come. When it did not materialize, there was a new approach. The publishing house of R. Voigtländer in Leipzig sensed a potential gold mine and published dozens of pamphlets and six or seven hard-cover books written in a lucid, popular style, a reissue of the original big work, and finally even a monthly magazine with the title "The Key to World Events." In the meantime, the Graeco-Roman term *Glacial-Kosmogonie* had been replaced by the German *Welteislehre*, which was "officially" abbreviated WEL and Hörbiger's office became the WEL-Bureau. Meetings and lecture series were organized; Hörbiger declared openly that since the jealous professional scientists had rejected his work, the acceptance of the WEL by the colleges would be accomplished by public pressure.

The public pressure certainly existed. I know of a manufacturer who would not hire anybody who would not declare himself to be convinced of the truth of the WEL. And the director of Treptow Observatory near Berlin —a popular institution of the type of Griffith Observatory in Los Angeles— told me that he spent more than half his waking hours answering letters and questions about it.

By 1930 the "carnival," as "reactionary scientists" called it, had become the equivalent of a political party, and a discreet flirtation with Hitler's rising Nazi party began. WEL agitators began to speak of their "movement" and began to use an Edda-like terminology for astronomical phenomena. An ice block was no longer "rough ice" *(Roheis)* as before, but had become an *Eisling,* a term which also simply means "ice block" but has a mytho-logical sound. And of course, the WEL was referred to as Nordic Science. I don't know about Hörbiger's private attitude, but his disciples fully ex-pected that Hitler, after coming to power, would declare their opinions to be the "official science" of the Third Reich.

Hitler did not do what was expected of him. In fact, I was told at the time that he had sharply rebuffed whoever broached the suggestion.

During the second World War the World Ice Doctrine died. It was a strange and weird phenomenon which—contrary to Hörbiger's hopes— remained restricted to the German-speaking area of Europe.

BIBLIOGRAPHY

Since all the pertinent books and articles have been cited in the body of this book in the proper places, only works on the history of astronomy are listed here.

Abetti, Giorgio. *The History of Astronomy*. New York: Henry Schuman, 1952. 338 pages. Original title *Storia dell'Astronomia*, published in 1951 in Rome. Translation by Betty Burr Abetti. A little too condensed to provide much detail, but very valuable for providing a general reliable survey and for quick reference.

Ball, Sir Robert S. *Great Astronomers*. London: Sir Isaac Pitman & Sons, Ltd., 1907. 372 pages. Short biographies of eighteen famous astronomers, beginning with Ptolemy and ending with John Couch Adams.

Berry, Arthur. *A Short History of Astronomy from Earliest Times through the Nineteenth Century*. New York: Dover, 1961. 440 pages. The original edition of this work appeared in 1898. The reprint is unchanged except for the substitution of better portraits.

Boll, Franz. *Kleine Schriften zur Sternkunde des Altertums*. Leipzig: Kohler & Amelang, 1950. 450 pages. "Short Writings on the Astronomy of the Ancients" by the famous German philologist who died in 1924. The widely scattered publications were collected (and occasionally annotated) by Viktor Stegemann.

Brunner, William. *Pioniere der Weltallforschung*. Stuttgart: Akademie Verlag, no date [c. 1955]. 295 pages. Dr. Brunner is a professor at the University of Zürich. The chapter headings are the names of famous astronomers, but the chapters deal mainly with the work of these men and less with their biographies.

Clerke, Agnes M. *A Popular History of Astronomy During the Nineteenth Century*. London: Adam and Charles Black, 1902. 489 pages. Still a good book for the period, though later authors have found some mistakes.

Cohen, Morris R., and Drabkin, I. E., eds. *A Source Book in Greek Science*. Cambridge, Mass.: Harvard University Press, 1958. 581 pages. Translations of classical Greek writings. Covers the whole field of science, including medicine, and includes a great deal of early astronomy, geometry, and other mathematics.

Crombie, A. C. *Augustine to Galilei*. Cambridge, Mass.: Harvard University Press, 1961. 2 vols., 296 + 380 pages. Volume I is subtitled: "Science in the Middle Ages, V–XIII Centuries"; Volume II, "Science in the Later Middle Ages and Early Modern Times, XIII–XVII Centuries."

Doig, Peter. *A Concise History of Astronomy*. With a Foreword by Sir Harold Spencer Jones, Astronomer Royal. London: Chapman & Hall Ltd., 1950. 320 pages. Recommended as an introduction to the history of astronomy for science students.

Dreyer, L. L. E. *A History of Astronomy from Thales to Kepler*. New York: Dover Publications, 1953. 438 pages. One of the "classical" works on the history of astronomy, originally published, under the title of *History of the*

Planetary Systems from Thales to Kepler, by the Cambridge University Press in 1906.

Grant, Robert. *History of Physical Astronomy from the Earliest Ages to the Middle of the Nineteenth Century.* London: Henry G. Bohn, 1852. 638 pages. Itself a work of historical interest by now.

Koyré, Alexandre. *From the Closed World to the Infinite Universe.* Baltimore: The Johns Hopkins Press, 1957. 313 pages. Originally one of the Hideyo Noguchi Lectures, delivered at The Johns Hopkins Institute of the History of Medicine on December 15, 1953. Dr. Koyré is a professor at the *École Pratique des Hautes Études* at the Sorbonne in Paris. The book covers the period from Nicholas da Cusa to Leibniz, specifically the philosophical aspects.

Holden, Edward Singleton, ed. *Essays in Astronomy.* New York: D. Appleton & Co., 1900. 536 pages. Excerpts (translated into English, where necessary) from the original writings of Ball, Harkness, Herschel, Huggins, Laplace, Mitchel, Proctor, Schiaparelli, and others.

Hoyle, Fred. *Astronomy.* Garden City, N. Y.: Doubleday & Company, Inc. 1962. 320 pages. A popularly written history of astronomy as well as an over-all picture of astronomical knowledge today. Lavishly illustrated with color reproductions of paintings, color photographs, ordinary photographs, woodcuts, steel engravings, and diagrams, so that it has virtually become a picture book, and there is some danger that the reader will neglect the text.

Jammer, Max. *Concepts of Space; the History of Theories of Space in Physics.* With a Foreword by Albert Einstein. Cambridge, Mass.: Harvard University Press, 1954. 196 pages.

Lodge, Sir Oliver. *Pioneers of Science.* New York, Dover Publications, 1960. 404 pages. Reprint of the 1926 edition. First published by Macmillan in 1893, this is a collection of eighteen lectures, all but two dealing with astronomers and astronomical discoveries.

Maier, Anneliese. *Die Vorläufer Galileis im 14. Jahrhundert.* Rome: Edizioni di Storia e Letteratura, 1949. 307 pages. A study of the natural philosophy of the later scholastics with much use of unpublished manuscripts of the Vatican Library.

Meurers, Joseph. *Astronomische Experimente.* Berlin: Akademie Verlag, 1956. 79 pages. This very unusual book is a collection of all attempts to duplicate astronomical events in the laboratory. An example is the appearance of Venus considered as a featureless white ball under proper illumination. Most of the work reported was done between 1890 and 1940.

Munitz, Milton K., ed. *Theories of the Universe, from Babylonian Myth to Modern Science.* Glencoe, Ill.: Free Press, 1957. 437 pages. A very useful collection of excerpts of older originals (translated into English, where necessary); some of them, dealing with Babylonia and early Greece, are excerpts from the classical historical books about these periods.

Pannekoek, A. *A History of Astronomy.* New York: Interscience Publishers; London: George Allen & Unwin, Ltd., 1961, 521 pages. Original title *De Groei van ons Wereldbeeld* ("The Growth of Our World-Picture"). First published in Amsterdam in 1951. A very fine work by the famous Dutch astronomer.

Pendray, G. Edward. *Men, Mirrors and Stars.* New York: Funk & Wagnalls, 1935. 339 pages. A popular history of telescopes and telescope making, with a list of telescopes and of observatories and their equipment in North America and in the southern hemisphere.

Rousseau, Pierre. *Man's Conquest of the Stars,* London: Jarrolds Publishers, 1959; New York: W. W. Norton & Co., 1961. 356 pages. Translation by Michael Bullock of a French popular work, its author was laureate of the Académie Française in 1957.

Sarton, George. *Introduction to the History of Science.* Baltimore: Williams & Wilkins, for the Carnegie Institution of Washington (Publication No. 376).

Vol. I, *From Homer to Omar Khayyam*. 1927. 839 pages.

Vol. II, Part I. *From Rabbi Ben Ezra to Roger Bacon*. 1931. 480 pages.

Vol. II, Part II. *From Robert Grosseteste to Roger Bacon*. 1931. 1251 pages.

Vol. III, Part I. *First Half of the Fourteenth Century*. 1947. 1018 pages.

Vol. III, Part II. *Second Half of the Fourteenth Century*. 1948. Pages 1019–2155.

Shapley, Harlow, and Howarth, Helen E., eds. *A Source Book in Astronomy*. New York: McGraw-Hill, 1929. 412 pages. Reprints (in English translation, where necessary) of fundamental astronomical reports. The first author is Copernicus, the most recent ones G. V. Schiaparelli and Sir George H. Darwin.

Shapley, Harlow, ed. *Source Book in Astronomy 1900–1950*. Cambridge, Mass.: Harvard University Press, 1960. 423 pages. A continuation of the preceding, reprinting the important papers of the first half of the twentieth century.

Stein, Walter. *Von Bremer Astronomen und Sternfreunden*. Bremen: Arthur Geist, 1958. 160 pages (quarto). Published on occasion of the dedication of the Olbers Observatory near Bremen on the bicentennial of the birth of Olbers. Rich in biographical material on Olbers, Schroeter, and Bessel, as well as on more recent astronomers of that city: Friedrich Nölke and Otto Sigfrid Reuter.

Struve, Otto, and Zebergs, Velta. *Astronomy of the 20th Century*. New York: Macmillan, 1962. 544 pages; many illustrations. An account of advances in astronomy—mainly stellar astronomy—since 1900, paying special attention to problems currently still unsolved.

Tollinton, R. B. *Alexandrine Teaching on the Universe*. London: George Allen & Unwin, Ltd., 1932. 184 pages. Originally four lectures delivered in Cambridge in 1930, describing the views of the universe held by Philo, Clement, Origenes, Plotinus, and the Gnostics.

Vaucouleurs, Gérard de. *Discovery of the Universe; An Outline of the History of Astronomy from the Origins to 1956*. New York: Macmillan, 1957. 328 pages. Originally published in Paris in 1951 as *L'Esprit de l'Homme à la Conquête de l'Univers—l'Astronomie, des Pyramides au Mont Palomar*. The French original was brought up to date and expanded for this translation.

Wolf, Rudolf. *Handbuch der Astronomie, ihrer Geschichte und Literatur*. 2 vols. Zürich, 1892. 712 + 658 pages. The author stated that he intended this work to "substitute for an astronomical library" for travelers and succeeded in carrying out his intention. The amount of information per page is incredible but results in difficult reading.

INDEX

(Figures followed by an n refer to footnotes)

Abetti, Giorgio, 384
Accademia dei Lincei, 112, 114, 118, 126, 191, 292
Adams, John Couch, 388n, 405, 407–414
Adams, W. S., 464–65
Ahnighito meteorite, 250–51
Ainslie, Maurice A., 396
Airy, Sir George Biddell, 405, 408–10, 412–14
Albategnius, 53, 54
Albertus Magnus, 60, 480
Albumazar, 52
Aldebaran, 7, 9, 55
Alexander, A. F. O'D., 371n, 386
Alexander II (of Russia), 44
Alfonsine tables, 56, 84
Alfraganus, 53
Algol, 55, 465–66, 467
al-Khwârizmî (Muhammad), 52, 54
Almagest, 53
al-Ma'mûn (Caliph), 52
al-Mansur (Caliph), 52
Althans, K. L., 236
al-Sûfî, 53
ammonia, 352
Anaxagoras, 27, 136
Anaximander, 26, 27
Anaximenes, 26
Andromeda galaxy, 461, 462, 472–74; discovery, 182; distance, 472–74
Angström, Anders Jöns, 447, 448
Antikythera machine, 39-41
Antoniadi, Eugenios Marie, 14n, 194–195, 207, 308, 375, 381
Apian, Peter, 67, 141, 146, 154
Arab astronomers, 53–54; star names, 54–55
Arab numerals, 52
Arago, D. F. J., 274, 401, 405, 410, 412, 414
Archimedes, 33, 106, 165
Argelander, Friedrich Wilhelm, 467
Ariosto, Lodovico, 481
Aristarchos of Samos, 33–36, 124
Aristotle, 25, 26, 27, 30-32, 49, 81, 107–108, 115, 136, 137, 138, 233, 479
Armitage, Angus, 75n
Arrhenius, Svante, 281, 299, 304–305, 492–93

Arzachel, 53, 101n
Ashurbanipal, 5
Asimov, Isaac, 499
Assyrians, 5ff
asteroids, see planetoids
astrognosis, 9n, 24
astronomical unit, 170, 181, 443, 509
astronomical tent, 80
atomic transformations, 475ff
Averroës, 56
Avicenna, 56

Baade, Walter, 330, 331, 335, 473, 475
Babylon, 4ff
Backhouse, T. W., 280
Ball, William, 387, 388n
Barberini, Maffeo, see Urban VIII
Barnard, Edward Emerson, 220, 280, 363–64, 365, 375, 376, 381, 395
Barringer, Daniel Moreau, 244–46
Barton, Samuel G., 364n, 365
Bartsch, Jakob, 127, 481
Barvetius (Barwitz), 96
Baum, W. A., 353
Baumann, Adrian, 295, 296
Bauschinger, Julius, 201
Bayer, Johannes, 55, 124
Bayle's letter on comets, 141
Becquerel, Antoine Henri, 459, 475
Beer, Wilhelm, 229, 290, 501
Bell, Louis, 397
Bellarmino, Cardinal, 123, 125
Berossos, 23, 25
Bessel, Friedrich Wilhelm, 63n, 151, 342, 374, 408n, 441–44, 456, 460, 464, 467
Bianchini, Francesco, 205–206, 208
Biela, Wilhelm von, 151–52
Biot, Jean Baptiste, 236
Bobrovnikoff, N. T., 46–47, 162
Bode, Johann Elert, 184n, 318, 319, 320, 400
Bode-Titius rule, 240, 319, 408, 410, 415, 432, 509
Bond, G. P., 309, 392, 394, 397, 462
Bond, William C., 231, 379, 390, 392, 393
Borchardt, Ludwig, 19–20
Borelli, Giovanni Alfonso, 144–45
Bouvard, Alexis, 405–406
Bradley, James, 436, 441

PTOLEMY

KEPLER

GALILEO

HALLEY

FLAMSTEED

DELISLE